Also by Guy Endore

NOVELS

The Man From Limbo (1930)
The Werewolf of Paris (1933)
Babouk (1934)
Methinks the Lady (1945)
King of Paris (1956)
Detour at Night (1959)

BIOGRAPHIES

Casanova: His Kingdom and Unknown Life (1929)
The Sword of God: Joan of Arc (1931)

PAMPHLETS

The Crime at Scottsboro (1937)
Sleepy Lagoon Mystery (1944)
Justice for Salcido (1948)

VOLTAIRE !
VOLTAIRE !

a novel by

Guy Endore

SIMON AND SCHUSTER
NEW YORK · 1961

· LIBRARY OF CONGRESS CATALOG CARD NUMBER: 61–9596
MANUFACTURED IN THE UNITED STATES OF AMERICA
BY H. WOLFF BOOK MANUFACTURING CO., INC.

DEDICATIONS AND ACKNOWLEDGMENTS

To my sister Adelyn Stoller (1905-1955), and to my friend Samuel Ornitz (1890-1957) for the encouragement they gave me, of which I was generally in need.

And to Voltaire and Jean Jacques Rousseau, for their lives and their works and their correspondence. To Moland and Desnoiresterres, and to Parton and Maugras. To Ducros and Guéhenno. And all the many other Voltaire and Rousseau experts and scholars, living and dead, whose works I mined so ruthlessly for the material used in this novel. Without asking for permission.

(I say novel, because this is a novel, even though there is not a single invented character in it, and scarcely a line that could not be documented with a footnote reference to some accepted authority or to the works of the men themselves. But it remains a novel nevertheless, because I wanted it to read like a novel even though the two main characters were professional philosophers, and because, while I have ample authority for any and all parts of this book, I have none for the whole of it. Which isn't surprising, since this is the first time this story is being told.)

And to Professor Francis J. Crowley of the University of California, Los Angeles, for permission to attend his seminars on Voltaire, and to Professor William F. Bottiglia of the Massachusetts Institute of Technology for reading my manuscript and catching some important errors, and to Mr. Theodore Besterman of the Voltaire Institute and Museum of Geneva, and all other Rousseau and Voltaire scholars with whom I have had the good fortune to be able to talk about my work while it was in progress. Which does not imply that all—or even any—of them approve this book.

And to Deputy Censor Georges Le Bas and Vicar General J. Millot, of the Catholic Church of France, of whom I know nothing except that, in spite of the fact that Voltaire's books are almost without exception on the Catholic Index of Prohibited Books, they nevertheless saw fit to accord their nihil obstat *and their* imprimatur *to a book in praise of Voltaire's unshakable belief in the existence of God and in the divine creation of man. And it would*

5

be nice to think that they might have extended the same liberality to this volume.

And to E. Beatrice Hall, who, writing under the pseudonym of S. G. Tallentyre, first gave the world (in her book The Friends of Voltaire, *1907) the phrase, "I disapprove of everything you say, but I will defend to my death your right to say it," which ever since has been accepted as the very quintessence of Voltaire's philosophy and has been more widely "quoted" than anything else by him—even though no scholar has ever been able to discover such an expression in anything that Voltaire ever penned. And some doubt that he could—or would—have written such a line. But I don't.*

And finally to my daughter Gita, for the pleasure of dedicating a book to her.

CONTENTS

1: THE FIRST LETTER

Voltaire! Voltaire!

How that name must have rung through the eighteenth century! And surely for no one so much as for Jean Jacques Rousseau, to whom, even as a youth, the name Voltaire must have sounded like the scream of an invisible eagle. Something majestic and faraway, something mysterious and powerful. A giant bird winging its way high above the clouds, straight toward the sun.

Was it really conceivable that a day might come when a now still totally unknown Jean Jacques Rousseau would be entitled to stand before that celebrated man?

The very thought was enough to make young Rousseau feel dizzy.

But no. It was unthinkable. He was too poor, and Voltaire too rich. He was too ignorant, while Voltaire's range of knowledge was the astonishment of his times. He was too sluggish in his thinking, while the quick leap of Voltaire's wit was already legendary.

And worst of all, he was incurably lazy. While Voltaire was known to keep himself busy night and day, his favorite aphorism being "How wonderful it would be to rest, if rest were not so awfully boring."

And yet, in spite of all these differences, each one to the disadvantage of Jean Jacques, he remained haunted by the conviction that someday he would prove himself worthy of Voltaire. Someday they would meet. Yes, someday they would stand face to face.

And what a moment that would be in the life of Jean Jacques Rousseau!

That is why, poor as he was, he had somehow to find the means to acquire books. And lazy as he knew himself to be, he must somehow battle his desire to sleep and to daydream and, if need be, stay awake all night to study and to work. And bad as his memory was, yet by dint of endless repetition he must manage to accumulate a store of solid, fundamental knowledge. And more than that, untalented as he had to admit himself to be, he must yet, by sheer force of will, squeeze out of himself something so startling that people would simply have to take note of him.

9

Rousseau! Rousseau! Yes, that name too would have to ring some-day!

Yes, somehow, somehow, and cost what it may—and how it did eventually cost, what terrible sacrifices it entailed!—he must pierce through and achieve fame.

And then Voltaire!

How often, and in how many different ways, he had pictured to himself that moment when he would have proved himself worthy, and Voltaire would open his arms to him! He knew already that it would be too much for him. That his knees would turn to water. And that, blinded by tears, he would precipitate himself at the feet of Voltaire, sobbing, "Master!"

But that justly honored man would be far too gracious, far too genuinely great, to permit such adulation and humiliation. Tenderly he would raise Jean Jacques to his feet, embrace him and present him to the company of distinguished Parisians, among whom, of course, there would not be a single dry eye.

"Gentlemen," Voltaire would say, "allow me to introduce my col-league, Jean Jacques Rousseau, the worthy citizen of Geneva, whose amazing literary work you have so often applauded."

Or, depending on which way Jean Jacques's fancies happened to be turning, Voltaire might say, "Whose wonderful philosophic studies will influence mankind for centuries to come." Or "whose acute mathematical demonstrations have changed our conception of the uni-verse."

Yes, the dream might vary, but essentially it was always the same: that unbelievable moment of triumph when Voltaire would take the weeping Rousseau into his arms.

An unbelievable moment, because even as Jean Jacques was spin-ning out this imaginary tale, he knew that his chances of ever making it come true were diminishing by just that much. For here he was wasting his time blowing still another soap bubble, while Voltaire by his undeviating application to work was already preparing his next great literary triumph.

Never had there been such a success as Voltaire's!

Brought up by learned Jesuits along with princes and dukes from the best blood of France. Admired for his wit and his poetry before he was ten. Recognized for his talent and his learning before he was twenty. World-famous before he was thirty. And, what was more, a polygraph whose like had not been seen for centuries. At home in every form of writing. Both in prose and in verse. Comic and tragic.

On the stage as well as in books. In fiction as much as in history. In philosophy as well as in science.

And so tumultuously acclaimed that on the opening night of his play *Mérope* the cry of "Author! Author!" resounded for the first time in any theater, forcing the actors and actresses to retreat before the playwright and creating a stage tradition that would sweep the world.

And to cap it all, so amazingly prolific in all these fields that when Voltaire was thirty-three, and Rousseau barely sixteen and not yet haunted by his dream of becoming worthy of the master, publishers were already issuing Voltaire's collected works. Merely the first of a succession of such editions which, over the years, were to come out in an ever increasing number of volumes, climbing well up toward one hundred.

How could Rousseau even dream of matching such a head start? Especially considering how ill-equipped he was. For in truth he was utterly lacking in any talent whatsoever. All he had was his emotions. But these emotions were so intense that, as he himself was forced to realize, they must someday be the death of him.

"I'm the story of the sword that wore out the scabbard," he would later write. "There you have my life in one sentence: the sword that wears out the scabbard."

As an illustration of his violent emotions, take that incident at table, when he was already well established with Madame de Warens, but before he had been offered that terrible and at the same time heavenly invitation to go to bed with her. . . .

Jean Jacques used often to eat two meals to her one, because she picked at her food, so that to continue to keep her company at table he, having already finished his meal, would nevertheless have to stretch his capacity and start all over again. Not that he really minded so much; he had so many years of near-starvation to make up!

One day Jean Jacques watched her as she slowly cut off a piece of meat and brought it to her mouth. Wearily she parted her lips and slid the food from the fork and chewed it lazily. There was something so infinitely voluptuous about the movements of her mouth, about the indolence of her jaws and her lack of appetite, contrasting somehow with her plumpness, the fullness of her bosom . . .

An irresistible craving welled up in Jean Jacques, so that as she had just taken the food into her mouth and was beginning to chew it, he had to pretend that he had seen a hair on the meat.

"Wait! Wait!" he cried. "There's a hair . . ."

Upset, she quickly took the bolus of food from her mouth and put it on her plate. And before she could stop him, he had snatched up the half-chewed meat and devoured it.

She stared at him for a moment. While a warm blush mounted from her bosom and flooded her face. She shook her head reprovingly. "*Petit . . . petit . . .*" she murmured reproachfully. Being without children, and he, despite his young manhood, being still so under-sized and childlike, she had, so to speak, adopted him without ever discussing the matter with him.

Nor had he ever discussed it with her. But as she had taken to calling him "little one," he had come to call her "Mama." As he did now in a tone of deep contrition.

And unspoken between them lay their strange love, half parental and filial, and half incestuous.

Then the silence was broken by his fear of losing her love. He wept. He begged her forgiveness. He fell at her feet and embraced her ankles. He did not dare explain himself to her. He did not dare tell her of the white heat of passion that flamed in him. Of the times he had found a towel with which she had wiped herself, or one of her undergarments, and would feel himself tortured until he had sur-reptitiously appropriated the cloth and pressed it a thousand times to his burning lips. Because he literally worshiped the very ground on which she set her foot, and would have rejoiced and promptly cast himself down before her if, like some angry queen of antiquity, she had expressed the slightest whim to trample him to death under her heels.

It's that intensity that explains Rousseau. Passions too big for words. And therefore tying up his tongue. So that late in life he would still feel that nowhere and never had he really elucidated himself. And as a result that no one had ever properly understood him.

It was of course particularly his passion for Voltaire that was to re-main almost beyond words with him. But as an example of the fury of his drive in that direction, we have the incident that occurred when a citizen of Geneva, Bagueret, an adventurer who had once worked for Peter the Great of Russia, drifted into Chambéry and tried to engage Madame de Warens in some sort of speculation.

One day, after dinner, this Bagueret proposed a game of chess to Jean Jacques.

"Chess?" Rousseau mumbled. He suddenly was stricken with shame that before this far-traveled man he should have to appear so utterly ignorant of a game known to everyone.

"You mean you don't know how to play chess?" Bagueret asked with a smile.

Jean Jacques stuttered, "Yes, of course. Or, rather, no. Just that I've never tried to play it."

"You look like a bright lad," Bagueret said. "Come. Bring out the board and I'll give you your first lesson."

The disgrace of it! Not to know chess. Surely Voltaire played chess. And probably with the same acumen he showed in everything else he did. Only he, Jean Jacques, didn't know the first thing about this great game that was the traditional sport and relaxation of all intelligent and cultured peoples.

Madame de Warens's home didn't even have a chess set. So Bagueret took young Jean Jacques to the coffeehouse. At first the various pieces and their different moves were confusing. Especially to someone who was trying to pretend that he already knew something of the game. But in a half hour the eager lad had struggled through the fog and picked up the rudiments of the art. In an hour he had managed to beat Bagueret, who, it is true, had spotted him a rook and besides wasn't playing to win.

"Now it is *I* who will spot *you* a rook!" Jean Jacques cried.

Bagueret laughed. "What a cocky little fellow you are," he said. "Don't you realize that I was more interested in showing you the various aspects of the game than in beating you?"

"You lost!" Rousseau crowed. "I can beat you!"

"Oh, very well," said Bagueret. "If you like. Go ahead. Spot me a rook."

Of course Jean Jacques found himself trounced by the fool's mate in a couple of moves.

And it was Bagueret's turn to roar at the lad's discomfiture.

"I've played with champions, my lad," Bagueret said. "I've played against the pupils of the Sieur de Légal, the star of the Café de la Régence of Paris. How could you even dream of matching my ability in one lesson?"

But of course that was precisely what he had to do: catch up! Catch up fast! Catch up with Voltaire no matter how great his head start. And even outrace him.

And so a new world was opened up to Jean Jacques's imagination. Chess! An international game whose champions toured Europe, challenging the best players of every country, of every city. And were feted and revered everywhere.

How about himself, Jean Jacques, becoming such a champion?

Why not?

Already he saw himself astonishing all Europe, knocking over all the star players. And even invited into palaces to demonstrate his skill before royalty and aristocracy. And then, with a vast reputation already attached to his name, he would compose epics, write dramas, invent machines.

And finally Voltaire! And what a Voltaire! Respectful. Admiring. Turning to his guests to say, "Gentlemen! Allow me to introduce to you the world's master of the chessboard: Jean Jacques Rousseau of Geneva!"

The very next day he went to procure himself a chessboard and the necessary pieces. Madame de Warens, as difficult as her finances might be, somehow always managed to scrape together a little money when it concerned something new that her Jean Jacques wished to learn. She could not resist that hot passion of his which he brought to bear on every new subject he attacked.

He got himself a copy of *The Calabrian,* which was the standard work on chess at this period, written by the famous Greco and not to be surpassed as a textbook until the great Philidor would come along nearly a quarter of a century later.

And now, day after day, Jean Jacques would retire to his room, just as early as Madame de Warens could spare him from the work he did in the preparation of those drugs and elixirs with which she was always hoping to make her fortune. It was not to idleness or sleep that he retired. It was to study chess. All the different openings must be mastered. All the various defenses must be memorized. And all the winning combinations must be burned so deep into one's brain as to become a kind of second nature.

His candle guttering at dawn found him still awake, still poring over his board and his book. Until sleep grabbed him in spite of himself, but only his body, not his mind, which went on moving chessmen in wild dreams until he awoke.

And so, one day, he issued from his room. He was thin from hunger, yellow from lack of sleep and stupefied from incessant study. But he felt that he had mastered chess. And could spot Bagueret not just a rook, but even a queen!

Yes, so he thought. Until he sat down opposite Bagueret and, in the face of the latter's derisive smile, actually insisted on giving him the advantage of a queen.

The chess addicts of the café began to gather around to watch this strange contest between an unknown beginner and an old hand. Their mood was obviously skeptical toward Jean Jacques, and he could feel it, too. They made a ring of chilliness around the table. A chilliness ever ready to break into scornful laughter.

Well, he would show them. He would not even accept the gift of the white pieces which would have settled the question of who had the opening move. He put that to the throw of a coin and lost.

Bagueret made the usual opening, with Jean Jacques following suit. Not until the third move would the game reveal what direction it would take. If Bagueret moved his bishop to bishop four, then Jean Jacques had no choice but to . . .

Wait a moment! What was it that he would do?

For just a second Jean Jacques felt a little haziness creeping into his thinking, but then he was quickly clear again. He knew exactly what to do.

But what if Bagueret played bishop three? Or if instead of playing the bishop he played his pawn? What then?

He took hold of himself. But when he saw Bagueret playing his king's knight, he was startled. And he began to feel how dim and ragged his knowledge of chess was.

He would have to play his pawn . . . No. Better his knight.

As he hesitated he heard whispers in the circle of addicts around him.

To hide his confusion he made a quick move. He thought he heard a giggle from one of the audience.

And that giggle undid him. It was as if his brain were melting. All the vast mass of moves and countermoves which he had studied and restudied were flowing together into one great blizzard of leaping chessmen in which he groped about helplessly.

He could no longer think.

Bagueret moved again. He seemed very sure of himself. And still wore on his face that same derisive smile that Jean Jacques remembered from before. Without really knowing what he was doing, already sensing the debacle ahead, and almost as if anxious to get it all over with, Jean Jacques played at random. And, hearing further snickers behind him, his anger burst into an undignified cry of "Silence!" Which he immediately repented.

He realized that his fury was just a childish effort to put the blame for his coming defeat on someone other than himself, and he was ashamed of having given in to so transparent a maneuver. But even as he felt himself caught in this welter of shame and fury, the game was already over. Bagueret made a move and said, "Check!" And Jean Jacques saw that his king was hopelessly pinned.

Exposed, disgraced, Jean Jacques pushed the board away from him so violently that the chessmen toppled to the floor. He jumped from his seat and ran out of the café, laughter washing after him. He ran blindly through the streets, out into the fields, up into the hills.

He didn't know where he was going, and he didn't care. All he knew was that he wanted to hide himself away forever.

Voltaire! Voltaire!

No. That dream was finished forever. Voltaire was forevermore unattainable. And without his dream, Rousseau felt like an empty shell. There was no strength within him to buoy him up.

He collapsed. Exhausted. And racked by such sobs that he had to bite his teeth into the ground to keep his ribs from being torn apart. He wanted only one thing, to die, and that as quickly as possible.

All those nights of labor, and nothing to show for them. Nothing but a brain befuddled with chessmen and chess moves. And cutting across it the rude laughter of the coffeehouse addicts, a sound that he felt would never stop ringing in his ears.

And from the way his heart beat, from the cold sweat that chilled him on the outside, while within he felt as if he were being consumed, he knew he had not long to live.

But of course he was actually too young to die. He was still too strong to be permanently cast down by a single defeat. There was still his beautiful mama, Madame de Warens, there were still his books and his studies. And the dream of Voltaire.

And in fact there was even still chess. Which it would subsequently turn out he had learned much more of than he supposed.

Years later, in Paris, he'd often go strolling with his good friend Diderot (who was already becoming known as a writer, while Rousseau still remained as unknown as it seemed he would always be), and the two of them would sometimes stop at Maugis's coffeehouse to have a drink and play a game of chess.

And Rousseau would always smash Diderot in short order.

"You always win," Diderot once complained. "And so fast."

"You don't apply yourself," Rousseau retorted. "Get yourself *The Calabrian!* Learn the chief gambits and defenses! That's what I did."

"I've studied too!" Diderot cried. "But you're still far ahead of me."

"You could catch up, if you really tried."

"How about spotting me a piece? Say a rook," Diderot suggested.

"What's the matter?" Rousseau asked. "Are you so anxious to have the pleasure of winning? In that case I'll spot you not only a rook but a queen too. Then you can be sure of beating me whether your game merits it or not."

"You misunderstand me," Diderot said. "My wonder is simply that you can derive any pleasure whatsoever from beating me. If you would set up some odds, you'd have a harder fight and consequently more honor out of it."

"If you don't think our game of chess is fair," Rousseau said, "then better let's not play."

"I didn't say it wasn't fair," Diderot quickly corrected. "I just thought by this time you'd be bored with always whipping me so easily."

"No. I'm not bored. So if you don't mind, we'll keep the game the same as usual."

"Very well," said Diderot, resigned to the necessity of a permanent loser's role.

But long afterward, when both men had achieved fame, but Rousseau far more so than Diderot, and they had become separated by a bitter quarrel, Diderot would write, "What a craving there was in that man Rousseau to feel superior to me. Even in such a small matter as chess."

From which it is obvious that Diderot never really understood his one-time friend Rousseau. Certainly he never understood the meaning of a game of chess in the inner life of Rousseau. And therefore how absolutely indispensable it was that he win.

Not merely in order to keep rubbing out that vile sound of the giggles of the chess addicts who had watched him lose his match to Bagueret, a sound that could at any moment come surging back into his ears. No, not just that.

But Voltaire!

How could chess have assumed such significance for Rousseau? Wherein lay the necessity of beating Bagueret? Was it not because chess had become connected in his mind with his whole fate? And in particular with his dream of someday proving himself worthy of Voltaire? There lay the jeopardy of losing a game.

It was the game of his whole life that would be lost. At least symbolically.

This clue to Rousseau's manner of seeing and feeling things is revealed in that strange story of which he himself tells us. The time when he found himself out walking in the woods and wondering about the question of religion.

He had been brought up a Calvinist. Until the age of sixteen, when, lonely, hungry, frightened and desperately in need of something to sustain him, he had let himself be induced to change his religion to Catholicism. Later he would change back to Protestantism.

But now, in the dust of the road, he had seen a dead bird lying on its back, its shriveled claws stiff in the air. Gone forever its song and its flashing wings. Ants and beetles already half finished with it. Soon it would disappear as if it had never been. As thousands and thousands of generations of birds had leaped for a moment into the air, trilling their notes, and then had vanished.

Leaving no trace of their existence.

And man? What about him? Is that the way he goes? Finished? Done with? Just the flesh and the bones remaining around for a while to decay and dry up and finally disappear into dust, too? Like a tree stump that slowly rots down until nothing is left aboveground and it seems as if the earth and the weeds had devoured it?

Or is man an exception? Is he unique among living creatures in the possession of a soul? An immortal soul. And will that soul be damned or saved, according to whether in life this man distinguished correctly between that which God considers a sin and that which He considers a virtue? Distinguished correctly whether God was a Catholic or a Protestant. For the Catholics all said that every Protestant is damned and must burn in hellfire for eternity. And the Protestants, on the contrary, said that it was the Catholics who must go to hell.

And Rousseau therefore had to wonder whether by changing his religion he had damned himself. Or on the contrary saved himself.

As he pondered these heavy and doleful questions, Jean Jacques was at the same time picking up stones and casting them at different tree trunks in a kind of fit of petulance. It added to his irritation to find himself sometimes hitting his target squarely in the center and, then again, missing it by yards. And suddenly it occurred to him to say, "If my next throw is a hit, then it means I have an immortal soul and that I shall be saved!"

The thought of beating off the threat of hell so simply overwhelmed him with joy. But at the same time he realized that he was just then taking his aim at a rather distant tree. One with a slender trunk, too.

How hazardous!

If he missed that target, then he was damned to an eternity of torture. Or even what was worse. Namely, he might not have a soul at all. And death would then be nothing but ants and beetles consuming a now useless corpse. Just so much offal.

How dared he set his salvation on so risky a throw?

But then it occurred to him: Was he bound to aim at that particular tree? In making up the rules of this trial—which was, after all, his own invention, so to speak—had he definitely indicated which of all the trees around him he must hit?

No. He hadn't. He had merely specified, "If my next throw is a hit . . ." Very well, then. What was to prevent him from casting his stone at a different tree? Say the one right near him, with a trunk so broad that it was almost impossible to miss.

But, impossible to miss or not, Rousseau could not forget that his soul was at stake in this throw, and with such weighty matters in the balance, no matter how certain the outcome, he still trembled as he prepared to cast his stone, and cold drops of sweat gathered under his armpits and snaked slowly down along his skin underneath his clothes.

What a relief when he saw his stone strike the tree and drop to the ground.

"Saved!" he exulted. "I'm saved! Death will not be the end of me. Hell has no more terrors for me!"

But his exultation was not unalloyed. A little itchy feeling persisted and robbed him of the full measure of joy which he should have derived. The question was, hadn't he loaded the dice in his favor? Hadn't he cheated just a little bit? Well, what of it?

In short, the game could not be made too easy for Jean Jacques, when the import of that game was so great. He had to win at chess, because chess meant to him much more than beating Diderot. Spotting Diderot a rook—why, that would be like throwing his stone at that thin and distant tree trunk. Why risk it? For just as that tree became linked in his mind with the question of hell and heaven, so his chess game had become linked with his dreams of success.

Such was Rousseau's obsession. And such his yearning for Voltaire. Just how and when had this obsession seized him?

The name of Voltaire could not, of course, have been totally unknown to Jean Jacques. Just as he had obviously known something about chess long before Bagueret had turned the game into an addiction with him.

But for the true story of how Voltaire came to haunt the life of Jean Jacques Rousseau, we must go to Rousseau's own written statement, which he made in the very first sentence of the very first letter that he ever sent to Voltaire. (Though how many imaginary ones he must have composed in that overactive imagination of his, before he finally thought he had a valid excuse for taking pen and paper in hand—that, of course, one can only surmise.)

MONSIEUR:

For fifteen years I have been laboring to make myself worthy of your notice, and of those attentions which you are known to bestow upon young people in whom you discover some talent . . .

Young people? Alas, he was no longer so young! He was thirty-three, or near it. And in truth he had a better reason for writing to Rameau, the famous composer, than to Voltaire. Since it was as a musician that he had been assigned the task of revising an extravaganza, *The Princess of Navarre,* written by Voltaire, with music by Rameau, an opera originally composed for the marriage of the Dauphin of France to the Infanta of Spain, but now scheduled for another performance as a *divertissement* for the court at Versailles. And for that reason requiring alterations which neither Voltaire nor Rameau had the time to make, since they were both occupied with another and more important extravaganza, *The Temple of Glory,* intended for the celebration of the recent French military victories over England.

In short, it was a mere musical patch job. For a secondary occasion. And Rousseau knew it, and wrote:

. . . whatever may be for me the success of these feeble efforts of mine, they will nevertheless be forever glorious to me, if they should procure for me the honor of becoming known to you, and of proving to you the admiration and profound respect with which I have the honor of being, sir, your most very humble servant . . .

This flowery ending was in part merely the usual style of letter writing of the period. But that bit about his feeble participation in this extravaganza remaining forever glorious to him, should it procure for him an acquaintance with Voltaire, that was seriously meant.

And especially serious was that opening sentence, "For fifteen years I have been laboring to make myself worthy of your notice . . ."

Never in his life, and certainly to no other writer, did Rousseau use such language. But to Voltaire, repeatedly.

"Written with painstaking care." Such was the marginal comment which the first editor who published this letter felt compelled to make. Well, naturally it was written with painful accuracy. It meant nothing to Voltaire, but to Jean Jacques in his Parisian garret, practically unknown and constantly pinched for money, it meant everything.

It was nobody writing to somebody.

The date was December 1745, when both men were in Paris, Voltaire being about fifty-one years of age, and Rousseau, as I have said, about thirty-three. Voltaire's name was just then more than ever on everyone's tongue, for he had recently dashed off his poem on the battle of Fontenoy, the great French victory over the British, and the presses could scarcely keep up with the demand as edition after edition was sold out. All Paris prided itself on knowing by heart the lines of that vigorously martial poem celebrating what had become so rare, a French military victory. And Voltaire had not only come out first with his poem, ahead of all other French poets, but he had cleverly worked in the names of all the heroes of the battle, so as to flatter as many important people as possible. And of course, above all, the King of France, who had been personally present on the field of combat.

As a result Voltaire had been appointed official historian of France. And then first gentleman of the King's chamber, a post that not only carried with it a substantial salary, but also provided Voltaire with a free apartment in the King's palace at Versailles. In addition the poet, with the ardent support of Madame de Pompadour, the King's new mistress, was slated for the next vacant seat in the French Academy.

And, mind you, it wasn't as if the man needed these new honors. Nor the salaries attached to them. He was already known and translated into every tongue of the civilized world. Besides, he was an astute financier in his own right. Even as a youth he had dabbled in investments. And with almost invariable success. He was one of the earliest men in history to see the advantage of skillful agiotage for quick profits. In addition he had recently inherited the family fortune as a result of the death of his older brother. But even long before that he had become a millionaire, with his money safe in such solid securities as bonds of the city of Paris and in such lucrative shares as those of the Paris-Duverney banking and trading firm, and in a number of carefully selected private loans to such important personages as the Duke de Richelieu. All of which would combine eventually to make him one of the richest men of France.

Nor did he need that apartment at Versailles. Which he rarely used. He had better quarters of his own in town. Furthermore, the Paris palace of his mistress, the Marquise du Châtelet, stood at his disposal. To say nothing of dozens of other houses, whose owners would have been only too glad to pay him to come and be a guest.

None of this was unknown to Rousseau, who was then an out-of-work secretary. Yes, an unemployed secretary, and this at a time when, as Voltaire himself said with sarcasm, "A good cook costs you fifteen hundred a year. At that price you can have three secretaries." No, none of this was unknown to Jean Jacques when he sat down to write this letter in one of the several garrets which at different times of his life he inhabited in Paris. Probably just then the one on the Rue des Cordiers.

He knew that Voltaire was invited out so much that on one single evening he would have to dine at three or four homes, nibbling a bit here and a bit there, dazzling everyone with a flash of his wit and a burst of his infectious laughter, and excusing himself to leap into his carriage and be off to another party. While Rousseau, on the rare occasions when he found some salon open to him, might be requested to eat with the servants, there being no place for him at the table. An insult to his pride that would make him stalk out in a fury, to go back supperless to his garret room.

Did he ever manage to catch a glimpse of Voltaire at that period?

Surely in the crush of the theater lobby someone must have once whispered to him, "There's Voltaire! See him? Over there. The one with the sharp face and the long pointy nose. And those pipestem legs."

But really it was hardly necessary for anyone to point out Voltaire. You couldn't miss him—though you might not actually see much of him, so surrounded was he by friends, admirers and supplicants. How could anyone ever mistake him, once having laid eyes on him? He was thin as a reed. And he had that curiously twisted spine, that oblique hunch of the right shoulder and droop of the left, that proclaims the scholar who has dedicated his life and his body to poring over books and papers.

On his feet he seemed like some sort of water bird. The stilt legs, for one thing, so that despite his diminutive body, and his hunch, he was nevertheless of average height or slightly more. And then his nose, like a beak, growing ever longer as the number of his teeth diminished and his mouth gradually caved in, endowing his face with a look that was keen and prying, as if nothing could resist that insatiable curiosity of his.

But it was especially his emaciation that struck one. For already Voltaire had discovered that cruel law of his continued existence, *"Ma bisogna in verita, morir da fame per vivere,"* as he had written once in Italian (a language of which he was very fond and which he knew perfectly, even though he had never yet set foot in Italy—and never would)—"I really have to keep killing myself with starvation in order to remain alive." It was the only sure way he had ever found to master his painful attacks of colic, when his intestines would knot up like the snakes on the head of Medusa.

Starve, starve, starve! That was to be the tribute that life exacted from him for the pleasure of remaining alive.

And he paid that tribute gladly. Even though it irritated him to be stared at. Once, in Germany, dismounting from his carriage to enter an inn, and noting the gaping crowd about, he threw back his coat and shouted, "All right. You want to see the only living human skeleton! Here he is!"

Everything about the man, even the state of his health, somehow had the power of evoking endless public curiosity, which Voltaire astutely fed by writing about it to all his friends, so that his endless struggle against death grew in time to be a matter of universal interest.

"I was born killed," he would say, referring to the fact that at his birth the midwife had thought him stillborn and had set him aside as dead. And his famous phrase "I interrupt my agony" he had finally used so often as to make it a kind of password for laughter, as again and again he rose from his deathbed, to write another letter, one last poem, still another play, or one final book.

His enemies, who were numerous, would say, "Won't someone finally bury that man who died long ago?" But his friends loved him all the more for his heartwarming pretense of being forever about to die. After all, isn't that the lot of man?

"If I have lived so long," Voltaire would explain, "it is because I was born an invalid." And the millions of this world, always conscious of how tenuous and insecure is the life of man, were grateful to him for his ability to extract laughter from our common tragedy and applauded him when he described himself as having "one foot in the grave, and doing kicks with the other."

What a fire of emotions must have blazed up in Jean Jacques at the sight of this great man on whom his heart had set its goal! How tempted he must have been to throw himself right then and there at the man's feet! But how silly that would have been! What reason would Voltaire have to lift him up and present him to his friends? Who was he? What had he done—so far—to make him worthy of even a moment of Voltaire's attention? Such an act, on his part, would have no meaning.

It would only be when he had demonstrated his own worth, that casting himself at Voltaire's feet would be a real gesture.

Besides, it was not so easy to cast oneself down before Voltaire, a man who was forever surrounded by admirers and favor seekers. There was always, for example, the ubiquitous and irritating Thieriot, known everywhere as the Trumpet of Voltaire, because his only function in life seemed to be to talk about that great man.

Many years ago he had been a clerk in the same law office where

Voltaire had worked—or, rather, loafed. That was when Voltaire's father still stubbornly refused to let his son devote his life to a literary career. And at that time Voltaire had assumed such an ascendancy over Thieriot's mind that both, so to speak, left law together, the one to write and the other to proclaim throughout Paris that there was no other writer like Voltaire.

Thieriot knew nothing except Voltaire. He ran errands for him. He took charge of minor business matters. And when Voltaire happened to be out of Paris, Thieriot took his place. Never letting the name of Voltaire die away from the public tongue. He would go around town all day long, endlessly repeating Voltaire's latest witticism. He would pull out of his pocket Voltaire's latest letter, read extracts from it and give the news of what Voltaire's next literary activity would be.

This information was Thieriot's *carte d'entré*, opening up almost all of Paris to him. Thus equipped, he ate at the best tables, saw all the highest personages of the realm. And long before the *Mercure de France* would bring out Voltaire's most recent letter, the favored element of the capital had already heard it from Thieriot, read in that man's most worshipful nasal voice, which made people refer to him as "the begging friar."

That was Thieriot, Voltaire's alter ego. Borrowing money from the great man and forgetting to repay it. Pocketing Voltaire's royalties, and Voltaire shrugging. And even stealing Voltaire's manuscripts to sell them to people who couldn't wait for publication, and Voltaire doing nothing about it. Living and breathing nothing but Voltaire, except when Voltaire was in trouble with the authorities—which was often—and then suddenly Thieriot had never heard of Voltaire. And was even capable of betraying him. With Voltaire later forgiving him.

And in this swarm about Voltaire, there would also be the Abbé Moussinot, who was Voltaire's business agent, and who had to seize whatever free moment he could find to get Voltaire's signature to some document, or his consent to purchase an interest in some grain shipment from Algeria, or to lend money to this or that would-be borrower.

And then there would be Voltaire's latest protégé, Linant, Baculard d'Arnaud or Marmontel (the last at that time still dressed in the violet cloak of an abbé, and not yet in the wig, the lace and the satin which he would wear after Voltaire had erased from his mind the idea of turning ecclesiastic).

And of course there would be actresses trying to get Voltaire to give them a part in his next production. And footmen trying to hand

Voltaire notes inviting him to this or that loge in the theater, or to this or that supper party afterward.

How fiercely Jean Jacques must have stared at that adulated figure who, from the cascading curls of his fine monarchical wig (of the most expensive variety, natural gray horsehair) down to his scarlet heels, expressed impeccable elegance and refinement. A man of unshakable poise, too, whose smile, whose ready wit, whose vast erudition and unfailing talent were both the envy and the despair of all.

Asked once whether he had ever felt himself intimidated in the presence of the great, Voltaire replied, "Not so far. But since I have only *one* soul, I shall certainly feel embarrassed and tongue-tied if I should someday find myself in the presence of a man who has *two*."

How could a Rousseau not be stricken with the seemingly unbridgeable gulf of contrasts that separated them? Here he was, almost penniless, still struggling to get on that first step, and at the moment reduced to living with a woman, Thérèse Levasseur, a laundress and a waitress, who was just a cut above being a prostitute, a woman so ignorant that she never learned to read or to write and in all her life would never manage to get the twelve months of the year straight in her head. And there was Voltaire, engaging at this very time in his most publicized love affair, the one with the rich, the beautiful and the learned Marquise du Châtelet.

All France knew of these two philosophers, male and female, and of how they had converted an old château into a combination of palace and physics-chemistry laboratory plus private theater, and how magnificently they lived there, devoting their days to a riot of scientific experiments, studies and lectures (the Marquise preparing herself to write her treatise on the mathematics of Newton, while Voltaire was writing his great study of the morals and customs of mankind, which, when eventually printed, would be a landmark in the art of historical writing), and reserving their evenings for a feast of private theatricals, with Voltaire himself not only acting but also dashing off new plays as often as required.

What was a Rousseau in comparison? A nothing. A pathetic nothing.

And the letter he was writing from his garret was thus an appeal from the depths to the heights. How else, then, should it be written, except with painstaking accuracy? So much depended on it!

How he must have thundered, "Quiet!" if his little Thérèse so much as clicked with her knitting needles. And, mentally limited and submissive as she was, that poor creature must have kept still as a mouse, totally unaware of the fact that in this struggle she too was involved, and that the man she loved was ready to sacrifice his life as well as hers (and indeed he would sacrifice her life!) just as he might sacrifice a pawn to win a game of chess.

Well might that first editor to publish this letter comment, "Written with painstaking care."

A Voltaire, to be sure, might make it a habit never to write anything but a first draft, sending out his letters *currente calamo,* as he used to say, just as they dripped from his pen, and leaving his secretaries to make a copy for his files before they consigned them to the post. But such practices were not for the likes of a Rousseau. That was all right for a Voltaire, with his fabulous facility, such that he could break into verse in the midst of a letter, for all the pain or effort that it would cost him. He could do that when he was still a child. And still do it when he was nearing eighty, as for example when he sent the Duchess de Choiseul the first pair of clocked silk stockings to come from his most recent business enterprise and in his accompanying letter suddenly burst into those charming verses beginning "Madame, behold me at your feet, with designs on your leg . . ."

To make matters even more difficult for Rousseau, he did not have a mastery of the language. Voltaire was Paris-born and Paris-bred. And he spoke the purest of French with a limpid clarity and a precision that made it a delight to follow him. While Rousseau's language was still full of those stubborn Geneva expressions, so much so that only recently, when he had managed to get out a little pamphlet (which, incidentally, fell quite dead from the press), he had had the exquisite torture of seeing the only critic who reviewed it leap on it most brutally because of its barbarous French.

It is this, all this and more, oh! far more! that one must have in mind when one reads those first tragic lines of that earliest of all of Rousseau's letters to Voltaire: "Monsieur, for fifteen years I have been laboring to make myself worthy of your notice . . ."

Is it not like a cry of pain? A cry for help?

Voltaire! Voltaire!

Fifteen years of effort to reach a man.

2: BEWARE OF VOLTAIRE

And if we go back those fifteen years of which Rousseau wrote in his first letter to Voltaire, what do we find? Rousseau would then be about seventeen or eighteen years of age and was knocking around the little towns near Neuchâtel in Switzerland, and just barely managing to exist by teaching music, and meanwhile desperately trying to learn some music himself so as to stay at least one step ahead of his pupils.

For with music it was the same with him as later in the matter of chess. He craved to know it, as he craved to know everything, and had to confess to himself that as yet he knew nothing. For example, harmony. Rameau's book was at that time the only available work on the subject. Rameau was then climbing to the heights of the honors and the powers he was finally to acquire in the musical world. He was becoming known as the most famous musical figure of the day, and as such naturally he would eventually link himself in several operatic works with the most famous literary figure of the day, Voltaire.

Night after night Rousseau would dig into Rameau's book. There was not a thing in it he could claim to understand. But that did not stop him. He read on anyhow. And he went back to read again. And then, thinking that perhaps copying might help, he copied and re-copied the text endlessly. Studied and restudied every example. Until at last he despaired of ever making the subject penetrate his dull mind. But even despair could not stop him.

And then, having forfeited his last pupil in Neuchâtel, with scarcely any money in his pocket he wandered off to the little town of Boudry, where he happened to enter an inn one evening and there saw a violet-cloaked Greek prelate, a man who styled himself the Archimandrite of Jerusalem, exhibiting richly engrossed certificates signed by such exalted personages as the Czarina of Russia.

"I am delegated to collect money for the Holy Sepulcher!" he cried, and pointed to the august signatures on his documents.

His problem was a lack of languages, and since Rousseau understood Italian and also French, and even some bits of German, the Archimandrite invited the youth to join him as interpreter while he went on his collecting mission throughout Switzerland. And Jean Jacques, who loved nothing so much as vagabonding, particularly if he could be sure of a good meal at the end of a day of walking, gladly agreed.

And so the two of them went from town to town. Until they hit Soleure, known also as Solothurn.

Here the French had an embassy, under the direction of the Marquis de Bonac, a diplomat of long standing, who had served so many years in the Levant that there was not a single trick of so-called Greek prelates that was unknown to him.

The Archimandrite was immediately arrested and turned over to the civil authorities for trial and punishment as a fraud, while young Rousseau, in terror, cast himself upon the mercy of the ambassador, explaining how in utter innocence he had let himself become involved, swearing that he was ready to accept any correction and follow any advice that might be given to him.

As usual in such cases when he was caught in some wrong-doing, Rousseau was quick to excite sympathy and explain his way out. He had his youth and his rather feminine looks to help him. And he could tell such moving stories of how his mother had died when he was born, and of how his father had remarried and abandoned him, and of how he had been forced to run away from a master who had treated him too brutally, that he could draw tears from a stone.

Touched by this recital of woe, the ambassador decided to reserve decision and meanwhile invited the lad to dinner, and after dinner turned him over to his secretary to give him a room for the night.

And as this secretary, M. de La Martinière, showed the lad into his room, he said in a bantering tone, "Now, here's a coincidence for you. Rousseau is to sleep in Rousseau's room. What do you think of that!"

And seeing a blank look on Jean Jacques's face, he added, "What? You've never heard of the great Rousseau? But your name is Rousseau, isn't it?"

"Yes, sir," said the young man.

"Your real name?"

"I swear it. You can make inquiries if you like."

"Then I'm really surprised that you've never heard of your great namesake."

The fact was that Jean Jacques might well have heard of a great Rousseau before, but he had certainly never given the matter any thought. However, as usual he refused to admit total ignorance, and the light of a candle happening just then to shed some illumination on a little shelf of books, Jean Jacques was able to notice the name "Rousseau" in gold letters on the back of several volumes and thus deduce that this Rousseau must have been a writer.

Quickly seizing on this fact to restore his ego, he said, "You mean the writer Rousseau?"

"I should think you'd be related in some way," the secretary said.

"No, sir," Jean Jacques admitted. "But I wish I were, for I too have often dreamed of becoming a writer." Which, of course, was true only to the extent that he had at one time or another imagined himself in every possible career, and therefore as a writer too. But now, suddenly and for the first time, he became intense about the subject.

"So you really intend to be a writer," the secretary said with a little smile. "Well, well. Then you'll have to beware of Voltaire. Especially with that name Rousseau."

Beware of Voltaire? Especially with that name Rousseau? What did that mean?

Jean Jacques realized that the secretary was teasing him, but his curiosity had been aroused. He had to know what was behind that warning. Who was this Voltaire? Here too it cannot be said that Jean Jacques had never heard of Voltaire before. Considering all the pains that Voltaire took to publicize himself, that was really extremely unlikely. But it was in this case as in every other similar case: up until now the name Voltaire had meant nothing to Jean Jacques. Now, suddenly, the name Voltaire began to ring.

"Why should I beware of Voltaire?" he asked.

M. de La Martinière explained, "Well, in the first place, because everyone who writes today has to beware of Voltaire. Because Voltaire is our greatest writer, and he has declared war on all writers who do not take their craft seriously, or have not the necessary talent to practice it and try to substitute tricks for ability. And when it comes to criticizing, there's no one in the world like Voltaire to ferret out a writer's weakness and thereafter belabor and lampoon him so brutally that a man would sooner sink into the earth than ever put pen to paper again."

There rose up in Rousseau's mind an image of Voltaire, like some king on a throne, sitting in judgment on all the writings of mankind.

Monsieur de La Martinière added, "And in your case especially, it's possible that Voltaire would want to squelch you fast. Very fast."

"Just because my name is Rousseau?"

"Yes. Oh, of course, you could conceal your name. You could write anonymously. Or under a pen name. But don't think that you can fool

Voltaire. That man finds out everything. Your Christian name doesn't happen to be Jean Baptiste too, does it?"

"No. I'm Jean Jacques."

"Well that's one thing you can be grateful for."

"What did Voltaire have against this Jean Baptiste Rousseau?" Jean Jacques asked.

"He was an informer."

"An informer? You mean he informed on Voltaire? What did he say about him? To whom? To the police?"

"No. Not exactly. He merely said that Voltaire was the author of the poem *Le Pour et le contre*. And of course everybody knew that already."

"But in that case, what difference if he said what everybody already knew?"

Rousseau was puzzled. Apparently writing was like harmony, or any other study. Things were always more complicated than you imagined. Everything was so ramified. Nothing was ever simple. There was always so much, so very much that one had to know!

"Yes," said the secretary, "everybody was aware that Voltaire must have written *For and Against,* for who else could have written this antireligious poem? Chaulieu, the poet Chaulieu, was antireligious enough to have wanted to write it, but he was hardly capable of writing such a fine poem. So the theologians and the clergy were up in arms, demanding that there should be a public burning of the poem and the immediate arrest of Voltaire.

"As for the authorities, I mean the civil authorities, tired of all the religious disputes which have been disturbing Europe for so many hundreds of years, they were happy to be able to say, 'We'd love nothing better than to arrest Monsieur de Voltaire for the crime of having written this terrible, terrible poem against religion, and we'd love nothing better than to throw him into prison, or exile him, or even burn him, but first we must have absolute proof that he actually wrote it. Merely because everyone says that no one else but Voltaire could have written such a wonderful—I mean terrible—poem is not enough for the law to act.' "

"And that's where Jean Baptiste Rousseau informed?" Jean Jacques asked.

M. de La Martinière nodded. "Yes. He provided the necessary proof. And Voltaire had to run away and hide. By the way, you've read *Le Pour et le contre,* haven't you?"

Rousseau was drinking all this in as if it were some precious balm.

It was only recently that he had changed his religion from Protestantism to Catholicism, and he had since felt himself oppressed from both sides with the threat of eternal damnation. And now for the first time he heard of an antireligious man. A celebrated antireligious man. A man afraid of neither side. Neither Protestantism nor Catholicism. How wonderful!

"No," Jean Jacques had to admit to the secretary, "I've never read *Le Pour et le contre.*" Much as it embarrassed him, he had to confess it, for he wanted very much to know what was in that poem with the intriguing title *For and Against.*

M. de La Martinière sat down and began: "Let me explain that the story goes that Voltaire wrote this poem while he was taking a trip to Brussels with Madame de Rupelmonde. I've heard that this wealthy woman lives as she pleases during the day, and her religious scruples bother her only at night. You see, she was in love with Voltaire, but not married to him, and all day she was delighted to be traveling with the poet, but at night she wept and could not sleep for fear that her sins would put her in hell when she died.

"And so, in order to calm this lady's fear, Voltaire wrote this poem, saying, 'Let my philosophy teach you to despise the horrors of the tomb and the terrors of a future life.' Do you understand that?"

"Yes, sir," Jean Jacques breathed.

Oh yes, he understood only too well. Did he not have sexual sins on his conscience, too, not quite like those of Madame de Rupelmonde, not yet at any rate, but similar? And was he not assailed at night by the terrors of the grave? Terrors that as yet he had never confided to anyone. Was it possible that Voltaire had the answer to all these dismal problems?

"Thus," the secretary went on, lowering his voice, "Voltaire begins his attack on what he calls 'the sanctified lies with which the earth is filled.' You know what he means by that?"

Jean Jacques thought he knew, but he wanted it spelled out for him. "No, sir," he whispered.

"He means all the world's many religions."

"That's what I thought, sir," Jean Jacques said.

The secretary continued: "Voltaire then declares that he wants nothing so much as to love God, in whom he seeks the father of the universe. But the image of God which he is shown in the Bible is of such a tyrant that he cannot help but hate Him. Was there ever a monster so cruel as that God of the Scriptures? What else but cruelty can explain a God who with all the power He has, nevertheless creates a man with a love for certain pleasures, pleasures which God proceeds at once to deny him, apparently only in order to have the right to torment this creature of His not only during life but after death and through all eternity."

Rousseau listened without saying a word. But he thought, How true. How true and how well said. And why did not I ever say that to myself? Somehow, deep in my heart, I thought that. But I never said it to myself. I never dared say, "I hate God." I mean that God about whom the different religions quarrel.

"And no sooner has this tyrant God created us," M. de La Martinière pursued, "than He repents Himself of the miserable job He's done. And He orders the oceans to rise up and drown this wretch whom He Himself fashioned in His own image. Having thus exterminated this original man, so Voltaire reasons, surely now God will produce a better mankind! Wrong! The new progeny turns out to be the same breed of brigands, of tyrants and of slaves. Indeed, far meaner than the first batch! And now one asks oneself, What terrible scourge will God launch upon these new miscreants to destroy them? Undeceive yourself! God drowned the evil parents, but for the evil children, God will come to earth Himself, to die for them on the Cross."

Jean Jacques had never seen logic used so powerfully. And he could only stare and listen, his mouth half open, his whole being gripped.

"Voltaire then goes on to argue that with God Himself come to die for our salvation, surely now we are all saved. Surely now we are all reclaimed from the clutches of the Devil. Surely God cannot fail. Not if He gives His life for us. But wrong again! Yes, God perishes on the Cross in vain. And yet with that sacrifice so obviously useless, as anyone who looks around the world can see for himself, noting the vast areas and vast populations who do not know Christ, it will nevertheless be demanded of man that he believe just the contrary, namely that Jesus saved the world. And what is the penalty for not believing what our eyes tell us is false? Eternal hellfire!

"But there's worse still: Scarcely has God mounted back to heaven than his fury is once more unleashed against mankind. And he not only continues to punish us for our sins, which may perhaps be justified, but he punishes us for an original sin in which we never had a hand. And in His blind anger, this God not merely exacts such punishment from us who at least know the story, but He even demands obedience from a hundred different nations enveloped in the night of utter ignorance of His law, through no fault of their own, and kicks their inhabitants into hell, even though it was He who created them ignorant!

"Moreover, even among those who are supposedly enlightened, there is no agreement as to what God's law is, and they divide themselves into sects each of which abominates and murders the other, and each of which declares that only one sect—which happens to be his—can get into heaven. All others must go to hell!"

Yes, Jean Jacques saw it clearly now, what Voltaire meant by "those sanctified lies with which the earth is filled."

The secretary resumed: "Voltaire declares that he, for his part, must reject such an unworthy conception of God. He wants a God whom he can adore. He demands to know if it is not dishonoring God to attribute to Him such follies and such crimes. And Voltaire concludes with the following prayer: 'Listen to me, God of all the vastness. Listen to my plaintive sincerity. If I'm no Christian, it is in order to be able to love you all the more.'"

The secretary paused, while Rousseau, drenched with new ideas, was for a moment unable to break the silence. But finally he asked, "And Jean Baptiste Rousseau?"

"Ah, yes," said M. de La Martinière, "you want to know how your namesake comes into this story. Well, when Voltaire and Madame de Rupelmonde arrived in Brussels, one of the first things the poet did was to call upon Rousseau. For you must know that Voltaire thought very highly of Jean Baptiste. When Voltaire was a boy in school, with the Jesuits, Rousseau was the great poet of France, and every year he would be invited to the graduation exercises of the school to hand out the poetry prize. And each year it would be Voltaire who won that prize, and Rousseau would be there on the platform and would kiss the young boy, crown him with the wreath of laurels and give him whatever book or other gift went with the prize."

Rousseau, Jean Jacques Rousseau, who had never gone to school in his life, stared off in envy, hearing of these advantages that Voltaire had enjoyed.

"And ever after, Voltaire sent everything of his that was published, and even some things still in manuscript, to Rousseau, whom he addressed as 'my master' and whose criticism he humbly invited. And Rousseau was always severe. He never quite approved of Voltaire's work. Even Voltaire's best he would sometimes reject. Nevertheless Voltaire continued to respect him. For he didn't realize, or didn't care to realize, that Rousseau had become more and more jealous of Voltaire's rising fame, which was so rapidly eclipsing his.

"This time, too, when Voltaire arrived in Brussels, he immediately called on Rousseau and invited his master to dinner and to the theater. But Rousseau was not able to suppress his feelings. And when Voltaire began the evening by reading to him the poem he had just written to calm Madame de Rupelmonde's fears of death and hell, Rousseau stopped him, declaring that such irreligious poetry shocked him. He called it blasphemous, and he berated Voltaire for such impiety."

"So Voltaire became angry with him?" Rousseau anticipated.

"No. Voltaire did not become angry yet," M. de La Martinière replied. "He continued to call Rousseau *'mon maître.'* It was not until they came back from the theater and Rousseau read to Voltaire his own latest poem, Rousseau's *Letter to Posterity,* that Voltaire was tempted to say the obvious: 'I'm afraid, my dear master, that there's a letter that will never reach its destination.' You can imagine how furious Rousseau was at this pupil who for the first time had dared to criticize back.

"But even that would not have made them the irreconcilable enemies they have since become. That resulted from Rousseau's taking revenge on Voltaire for his witticism. When Voltaire's irreligious poem gradually spread around, by manuscript copies, and was finally surreptitiously printed and sold, the author immediately denied having had anything to do with it. That was his usual procedure. But this time he found the authorities had documents in hand with which to confront him."

"Documents from Jean Baptiste Rousseau," said Jean Jacques.

"Exactly. Rousseau had written letters all over, telling of how Voltaire had read this poem to him, and how proud he had been of having written it."

"What happened to Voltaire?" Jean Jacques asked.

"I don't know. He had to make himself scarce for some time, that's obvious. He had to run away from his beloved Paris, that's certain. But whether he hid out in France, or went to some other country, I don't know. And how much conniving, how many princes and ministers he had to flatter, to get back into good graces and reappear in Paris, that I don't know either. Except that now he never misses an opportunity to deride Rousseau and has done much to wreck Rousseau's reputation."

M. de La Martinière rose from his chair. "And now, for such is fate, here you are sleeping in the room where Jean Baptiste lived when his friend the Count du Luc used to be ambassador in Soleure. And it only depends on you to write such great works that someday people may say, not 'Here is the room where Jean Baptiste Rousseau stayed,' but 'Here is the room where Jean *Jacques* once slept.' " M. de La Martinière smiled.

34

But Jean Jacques nodded, as if already he could see such a day ahead. He felt himself under the spell of greatness.

"Why not?" the secretary asked, still smiling. "Someday perhaps, when people speak the name Rousseau, no one will think of Jean Baptiste, they will think only of Jean Jacques. That's up to you."

Rousseau nodded again, carried away by vague but grandiose dreams.

"What has happened to Jean Baptiste?" he asked finally.

"They say he's still living in Brussels, but in quite straitened circumstances. His former patrons have died. And he depends now on a rich Jew for his living, a circumstance of which he is so ashamed that he never enters this Jew's home until he has first looked up and down the street and made sure that no one is watching him. . . . You see, Voltaire sweeps everything before him!"

Rousseau shuddered. "Poor man!"

The secretary laughed. "That's why I warned you, be careful of Voltaire. Don't let Jean Baptiste's fate happen to you."

And then M. de La Martinière said good night and left the boy alone with his fantasies.

And what fantasies he had!

He went to bed. And then reached out to extinguish the candle with his fingers. But he could not sleep.

He felt the presence of great forces in the darkness of that room. In the first place, Voltaire. Voltaire bringing him a new God such as Jean Jacques had never dreamed of before—a God not to be feared, such as the Calvinist God whom he had been taught to believe in as a child in Geneva, or the Catholic God who had been given to him when he had converted himself to Catholicism in the city of Turin, but a God to be admired and adored and respected. A God who would never have been so cruel as to create us such as we are if he had not intended us to be that way. A God, therefore, who will not punish us with hellfire for not being able to believe everything that we are told to believe, or to do everything we are told we must do.

Rousseau felt better because of Voltaire's God. For he had many sins on his conscience. Wild sexual fancies harried and delighted him, so that the more he fought them, the more he was prone to indulge in them. Sin and repentance coursed through him, tearing ever new promises of reform from him, promises which he could not keep.

Protestantism and Catholicism both threatened him with hellfire and tormented his life. He felt himself trapped between the two. In particular he could not forget a certain horrible moment when he

35

had appeared before a member of the Inquisition at Turin, whose duty it was to test a new proselyte's strength of faith, prior to approving his admission into the Catholic Church.

This examining friar had shouted at him, "Your mother was a Calvinist heretic, was she not?"

Frightened, Jean Jacques could not answer for a moment. His dear mother, whom he loved all the more because she was so completely imaginary, since she had died in giving him birth, his dear mother was a criminal of the worst kind.

"She died a Calvinist heretic, did she not?" the friar pursued with fury.

The frightened boy—he was then scarcely sixteen—who had had no choice except either to die of hunger on the streets of Turin or to accept the hospitality of the home for catechumens, felt compelled to admit that yes, his mother had been a heretic. And yes, she had died as such.

Whereupon the monk had cried out, "Then you know that right now, at this very moment, and forever more, your mother is burning in the deepest pit of hell, where all heretics are scorched with hot flames and scream in eternal pain?"

Jean Jacques had not known how to answer this terrible question. And as he remained silent, the Inquisitor had pounded away at him: "What? You do not know that as an excommunicated heretic, she must be burning in the fires of hell? Or do you perhaps deny it?"

Holding back the scalding tears that were forcing themselves into his eyes, Jean Jacques had finally said, "I can only pray that she may have seen the light before she died, and in time for God to forgive her."

The Inquisitor had glared at the boy for a couple of seconds and then had nodded his reluctant willingness to let that slightly dubious answer pass.

And now it was as if Voltaire had given him back his mother and had wiped out the stain of his answer. But it would be years before Rousseau would find his way safely to Voltaire's God. He would find his way deeper into Catholicism first, and then back to Calvinism. But always that God of Voltaire would beckon to him, and there would come a time much later when he would write his "Profession of Faith of a Savoyard Vicar," which would celebrate the glory of the Voltairean religion and the Voltairean God. And would be almost indistinguishable from Voltaire's poem *For and Against*. But so well done that even Voltaire would say, "I shall have my copy bound in the finest Morocco leather."

And in all his subsequent tortured relationship with Voltaire, Rousseau would never be able to forget the debt he owed to Voltaire for that Creator of the Universe, kindly, sensible, believable. A God who played no favorites with some nations and peoples as against others, but had scattered them over this globe to have their various fates, their mixture of sorrow and happiness, as chance and circumstance might apportion it to them.

No, never would Rousseau cease to feel grateful to Voltaire for this immense gift.

But at the moment there was still another force in the room besides Voltaire. It was that other Rousseau. The great Rousseau, the enemy of Voltaire. Rousseau the poet—his namesake!

So powerful was the attraction of the celebrity that had once inhabited these rooms that Jean Jacques had to strike a light and get the candle burning again.

He rose and took the candle over to the little shelf of books. But for a while he did not dare touch them. They frightened him as much as they attracted him. There was something magical about seeing his own name on the cover of a book. It was as if he had written it. As if he shared in the greatness of it. But at the same time there was something prophetic in it. As if it involved him, in spite of himself, in a fight with Voltaire.

That is why he couldn't bring himself to touch these volumes for a moment. No doubt the inside title page bore the name "Jean Baptiste." But as far as the outside of the book was concerned, it was as if it were his own work. And it seemed to him that if he were to touch one of these volumes, or even go so far as to open one and read it, then he would have sealed his fate to that of the other Rousseau, with the promise both of eventual literary fame and of a dangerous involvement with Voltaire.

So, for a little while, all he did was stroke the leather binding, letting his fingers feel the gold impressions that said *"Rousseau, Rousseau . . ."*

And which at the same time seemed to whisper, "Beware of Voltaire! Beware of Voltaire!"

In the end of course, come what might, he had to take the volumes down and look into them. They were filled with plays in verse, and with shorter pieces of poetry. And the poems seemed largely in a form that Jean Baptiste Rousseau called "cantatas."

Jean Jacques did not know that this was Jean Baptiste's favorite form and that a large part of his fame was based on these cantatas. He could not even understand too well what the poet was trying to say in

37

them. But he could feel their beauty, their polished charm. And their gracious fluency. Indeed, they read so easily that Jean Jacques was convinced that they could not be so very difficult to write. And seeing on the night table some writing material, he sat down at once to try his hand.

What kind of poem should he write? A cantata, of course.

But to whom?

To Madame de Bonac, of course, the wife of the ambassador. He had seen her at dinner the previous evening. Elderly, but at the same time still motherly. Perhaps, as a result of this poem, she would take him into her home.

Having lost his own mother at birth, Jean Jacques never ceased looking for a mother. In his wanderings about the country he would often go out of his way to sing beneath the window of some fine country home, always dreaming that a casement would open up and a feminine voice would invite him in.

Which never happened. And yet in the course of his life he was to make his way into the home of Madame de Warens, and then into the home of Madame Dupin, and that of Madame d'Épinay, and finally into the home of the Duchess de Luxembourg.

Madame de Bonac was naturally flattered by Jean Jacques's poem, which he showed to her the following morning. She was not too surprised. It was an age of much poetry writing. But she was touched. However, she did not consider adopting this boy. All she did was discuss with her husband and with the ambassador's secretary what might be done to help him. He was a charming young lad, without much formal education and not at ease in good society, but obviously ambitious and willing.

The result was that Jean Jacques was provided with one hundred francs, with which it was expected he would manage to make his way to Paris. On foot, of course. And with a letter of introduction to a certain Colonel Godard, who was in need of a tutor-companion to his son, the latter being about to join his father's regiment as a cadet. Jean Jacques would enter as a cadet, too, and would help out young Godard by studying with him military history, geometry, engineering, fortification and ballistics.

So off went Jean Jacques, who during the night had dreamed of nothing but Voltaire and poetry, to become a military man, with his mind now spinning fantasies not of cantatas nor of Voltaire, but of troops, ramparts, gabions and batteries. He saw himself already in an officer's uniform, with a great white plume on his tricornered hat, standing calm and brave, a field-glass in his hand, the din of cavalry and cannon fire all around.

But when many days later he reached Paris, with his clothes discolored from sweat and dust and his shoes slit where he had cut the leather because of his corns, and presented himself thus to Colonel Godard, the latter laughed at the idea of making him a companion cadet to his son. He offered him nothing more than a job as valet to his son, and that at no wages except food and lodging.

Jean Jacques rejected this gift that was no gift.

His first sight of Paris had been a big disappointment, too. He had dreamed of a city more magnificent than anything in fairyland. But he had come in by way of the suburb of St. Marceau. Instead of streets of gold and towers of marble, he saw dirty, stinking little alleys, ugly black houses, swarms of beggars. And carters, menders of old clothes, criers of decoctions and pastry vendors threading their way through the crush.

So he escaped from Paris back to Switzerland before his money should give out. And was happy to take to the road again and dream new dreams.

Dreams that faded in turn and gave way to other dreams.

With only one dream persisting and growing ever stronger.

Voltaire!

3: THE CENTURY THAT SPARKLED

Impossible to exaggerate the impression that Voltaire made on young Jean Jacques. The poet's plays especially. One of them, *Zaïre,* when Rousseau read it for the first time, literally transported him, so that for days on end he walked about as if in some kind of enchantment. But it is in particular his description of the effect upon him of seeing a performance in Grenoble of Voltaire's *Alzire* that must be studied, in order to gain some conception of the intensity of his feelings.

Jean Jacques was then about twenty-five years of age, and still as lost as ever, having no status, no family, no religion, no career, no money that he could really call his own. He was in every respect a beggar. Poorer than the poor, because the poor have arranged themselves inside their poverty, while he remained perpetually mortified by every single link of the chains.

It is in a letter to his Mama, Madame de Warens, that he writes of attending a performance of Voltaire's *Alzire,* and of how as a result his health was grievously damaged.

It wasn't even a good performance, he says as if to emphasize that neither the skill of the actors nor the costumes and scenery had anything to do with the impairment of his health. Nothing but the lines of Voltaire.

One can see him there in that provincial hall, waiting for the curtain to rise, and already his heart beginning to pound. And then, with the rise of the curtain, falling completely under the spell of Voltaire. He hardly dared breathe. The noise of air rushing into his nostrils might cover the voices from the stage, and he might thus lose a single one of those precious words.

So fierce was his concentration that he glared at his neighbors as if they too ought to stop breathing. Indeed, as the play developed and he found himself more and more magnetized, he would catch himself clutching at his rib cage, where his stupidly beating heart was making such a bother as to threaten to interfere with his attention.

He must have greeted the intermissions as lifesavers, to give him a chance to master his emotions. Nevertheless, by the time the play was nearing its end his misery must have become acute—there would be the usual buzzing in his ears, the usual mounting of turmoil in his head, such as he always experienced when too aroused. One feels, in fact, that he would have been capable of beating his head into insensibility in order to keep it quiet, except for the presence of other people around who might have been shocked.

How he managed to hold out until the curtain came down at the end of the fifth act is impossible to say. But somehow, despite his torture, he held himself in check until he was able to rush from the theater and back to his room, where he no doubt took to bed at once, fearful of the worst consequences and vowing never to see another Voltaire tragedy again.

What could possibly have moved him to such a degree as to fear for his life? Why should he cry out in his letter to Madame de Warens, "How can there be such hearts, so sensitive to that which is great, to that which is sublime and pathetic? While other hearts seem doomed to crawl in the gutter?"

There was of course in the first place the startling novelty of Voltaire's message. And then the great humanity of it! For *Alzire* is the prototype of all those plays that contrast two different civilizations and two different religions, the sort of thing that has since then been followed by so many other playwrights, notably, of course, some forty years later, by Lessing in his *Nathan the Wise*.

Alzire concerned the virtual extinction of the kingdom of the Incas by the brutal Spanish conquistadors, and its theme can be easily summed up.

QUESTION: What is your definition of a savage?

VOLTAIRE: A savage is a man who pursues his enemy in order to offer up his smoking corpse to his gods.

QUESTION: And what is your definition of a civilized Christian?

VOLTAIRE: A civilized Christian is obviously a man who does not pursue his enemy in order to offer up his smoking corpse to his gods. But pray tell me, in what country of Christian Europe shall I look for an example of this civilized Christian?

But it was more than just the novelty and acuteness of this play, and the masterly manner in which Voltaire had developed it, that stirred Jean Jacques to the core of his being. It was more than just the fact that Rousseau too was caught between two religions. And more than the fact that Voltaire's contrast between the rude virtues of the savage and the refined virtues of civilization was someday to be at the very heart of his own philosophy.

It was the world-wide success of *Alzire*. And the feeling that, as Voltaire achieved ever and ever greater successes, the gap between them, instead of narrowing, only widened, making more and more impossible that great moment when he would be worthy of prostrating himself in tears at the feet of Voltaire.

To be a Rousseau, poor, unknown, provincial, and yet be on fire with vast longings and meanwhile have to watch year after year go by without results, while one merely fretted or mooned around, unable to fix on any particular career or project, one's genius thus remaining locked up or perhaps, for all one could know, nonexistent, but nevertheless something there within one, bursting to be liberated, yes, bursting—and meanwhile a Voltaire goes marching on from one success to another, from his antimilitaristic *History of Charles XII* that was more exciting to read than an adventure story, and that was going through edition after edition, to his *Philosophical Letters* that were as amusing as they were profound, and that continued to cause a turmoil; from his epical *La Henriade* to his daring *For and Against;* from his starkly

Greek *Oedipus* to his deeply moving *Mérope*. Each one a more impressive success than the last. And important people considering it a matter of honor that they had been privileged to see in manuscript some portion of Voltaire's licentious poem *La Pucelle* (in which the English, despairing of winning battles against Joan of Arc because she is a virgin, send a handsome Englishman to win her love, and the fate of France is thus brought to teeter on a moment of passion between sheets); or being able to boast that they had had a glimpse of Voltaire's long-announced but still unpublished *Century of Louis XIV*. (So avid was the public for Voltaire's works that any excuse was enough to bring out a new edition, and printers constantly besieged and tempted his secretaries to copy out or steal for them some manuscript, in no matter what state of completion it might be in, and this would be published, full of errors, often completed by some hack, forcing Voltaire to deny, to repudiate, to scream out his fury, and leaving his scholars to this day lost amidst varying editions.)

In short, to be a Rousseau, and to be aware of all these accomplishments of Voltaire's past, and to feel that there were still more to come in the future from that busy and talented pen, whereas for oneself, one still had to make one's very first contribution—how could all that fail to put one to bed with palpitations of the heart?

And there was more! For it seemed that Voltaire said only those very things which one might have been on the point of saying oneself. Voltaire's works had that infuriating quality of just anticipating what was on the tip of your tongue. But saying it so well that it cleaned you out and left you with nothing to do but keep silent.

There was some kind of sleight of hand to it. You were dazzled and robbed at the same time. Left penniless and full of admiration.

Ah, if only one could write a play. A magnificent play. If only one could have a huge success with a play and thus leap to fame beside Voltaire!

Voltaire had begun that way. His first play, *Oedipus,* had piled up a run of forty-five consecutive performances, establishing a new record for any theatrical production up to that time in the history of the French stage.

Nothing more was needed to make Voltaire world-famous.

If ever there was a century that was crazy about the theater, it was the eighteenth century. All Europe seemed to have gone theater-mad. (Except, of course, Geneva, the city of Jean Jacques's birth, where the theater was still forbidden.) But everywhere else, not a princeling too poor to have his own court theater, and even his own private troupe of actors and actresses. Italian or French preferred. And no city too small to afford a public hall to accommodate one of the dozens of roving bands of players who tramped the continent from one end to another.

Not only did Paris have its theaters supported by the state, but strolling comedians spread their boards wherever they could, and in particular at the so-called theaters of the two fairs, that of St.-Germain and that of St.-Laurent, where more or less unlicensed shows were given for the amusement-hungry populace.

In addition the city swarmed with private theatricals. With the King of France setting the example by having plays performed at the Tuileries, at Fontainebleau and at Versailles, wherever the court happened to be residing. And the Queen, too, having her weekly *grand spectacle,* which was so lavishly mounted with costumes, musical numbers, skits and dances, that there had to be daily rehearsals, and thus her one show a week nevertheless filled out the whole week with theatrical business.

And of course what the Queen had, the King's mistress had to have, too.

And the dukes and counts, right down the line, each according to his means. Or, rather, beyond his means. For nothing was so common nor considered so elegant in this age as a family fortune dissipated in a passion for the theater. And in this race ecclesiastics joined with the financiers. And convents too. And even the Army. So that there were times when war seemed to take place only between plays, and one might see in camps such signs as this: "No play scheduled for tomorrow because of military engagement. *The Village Cock* will be shown the day after."

So that all a Rousseau really needed to become known was to write a halfway decent play. Were not theaters everywhere clamoring for new plays?

Then why couldn't he? Why couldn't he, Rousseau, do what so many others were doing? Here was the century literally waiting with wide-open arms for a Rousseau to show his talent, and he couldn't.

He couldn't write a play to save his soul.

Furthermore, it might be said that had Voltaire never written his *Oedipus,* he would surely have become famous anyhow. As a wit. He wrote, for example, some savage lampoons against the Duke d'Orléans, who was Regent of France after the death of Louis XIV, while Louis XV was still too young to take the throne. The Duke was not difficult to lampoon, since he was addicted to orgies and was supposed to have drawn his daughter into these parties and perhaps even made her pregnant. But it was particularly because of the severe economic crises through which the country passed under his rule, and which eventually culminated in the crash of the John Law system, that he was disliked in certain quarters.

Voltaire was arrested for these lampoons (some of which he hadn't written, but which were attributed to him nevertheless) and went to the Bastille for eleven months. When the Regent permitted his release, the Marquis de Nocé undertook to bring the two men together and to secure for the poet the favor of the Duke.

While the Marquis waited with Voltaire in the crowded antechamber of the Palais-Royal for admission into the Duke's presence, a furious thunderstorm broke out. Lightning flashed, rain and hail fell in fierce torrents. Windows were smashed and chimney pots went flying. And the streets of Paris were flooded.

"Right now, there's no doubt a regency in heaven too," Voltaire couldn't help remarking.

The laughter in the antechamber was so boisterous that the Duke inside wanted to know the cause of it and himself came out to inquire.

The Marquis de Nocé said, "Sire, I bring you Voltaire, whom you have kindly released from the Bastille, and whom you are now going to send back there." And he proceeded to relate Voltaire's witticism.

The Duke was typical of his century. He found it difficult not to yield to wit. He forgave Voltaire and even made him a grant of money.

"I shall be only too pleased to have Your Majesty provide for my board," Voltaire said in accepting the money. "But let me please provide my own room."

The Duke laughed again, charmed once more not only by Voltaire's wit but by the deft manner in which he had covered up their past enmity by allowing it to be inferred that by putting him in prison, the Duke had only been providing for his living quarters.

Yes, it was that ability to give utterance to something bright and appropriate, that ability to arrange words in such a way that they twinkled as if from a light within them, just that alone would have made Voltaire famous even if he had never written a play.

For if ever there was a century that could be said to delight in sparkling, it was the eighteenth century. From the jeweled buckles on a man's shoes to his powdered wig, from the satin slippers of a lady to the beauty spot on her cheek, it was as if everything schemed to catch a ray of light, splinter it into rainbow-colored fragments and scatter it to all sides.

Voltaire understood the passion of his times for witticisms, and he charged his trumpet Thieriot with the task of picking up the flashes that dropped from his lips, and spreading them about town.

Thus to a bore whom Voltaire despised, and who happened to be discussing at length what he should wear to a coming masquerade party, the writer suggested, "Go disguised as a man. You can be sure of not being recognized."

And to a lady who, as Voltaire entered, rose from her bed saying, "Only for a genius such as you would I rise from my bed," Voltaire replied, "I would be more flattered if you thought me worthy of the opposite."

Piron, who liked to think of himself as even wittier than Voltaire, used to say that some of these lines didn't originate with Voltaire at all. "If I had a ship," Piron once said, "I'd name her Voltaire. She'd be bound to make a fortune in piracy."

Imagine a Rousseau alive in this century of wit and burning to have himself recognized, and yet unable to produce a single bright remark. And the more the conversation around him crackled with cleverness, the more he felt himself unable to utter a single word, however banal.

And later, years later, how he would tear to shreds this frivolous Parisian chatter, while at the same time confessing how desperately he wished he could have found something to contribute. How embarrassed he would feel, sitting there, so caught in this conflict of emotions that he would lose the whole trend of the conversation and go so far as to imagine that Paris was full of secret codes from which he was excluded, so that while others were constantly exploding with laughter, he had no idea of what it was all about.

And if by chance he did feel that he had something to say, his thoughts would be so slow in organizing themselves that by the time he had the words ready he would discover to his dismay that the topic of conversation had meanwhile moved on to something totally different, and the moment for his remark was no longer opportune.

"Oh, why must my thoughts be so sluggish!" he would cry in his *Confessions,* though by the time he wrote that work he had long since become famous and had no need to envy the brightness of others.

But the envy was still there. Because the memory of a thousand moments of humiliation had engraved themselves forever on his sensitive soul.

It was Fontenelle, you might say, who first set the tone for this period, the scientist who considered that even a book on astronomy ought to be written so as to delight the ladies. In Fontenelle's opinion it was only stupid pedants who insisted that science must always and inevitably be abstruse and forbidding. And the bachelor Fontenelle, who never stayed home of an evening, but dined out every night of the week, either at Madame de Lambert's salon or at that of Madame de Tencin, or later at Madame Geoffrin's, or at some other house of wealth where there were hospitality and good cooking, was never guilty of what the eighteenth century knew as the greatest crime of all: the crime of boring people to death, which is in effect the assassination of little bits of their lives.

In those rich salons, if you had nothing bright to contribute to the conversation you were not likely to be invited again. The salon was, so to speak, just another theater, where if you couldn't play your role, you didn't stand a chance of remaining on as an actor.

The one exception has so often been told in that famous anecdote: "Whatever became of that strange gentleman who always used to come to your dinners and was the only one who never had anything to say?" one of her guests once asked Madame de Geoffrin.

"You must mean my husband," she said. "He died."

Fontenelle, surely, was one who never failed to be interesting.

"You're right," he once said to a medical man, "coffee is a slow poison. I've been drinking it for ninety years and it hasn't killed me yet."

When Fontenelle was ninety-four and still going out every evening to dine, he was nevertheless able to jest about his failing hearing and eyesight. "I'm sending some of my baggage ahead," he would say, and he would lift his ear trumpet so as to catch the laughter.

And when he finally did die, just weeks short of his hundredth birthday, and his funeral cortege was passing, Piron, Voltaire's rival, commented, "Now, isn't that just like Fontenelle. Won't stay home. Not even on the day of his funeral."

Always the apt comment that spares people's feelings by drowning all sense of personal tragedy in a laugh.

Dark ideas were as if forbidden. The grandmother of George Sand would later tell her, "In those days we didn't know what it was to grow old. It's the Revolution that brought the idea of old age into this world. We insisted on being graceful, elegant, perfumed and gay until we were ready to go to our graves. What difference if one had the gout or lacked money, one could still manage to put on a smile and say something witty. Wasn't it better to die at a ball, or at the theater, than to perish in some dark room with black-clad priests around?"

Superficial? Yes. Perhaps.

46

But they saw themselves as those "atoms of a day" of whom Voltaire used to say, ". . . born like me to suffer everything and be ignorant of everything." What is all this talk about space, light, awareness, soul, he would ask in his article "Ignorance," when we don't know what we're talking about?

Since we know in advance that we cannot solve the deeper mysteries of life, why keep probing the wound? It can only cause additional pain. Delicacy rather than depth. That should be our ideal.

So there developed this peculiar way of living. Unreal, perhaps, but charming. And suited to those rooms where the walls were either paneled or carved and then either painted with gay scenes or else stretched with brocade, and everything was chosen to delight—and even, at times, overdelight—the eye: the mirrors, the silver, the glassware, the colorful liveries of the servants.

When Louis XV was not yet of age to take the throne, he went out walking once with his tutor. At the palace gates stood a beggar. The King tossed him a coin. The beggar made a deep reverence, while the King walked on with his preceptor.

"I have just seen the most remarkable event of my life, Your Majesty," the tutor observed.

"Yes? What was it?" the King asked quickly.

"A beggar who could outdo a king in courtesy."

The King understood. He walked back to the palace gates, faced the beggar, put forward his buckled shoe and bowed low while sweeping his plumed hat from his head and bringing it to his heart. And thus regaining his right to be king.

But of course leaving the beggar as poor as before—if not poorer. Outdone now in courtesy too.

No doubt this French courtesy could be carried to extremes. As when Louis XIV asked the Duke d'Uzes when his wife expected to give birth.

"It will be whenever Your Majesty desires," said the Duke, bowing low.

But it had its beautiful as well as its ridiculous side.

When Madame Geoffrin sold her Van Loo paintings for fifty thousand francs she remembered that she had bought them for five thousand, and she sent the difference to the widow of the artist. No depth, no. But what superficial sensitivity!

And perhaps this beautiful superficiality is the explanation of why there were so many long-lived men and women in this era. Like Fontenelle, who lived to almost a hundred. And his friend the poet

Sainte-Aulaire, who lived to be ninety-nine, too. And Mairan, Fontenelle's friend and successor at the Academy of Sciences, who lived to be ninety-three. Voltaire himself lived to eighty-four. And Piron, who tried to match Voltaire in wit, but at any rate matched him in age: he lived to be eighty-four also. While Voltaire's lifelong friend, the woman-crazy Marshal de Richelieu, lived to be ninety-two. And Largillière, who painted the well-known portrait of the young Voltaire, lived to be ninety. While Houdon, who did the famous statue of the old Voltaire, reached eighty-seven. And Saint-Lambert, who had the peculiar privilege of being the successful rival to both Voltaire and Rousseau in the matter of their greatest love affair, lived to be eighty-seven, too. And Voltaire's first female admirer, Ninon de Lenclos, lived to be eighty-five and his last female admirer, Madame du Deffand, lived to be eighty-three. And even the poet Chaulieu, who never went to sleep except drunk and tried in vain to drag Voltaire into his orgies, lived to be eighty-one.

But Jean Jacques Rousseau died at sixty-six.

Was it the joy of living in this sparkling era that gave them such long lives, these men and women who delighted in laughter, who, if the conversation threatened to fail, would do anything to keep themselves amused? Flooding the floors with water to make them slippery, and extinguishing all the lights, in order to engage in a handkerchief battle in the dark, or play crazy guessing games, ending up exhausted, their sides aching from laughter, their clothes torn and wet, to sing such songs as no one would dare sing today, or recite verses, such as those that George Sand's grandmother collected and that George Sand couldn't even begin to read, so horrendous did they appear to her, and that she therefore burned, verses perhaps such as this one:

> *Le trou du cul, le trou du con,*
> *Sont deux trous qui me semblent farces.*
> *Par l'un on jouit du garçon*
> *Et par l'autre on jouit des garces.*
> *Tous les deux me sont défendus,*
> *Mais puisqu'il faut que je me perde . . .*
> *Je préfère le trou du cul,*
> *Malgré mon dégoût pour la merde.*

Which was evidently the work of some perfumed abbé of the period, as the words "both are forbidden to me" would seem to indicate.

And how violently, later, these men and women would condemn that Rousseauan rage to make everything better, which had brought on the Revolution and taken the joy out of existence by being too serious about it. So that Talleyrand would then be able to say that no one who had not lived under the old regime could understand what was meant by "sweetness of life." And the peasant-born Rétif de La Bretonne would say the same.

But how sweet was that life for Rousseau?

How sweet was it for the millions of poor? How sweet was it in the slums of Paris, amidst mud, animal excrement and clouds of flies? How sweet was it for the porters who carried ladies and gentlemen in chairs up and down the streets of London, Paris, Genoa, everywhere through those impossible old tortuous and climbing streets of Europe, which, if we could see them again today, would make us think of Asia, crowded with palanquins and jinrikishas.

Did that century sparkle, for example, for the victims of syphilis, for those prostitutes and laborers who, unable to pay for the expensive private treatment for syphilis, had to go to a free hospital such as that of Bicêtre, there to take the mercury cure which brought them so close to death, so very close that often indeed they did die? And even when cured, they could not be released until they had submitted to a punishment for their licentiousness: a thorough fustigation, that is to say a drubbing with a stick by an expert in the art of imparting pain.

Nor could the century be said to sparkle for a *faux-saulnier,* a contraband-salt dealer, hiding out from the taxgatherers for fear of prison or worse. And what about a Negro slave sweating on some French sugar plantation in San Domingo? Nor did the era sparkle for a Protestant minister found preaching secretly to his little flock of faithful in the mountains of the Cévennes. Who if caught would be condemned for the rest of his life to pull an oar on some ship of the line of the French Navy and there be exposed to the first raking enemy salvo, since to cripple a ship's maneuverability there was no surer method than to cripple its galley slaves. And what of the hundreds of thousands of French girls who hid the disgrace of their faces, ruined by smallpox, in the depths of some provincial convent?

When King Louis XV recovered from a dangerous illness, all over France the church bells rang with joy. And the rich of Paris, and indeed of the whole nation, took to having their tables set out in the streets, and throughout the good season they dined out of doors, inviting whoever wished to sit down and eat with them.

But when Damiens, a few years later, during a severe winter, struck at the King with a penknife, barely scratching the monarch's skin, he was given the torture of the diamond, which is beyond description, and later quartered by four horses, each attached to a different limb and then driven apart. But even that would not have separated his limbs from his torso if, after an hour of useless pulling, the sweating horses had not had the assistance of surgeons who cut some of the man's tendons.

"All I wanted to do was call His Majesty's attention to the condition of the poor," was the only explanation that Damiens would offer for his deed. And in truth it had been a severe winter. The coldest seen in France for a hundred years. No one could remember when the Seine had frozen over so solid before.

All Paris crowded to watch the spectacle of Damiens' execution. Adjoining houses were able to sell window space to spectators for fabulous sums.

"What beautiful white skin he has," one lady is reported to have said when the naked man was being tied to the horses, after his right hand, the hand that had held the penknife, had first been punished with burning sulphur for its criminal act.

There was much talk about the cruelty of the Parisian mob for coming to see this spectacle. And Voltaire felt called upon to correct a misapprehension: "It was the execution that was cruel. The people were only curious."

No, the century did not sparkle for everyone, that's obvious. There were the wars and injustices of every century. And yet it did sparkle. And one of the main reasons why it sparkled was Voltaire.

4: THE THREE ROUSSEAUS

Inasmuch as there would come a time when Voltaire and Rousseau would seem to be enemies, indeed the greatest enemies of the century, and would go down in history as such, it is well to emphasize that even when he was already thirty-eight years old, and when nearly twenty years had passed since he had first dreamed of making himself worthy of Voltaire's attention, Rousseau could still write the most abject and pleading letter to the master.

The proof of that is to be seen in what happened one morning in January of the year 1750, when some friend of Rousseau's, whether Diderot, or d'Alembert, or Grimm or Klüpfel, I don't know who—

and, incidentally, all these unknowns were eventually to attain fame, Diderot and d'Alembert for their great *Encyclopedia,* on which they were just beginning to work, and Grimm for that correspondence of his through which he kept half the royal families of Europe supplied with the literary news of Paris and which would be compiled and published under the title *Correspondance littéraire,* and Klüpfel for his *Almanach de Gotha,* which he was to establish later—anyhow, whoever it may have been, he came up the six flights to Rousseau's room in Paris, either in the Rue Jean-St.-Denis (where also Condillac used to visit Rousseau—that same Condillac who would later be considered the founder of the science of modern psychology) or in the Rue Grenelle-St.-Honoré, where Rousseau for a time, beginning early in 1750, had tiny lodgings with his mistress Thérèse.

Anyhow, this visitor (and it would be ironic if this visitor had been Diderot, for Diderot had just recently received what Rousseau wanted so badly, the accolade from Voltaire) this visitor exclaimed, "Well, well. You sure had your nerve last night."

"What do you mean?" Rousseau asked.

"To break with Voltaire. Openly."

"Break with Voltaire?" Rousseau cried out. "Are you mad?"

"That's what *I* am wondering about *you!* Why did you hiss his play last night?"

"I? Hiss Voltaire's play? Why, I wasn't even out of the house last night."

"But you must have been. Everyone is talking about it. You even tried to incite others against it. And Voltaire was furious! He screamed at you from his box. Calling you 'the little Rousseau'!"

Rousseau was stricken. He moaned, "But I was sick last night. I was lying here in bed, thinking that I must die. Thérèse can tell you."

The truth was that Jean Jacques had been sick. He had been staying home often recently with his ever recurring trouble: his inability to thoroughly empty his bladder. When these attacks came he would be dizzy, feverish, with hot and bloated flesh, and he would despair of survival. The urine would literally have to be milked out of him, one painful drop after another.

Thérèse would help him in this terrible and ugly operation, which as the years went by became an ever more serious problem, and which would always somehow deepen his usual misgivings about his life. What had he achieved in all these years? He was secretary to the enormously wealthy Madame Dupin, wife of a tax farmer.

For eight hundred to nine hundred francs a year, worth perhaps three thousand dollars today, scarcely enough to live on, he would help entertain her guests with music and with skits or plays. And he would cull out Latin and Greek quotations which she might insert into various places of the book she was writing on women, in order to give that work an appearance of profound learning. And now and then he would have to take charge of a semi-idiotic son of hers, who had to be prevented from doing any harm to himself or to others.

How he hated himself for this trivial and spurious work! In which his only satisfaction came from the chemistry courses which he and Madame Dupin's son-in-law pursued together.

And thus time had passed. Four years had gone by since that first letter to Voltaire, in which he had confessed that for fifteen years he had been laboring to earn that great man's esteem. And still nothing accomplished. Nothing except that, from hanging around the outskirts of the literary crowd, he had become known to some extent as "the little Rousseau" to distinguish him from now still another Rousseau, the much better known and more important Thomas Rousseau, editor of the magazine called *The Encyclopedic Journal*.

The worst of it was perhaps this: that a few months before, Diderot had issued an anonymous booklet entitled *Letter on the Blind,* with the intriguing subtitle *For the Use of Those Who Can See*. It was a very clever sideswipe at man's passive acceptance of the existence of God on no stronger evidence than the fact that this existence has been accepted by our forebears.

Diderot had to go to prison for this book, whose authorship he at first tried to deny. But meanwhile he had proudly sent a copy to Voltaire.

And Voltaire had answered!

And what a wonderful answer, of which Diderot was so vain that he exhibited it everywhere and promptly replied, "The moment when I received your letter, my dear sir and master, was one of the happiest of my life."

It's true that Voltaire had taken issue with some of Diderot's ideas (but all the better, since that showed that Voltaire had read the book and appreciated it). In particular he objected to Diderot's leaning toward atheism (Voltaire always fought atheism, wherever he found it): "But let me confess that I am not at all inclined to the opinion of the Saunderson of your book, who denied God because he happened to be born blind. I may be mistaken, but it seems to me that in his place I should have argued thus: Who has given me so many supplements to sight if not a very intelligent Being? And how is it that my mind can recognize the manifold relationships between all things, if there is no infinitely clever Workman behind it all?"

But the full extent of Rousseau's checkmate in this chess game of life, whose victory Jean Jacques had craved so hotly, was in Voltaire's invitation to Diderot, "You must do me the honor of sharing a philosophical repast with me at my house, along with several other sages, for I am passionately anxious to have a talk with you."

Diderot invited to dine with Voltaire! That was a blow!

It's true that Voltaire never set the date. Voltaire's mistress died. Other misfortunes occurred, and the philosophical repast never came off. But still it remained clear that Diderot had now far outdistanced Rousseau.

And then, to add to Rousseau's miseries, there was now this: that after all his years of dreaming, somehow Jean Jacques had managed to get himself confused with Voltaire's enemies. Perhaps irrevocably.

For just at this moment the suspicion of having hissed Voltaire was a very important matter. It was the period of the great Crébillon-Voltaire battle for first position in the world of the theater. Really a completely synthetic feud over the respective merits of these two writers. But at the moment the enemies of Voltaire had no other contender against the master except this seventy-five-year-old playwright whose popularity had long since waned along with whatever talent he had once demonstrated.

They were not stupid, these concocters of plots against Voltaire. Nor blind either. And they worked tirelessly, year after year, to humble Voltaire. For they recognized that literature was always a potential threat to the state. And particularly since the advent of Voltaire.

They recognized that due to the constant increase of printed matter and the ever spreading ability of people to read, literature was turning into an enormous realm—true, a realm without precise geography, but a realm nevertheless—in which a thousand or more writers ruled with unquestioned power over untold millions of readers, commanding them as if they were their sworn subjects.

Here was an army, a vast army, an international army, which someday might rise up in irresistible battalions, as indeed to this day it still may.

And if as yet this new domain had not constituted itself as an independent power, it was only because hitherto writers had not yet been fully awake to their own strength. They had developed the habit of fighting amongst themselves, of sneering at each other, engaging in ridicule and backbiting, in a doglike greed for the few scraps of favors that fell from the tables of the patrons.

Literally throwing away the world in their haste for a crumb.

But what would happen now? What would happen now that they

were becoming increasingly independent of patronage and appealing more and more directly to the general public? And particularly now that Voltaire had become so dominant in the world of letters as to be the acknowledged leader, a writer who was gradually bringing artists to see themselves as a body of workers armed with common sense and good taste, able, if they chose, to lock arms in the task of bringing truth and beauty into the lives of people?

Yes, what might happen now when a writer as outstanding and clever as Voltaire came into being, endowed with a genius and with a logic that no one could resist? Would he discover himself someday with an army at his back stronger than the Church? Stronger than the state? Stronger than the King himself? Stronger than all nations and all peoples?

Such a potential menace must be met and resisted before it went too far. Writers must be shown up as a quarrelsome lot of rowdies, unreliable, vicious, ridiculous and incapable of making a living for themselves without the charity of the aristocrats or the Church. And the fame of any writer must be shown to be nothing more than the evanescent manifestation of an always fickle public.

The public and the writers of the time had to be shown that a Voltaire could be made and unmade at will, at the behest of the King or any other important personage.

But it was difficult, if not impossible, to get the better of Voltaire. Because of his genius. Take for example Voltaire's book *Elements of the Philosophy of Newton*. Newton's great revolution in physics, optics, and especially in our view of the universe, was already fifty years old and had still not penetrated public thinking, being confined to scholars. Then Voltaire undertook to write a book on the subject.

He didn't even finish it. A publisher had the first part of the manuscript and got tired of waiting for Voltaire to provide the conclusion. He hired a mathematician to supply an end. And he added to Voltaire's title the following words: "Adapted to the capacity of the general public."

And at once sensation! With Voltaire furious that his book was being published without his permission, and incensed that someone else should have completed the manuscript. Crying out that the book was full of errors and that he repudiated it.

But it was still Voltaire. Bad as it was. Bad as it would always be, even when Voltaire rewrote it and finished it in a subsequent edition.

Suddenly Newton was known to everyone. And in some measure everyone now understood a little of Newton's philosophy, if only from that story which Voltaire was the first to publish (and which he perhaps invented), the famous story of Newton under the apple tree, seeing the apple fall to the ground, and his mind at once leaping to the whole universe and visualizing the great principles of universal gravitation, the attraction of all bodies to each other.

Voltaire gave Newton to the world!

What a hubbub! With the Abbé Desfontaines, that unfrocked priest whom Voltaire had saved from being burned at the stake for pederasty with a little Savoyard chimney sweep (the abbé had appealed to Voltaire from his prison, and Voltaire had appealed to his most powerful friends, while at the same time making fun of the whole business by claiming that the little chimney sweep with his brushes had looked to the abbé like Cupid with his bow and arrows), the Abbé Desfontaines who was now making his living by attacking Voltaire (what else could he do? he had to make a living somehow, and attacking Voltaire was a business for which he could always find a patron)—the Abbé Desfontaines made a famous pun about the subtitle to Voltaire's book on Newton, *Adapted to the Capacity of the General Public,* which in French is *Mis à la portée de tout le monde,* changing just one letter of it to make it read: *Mis à la porte de tout le monde,* meaning "shown to the door by everyone." A truly diabolic pun.

But somehow the more one attacked Voltaire, the greater he became. And yet the attacking had to go on. This man with the independent mind had to be brought to heel!

Of course the truth was that Voltaire was far from being the danger to society that he might have been. He personally just did not believe that by overthrowing the government one could suddenly create better human beings and thus a better, happier society. Men like Desfontaines—and how many others!—who had crossed his career, and whom Voltaire had helped or even saved, and who repaid him with lies and bitter enmity, had convinced him that the human race would improve only gradually.

If at all.

And that couldn't be helped. That lay in the nature of man. In his passions. Suppose, for example, that you could cure man of his greed. What would result? Society would stagnate! No one would crave anything with sufficient force to drive him either to work or to fight for it. Men would lie around in a state of apathy. They would degenerate to a level below cattle.

So human beings must have their passions. But once you have passions, and society is bubbling with activity as a result, how are you going to make absolutely sure that no one will ever let his passions get the better of him and lead him to violence, to arson, to theft, rape or murder?

The best one could hope for was that in time the light of reason would spread and prevail, and thus that man would gradually ameliorate.

But though Voltaire himself had no desire to upset applecarts, his genius was there. The power was there. And even though he would use it only cautiously, still it was with him, and even years after his death the authorities would still tremble with fear over the words that Voltaire had put down on paper.

So much so that the Catholic Church would put all his works on the Index of Prohibited Books, even though during his lifetime Voltaire had been a friend of the Pope. And some countries, such as Italy, would never permit the sale of Voltaire's books. And later, even in France itself, Napoleon Bonaparte for twenty years would subsidize newspapers and magazines to carry on a campaign of besmirching the name of Voltaire. Why? Was it perhaps because Voltaire had written in his *History of Charles XII:*

"Certainly no sovereign, reading the life of Charles XII, can fail to be healed of the folly of conquests. For where is the sovereign who can assert, 'I have more courage, more energy, a body more robust and a soul more steeled than Charles XII'? Or 'I have better troops than he, and I understand the art of war better'? And if, with all those advantages, and after all those victories, Charles XII nevertheless perished so miserably, what can other sovereigns expect, driven by the same ambition, but backed up by less talent and fewer resources?"

Such, then, was the origin of the Voltaire-Crébillon feud: in the desire of certain people, indeed in their necessity, to humble Voltaire, if only by raising up a rival playwright.

It was true that Crébillon had seen his best days. He was really no longer a playwright at all. Still, the enemies of Voltaire were not stupid. Something had happened recently: Madame de Pompadour had become the mistress of the King of France.

The enemies of Voltaire knew that Crébillon had been a friend of the Poisson family and had taught their daughter (who was later to become Madame de Pompadour) how one stands with grace and walks with beauty. And how one pitches one's voice so that it rings and it becomes an enchantment to listen to.

And the little girl had been so lively, so quick-witted and so eager, that Crébillon had called upon his theatrical connections to complete her education. To teach her to sing and accompany herself on the piano. To give imitations that were tinctured with just the right amount of malice to make them exciting and funny without being insulting. To wear clothes so that every fold of material, every fall of lace or ribbon, would speak of charm and of distinction. And to converse with just the right touch of irony and roguishness to procure her as many friends and as few enemies as possible.

And now that she was Madame de Pompadour and the most powerful woman in France, these enemies of Voltaire approached her and informed her casually that poor Crébillon was living in misery. Which wasn't exactly true.

"My dear Crébillon in want?" Madame de Pompadour exclaimed. "Why has no one told me before? Here. Quick, my purse! Take this gold to him. Tell him there is more if he needs it."

"It's the neglect of his works that really distresses him most," she was told. "You know how great a dramatist he once was."

"Why doesn't the Théâtre-Français revive his plays?" Madame de Pompadour asked.

"With Voltaire so powerful there?" was the answer. "It's well known how much he despises everything that Crébillon has written. So long as the Théâtre-Français remains on the side of Voltaire, the actors and actresses there will keep on spurning Crébillon."

Thus they tried to turn Madame de Pompadour, who always liked Voltaire, against him, while Crébillon, a nice enough fellow, was brought to court and showered with attention. And the story would go the rounds that at his first interview with Madame de Pompadour, when she received him at her bedside and he bent down to kiss her hand, the door opened.

"Madame, we are lost!" cried the gray-haired Crébillon in mock terror. "It is the King!"

These and other stories were purposely circulated in order to swell the wave of sympathy for Crébillon, and to give those people who always lean with the prevailing wind something to gossip about, and to demonstrate that Crébillon's wit was fully as good as, if not better than, Voltaire's.

The result of all this fuss and fury was to give the impression that somehow it was Voltaire who had contrived by trickery to keep the great Crébillon off the stage, but that the court was now determined to see justice done to this neglected genius. The actors and actresses of the Théâtre-Français, being after all employees of the King and paid out of his pocket, could not resist what seemed to be royal orders and began to schedule Crébillon for performances, and to give his works extended runs whether the public showed up or not.

Voltaire knew, of course, of the plot that was being cooked up against him, and though it came at a difficult moment of his life, when he had just suffered the death of his mistress the Marquise du Châtelet, he took up the challenge. In order to be able to call upon the enlightened opinion of the general theatergoer, he first issued a statement avowing his own high regard for Crébillon and thus cleared the decks for a public demonstration of who was the better playwright.

In a matter of weeks he had ready for the stage a number of plays paralleling Crébillon's best. To make the comparison all the more vivid, he chose to use Crébillon's own themes, writing a *Semiramis* to match that of Crébillon, writing a *Rome Saved* to match Crébillon's *Catilina,* and an *Orestes* to match Crébillon's *Electra.*

"Let the public judge," so Voltaire was saying, "which of us can handle these themes better!" And while the big Théâtre-Français was occupied with Crébillon, Voltaire fixed up his own private theater on the Rue Traversière, a place so tiny that the steps of the staircase were considered boxes, while the reserved "seats" were nothing but standing room.

It didn't take the public long to see where the real talent lay. The tiny theater on the Rue Traversière was mobbed. And the Théâtre-Français, playing to empty houses, was soon compelled to invite Voltaire back. For it is easy enough to fill a theater with a claque, but not so easy to fill it with an audience.

But the Crébillon cabal fought on, and at the première of Voltaire's *Orestes,* at the Théâtre-Français, there was such an organized attempt to howl down the author that the noise was deafening, and three hours after the curtain had risen the actors had still not been able to speak a single line.

It was during such a disputed performance of a Voltaire play, when the power of the public was definitely winning out over the power of patronage, after the hired claque had been finally forced into silence by the audience's determination not to leave the theater until the piece had been played—it was at such a juncture, and just when the audience was listening to a particularly effective Voltairean scene, that suddenly there was a long-drawn whistle of contempt.

Voltaire, sharp-faced but purblind, rose from his box and stared blinkingly into the parterre. "Who was that?" he yelled in hot fury.

There was no answer. But somebody in the pit was talking angrily and rapidly.

"Coward!" Voltaire screamed. "Show yourself, you Boeotian!" Referring to the stupid peasants of that province of ancient Greece.

Someone spoke up: "That was Rousseau who whistled."

"Rousseau?" Voltaire thundered. But then he had to recollect himself and ask, "Which Rousseau? Thomas Rousseau? Is that who it was? Or the ghost of Jean Baptiste Rousseau? Or perhaps the little Rousseau?"

He would have gone on storming if the wife of the famous engraver of Watteau paintings, Jacques Philippe Le Bas, had not yelled at him, "I want to listen to the play! Now are you going to shut up? Or must I come over and smack you?"

Voltaire shouted back, "Learn, madame, that I am the author of the play you are so anxious to hear."

But this tempestuous lady cut him short with a withering comment: "I never go to the theater to listen to an author! I go there to listen to his play! And now silence, please!"

Defeated by a witty woman, but pleased nevertheless that he should be called to order by someone so determined to listen to his play, Voltaire said, "There is no known defense against an attack that is a compliment." And subsided amidst titters while the actors began the scene over again.

Of course it was unthinkable that Jean Jacques Rousseau should hiss Voltaire. There can be no doubt on whose side he was in this dramatic feud. He could not have watched Voltaire's play except with admiration and stupefaction.

And, of course, considerable envy.

The spectacle of a Voltaire girding himself to combat against a Crébillon and in a matter of weeks tossing out his plays like so many bombs, that was something that Jean Jacques could only view with amazement. Here he had been trying for almost twenty years to write just one play for production, and he had not yet succeeded, while Voltaire wrote them at command, one after another, in a matter of days.

Was it not enough to make one gnash one's teeth with envy and frustration? And now this false accusation of having hissed his master! If, nearly five years before, he had shed tears over a letter and written it with painstaking care, over this second letter to Voltaire he must have shed gouts of blood.

For now he renounced writing, was through with it forever, aware that he was totally lacking in the kind of talent that was required for a literary career. Diderot had it. But not he.

Here is what he sat down to write, on January 30, 1750. And as usual making copy after copy until he had it perfect, and as usual commanding absolute silence from his Thérèse.

He began by recalling that night in Soleure two decades ago, when he had first sensed the power of Voltaire.

MONSIEUR:

There was once a Rousseau, I mean Jean Baptiste Rousseau, the poet, who was your enemy because he was afraid that otherwise it might be too evident how much he was your inferior.

There is now another Rousseau, Thomas Rousseau, the editor, who supposes that by also making himself into your enemy he may pretend to some share of the talent that Jean Baptiste had.

As for me, who bear the same name as these men, I have neither the talent of the poet nor the influential position of the editor, and my only merit is that I would never permit myself the injustices that those two men have displayed against you.

I do not mind living unknown. But it would horrify me to live in dishonor. And I would indeed consider myself dishonored were I to show myself lacking in that respect which all men of letters owe to you, and which all writers who are worthy of their profession gladly accord to you.

As a lone man with no powerful patron, as a humble man lacking the art of speaking, I have never dared present myself to you. On what pretext, on what basis, would I have done so? It was not for lack of zeal, but out of pride, that I never dared show myself to you. I was waiting for some more favorable occasion when I would truly have the right to show you my respect and my gratitude.

Yes, he must have been in tears at this point. And even before he reached that next line, the bitterest of all:

Now I have renounced the practice of literature. I have rid myself of the illusion that I might someday acquire a reputation. But, despairing of ever achieving fame as a result of genius, as you have so brilliantly succeeded, I continue to disdain the schemes that others employ. For never shall I give up my admiration for your works.

You have depicted such friendship and virtue in your writings that it is obvious you know them and love them. Yes, I have heard the envious muttering against you, but I have despised their accusations, and I have said it out loud, with no fear that I could possibly be mistaken: "Writing that can elevate my soul and inflame my courage can never come from a man who is indifferent to virtue."

I protest then, sir, that not only could I, the Rousseau of Geneva, never have been responsible for the hissing which you attributed to me, but that I am utterly incapable of such an action. I cannot flatter myself on having merited the honor of being known to you, but if that happiness should ever be mine, it will, I trust, never be the result of anything but efforts worthy of your highest esteem.

I have the honor, sir, to sign myself your very humble and respectful servant,

JEAN JACQUES ROUSSEAU . . .

He must have paused here, asking himself, How can I make sure that this great man will realize that every word written here is truth? Bitter, meaningful truth?

How does one distinguish truth from falsehood in this century when everybody is so fulsome with politeness?

How, in this sparkling age of lightheartedness, in this age of flattery and counterflattery, in this age of cabal and intrigue carried on amidst wit and laughter, where nothing is serious or honest, how in this age when everything is as false as the gray hair of men's wigs, as false as the sword that everyone carries but not one in ten knows how to use, how in this age when women wear beauty spots to give themselves an air of having spent their lives in dissipation, how in this age that has ruined the meaning of every word, how does one convey to a Voltaire that this letter is something more than the usual effusive note that Parisians toss off by the thousands every day?

It was in order to draw a sharp distinction between himself and others, in order to show that this was really a cry of despair from a man about to give up a profession that he had tried to follow for so long, that Jean Jacques, for the first time in his correspondence, used an appelation which he was eventually to make famous.

"Citizen of Geneva"—so he signed himself, as if he were breaking now and forever with that spirit of Paris, with that spirit of Catholic Paris, with all the illusions that he had entertained ever since he had run away from his engraver's workbench in Calvinistic Geneva.

And so he signed himself "Jean Jacques Rousseau, citizen of Geneva."

That should make it clear to Voltaire.

But for all Rousseau's labors, and for all his new signature, Voltaire could see nothing unusual in this letter. Had he been less the polite gentleman of the eighteenth century he might not have answered it at all. But being the sensitive person that he was, he dashed off a note so quick, so truly in his *currente calamo* style, that he didn't even give himself time to make capital letters.

to m roussau of geneva [so he wrote, cavalierly misspelling Jean Jacques's name], by your probity you rehabilitate the name of roussau, the man who hissed me was obviously no citizen of geneva, but a citizen of those quagmires that lie at the foot of mount parnassus. such a person has faults of which you are surely incapable, just as you must have merits of which his kind can have no inkling.—V.

It was really a very sweet note, but it had obviously occupied the great man for no more than a couple of seconds. And when Rousseau thought of all the care and anguish on his part! For what? For what indeed? Voltaire, evidently under the quick impression that Rousseau had blown a whiff of perfume in his direction, had done the polite thing, according to eighteenth-century etiquette, and had shot right back with a little whiff in Rousseau's direction. Phuit! Phuit! And two perfect gentlemen sheathed their perfume bottles, pirouetted on their scarlet heels and retired from the field of honor, the incident obviously closed with credit to both sides.

Is that all life was? Two squirts of flowery compliments?

How lost, how abandoned, how remote from human warmth and true friendship such a note must have appeared to the poor unknown acolyte, lying sick with uremia, his body bloated, his breath fetid, his mind unclear! And how he must have vowed through his semidelirium that someday he would be known as the most impolite man in France—but at the same time the most honest!

5: A SHOWER OF GOLD

In his calmer moments Rousseau might realize that he was expecting the impossible from Voltaire. (But then, when was Rousseau ever calm?) For Voltaire was obviously busy with a thousand matters, as Rousseau well knew, since almost everything that Voltaire did was public knowledge.

There was, for example, Voltaire's voluminous correspondence with the King of Prussia, an exchange of letters that ranged through every aspect of life, from the most grotesque to the most sublime. Thus Voltaire might petition His Majesty to send him some of Dr. Stahl's pills. "A goodly supply, please, because those we get here in Paris are miserable imitations that have no effect whatsoever on my obdurate gut."

And Frederick would answer, "Are you mad? What? The great Voltaire still has faith in those charlatans of doctors? Let me tell you about Dr. Stahl and his pills. The doctor is dead now, and those pills of his were really compounded by his coachman and were never intended originally for anything but horses. Here in Prussia, it is only girls who have to bring about an abortion on themselves who resort to such violent drugging."

To which Voltaire would answer, "No. I don't believe in doctors or in doctoring. But when I stumble on a remedy that finally has some effect on me, I am forced to put my faith in it, abortion or no abortion."

What Frederick the Great wanted was for Voltaire to move from Paris to Potsdam. And when Voltaire had lost his great love, the Marquise du Châtelet, who had always disliked the Prussian, Frederick could not understand why Voltaire should not yield to his entreaties.

"I have a chattel mortgage on your works!" he would write. "You must come and live with me. And bring me all your manuscripts!"

And to the members of his court Frederick would gloat, "If I can lure that man away from France, I shall have attained more than if I had kidnaped their whole French Academy of Belles Lettres. For Voltaire is at one and the same time their best dramatist, their only epic poet, their most capable historian, their sharpest essayist, their most enlightened philosopher, one of their best scientists and their most learned grammarian."

It was this German King's desire to go down in history not only as a great monarch but also as one of the great writers of French poetry and prose. And for that he needed Voltaire. He needed him to correct his lines and give them additional poetic values. With the result that in the letters these two men exchanged they were forever leaping from prose into verse and back again.

"Is it money you want?" Frederick would write in a poem to Voltaire. "Then let me be your Zeus, coming to you in a shower of gold as he did to Danaë."

And Voltaire, versifying back, could only plead that it would take a lot of gold to move his sickly carcass, but that it was not really gold that he wanted, but just to go and die at the feet of his great and noble friend. However, he was not only sick, he was also first gentleman of the chamber to His Majesty the King of France, and his duties retained him in France.

"Come and be *my* chamberlain," Frederick would write. "I shall put the golden key around your neck. And hang upon your breast the Order of Merit, the highest decoration I can bestow."

"What about my establishment in Paris?" Voltaire would counter. "It costs me thirty thousand francs a year to maintain it."

"Keep it!" the King would say, tossing another poem at Voltaire. "As for your accommodations here, they will not cost you a single penny. You shall have your room in my palace here at Sans Souci, and it will be the same room that was once reserved for Marshal de Saxe. And as for food, there's my kitchen, open day and night, to serve you with whatever your body needs or your heart desires. Carriage, coachman, groom, everything will be at your disposal. And for your purely personal expenses, you shall have twenty thousand francs a year."

Twenty thousand francs a year! A fortune! And just for personal expense. While Rousseau earned altogether only eight hundred francs a year.

"But moving is such a damnably expensive business," Voltaire would argue.

"Enough!" the King cried in a poem which allotted Voltaire an extra sixteen thousand francs for the expenses of the voyage. And he added, "Since my banker in Paris may not honor a draft drawn up in lines that scan and rhyme, I am sending you another draft done in ordinary prose, which I am sure he will cash for you in gold."

And still Voltaire delayed. While the King grew furious.

The degree to which Voltaire would eventually irritate Rousseau was already to be seen in his ability to rouse the King of Prussia to such a point that he would write to another correspondent, "That Voltaire! Someday my guards will climb Mount Parnassus and horsewhip him there! The monkey! That's all he is. Cute little mannerisms, just like a monkey and full of monkey malice. God! Why should such a vile animal be endowed with such genius?"

And sometimes the King would come right out with it to Voltaire himself: "Tell me, were you born out of the icy flanks of the Caucasus? Were you suckled by the teats of a tigress? What is it that has made your heart just as cold and flinty as the rocks of the Alps? How can you be so ungrateful to me? To me who would strangle with my bare hands any man who dared deny your genius?"

But Voltaire wasn't in any hurry to commit himself. What a trick if he could pull it off, to have the King of France and the King of Prussia bidding against each other for his services. Voltaire, the most wanted man in the civilized world!

Then perhaps his great dream might come true. The great Voltairean dream of the philosopher-king. For he had been studying history closely and had come to the conclusion that the best government was that of the tyrant-philosopher, the ruler with irresistible determination and will power, who devotes himself single-mindedly to making his country happy and knows that *there,* where the most work is done, *there* the people are most prosperous.

Then one would see the day when instead of weeping over the ruins of Jerusalem, or standing with gaping mouths before the Pyramids of Egypt, modern man would build more colossal monuments than had ever been dreamed of. The ugly narrow streets of Paris would be torn out and yield to broad avenues. Great palaces with vast open places before them would create a city of beauty, light and air. Theaters, museums, fountains! Build! Build! Build!

And agriculture, as the basis of all wealth, would be protected and encouraged. Monks, whether brown, gray, white or black, shod or unshod, would be put to work. As would all other beggars. And nuns would be taken out of their convents and turned into good wives and good housekeepers. Work! Work! Work! And fill the earth with children! The God who made the sun doesn't need candles lit for Him.

And no more of this insane habit of burying people in churches! Which in hot weather caused Paris to stink. Would the God of a million universes be any worse off if several hundred thousand monks and nuns stopped their prayers and went to work? Would the dead be any nearer or any farther from heaven if their rotting corpses were buried in fields to enrich the soil and grow trees?

Enough of this praying business!

Come on, Louis XV and Frederick the Great, be the tyrants of your countries, but let a Voltaire or his equivalent be the guiding philosopher at your side.

Thus, as historiographer of France, with access to the secret archives, Voltaire labored in the accumulation of material for his great work on the century of Louis XIV, which he was to follow with his study of the times of Louis XV (for, having declared to the world in his *Philosophical Letters* the superiority of the English parliamentary and more democratic system, he was now annoyed at English ridicule of the French system and wished to show that a monarch like Louis

XIV had been able to make France into the greatest country of the world because he regarded the country as his property, and the people as his children, and wanted the best for them, and that there was nothing inherently bad in the monarchical system that could not be cured by a great king), and with all that, Voltaire nevertheless did not neglect his duties at court as chamberlain to Louis XV, nor did he give up the management of his growing fortune. In addition he continued to fight off the enemies who were forever sniping at him, of whom the Crébillon cabal is only one example among many. And somehow he also found time to prepare pamphlets on a variety of subjects, such as the one on the beautification of Paris, and another on a better system of taxation for France, a system that would force the aristocrats and the Church in line with the rest of the nation, compelling them to pay taxes like merchants and farmers, and putting an end to the exemption they enjoyed. In this pamphlet he exposed as false the claim made by the aristocracy and the Church that the donations they voluntarily made to the treasury in times of emergency more than equaled the taxes they would have paid. It is true that these donations were often spectacularly enormous, but Voltaire, who hated to have the wool pulled over his eyes, added them all together and discovered that if spread out over the years they would amount to only one half the rate paid by the commoners.

There was such a thirst for life in Voltaire!

And that thirst for life began with him, so the story goes, when the midwife first pulled him from his mother's womb and he showed no signs of life whatsoever and was therefore simply set aside on a chair, while the midwife occupied herself with the mother. But then a grandparent, groping about in the dim candlelit lying-in room, sat down on that chair, whereupon a faint noise was heard, like the escape of air from a pair of bellows.

What? A noise of air? Then there must be a flicker of life in those tiny lungs. And so indeed it turned out.

That faint noise was Voltaire's earliest protest against being sat upon by the superstitious, by the ignorant, by the past. It was a noise that would grow from year to year, until in time it would fill the world. But for a long time it would be so feeble that night after night his nurse would come down to the family room to weep and to tell the parents that their offspring could not possibly survive until the morning.

But Voltaire's struggle to live never stopped. It only broadened. And opened up to include a struggle against everything in the world that leaned toward the side of death.

He struggled against idleness, for example. For was not idleness a kind of death? Not a total death, it is true. Just a temporary death. But those minutes and those hours thus thrown out of one's life would never return, no more than gold coins thrown from the port-hole of a ship at sea.

And he struggled against ignorance. His own and others'. For wasn't that a form of death, too? The body remaining alive, while the mind was already clothed in its shroud and put away in its coffin.

And against sleep. Except for that basic minimum required for one's health.

And against boring company. Against those people who killed part of your life and gave you nothing in return.

And against darkness and cold. (Oh, the wretched cold of chilly rooms, where one could only sit and shudder and all work became impossible! Even as a boy in school he schemed to get closest to the hot stove and for a long time puzzled his Jesuit masters by an occasional stubborn stupidity, which it was later discovered occurred invariably in cold weather, because then the stove was lit in the rear of the room, to which the backward pupils were relegated.

(And years later, when he decided to compete for the annual prize of the French Academy of Sciences, the subject he chose to investigate was the nature of fire. His love of warmth was so intense and his fear of cold so great that Madame de Graffigny would exclaim with horror at the enormous flames in his fireplace. "Whole forests are swallowed up in such a furnace!" she would declare with indignation. But long before Montesquieu, Voltaire knew that a man had to have the right climate to develop himself in.)

For what are cold and darkness, if not forms of death? Do they not limit life? Everywhere that Voltaire looked, his beady black eyes and his sharp, inquisitive nose detected the sly and semiconcealed coils of death. In dirt, in poverty, in ugliness, which make people hate life instead of loving it. In sickness, in bodily infirmities, in old age, which turn life into a kind of half-death. In lack of friends and lack of enemies, which are the indicators of the dying down of our emotions and our enthusiasms. And in all forms of cruelty: in torture, in prisons, in war, which are the results of man allying himself with death instead of with life, allying himself with injustice and intolerance and ignorance, which are the enemies of life.

How vast are the armies enrolled under the banner of death!

And Voltaire would never stop fighting them.

Of course, Jean Jacques knew that Voltaire's mind was occupied with great projects, and that at the same time he faced the question of whether for his own good he ought not to exile himself, this time to Prussia, instead of to England as he had done years ago. Rousseau followed with excitement, as did all Paris, the question of whether Voltaire would leave France. Voltaire's enemies were ever active and even gained Louis XV himself, who openly declared that writers were a bore and that he saw no reason for lavishing any money on them.

Frederick, meanwhile, was scheming how he might, by trickery, bring Voltaire to a quick decision. And one way was by feeding material to Voltaire's enemies. Among others to the bishop of Mirepoix, a violent hater of Voltaire. In addition Frederick let the rumor be circulated in Paris that he no longer wanted Voltaire. He had found someone far superior, namely Baculard d'Arnaud.

"You are the brilliant dawn," he versified to Baculard. "Voltaire is the setting sun." And he saw to it that copies of this poem went around Paris.

Voltaire was at first furious. But then he only shrugged. He had himself foisted Baculard on the King of Prussia, because he had grown tired of supporting that blond giant, who was evidently cut out to be nothing more than a perpetual protégé, always giving great promise but never any fulfillment.

To Frederick, Voltaire wrote, "What a devil of a patron you will turn out to be. Clawing with one hand, while you caress with the other."

Still, in the end, tired of his perpetual battles in Paris, and seeking peace for finishing some of his more important works, particularly his *Century of Louis XIV*, Voltaire resigned his position at the French court, took leave of his dear niece and journeyed to Potsdam. And the moment he was out of the country, his enemies had prints struck off of Voltaire in Prussian uniform, and they hired colporteurs to hawk these caricatures on the streets of Paris, crying, "Voltaire, the traitor! Buy a print of Voltaire the Prussian!"

How deeply hurt Jean Jacques must have been to hear of the departure of his wonderful Voltaire to far-off Prussia, leaving him farther behind than ever. Twice in twenty years he had thrown himself at the feet of his hero, but only in letters, and twice he had received nothing more than a kindly nod and a perfunctory pat on the head.

But for all that, how excitedly he must have followed the news that told of how Frederick was planning for Voltaire's reception one of the greatest spectacles ever put on by man. How the courtyard of the royal palace in Berlin was to be turned into a great amphitheater, with forty-six thousand tiny lanterns of glass for illumination. And how a long schedule of balls, fireworks, concerts, operas and plays was being readied.

Three thousand of Prussia's finest troops were being trained to guard the area. Four princes of the royal family, each costumed differently, were rehearsing to head quadrilles of mounted knights clad in extravagant Roman, Carthaginian, Greek and Persian armor, who were to march and countermarch in a grand and glittering display of splendidly caparisoned knights and horses.

And as Voltaire came into the arena, attended by the foremost lords of the Prussian realm, and went to meet the King, who would himself deign to meet him halfway, the crowd would set up a cry of "Voltaire! Voltaire! Voltaire! Voltaire!"

It was to be the greatest reception ever planned for a writer in all recorded history. And certainly its like was never to be seen again.

These must have been the worst months of Rousseau's life. Sick, resigned to never amounting to anything in literature, with his Thérèse pregnant once more, and with nothing for Jean Jacques but his duties as secretary to Madame Dupin and a few articles on music which his friend Diderot, now editing material for the world's first great encyclopedia, was commissioning from him, he had to watch Voltaire leave France and go to this magnificent reception in Prussia.

But just then came the first sign of his own piercing through. Voltaire reached Potsdam on July 10, 1750, and moved into the suite of rooms assigned to him in the palace of Sans Souci. And on July 9 the Academy of Dijon announced that it was awarding first prize and gold medal to anonymous essay number seven, bearing the quotation from Horace *"Decipimur specie recti."* Meaning: "We are deceived by the righteous."

The anonymous author was Jean Jacques Rousseau.

This was, of course, still not much. Compared to Voltaire. But within a few days the *Mercure de France,* foremost literary periodical of the day, had sent a representative to Rue Grenelle-St.-Honoré to interview Rousseau and beg him for a contribution.

No, it was not much, but it was growing. For a day would come when Diderot (who, with Rousseau sick in bed, had himself undertaken the task of finding a printer for Jean Jacques's prize-winning essay) would come running up to Rousseau's apartment crying, "All Paris is thunderstruck! People are battling each other for a copy of your essay. The booksellers are all sold out and are clamoring for more copies. You are famous!"

It would still take time before Rousseau's new fame would spread beyond Paris, but already his situation had changed completely.

It had finally been demonstrated that he could write! A gold medal was specially struck for him by the Academy of Dijon. One hundred écus were awarded to him. And everywhere in Paris people were reading, discussing, criticizing, approving and disapproving his *Discourse on the Arts and Sciences.*

Was he not now finally worthy of Voltaire's esteem?

6: LIFE IS A SNARE

Yes, he was famous at last. He had finally pierced through.

And those rich salons of Paris that had formerly barely tolerated him, or had even relegated him to eat with the servants or actually closed their doors to him, especially on evenings when the truly great wished to be by themselves, these salons now vied with each other as to which might claim him as their most frequent guest.

Oh, yes, they all wanted him. Now.

But just at this time he was often too ill to rise from his bed. Madame Dupin, only too proud of the achievement of her secretary, sent him her own physician, the well-known Dr. Morand.

Other friends recommended Dr. Helvétius, father of the writer, and still others praised Malouin and Thierry.

In the despair of his pain, Rousseau saw them all.

They came to his bedside, where he rolled about in agony. They had no trouble locating the cause of his affliction. The inflamed belly, the burning in his loins, his bad breath and utter lassitude—everything pointed to the true seat of his malady.

"The fault is not in the kidneys themselves," they agreed. "We can find no evidence of stone. The disease comes from the bladder. Or, rather, from the condition of the urethra, which prevents the bladder from emptying itself thoroughly. With the bladder constantly engorged and the urine backing up, the kidneys are also affected. And finally the condition of the kidneys transmits itself to the whole body."

They also agreed that there was only one way to obtain relief: widen the urinary duct so that the bladder could be relieved.

But from this point on they all differed. Not only did each doctor have his own particular favorite type of bougie, or sound, which he wanted to introduce into the urethra in order to stretch it, some being made of metal, others of ivory, still others of parchment or of quills and some even of fine mouse leather rolled over a core of brass wire, but the question of what, if any, sort of emollient ought to be used to facilitate introduction, and whether the end ought not to carry some caustic substance into the interior in order to burn away supposed carbuncles or fleshy excrescences which presumably must be there obstructing the free flow of urine, all this divided one doctor sharply from another.

On only one point were they all united: in the pain they caused when they explored the sensitive canal or introduced searing medicaments, such excruciating pain that Jean Jacques's face broke out into a cold sweat, and Thérèse, standing at his bedside, had to give him a cloth to bite into in order to keep him from screaming.

There was even one ghastly time when a too delicate sound snapped off, leaving the broken piece buried in his urethra and blocking the passage completely. Jean Jacques nearly went crazy in his agony and fear of imminent death before the broken end was successfully, but oh, how painfully, extracted.

Such, then, was the price of civilization! he exclaimed to himself. Such was the cost in health exacted from those who spent their lives in study instead of in hard labor in fields and forests. And to relieve man when his functions failed, the cleverness of man had devised nothing better than these hellish bougies, which could as easily kill him as repair him.

What compensation was there for man to discover the most subtle laws of mathematics or hydraulics if the result was that one's body, for lack of sufficient exercise, degenerated to the point where one's own hydraulic machine failed and the body could not void its liquid waste?

It was only when old Dr. Daran appeared with his very thin and very flexible whalebone sounds that Rousseau was finally able to secure some relief without going through repeated agony. And because Daran was so old and so feeble that it seemed as if he might die at any moment, Rousseau ordered from him a huge quantity of his wonderful bougies, which cost him all the cash he had. Apparently one gained literary prizes only to expend them on doctors.

Daran had also to instruct Thérèse in the art of introducing the sounds. As well as how to keep them clean and supple.

Meanwhile, sick as he was, Rousseau never stopped working. He couldn't. Not now. Such influential scholars as Abbé Raynal, editor of the state-supported *Mercure de France,* who had so often in the past turned down Rousseau's work, now honored him with a lengthy refutation and held the columns open for Jean Jacques's reply. The well-known mathematics professor, Gautier of Nancy, also attacked Rousseau, and he too had to be answered. So did Academician Bordes of Lyons, and Academician Lecat.

And even a king. Yes, that too Rousseau had now acquired, a king who took notice of him. Nothing yet so grand, of course, as Voltaire's King of Prussia, in fact only an ex-king, Stanislas, formerly ruler of Poland, now Duke of Lorraine and father-in-law of Louis XV of France, who also brought out in the *Mercure* an attack on Rousseau's theory and received his reply in a subsequent issue.

Only from Voltaire, not a single word. Voltaire, Voltaire . . .

But in Paris, wherever Rousseau might appear now, people would point him out as the philosopher who condemned all the proudest accomplishments of man. Pointed him out as the writer who boldly castigated all modern civilization. The man who wanted to turn back the world to the time when we were all savages and barbarians, without books or paintings or any of our wonderful arts and sciences.

Just healthy, free, naked savages.

On the streets, in cafés, in the lobby of the theater, in the homes he visited, people, even strangers to whom he had never been introduced, considered it now their right to buttonhole him and force him into a debate.

It was after all such a fascinating point of view: that the more man struggled to improve himself, the weaker and the more unhappy and the more evil he became. Could it possibly be true? Was everything really upside down?

"What?" people would cry at him. "Poor nations are stronger than rich ones? How can you maintain such an obvious untruth?"

"Doesn't history demonstrate it to us on every page?" Rousseau would find himself forced to argue. "Wasn't China in her greatest glory humbled by the fierce Mongols? And Greece, did she not go down to defeat at the height of her wealth and her arts? And Rome, mistress of the world, living amidst marble and bronze, drawing revenues and slaves from a hundred conquered provinces, was she not overrun and destroyed by barbarians who owned nothing but the miserable clothes on their backs and the crude weapons in their hands?"

"You may be right, that wealth does indeed corrupt," people would grant him. "But you say the same of the sciences. Surely knowledge can't corrupt man."

"Knowledge itself is corruption," Rousseau burst out. "The man who reflects is depraved!"

"What a thing to say! My dear Monsieur Rousseau—depraved?"

"I say it because it is true! Aren't all the sciences born out of depravity? Medicine? Is it not man's effort to save himself from the bother of obeying the laws of nature, of observing the rules of hygiene? And as for astronomy, did it not arise from the superstitions of astrology, man's ungodly efforts to pierce the mystery of the future? And geometry? Was it not due to the avarice of landowners who wanted to measure and hold on to their properties even if war or flood should obliterate all boundary marks? And what, may I ask, gave rise to all our arts of composition, of oratory, of eloquence and persuasion, if not the ambition of office seekers, the money lust of lawyers and their clients. Yes, all the sciences together are nothing but the outgrowth of human greed, human pride and curiosity. And their ultimate aim is to enable man to indulge in ever greater laziness, gluttony, luxury and concupiscence."

"Ah, well, one must grant you that some sciences have their faulty origin. But surely you go too far when you call the invention of printing a scourge. Surely the gift of books to man— Why, I can't imagine what man would do without books!"

"Precisely!" Jean Jacques would say with scorn. "What would we do without books? How necessary they have become to us! And what is the result? Man everywhere greedily devours books, seeking in the opinions of others the clue to happiness and to understanding, when all along he should be searching for these gifts within himself, which is the only place where they can be found."

"How persuasive you are, Monsieur Rousseau. But certainly there is one aspect of modern society which you cannot condemn. The art of pleasing, in which we French have advanced beyond any other people. Really, you cannot mean to deprive us of our good manners, our politeness, and all the charms of our French talent, the Parisian theater, our opera, our paintings, our architecture."

"The worst of all!" Rousseau cried. "What are they but disguises! We live in an age when no man dares be himself. All of us, whatever we may really be, the coward, the cripple, the diseased, the suborner, the weakling, the liar, all now speak the same language, all mouth the same formulas of good breeding. All wear the same dress, and observe the same rules of good behavior. Don't talk to me of the charms of

73

society, which have produced nothing but a herd of sheep. How different from each other we would be were we naked, and if we expressed our real thoughts, our true feelings, and bartered the products of our hands against the handiwork of others. How varied and individual we'd be! Crude and intolerable, perhaps, but at any rate healthy and honest, without pretense or deceit."

Endless were the questions thrown at him. Should we really close our schools, our academies, our institutions of learning? Did he really think that we should burn our libraries? Could anyone really argue that the world might be better off had there never been a Kepler, a Galileo, a Newton?

Rousseau hated all this fuss. Hated it and loved it at the same time. Loved it because it meant that he was finally being recognized. Hated it because it drew him into conversations, where he was never at his best. He could not seem to summon his arguments quickly enough. Nor put them into a sufficiently telling form. He lacked vigor in his expressions. He fumbled for words. In short, he needed time for reflection.

But of course he did not dare say that. He had visions of someone retorting, "I thought you said that the man who reflected was depraved."

As a result of his dubious position he was often curt with his interlocutors. He would pull away abruptly and tell people to read his essay and tear it up if they didn't like it. But as for himself, they should leave him alone.

But the more impolite he became, in this city of exaggerated politeness, the more of an attraction he became. All Paris insisted on adopting this ill-behaved boor, calling him affectionately *"notre Jean Jacques."* Our good Jean Jacques. For all the bored and rich people of the nation seemed suddenly to have found a new and exciting sport: to be scolded by Jean Jacques. Everyone flocked to see him, and if they couldn't get him to talk they could stare at him as if he were the man from the moon.

Yes, everybody seemed excited about Rousseau and his thesis. Everybody, that is, except Voltaire.

Jean Jacques had naturally sent him a copy of his essay the very moment it had come off the press. Just as Diderot had done with his *Letter on the Blind.* But, unlike Diderot, he had received no word from Voltaire. Not even an acknowledgment. And certainly no invitation such as Diderot had received, to a dinner of sages. Which would be at the moment the famous circle of intellectuals gathered about Frederick at Potsdam.

74

Not a word. Not a single word.

Was it perhaps because Voltaire was maturing a thoughtful and lengthy letter for him? A refutation, no doubt. Since Voltaire certainly cherished the sciences and the arts. And yet, ought not precisely such a great philosopher as Voltaire appreciate man's degeneration from his primitive nobility?

But even a refutation—or an excoriation—would have delighted Rousseau. As an excuse to escape from his present position, a position that was becoming ever more involved and difficult to defend: that he who had spent so many years struggling to perfect himself in the arts and the sciences should now be rejecting them.

How wonderful, then, if Voltaire should offer him a way out! How wonderful to find himself forced to bow to Voltaire's superior reasoning. And thus give up his stand without making himself ridiculous and without sacrificing the notoriety that had come to him with it.

But at any rate something. Whether praise or blame. At least some word from Voltaire, even if only another squirt of perfume.

But nothing. It was as if Rousseau did not exist for Voltaire.

And then, suddenly, there began to circulate through Paris a witty epigram, which those who repeated it claimed to have from the mouth of Voltaire. By way of his trumpet Thieriot.

The King of Prussia had supposedly asked Voltaire, "Have you read Rousseau's essay?"

"Sire," said Voltaire, "I have read it. A very eloquent essay. Indeed, I may say that never has eloquence been so eloquently condemned."

That hurt. That hurt profoundly. Coming from Voltaire. But then it might be a false report. Wags were constantly attributing to him things that he had never said.

But the line, whatever its origin, had its effect in Paris. Already Rousseau could sense that people were thinking more and more about the paradoxical nature of his position.

And smiling to themselves in a superior way as they argued with him.

All the way from Prussia it seemed one could hear Voltairean laughter. "Who is this Jean Jacques Rousseau who uses the printing press to print an essay against printing?" Voltaire was supposed to have written to one of his Paris correspondents.

Jean Jacques still would not credit these lines to Voltaire. But he began to appreciate more than ever the knifelike edge on which he had taken his position. He dreaded the thought of finding himself committed to walking forever on a tightrope of sublimity across an abyss of the ridiculous. Swaying perilously to the wind of every waggish line from Voltaire and forced eventually to fall and be laughed at as a clown.

It was notorious that in Paris everything was a seven-day wonder. These same people now so excited about him could at any moment begin to scorn him.

Was that to be the end of his fame?

Well, he would show them. He would prove to everyone that here was one man who adhered to what he wrote. To whom life was no mere persiflage. A man who was prepared to back his position with his life.

Vitam impendere vero! That would hereafter be his motto. "I have dedicated my life to the truth!"

Only recently, now that he had become well known, the Dupin family had decided to distinguish their secretary and enable him to live in a style more fitting to his reputation. And therefore the son-in-law of the family, the same M. de Francueil with whom Rousseau had pursued serious studies in chemistry, gave Jean Jacques an additional position: he was to be head of the Dupin countinghouse.

Since the Dupins were members of the little clique of tax farmers who annually participated in the bid for the right to collect the national revenues of France, Jean Jacques, as cashier for one of that group, was suddenly in line for real wealth. These farmers-general, as they were called, would estimate each year the probable tax returns and would pour this sum immediately into the French treasury, which, being chronically up against a deficit, was in constant need of ready cash.

At this particular period, the society of tax farmers would have to advance each year about sixty million francs. A sum which they would then have to squeeze out of the people in tariffs, poll and property taxes, duties on salt and tobacco, and other internal revenue. Whatever they collected above the sum they had already paid out accrued to them as profit. And usually that profit was enormous. So that the Popelinières, the Dupins, the Saint-James', the Lavoisiers, etc., lived in a style that rivaled dukes and even the King himself.

As head of the Dupin countinghouse, Rousseau might reasonably expect to be allowed to purchase some slight participation in the tax-farming pool. And in time, perhaps, become a full-fledged partner. The fortune of the witty philosopher Helvétius, son of the doctor, stemmed from this source. Why not, eventually, that of Rousseau?

But he could just imagine the Voltairean epigram! Jean Jacques the tax collector!

Abruptly he wrote a letter of resignation to the Dupins. He might continue to be their secretary, since he felt that he rendered services commensurate with his pay. But he could no longer be their cashier.

The Dupin family was dumfounded. They had given him this position only as a reward, as an honor, as a testimony of their admiration. They therefore visited him to find out why he was now turning it down. They came to beg him to reconsider.

But Jean Jacques's mind was made up.

"One cannot preach freedom, disinterestedness and poverty and then not practice what one preaches," he said. "One cannot accuse the world of hypocrisy and oneself remain a hypocrite. People must see that in this age without convictions there exists one man who is not afraid to reach convictions and then abide by them."

When they continued to argue with him, Rousseau pulled them up sharply: "Apparently you have not seen, as I have, peasants who have to hide their bread, their wine, their meat, because they are lost men if revenue officers should ever learn that they are not starving. Or should excise men ever learn that they have something else to drink besides plain water."

Jean Jacques concluded brutally, "No. When it comes to choosing whether I shall live with the oppressors or the oppressed, I cannot hesitate for a moment. It is not you who should be surprised that I resign, but, rather, I who should be surprised that you should not yourself give up a livelihood which is founded on so much injustice."

In vain the Dupins argued that they did not set the tax laws. They only bid for the right to collect them. "If we resign, will not the taxes still be collected? And perhaps by people who will be far more severe than we are. In resigning from the tax farmers' group, who can say whether we shall be doing the people a good turn or an evil one?"

Jean Jacques shrugged. This was something he refused to answer. All he knew was that he had a duty to his conscience.

Through Paris spread this story of the man of virtue. This man who was absolutely incorruptible.

Diderot, Grimm, Klüpfel, Duclos and others came running to find out what was happening. They all wanted to know how Rousseau meant to manage. There was so little money in writing. What had he got out of his essay, in spite of all its popularity?

Diderot said, "I considered myself lucky to have found a printer for you: Pissot, who was willing to print your essay at his own expense. All the others wanted to be paid. No one could be sure that it would sell more than a dozen copies."

Rousseau could not gainsay that. He knew that there was precious little money in the sale of books. At any rate, for authors. It was only the resulting fame and the patrons it might be expected to bring that gave one any compensation for putting one's books into print. One might expect invitations to dinner as a result, or a stay in the country home of some important and rich man. There were sinecures to be had from the wealthy and pensions from the King. It was these rewards that counted in the life of an author.

From the publishers one could expect very little. And that was not entirely their fault. They themselves were not certain of any revenue. No sooner did a book hit the stalls and show some signs of becoming popular, than another printer had quickly issued it in an edition pretending to come from abroad and bearing the word "London" or "Geneva" or "The Hague" on the title page, as if it had been smuggled into the country.

Indeed, even when you paid a printer to print up for you a given number of copies, intending to sell them yourself, you had to beware lest unknown to you he print up a secret batch for himself and put himself in a position to compete against his own client.

In the matter of plays, there was some reward from the theaters of the capital, but any play that was a success was immediately played all over Europe with no additional royalties paid. And as for plays in book form, all the printers sent their stenographers to the performances, and a successful play was already in print and for sale the following morning. Full of errors, naturally, and with no money for the author.

Well known were the stories of how Voltaire revenged himself on the crooked printers of Paris. When he wanted to bring out his philosophical romance *Zadig,* for example, he took the odd-numbered sections to one printer, pretending that he had given him the whole book. And then took the even-numbered sections to another printer, under the same pretense. He then hired needlewomen to sew all the signatures together in their right order and thus found himself the only person with complete copies for sale, and with two rival printers both offering mutilated editions to a mocking public.

The printers cursed him, but Voltaire had his laugh on them for the years of cheating they had practiced on him.

In this dog-eat-dog world of writing, how would Rousseau earn a living?

"I will do what most people in this world have to do in order to eat," Rousseau said. "Has no one ever heard of honest work with one's hands?"

"What honest work will you do with your hands?" they asked.

"I can turn out a very neat page of musical notation," Rousseau decided. "For the short span of life remaining to me, I shall copy music, and I am sure that my little earnings will suffice."

He could see that such an answer did not sit well with Diderot, with Grimm, with Klüpfel and the others. It seemed to accuse them of earning their living by somewhat less than honest means. It seemed to say, "People with fewer scruples may not mind whence comes the money which supports them. But I do." It seemed to relegate them into the class of parasites.

Where, indeed, to some extent they all belonged.

Certainly Grimm did, the man who used his literary correspondence to establish relations with all the best families of Europe, and who would eventually bow and scrape his way into an Austrian baronetcy, a Russian colonelship, and medals and stars without number.

And surely Klüpfel, who with his *Almanach de Gotha* established what is without doubt the world's supreme snob book of all time.

And even to some extent the democratic Diderot, rough son of a bourgeois producer of surgical instruments though he might be. For when Empress Catherine of Russia would eventually buy his library for sixty thousand francs and leave it in his care, Diderot would erect her bust in the center of it and go there to pray and to write panegyrics to her.

Such men, with their ambitions and their mental acuteness, could not but suspect in Rousseau's determination to live on a couple of francs a day, which was all he could make by copying music, a kind of hypocritical shortcut to the same fame they were all after, but where they could no longer compete with him.

And Rousseau, for his part, knowing that their position was not without its justification, could not help but despise them for not having his kind of courage, no matter how hypocritical it might be. For he was staking his whole life on this play, where they were gambling only a little bit of themselves at a time.

Thus, where formerly there had been a great friendship of talented but impecunious men, there were now suddenly deep rifts of suspicion which would only widen with time.

Diderot expecially, who was so closely involved in the origin and in the printing of that prize essay that had touched off this new trend in Rousseau, felt himself particularly called upon to suspect and attack his friend's motives.

But Jean Jacques would not budge. "Music copying is a highly prized skill," he said. "It is an honest profession. It is useful. And there is no one whom I can harm in this way."

"What makes you think so?" Diderot countered. "Take my copyist,

79

whom I have to employ now and then when my pages become almost indecipherable from too many corrections. This poor man knocks at my door two or three times a week to ask if I have work for him. Only recently I wanted something done immediately, and so went to look him up, and for the first time saw the place and the condition in which he lives.

"Not in a room. For he can't afford a room. Just a piece of a room, and that the cheapest, ugliest, dirtiest room you can imagine, where he rents a corner which is divided off by a curtain that is rotting with age. There he has just exactly enough space for a cot. And you can imagine how that cot looks when I tell you that it is there that he sleeps, there that he wakes up in the morning, there that he eats and works through the day and at night falls asleep again. And there he has his little library of Virgil and Horace, which he treasures. A couple of books, which is all he owns, and which he reads over and over again.

"Now suppose I said to this man, 'My friend, I shall have no more work for you in the future. In fact, I am going into competition with you. I too shall copy manuscripts. It is an honest profession. It is useful. My friend Jean Jacques is going to copy music, because he doesn't wish to be a parasite, and neither do I. And as for you, my good friend, if that happens to take the bread out of your mouth and gets you thrown out on the street, console yourself: I am taking the only honorable course. Jean Jacques Rousseau says so.'"

And Diderot asked, "Are you sure you are harming no one when you become a music copyist?"

Jean Jacques had to think about this for a moment.

Then he said, "I will charge more for my work than the other music copyists. In fact, I will charge double. Nor will I promise immediate delivery. Thus the theaters and orchestras will have to depend on their usual copyists. And I shall get only the orders of people who for some reason or other want especially fine and careful work, and who can afford to wait for it."

Diderot smiled. "In other words, you will be working for patrons who will disguise their patronage by giving you some music to copy which they don't particularly want copied."

Rousseau protested.

But Diderot shrugged and said, "I am merely repeating what you said. You intend to charge double for work that is not needed at any particular time."

Rousseau could understand that Thérèse should object to his decision. Since it involved her own well-being, and also that of her numerous relatives, her mother and father and any number of brothers and sisters, who were always hanging around hoping for a little food, a little money, some worn-out clothes.

Yes, Rousseau could understand her motive for objecting. But why should his best friends object so strenuously? Was it not at bottom because they could not forgive him for having suddenly outdistanced *them*, and that just as they all seemed about to outdistance *him*?

Still, he might have agreed with them and let them persuade him, if he had not been able to hear echoing in his mind that mocking laughter from Prussia.

"The rest of the world has only to imitate me," Rousseau said, "and all of us will be so much the better off for it. I cannot speak for the oppressed of this world without sharing their misfortunes."

"Well, if you are right," Diderot said, "then most of the decent hard-working people of this world must be wrong in the way they think and behave."

Rousseau agreed. "Yes. And my example will teach them."

Evidently it was necessary for him now to make a visible demonstration to the world of just how he felt. The very next day, therefore, he went into a pawnshop and laid his sword upon the counter.

"I have here an instrument invented and manufactured in order to cut up people. I have carried it around with me for many years and have never had occasion to use it. In fact, I have never had the slightest intention of ever using it. Wouldn't know how. Not even if I wanted to. In short, my wearing it has never been anything but a lie. I am not at all as cruel or as military as this sword shows me to be. Indeed, the wearing of it was never intended to proclaim my bloodthirstiness, but was merely a device to let others know at a glance that I do not belong to the class of people who have to labor for a living and who might be hampered if they had this long piece of metal dangling from their waists. And that I thus have the money to spare for this ornament and do not have to put everything I earn on the table for food."

"I understand, monsieur," said the pawnbroker. "And I shall give you in money what this sword is worth. But first I must tell you that if tomorrow everyone should come to feel as you do, then this sword would be worth nothing, and I could not afford to give you the going price of today."

Jean Jacques also took out his watch. "What do I need this for? The day will be only twenty-four hours long whether I carry an instrument to tell time or not. And what about the church bells? What about the light of the day? Will those not be enough to tell me the time? This watch, in short, is just another ornament that one carries around in order to prove at a glance that one is a gentleman and that one has more money than one needs to fill one's stomach. Besides, what if I am a few minutes late to an engagement? If those who expect me cannot wait for me, then they are not true friends."

The pawnbroker smiled and said again that it was fortunate that not everyone thought the same.

Rousseau took off his wig too. "What am I? A monarch? Why should I want to look like a king, who, if he has any human feelings at all, is not able to sleep at night, thinking of the thousands who must die for him in battle and the thousands who suffer from hunger on his rich lands?"

He bought himself instead a little round wig, just enough to protect his naked scalp from the cold wind.

At home he said to Thérèse, "All this gold braid on my suit is ridiculous. Take it off and sell it. And no more frogging and gold buttons. Buttons of wood or horn will do just as well. It is ridiculous that I should dress up as if I were a courtier, or a general on dress parade. Get rid of all my white silk stockings too. And my lace cuffs and my lace jabots. Why should I try to set myself off from people who work for a living?"

Could Grimm, d'Alembert, Diderot, Marmontel or any of the others now doubt for a moment the genuine desire he had to merge with the common people and live an obscure life working at an honest trade?

Alas, his new manner of dressing only made him all the more conspicuous in Paris. People who formerly had only wanted to meet him in order to argue with him about the validity of his essay were now joined by large masses of Parisians who would never read his work but who wanted to catch a glimpse of this strange character who was the rage of the town.

"Have you never seen anyone who just wants to live unknown, like most people of this world?" Rousseau asked. "Someone who seeks nobody's society and wants no special honors or preferments?"

Apparently no one ever had. For still they flocked around. Grabbing up, by way of excuse, whatever sheet of music happened to be lying around, and pretending that they had to have it copied. Soon Rousseau had orders for months and even years ahead. Even if he should do nothing all day except copy music, which certainly was not his intention.

But though he turned them down, still the curious came on. His apartment would not empty itself. And new visitors lined up on the staircase.

Gruffly Rousseau would fling at them, "Can't you see that you are robbing me of the most precious thing I have—my time?"

The ladies blushed and giggled at his fierceness and apologized so demurely, so prettily, that his heart melted. They put on all their charm, they used a thousand little artifices which only women know how to use. And before he knew it, he had accepted another dinner invitation.

But at the dinner his anger would explode again. What was it, after all, but the same old dinner that he had had a hundred times before? With the same old wits flinging their obscure allusions back and forth and exploding with incomprehensible laughter.

And the obviousness of their efforts to include him in the conversation by asking him if he thought that the savages of Africa and America would someday cross the ocean to put red or black kings on the thrones of Versailles and Buckingham. And their anxiety to load him down with presents of wine, venison, books or *objets d'art,* in order to compensate him.

While at the same time his pockets were so empty of coin that he could not afford to tip the servants who stood around despising him, knowing themselves richer than he, for all his glory, but still begging from him, since he nevertheless belonged to the world of givers and they to the world of receivers.

Gifts were one way to reach Rousseau. One couldn't very well shut the door in the face of a lady whose lackey followed her with a great package. Nevertheless, the way in which Thérèse received such presents with ohs and ahs, while all her relatives stood around ready to grab, aroused Rousseau to the point where he finally had to scream, "No more presents!"

Which evoked a new sport in this city always thirsting for some fresh experience. "Having one's gift refused by Rousseau"—that was the latest adventure: to test the incorruptible Jean Jacques with richer and richer gifts.

Bringing another laugh from Prussia: "Who ever heard of a poor man—a genuinely poor man—refusing a present?" The inescapable conclusion being that Jean Jacques's poverty was a fraud.

What a torture that was, that just now when he was realizing his ambition to make himself worthy of Voltaire, this great man should take to ridiculing him? Could one cast oneself at the feet of a man who was laughing at one?

And apparently the whole world was in a kind of conspiracy to make him look like a fool. He discovered that Thérèse was slipping downstairs just after he had turned down some lady and her gift and was secretly wheedling and begging for the receipt of it below, swearing that her master had no idea of the fact that they did not even have enough food in the house.

Now his anger exploded against Thérèse for making a clown out of him. She wept into her apron. If he had not vowed never to abandon her, if he had not found her fingers more deft than any other in taking care of him when he had his bladder trouble, he would have thrown her out.

What a snare life was! As if it lay in ambush at every turn of the road, to cast another loop around one. In his bewilderment, he would more and more often run out of the city, into the outskirts, where he would lose himself in field and forest and meditate upon his incredible situation.

Now when every woman was available to him, he, who had dreamed of possessing them all, could not take a single one. Now when fortune smiled on him, he who had craved wealth so much had to refuse it when it offered itself. And now when Voltaire finally knew him, he who had yearned for nothing so much as to throw himself at his feet could not do so.

The long walks in rain and sun did him good. His bladder eased itself as often as it liked, with no need for him to excuse himself from a crowded room into some antechamber or out into some courtyard under the scornful stares of coachman and lackey, who could watch him as he tried to piddle a few drops and knowingly assume from his pain and contortions that surely he must have the pox.

Out in the woods, too, the proper answers came to him for those bores who would slyly ask him tormenting questions: "Monsieur Rousseau, must we really burn down our libraries?"

"Beware!" he would cry. "What right have you, who never wrote a book, to burn one?"

New astonishment! Another paradox from the man of paradoxes!

"But you yourself have condemned them. You said that the burning of the library of Alexandria by the Caliph Omar was a praiseworthy act. And that if our Gregory the Great had done the same it would have been the most sublime act of his life."

"I have said, I have said!" Rousseau would repeat angrily. "But don't you see that man *must* have libraries? That we *must* have academies, and literary and scientific institutions?"

"But that is not what you said—"

"But can't you see that with man corrupted to the point he is now, such institutions are the only thing that keep him from being as evil as he otherwise would be?"

"Then you are not against printing books? And the invention of printing was not really a scourge?"

"Of course it was a scourge!" Rousseau would protest energetically. "Take our police! Does not the mere existence of our police force prove that we are criminal and corrupt? But are they not at the same time our one remaining safeguard against our very criminality and corruption?"

He would glare at the guests around him. "Let people laugh at me. But I shall go on printing books against printing. For that is the bitter satire of our century: that the very things that have corrupted us are now our only protection against further corruption."

They would all be startled for a moment, and then they would laugh awkwardly. "Our dear Jean Jacques. How delightful you are with your eternal paradoxes."

"Paradoxes?" Rousseau would shout. "Where is the paradox? When men have made themselves sick from too many doctors and too much medicine, what else can save their lives, except more doctors and more medicine? The fault was to have doctors or medicine to begin with. But for that it is too late now!"

"You mean, then, that we must not abandon our civilization?"

"We *dare* not!" Jean Jacques would cry. "Depraved as we are, to take away our civilization would be annihilation!"

There were times when he wondered how he had ever got himself involved in this almost untenable position. Did he really believe what he said? Why, then, had he struggled so to master all the world's knowledge, if this is what it led to? He was himself the best illustration of how a man ought never to live: perpetually glued to books.

If he was now caught like a fly in this spider web of arguments, the fault was Diderot's. And Voltaire's too. The fault of all the men whose literary success he had ever envied.

Yes, life was a snare. A snare laid for us by our ambitions.

7: FROM PARADOX TO PARADOX

How had Rousseau come to write this prize-winning *Discourse on the Arts and Sciences,* denying everything he had stood for until then?

It started with Diderot's becoming excited about an operation that was to be performed by a Parisian surgeon. A girl who had been born with cataracts in both eyes and who, as a result, had never been able to see, was about to undergo the daringly new operation of having her turbid lenses removed. She was to see for the first time in her life!

And what would she see? What would the world look like to her? That was the question.

"What an opportunity to learn how man acquires his knowledge of the outside world," Diderot exclaimed. "Voltaire already suggested this experiment years ago: that this would be the way to test the theories of Locke, namely that man is born without any innate knowledge whatsoever and only gradually acquires a store of facts and ideas that come to us through our senses."

"What you really want to know," Rousseau said, "is how do we know about God? If no one ever told us about Him, would most of us live and die without ever suspecting His existence?"

"Precisely what I'm after," said Diderot. "You know, of course, that blind people are notoriously insensitive to religious impulses. That's understandable. What can an *invisible* Creator mean to people for whom everything is invisible? An inaudible God would mean much more to them. Or an impalpable God. In fact, I have heard a blind man say that he did not crave eyes. What would he do with them? But if he could have arms twenty feet long, he would know what was going on across the street or upstairs."

But in spite of Diderot's eagerness he was not permitted to witness the operation or study the patient's subsequent stages of learning, which might or might not have gone to prove that God was gradually created by man himself through an accumulation of concepts. This, however, did not stop Diderot from writing his little book, called *Letter on the Blind, For the Use of Those Who Can See.*

Which he prudently published without his name.

The clergy were up in arms at once. Who was it who dared throw doubt on the existence of God? And Diderot was betrayed by the many efforts he had made to witness the operation. Sealed orders immediately consigned him to the dungeon at Fort Vincennes, where, however, he was soon treated very nicely, and from which he was released after a few months.

While he was there his close friend Rousseau visited him as often as possible. Walking all the way from Paris, because he did not have the price of a carriage.

It was during one such walk, late in autumn, when the heat was really excessive, about two o'clock in the afternoon, that Jean Jacques happened to look into a recent issue of the *Mercure de France,* which he had picked up just before leaving the city. And there he read of the Academy of Dijon's announcement of the latest subject for their annual prize essay: Has the advance of the arts and sciences purified or corrupted the morals of man?

And suddenly it was as if he were a different man. Not Jean Jacques, but that patient born blind, and now the cataracts of years had fallen from his eyes, and light, pure light, was suddenly streaming into his mind and dazzling him.

The universe opened up before him.

His heart began to pound, his breath came and went. And, unable to stand, he reeled about like a drunken man and finally allowed himself to sink to the ground at the foot of one of the trees that lined the road.

His senses seemed to leave him, and yet, at the same time, he felt that never in his life had he thought so clearly. He saw the network of greed, avarice, pride, envy, hate, suspicion that link and divide man into an intricate mesh. He saw all the necessary causes that lock event to event and that explain why things are the way they are.

"If only I could have written down a fraction of all the ideas of that one moment of illumination," he would exclaim later, "I could have changed the whole world by arguments at once brilliant and irrefutable."

When he woke up from this spell, he found that he had in fact been busy while unconscious. The whole front of his vest was drenched with tears. And in his hands was a piece of paper on which he had scribbled that Prosopopoeia of Fabricius which was later to become perhaps the most famous part of his subsequent essay. Fabricius was the old Roman of early republican days who was absolutely incorruptible. In the prosopopoeia, Rousseau imagines him returning to Rome in the days when it is no longer a town of thatched huts, but an imperial city of marble and bronze, mistress of the world. And Fabricius apostrophizes the Romans on the decay of their moral fiber because of excessive luxury and ease.

All this was so new to Rousseau, so contrary to his usual way of thinking, so contrary to the thinking of Voltaire, to that of all his literary friends, that Rousseau did not dare mention his vision when he arrived at Fort Vincennes, where Diderot now enjoyed a kind of semiliberty. But he did mention the subject of the prize essay.

"I'm thinking of competing," Rousseau said to Diderot.

Diderot reflected for a moment. "Whether the advance of the arts and sciences contributes to the corruption or purification of man's morals? Hm. Very interesting. Naturally you're taking the positive side?"

Rousseau shrugged. "Naturally," he said. "Is there any other side to take?" He was speaking now as Rousseau the mathematician, Rousseau the student of chemistry, Rousseau the man who had only recently predicted that human beings would eventually fly, and who was himself trying to construct a machine which would enable man to sail among the clouds. He was speaking as the man who years before had tried to convince musicians to adopt a new form of musical notation. He was speaking as the man who loved Voltaire and wanted to write plays like that great master. He was speaking as the person he had hitherto always shown himself to be: forward, progressive, devoted to the sciences and the arts.

"But you want to win, don't you?" Diderot asked. "You have seen how I've begun to make a name for myself by writing my pornographic *Indiscreet Jewels,* and now my sensational *Letter on the Blind.* Jean Jacques, you've got to learn to shock people. You've got to make yourself both friends and enemies. You've got to get people to talk about you. That's what you want, isn't it? That's fame!"

Jean Jacques had to admit that Diderot was right.

"Of course there's only one sensible side to take," Diderot went on. "That the arts and sciences elevate man, purify his morals, add to his well-being, civilize him and prepare him for a peaceful and useful life. Of course, of course."

When Diderot began to talk it was often difficult to stop him. He had a way of fighting you with his talk, of grabbing your shoulder, shaking his fist at you, of poking you with his index finger to emphasize his points. It was the sort of speaking which would later make Empress Catherine come away from an hour's talk with Diderot, her body covered with black-and-blue marks where he had emphasized his arguments on the Queen's poor flesh. It was the sort of speaking that would later make Voltaire say, "Doesn't that man know the meaning of the word 'dialogue'? That someone else must be permitted to utter a word occasionally?"

Diderot continued, "Yes, there's only one side to take. But that's the side that everyone will take. That's the side where you'll have competition. And where one man will say precisely what the next one does. Believe me! That's the bridge of asses. No. You must take the other side. The unpopular side. The different side. Then you'll stand alone. You'll get the attention you deserve. And you'll win. Don't you see that?"

Rousseau said, "Yes, but—"

But Diderot went on: "It's a bit fraudulent, I'll admit. But you've got to grab people's attention. You've got to be like the sellers at the fairs, who fire pistols into the air to attract a crowd."

Rousseau nodded, as if persuaded by his friend's arguments, and saying nothing of the violent emotional storm he had just been through, saying nothing of the prosopopoeia of Fabricius, which was still in his pocket on a tear-stained piece of paper.

No wonder that Diderot would later be amazed at Rousseau's behavior and wonder about his selling of his sword, his resignation from his position as cashier for the Dupins. Diderot could understand a little fraud in order to call attention to oneself, but this was carrying fraud too far.

And as for Jean Jacques, he would later deny the statement made by Marmontel and others that it was on account of a suggestion from Diderot that he had adopted the negative side of the argument. And since this is a subject that has caused so much flow of scholarly ink, it is well to call attention to Rousseau's own sentence in his *Confessions,* where he says nothing of a suggestion by Diderot, but where he does state, "All my subsequent misfortunes were his fault." Thus blaming Diderot for the very thing he refused to honor him for.

But of course the fault was really Voltaire's. And Diderot's only incidentally, in that, without Diderot's encouragement, never perhaps would Rousseau have dared suddenly reverse all his thinking. For twenty years he had been running breathlessly after a reputation like Voltaire's. Eating, sleeping, drinking nothing but Voltaire, dreaming and scheming of how he could make himself worthy of that great man. First fame, and then the arms of Voltaire.

And now suddenly he was famous. But by a trick that had only served to make him appear ludicrous to Voltaire. And yet he dared not let go of his new-found fame. He dared not take the risk of lapsing back into obscurity.

For then all would be lost. This way there was still hope. There might, for example, be a great thrashing out of his question, with Voltaire leading the party for the arts and sciences, and he leading the opposite party. As there had been about seventy-five years ago in European thought as to whether the writers of the day could ever hope to equal the writers of Greece and Rome. That had been the famous battle of the Ancients and the Moderns.

Or such a great quarrel as had more recently exploded between Newton and Leibnitz, as to which one of these giants of science had first discovered the use of infinitesimals in the solution of certain mathematical problems: the battle between fluxions and calculus.

Meanwhile, of course, Rousseau would have to play out the role that had brought him fame, even though in that very role there were contradictions. For example, it forced him to pretend that he wanted obscurity. Which was the last thing he wanted.

Had he not, some years before, when he had by a lucky chance found himself selected as secretary to the ambassador at Venice, prepared himself by borrowing money from every possible source in order to properly equip himself? The finest suits had to be specially tailored for him. And twenty-four of the sheerest white linen shirts. Twenty-four! No less. And expensive shoes. Silk stockings. And of course all the necessary lace, buttons and braids that went with such a select outfit. And how elegantly he had traveled! And what a furor he had kicked up in Venice when it came to the question of whether he had the right to the services of a private gondolier to be paid by the embassy!

Secretary to the ambassador, that's all he had been! And to what an ambassador! Just to the tiny republic of Venice, a government whose importance had become almost purely historical since world commerce had shifted to the Atlantic ports. Of course Signor Rousseau had palmed himself off as secretary to the *embassy,* which sounded so much grander, and made himself out to be a member of the French diplomatic corps, instead of what he had actually been: the ambassador's secretary, paid out of his own pocket.

But how unashamedly Rousseau, still years from his fame, had displayed his love of luxury, his desire for honors, his insistence on punctilio, his extravagance and elegance. Nor had his intimate friends ever forgotten it. And naturally now they were not too overwhelmed by this supposed conversion of his. Still, they did not turn against him. They too had played such games. It was part of the game of living. Hadn't Diderot, for example, sold sermons to priests who couldn't write their own? Diderot, mind you, this man whose atheism was too much for Voltaire. And Grimm, with his spurious catalepsy supposedly the result of an irresistible love for a famous actress of the day, Mademoiselle Fels. All Paris talked of nothing else for a week! Grimm got his first attention from the public that way.

So they didn't really blame Jean Jacques. They would have played along with this excitement if it had happened to come their way. But wasn't he carrying it a bit too far? Surely he might relax in private and give them a wink of understanding. Surely he didn't expect them to fall for his game. They knew him too well for that.

Ah, but this time they had the wrong man! Rousseau was determined that they should believe in him. There would be no retreat for him! There would be no confession of fraud from him.

And besides, was he a fraud? Hadn't he had a stroke of illumination on the road to Port Vincennes? Had he not written, while unconscious, that Prosopopoeia of Fabricius of which everyone was talking? Deep down, hadn't he always hated the rich and the elegant? Hadn't he always hated this salon life, this theater life, these wits and *persifleurs* who made him feel so inferior?

Of course he had!

He was paying them back well now for the years they had made him suffer!

No. There could be no retreat for him.

What was in his past—and there was far more there than even his best friends knew—would have to remain hidden. And God forbid that Voltaire should ever learn of it!

Was it not for Voltaire that he had committed the worst of his follies? The most terrible of his sins?

But of course Voltaire couldn't know that. And now there were circulating in Paris stories of a funny skit that Voltaire had directed against Rousseau, and with which apparently he had amused the King of Prussia.

That would be at one of those wonderful evenings at Sans Souci of which such marvelous tales were told in Paris. The round, candlelit table, the open palace window through which one could see the moon and the stars, and company of such intellectuals as could be found perhaps nowhere else in the world.

And dominating them all, Voltaire, the inimitable Voltaire, with that sparkling, malicious expression of his. So much the master here by the vast breadth of his knowledge, by that unexampled talent of his, that when someone addressed Frederick II as "King" at this table he cut him short: "I may be the King in Prussia, but here we are in the realm of literature, and Voltaire is king."

It was at the honeymoon stage of the two men's relationship. When

Voltaire felt that he had at last discovered a monarch who was also a philosopher, and Frederick felt that he had at last discovered a philosopher who was also a monarch.

And Voltaire would epitomize the magnificent reign of Frederick with a remark that became current all over Europe, and particularly in France, where he of course meant it to circulate: "For the first time in centuries a king is governing without women and without priests." What a contrast to the reign of Louis XV of France, with its unending frou-frou of women's skirts and priests' frocks!

But that didn't mean that sex was not represented at Sans Souci. Not when the walls were covered by those murals by Pène, in which priapic men and naked women embraced among doves covering, rams mounting and a flock of cupids playing a game of vaginal injections.

Voltaire had characterized this experience in a wonderful line: "Imagine the Seven Wise Men of Greece holding a conversation in a brothel!"

Nor did it mean that God was not represented, too. Voltaire said, "It is only that our respect for God is so great here that none of us dares pretend that he can speak in His name. Such monopolistic arrogance we leave to priests and preachers."

What a company! The lovable Lord Keith, diplomat and military leader. Algarotti, traveler, poet, mathematician. La Mettrie, the far-seeing doctor of medicine who wanted to reduce life to its mathematical and physical manifestations. And d'Argens, the irrepressible adventurer and writer. And Maupertuis, who had proved Newton's theory that the earth must be flatter at the poles than at the equator, an ambitious and jealous man of wild scientific ideas, which Voltaire would later excoriate in the most withering manner.

No wonder that evening after evening the sessions would prolong themselves, with no one willing to stop the flow of wit and learning, so that the liveried servants would later have to be helped to their beds, their legs so swollen from prolonged standing that they could not move from their places.

Once the King sought for the best definition of man. He suggested Plato's "birds without feathers." La Mettrie advanced his own famous definition, "Man is a machine."

It was Voltaire's discourse on this subject that drew everyone's applause.

"The Bible assures us that we are made in God's image," Voltaire began. "But Xenophon had the proper retort for that. He said, 'If horses could carve images, they would represent their gods with four legs.' In general the ancients were not very complimentary to man. Epictetus called man 'a little soul carrying around a big corpse.' And Homer called him 'the fool of fate.' To Petronius man was nothing but a 'bag of wind.' And to Aristotle he was only 'the political biped.' Only Protagoras thought enough of man to call him 'the measure of all things.'

"Modern times have raised our respect for man. Pascal calls man 'a feeble reed,' but he adds, 'He is a reed who can think.' But the most glorious definition of man is surely the one that that great barbarian playwright Shakespeare has given us in the words of Hamlet: 'What a piece of work is a man! how noble in reason! how infinite in faculty! in form and moving how express and admirable! in action how like an angel! in apprehension how like a god! the beauty of the world! the paragon of animals! And yet, to me, what is this quintessence of dust?'

"Yes, it is a beautiful definition," Voltaire went on, a sad-sweet mocking smile coming into evidence at the corners of his mouth, "but it misses the most important factor in human life."

"What do you consider that to be?" the King asked.

Voltaire did not answer for a fraction of a second. And in that brief fragment of time he must have realized that for this King, who had to lead men to battle where thousands perished, the life of man could never have the same significance that it had for him to whom each second was precious. Voltaire remembered that when this King was still a crown prince he had refused to take any interest in military matters and had even tried to escape his obligations by fleeing to England with his best friend, Katte. But his brutal, soldier-mad father had discovered the plot and locked his son in a cell, and right outside that cell he had hanged that best friend Katte, so close to Frederick that the latter could reach out and shake the hand of his doomed companion. What that father had begun, the glory of Prussia and the Silesian War had brought to sanguine blossom. No wonder Frederick now liked Plato's definition of man: a featherless biped, a plucked chicken, ready for the pot. Not long ago Voltaire had heard of one of Frederick's cavalrymen about to be executed for having had unnatural relations with his mount. Instinctively Voltaire had pleaded for the man's life. Just as he had pleaded for Desfontaines's life when the latter was to be burned for sodomy with the little chimney sweep. And just as he would do when Admiral Byng was to be shot for his defeat by the French. Just as he would always do where life was involved. But Frederick had refused. The man must die. The fighting spirit of the cavalry must not be endangered.

"What was the most important factor in human life that Shakespeare missed in Hamlet's definition?" Voltaire repeated. "It is this: *Man is the only animal that knows it must die . . .*"

His voice hung in the air for a moment. There was something he wanted to add, but wasn't sure he should. His tongue meanwhile sought the glossy spaces of his gums where of late he had lost tooth after tooth. Recently, when someone had written to him of a prisoner in the Bastille who had lost nineteen teeth there, Voltaire had written back, "It is not only in prison that one can lose teeth. I have lost just as many at the court of Frederick of Prussia." That was why he had wanted to say, "Man is the only animal that knows it must die. *And can watch himself doing so, day after day.*" In prison or out of prison God executes us a little bit more every day.

Instead Voltaire said, "I am preparing my *Century of Louis XIV* for publication. And in that connection I am compiling for it a list of the great writers, artists, scientists who together made that century one of the four glorious periods of man's history. For it seems to me that man has had only four great flowerings so far. The first being the age of Pericles in Greece, when Plato, Aristotle, Alexander, Demosthenes, Praxiteles and other geniuses lived.

"The second such flowering was at the time of Caesar, which was also the time of Cicero, Virgil, Horace, Lucretius, Ovid and so many others. And the third, of course, was the period of the great Medici, when Michelangelo and Raphael and Leonardo da Vinci flourished.

"In the course of compiling this list for the age of Louis XIV, I learned to know the poet Maucroix. And I am tempted to quote from this now almost forgotten writer, these four lines which he wrote when he was over eighty years old:

> *"Chaque jour est un bien que du ciel je reçoi;*
> *Jouissons aujourd'hui de celui qu'il nous donne.*
> *Il n'appartient pas plus aux jeunes gens qu'à moi,*
> *Et celui de demain n'appartient à personne.*

"Which one of us," Voltaire asked, looking around the table, "will be able to write lines as philosophical as that when he is eighty years old?"

He stopped talking, wondering if at eighty—if ever he should reach that age, which was highly unlikely—he too would be able to think of each day as a special gift sent down from heaven and would be able to invite all mankind to enjoy that celestial present, because it belongs

94

to the young no more than to the old, and because the gift of tomorrow is certain for no one.

The King applauded when Voltaire ceased, and he exclaimed that surely there was no philosopher whom he would rather listen to than Voltaire. "You must compile a dictionary of your definitions," Frederick said.

"I hear and obey," said Voltaire. And indeed, when the session broke up, he did not go to sleep, but sat up in his study and remained at work the rest of the night, so that the following morning he could send to the King the first article of his subsequently so famous *Philosophical Dictionary,* the article on Abraham, who married his sister, who circumcised himself at the age of one hundred, who had a child when his wife was over ninety-five and who almost sacrificed his son to God.

It was a typical Voltairean article, learned, moving, with flashes of malice, with the sparkle of erudition and with moments of profound insight. And he had not minded staying up all hours in order to write it. What better way was there to enjoy the celestial gift of time than to spend it in work?

Yes, it must have been on such a typical night of brilliant conversation that the King asked Voltaire whether he had yet read the essay by Rousseau which was creating such a commotion in Paris. And Voltaire's skinny face, with its almost toothless grin, must have replied that no, he never had met Rousseau, but that it was easy for him to imagine such an encounter.

Would the King like to hear the story of Voltaire's imaginary encounter with Rousseau?

The King would indeed.

Voltaire thereupon put on, extempore, the sort of biting little skit for which he was already noted, in which he played all the roles, altering his voice with incredible facility to suit his characters.

Voltaire portrayed himself as an acquaintance of Rousseau, come to pick him up at his home because they were both invited out to dine at a friend's house in the country.

Voltaire finds Rousseau in the midst of burning his books, dancing with glee around the bonfire and congratulating himself on having finally rid himself of these corrupters of man.

Rousseau throws his gold watch into the fire, railing at man's ridiculous mania of carrying the time around in his pocket.

He invites Voltaire to follow his example, crying, "Only the savages are decent. But I'm afraid that now that Quebec has become a city with orchestras and tapestries, even the noble Iroquois will soon be corrupted."

Rousseau is so persuasive that Voltaire is almost convinced that he should burn his books, too. But while the two men are riding into the country, where they are going to dinner, they are attacked in the dark of the forest by a band of thieves, who strip them of everything, including most of their clothes.

"You must be a very learned man," says Voltaire to one of the bandits.

"A learned man?" the bandit laughs in his face.

But Voltaire perseveres. He goes to the chief himself. "At what university did you study?" he asks. He refuses to believe that the bandit chief never attended a higher institution. "To have become so corrupt," he says, "surely you must have studied many arts and sciences."

The chief, annoyed by these questions, knocks Voltaire down and shouts at him that he not only never went to any school, but never even learned how to read.

When finally the two bedraggled men reach their friend's home, Voltaire's fears are once again aroused. For it is such a distinguished place, with such fine works of art and such a big library, that there can be little doubt but that the owner has become depraved by all this culture.

To Voltaire's surprise, however, their host gives them fresh clothes to put on, opens his purse to lend them money and sits them down before a good dinner.

Immediately after dinner, however, Rousseau asks for still another favor. Could he have pen and paper, please? He is in a hurry to write another essay against culture.

Such was the impromptu that Voltaire gave to howls of laughter at Sans Souci and that was soon circulated in manuscript throughout the literary circles of Europe, to be printed sometime later, but with the name of Timon of Athens, the famous misanthrope, substituted for that of Rousseau.

How cruel!

But at the same time how understandable. How could the rich, for whom life was made so simple, ever understand the subterfuges, the lies, the frauds, the errors, sins and even crimes to which the poor were driven in their efforts to overcome the great advantages the rich had in the race of life?

How, for example, could a Voltaire understand the strange predicament in which a Rousseau would find himself when, soon after the furor of his first *Discourse,* he acquired still another title to fame?

This time as a musician. As a composer.

Ever since he had first begun to study music and to teach it, Rousseau had dreamed of piercing through to fame as the result of a successful opera. But his facility in this genre was not great. And his efforts to get a performance for his *Gallant Muses* invariably failed. And for good reasons. His operatic music had little merit.

But then one day, while on a week's visit to the country home of a retired Swiss jeweler, Rousseau amused the company with a few little melodies he had written, to which he attached no great importance. He was really amazed to discover the other guests so excited about these delicate little songs.

"Put a few such songs together," they urged him. "String them onto some sort of little plot, and you'll have a delightful operetta."

He didn't believe them. "Nonsense," he said. "This is the sort of stuff I write and then throw away!"

"Heaven forbid!" cried the ladies, enchanted by his music. "You must make an opera out of this material."

And they wouldn't leave off arguing and pleading until he had promised.

Oh, the irony and the bitterness of it! That after all his years of effort to become a composer, he should now, now when he was still stoutly replying to the critics of his *Discourse on the Arts and Sciences,* be so close to a success in music and have to reject it.

Or at least appear to reject it!

But what else could he do? You couldn't on the one hand decry the arts and at the same time practice them, could you? Well, yes, perhaps in literature, since you could argue that you couldn't keep silent about your feelings against literature and so were involved in spite of yourself. But now music too? No. That would be too much!

And the fault, of course, was Rameau's. The fault was Rameau's and that of the whole culture of this Parisian age. For it was Rameau's type of music that he had been trying to write, and that he couldn't write. These little songs, however, were sweet nothings from the heart, tender memories of his childhood, little melodies that anyone could hum and that would make one want to weep.

But no. He couldn't appear as a composer now. That glory, craved for so long, was now forbidden to him. Still, just for the ladies, and just for this once, for this one weekend in the country, he would make a little piece out of his melodies.

The ladies were delighted and Jean Jacques was applauded. And everyone went to work to learn the parts which he wrote.

But then, after the little operetta had been given its feeble amateur rendering, everyone insisted that it was too good to be lost forever, and that the Royal Academy of Music must now have the manuscript in order to give it the really first-rate performance it merited.

Rousseau was aware that he must seem like a hypocrite, standing there and arguing that he could not possibly permit a public performance. The ladies especially couldn't understand what troubled him. A contradiction? Bah, what was a contradiction in one's life? Every woman has had the experience of saying no when she meant yes, and saying yes when she meant no.

Rousseau had to admit that though he couldn't agree to a public performance, he would indeed, just for his own private satisfaction, dearly love to know how his work would sound when done by professional musicians and by trained voices.

"I'd simply like to know if it is as good as you kind people seem to think," he said.

Duclos, the historian, pointed out to Jean Jacques that this was impossible. The musicians of the Royal Opera would not rehearse a work merely to see how it would sound. Merely to satisfy the author's curiosity.

Rousseau agreed. But he recalled that Rameau had once had a private performance of his opera *Armide,* behind closed doors, just for himself alone.

Duclos understood what was bothering Rousseau: that the writer of the Prosopopoeia of Fabricius should now become known as the writer of an amusing little operetta. That would certainly be paradoxical. But Duclos thought he saw a way out.

"Let me do the submitting to the Royal Academy," he suggested. "Your name will never appear. No one will even suspect that it is your work."

To that Rousseau could agree.

But now what crazy twists and turns of his emotions!

Afraid at one and the same time that his work might be turned down—which would be a blow to his pride even though no one knew he was the author—and that the work would be accepted, and then that his violent feelings in the matter would certainly betray how deeply concerned he was in spite of himself. And how anxious this lover of obscurity was for applause! And thus torn between his desire to be known as the composer of a successful opera and the necessity of remaining true to his proclaimed desire for anonymity, Rousseau suffered through several painful weeks.

All these emotions were screwed up to new heights when, after ac-

ceptance and the first rehearsals, there ensued such a buzz of excitement among Parisian music lovers that Duclos had to come running to
Rousseau to inform him that the news had reached the superintendent
of the King's amusements, and that he was now demanding that the
work be offered first at the royal summer palace of Fontainebleau.
Imagine the honor of it!

"What was your answer?" Jean Jacques asked, striving to appear un-
impressed.

"I refused," Duclos said. "What else could I do? Monsieur de Cury
was incensed, of course. But I said I would first have to get the author's
permission. And I was certain he would refuse."

How infuriating all this was! Why had not this success come to him
before he had plunged into his *Discourse,* and before he had committed himself to a life of austerity and denial? Now, when everything was opening up to him—even the court of Louis XV!—he had
to play a role of self-effacement.

Back and forth Duclos had to go, between M. de Cury and Jean
Jacques and between the Duke d'Aumont and Jean Jacques again, as
his little operetta, *The Village Soothsayer,* though still unperformed,
took on ever more importance.

And of course the news of who the composer was did finally begin to
get around among his closest friends. But they, naturally, kept his
secret well, and the public at large knew only of a great excitement in
musical and court circles.

How titillating it was to go among people who did not know him
as the composer, but who talked in the most glowing terms of the promise of the piece after having heard the first rehearsals. The furor
was such that people who could not possibly have squirmed their way
into the rehearsals were pretending that they were intimate with the
whole affair and that it would be sensational. And listening to such a
conversation one morning while taking a cup of chocolate in a café,
Rousseau found himself bathed in perspiration, trembling lest his authorship become known, and at the same time dreaming of the startling effect he would make if he should proclaim himself suddenly as
the composer.

He felt himself now, as he himself says in his *Confessions,* at a
crucial point of his life. And that was why, on the day of the performance, when a carriage from the royal stables called to take him to the
palace, he did not bother to shave. On the contrary, he was pleased
that his face showed a neglect of several days.

Seeing him in that condition, and about to enter the hall where the King, the Queen, the whole royal family and all the members of the highest aristocracy would be present, Grimm and the Abbé Raynal and others tried to stop him.

"You can't go in that way!" they cried.

"Why not?" Jean Jacques asked. "Who is going to stop me?"

"You haven't dressed for the occasion!" they pointed out to him.

"I'm dressed as I always am," Rousseau said. "Neither better nor worse."

"At home, yes," they argued. "But here you are in the palace. There's the King. And Madame de Pompadour."

"If they are here, then surely I have the right to be here," Rousseau said. "And even more right. Since I am the composer!"

"But in such a slovenly condition."

"What is slovenly about me?" Rousseau asked. "Is it because of my slovenliness that hair grows on my face? Surely it would grow there whether I washed myself or not. A hundred years ago I would have worn a beard with pride. And those without beards would have stood out as not dressed for the occasion. Now times have changed, and I must pretend that hair doesn't grow on my face. That's the fashion. And fashion is the real king here. Not Louis XV, since even he obeys. Now, if you don't mind, I should like to hear my own piece performed."

But of course behind his boldness he didn't feel bold at all. He trembled lest his piece should fail. And this in addition to his usual fear of being among people of high society. His fear of making some inane or inappropriate remark. And even deeper than that: his fear lest in this closed hall he should suddenly itch to relieve himself. Could he walk out in the midst of his piece? Here, before the court? Before the King?

Already more and more people were staring at him as, bit by bit, the secret of his authorship was being communicated from one group to another, and soon the whole hall was looking in the direction of the shy little man in the poor clothes.

Meanwhile the lamps had been lit and the curtain had risen, and the first song was soon heard. Nothing could have been more in contrast with the audience than this glimpse of the Alps, with its simple characters, a young shepherd and a young shepherdess, with a chorus of peasants, and no plot except the yearning of two sweethearts to find the way to each other's happiness. The very first song showed that the work would be a success. And as one charming number followed another, the warmth of the reception only increased.

On all sides Rousseau could hear whispered expressions of praise, and among them particularly those of the ladies, who now seemed to him all as beautiful as angels, so that he wept with joy to think that he was the cause of their pleasure. And in the sad numbers, seeing them begin to cry, he was overcome with sensuality to the point where he felt himself consumed with an almost irresistible desire to catch their tears with his lips, those delightful tears which he had induced.

And in the end, what an ovation! Despite the restraining presence of the King, whose attitude was always watched by everyone as a guide to his own reaction.

That very same evening M. de Cury, the superintendent of the royal amusements, brought Rousseau the message that the King would like to see him at his audience the following morning at eleven.

"I am certain it is His Majesty's intention to bestow a pension upon you," said M. de Cury.

A pension!

A royal pension. Just such as Voltaire had received from the Regent.

Rousseau lay awake at night, glowing with the thought of it. Never had he felt so sure of himself. Never so close to Voltaire! It was only gradually that he realized that he could not possibly accept it. Why, just the ordeal of waiting in that crowded audience chamber, amidst the crush of nobility, until His Majesty deigned to notice him, while who knows what bladder pains began to stab and fever him, was bound to prove more than he could endure. And then, even if that stage were somehow surmounted, how could he possibly face the King and find at a moment's notice the appropriate words in reply to whatever was said to him? He, with his sluggish wit and his faltering tongue.

No. It was beyond him. He sweated at the thought of it.

Besides, what of the future? Would not his acceptance of a pension mark the end of his fame as author of the *Discourse on the Arts and Sciences?* What would the King be allotting him a pension for, if not for his work as an artist? No longer would he be "our queer Jean Jacques," "our incorruptible Jean Jacques who, just imagine, insists on earning his living with the labor of his two hands. Wants the people to be his only patron."

No. Now he would have the King for a patron. And he would be expected to pay court to His Majesty. He would be expected to follow up his little operetta *The Village Soothsayer* with something equally charming, or perhaps something even better.

Did he dare risk his fame on his musical ability?

True, he prided himself on the fact that he had this talent, and that while his friends, the Diderots and the Grimms and so forth, could no doubt write books, there was not one of them who could compose an opera too. But now, suppose his next composition failed. Suppose it were hissed at. Never again could he go back to being a critic of the arts. He would be laughed at if he dared curse the arts again. He would be exposed as just another envious failure who criticizes what he can't do.

(As a matter of fact, his position was already dubious enough. And in a few months when he was to allow himself to be persuaded to give his youthful tragedy *Narcissus* to the Théâtre-Français for production, it would be even worse. What an almost fatal mistake! The play failed miserably. And the best that Jean Jacques could do to recoup his prestige was publish his tragedy with a preface in which he said that he knew the play had no merit, but that while "it is too late to lead people into doing good, we can still try to amuse them, and thus prevent them from doing ill for at least one evening." He even went further, declaring, "Let the public hiss me for two hours. I don't care. I'll gladly give them a play a day to hiss, if it will restrain them for two hours from doing worse according to their corrupt natures."

(Which naturally evoked this comment, supposedly originating with Voltaire: "But what about the poor actors who must learn these miserable pieces? And the public that must pay to see them? Is the whole Parisian audience composed of would-be assassins who are better off being bored in the theater by Jean Jacques than hanged in the square by the public executioner? Many of them, perhaps, would prefer hanging.")

No. He must not take this pension from the King. He must stick to his music copying, and to essays written by the man of virtue, the Citizen of Geneva. Still, he was tempted. Naturally. For his long years of dreaming had stimulated him to crave every distinction. But he realized that he could not play the role of courtier and artist, which would involve his developing a polished social deportment that he had to admit to himself he could never attain.

And thus, alone at night, when his mind worked best, Rousseau fought out his destiny. A pension, he argued, was not really a gift. Since it was paid annually, it was rather a golden chain of which one end would always remain in the hands of the patron, since he could always stop payment at the least sign of insubordination.

Yes, he saw clearly then the truth of what he was to write later: *that the money you have in hand makes you free, while the money you hope to get makes you a slave.*

For a Voltaire, ah, that was different. For him a pension was but another item in the long list of the sources of his wealth. There can be no chains for millionaires. But for a Rousseau, such a pension was impossible.

The following day he failed to show up at the King's audience.

Two days later Diderot saw him from a carriage and beckoned him in.

"Are you a fool?" Diderot asked.

"Have you any doubts about it?" Rousseau countered.

Diderot shook his finger at Jean Jacques. "I can understand— No, I take that back—even your own indifference to a pension I don't understand. Take the money and do what you please! Write what you like! Let the authorities strike you from the pension list if they take offense at what you may say. That's their affair. But don't go striking yourself from the list! Remember, you are not alone in this world. Or have you forgotten that you have the responsibility of your mistress, and her aged mother, and their relatives, all of them so poor and so utterly dependent on you when other means fail?"

"Why talk to me about matters that are already settled?" Rousseau said coldly. "You know that I didn't show up at the King's audience. So the occasion is gone."

"The occasion is *not* gone. The pension is still there for you. Everyone says that the King goes around all day whistling your melodies, and that he wants your operetta repeated within the next week. You have only to present yourself. You will have your pension at once. You'll see! For yourself you have a right to hesitate. But since so many others are concerned, your hesitation is a crime."

"Thank you for the lecture," said Rousseau. "If you were not my true friend I would consider it an impertinence. But I know it comes from your heart, and therefore I am grateful to you. But I have a higher duty than the one I owe to my friends and my relatives. I have to be true to my principles. Embrace me, therefore, and pity me!"

And giving Diderot no time to formulate an answer, he excused himself and stepped out of the carriage, much to Diderot's annoyance.

The news that Rousseau had refused a pension from the King was even more sensational than his success as a composer, following now so soon upon his success as a writer. And there could be no doubt that it would soon reach the ears of Voltaire.

Now, surely, he would at least have to believe in Rousseau's sincerity!

It wasn't long before the answer came from Potsdam: "This Jean Jacques, seeing that he can never hope to be the richest author in the world, has decided that he will be the poorest. Let us wish him success."

Obviously, by the phrase "the richest author" Voltaire was referring to himself.

8: THE TERRIBLE SECRET

"Voltaire is the greatest genius of our time." So Rousseau felt and thought and wrote in letters dated as late as 1755. When Rousseau was already known both as a composer and as a philosopher.

Imagine! Voltaire first ignores him and then mocks him cruelly, and still Rousseau goes on blindly worshiping him. And this happens again and again.

"He is of all men the most amiable." So Jean Jacques continued in the letter quoted above. "And just for the sake of trafficking with that keen wit of his, I would consent to spend the rest of my days at his feet."

One is really amazed. How could he go on expressing himself in this laudatory fashion, while Voltaire was making all Europe chuckle over Rousseau's follies?

"Not for a moment," Rousseau concluded, "will I yield to those critics of unrelenting animosity who impute to Voltaire the most baleful character. I tell you it is impossible that a poet should depict friendship and virtue as Voltaire has done so often in his works and not himself have a heart that throbs with both."

Clearly, though that heart still did not throb for him, Jean Jacques remained convinced that someday he and Voltaire would meet as friends, that someday he would find his way into Voltaire's arms.

How is this undeviating loyalty and continued admiration to be explained?

By the passion of Rousseau. By the passion of a man who had waited for so many years that he could easily wait still longer. Take, for example, as an illustration of Rousseau's inexhaustible determination, the incident when he had promised a lady a copy of one of his works, still unpublished. He had the courage to copy it out in his best hand. Only a matter of five hundred pages or so. Using a special ink, and drying it with a blue-and-silver powder. God knows how many days and nights of work.

When it was all done, however, the effect did not quite satisfy him. The writing was not really dark enough. The pages seemed to shimmer a bit and make reading somewhat arduous.

Not for a moment did Rousseau hesitate. It's true that he hated desk work. That he loved the out-of-doors. That he was forever lazy. But for all that, he sat down and patiently retraced every single letter of those five hundred pages, giving an additional emphasis to each stroke with a second coat of ink!

Such was the character of this man who had caught the desire for glory from worshiping at the shrine of Voltaire. Was he going to give up all his hopes, all his yearnings, just because he had failed to impress that great man with his first literary effort? Not at all. Jean Jacques's dreams would go on. Indeed, they would never stop. Not even during those years when Rousseau would finally come to hate Voltaire with all his might. (But surely with tears in his eyes.)

Nor during those years when he would be mortally afraid of Voltaire.

How complex now the relations between these two men—who had still to meet. Who had still to speak one word to each other! For years it had been merely a question of whether Jean Jacques could manage to achieve some sort of fame and thus make himself worthy of Voltaire. And all through those years of unceasing endeavor Voltaire and fame had constituted but a single goal. Fame seemed to lead inevitably to Voltaire.

But then the unexpected had happened. He had acquired fame. And precisely for that reason Voltaire had become more unreachable than ever.

And now a frightening possibility! That a terrible sin committed by Rousseau during his years of struggle might be discovered. A sin that he had committed again and again. Committed because he had no choice: it was either sin or give up his dream of Voltaire.

Of course, as long as Rousseau had not yet become France's man of virtue or dreamed of ever becoming that character, the sin had not seemed so terrible. His conscience had not given him too much trouble. But now! What if Voltaire should find it out now? Never would he understand that this sin had been committed as a tribute to Voltaire! He would think only of how he could use it as a weapon against Jean Jacques. Another means of loading him with ridicule, exposing him before all Europe as a fraud!

As yet only a very few, and all of them very trustworthy people, knew of Jean Jacques's secret sin. Nevertheless, there was always the danger that it would get abroad. Whispered at first. And of course only on the promise of the strictest secrecy. But gradually making its way around. Until finally it was what the French call "the secret of Polichinelle," and it might as well be shouted from the housetops.

His fame had spread like wildfire, had it not? Then so might his shame.

Certainly the rich and ailing Madame de Francueil had somehow come into the knowledge of his sin. And she was obviously deeply disturbed when she arrived one morning at his apartment, unexpectedly, and begged him for a moment of his time. Alone.

No sooner had Rousseau unceremoniously shooed his mistress Thérèse out of the room than Madame, her low voice threatened by sobs, pleaded with him to assure her that it wasn't true.

He knew immediately what she meant. But he pretended not to, for a moment, while she explained herself further. Then he was roused to the utmost pitch of fury. There went his whole life! A quarter of a century of labor wrecked.

Standing over her as if ready to attack her, he demanded that she tell him immediately the source of such a vile story.

She cowered, trembling. Nevertheless she refused to give him her source. She had no right to do that.

"If it was Thérèse!" he raged.

She clutched his arm, and begged him not to do anything violent. She had anticipated this outburst, and that was why she had hesitated for a long time before coming to see him. For she admired him. She revered him. And for that reason she simply had to be reassured. Only when he gave her his word that the story was false would she feel herself entitled to give him the name of the person who had revealed the matter to her. She need have no pity for a liar!

Rousseau said nothing for a moment. He was searching his mind to discover from whom she might have received this information.

Obviously she could never have discovered it of herself. No. The styles of women were so voluminous about the waist that neither pregnancy nor delivery made any noticeable change in a woman's appearance. One really had to live in the closest intimacy with a woman to guess that she had conceived and carried a baby to term.

As for Thérèse, on second thought, he felt that she was hardly likely to have told anyone. He had impressed upon her that if the story of her babies should be bruited about, it could only be to her own dishonor. She would become known in the quarter as a person of loose character. Naturally he would be compelled to cast her off, and she would have no choice but to become the lowest sort of prostitute.

It was true that he himself, originally, had not felt any particular need for secrecy. What for? Indeed, at the time he had been rather proud of having had a sexual adventure. And yet he had nevertheless been secretive. Not just for the sake of Thérèse, but only as he always tended to be secretive about himself. With the result that only a few of his closest male friends knew anything about his children. Diderot. Grimm. D'Alembert.

And while deep rifts were now showing up between him and these philosophers—for example, in the matter of the parsley debate that Diderot had launched (writing anonymously, Diderot had put forward the proposition that while it was a matter of life and death that man should know how to distinguish parsley from hemlock—which so closely resembles parsley but is violently poisonous—it was not so important for man to know which of two religions was the better)— nevertheless he was still friends with these men, and they were men of honor who would never reveal his secret. Besides, he knew secrets about their lives too. They would therefore be just as anxious as he was to keep the matter quiet.

Nor could it have been the midwife, Gouin, who had talked. Her lucrative practice was based precisely on her dependable professional secrecy, which naturally she would be the last to violate.

That left only Thérèse's mother, who could have let the secret out. But would not this old woman tend to guard her tongue, seeing that she was so utterly dependent on her daughter, who again was so utterly dependent on him? Still, there had been one occasion when she might have felt that to talk would be the right course. That was when everyone was trying to dissuade him from resigning his well-paid job as cashier for M. de Francueil. She might have thought then that a word whispered to Madame de Francueil about Thérèse's longing to keep at least one of her babies would add an argument to prevent Rousseau from throwing up his good position.

In any case, the secret had escaped at least so far as Madame de Francueil, and there she was, wanting assurance from him that it wasn't true.

His first thought was to lie to her. To deny everything. Out of hand. Attribute such shameless rumors to his enemies. Pretend amazement that she should credit such an ugly story even for a moment.

But instead, driven by some obscure but powerful impulse to hurt this woman, this extremely rich woman who had never in her life had to face the terrible problem of an additional mouth to feed in a poverty-stricken household, this rich woman who had never had to face the problem of an additional person to accommodate in already overcrowded quarters, this rich woman who had been surrounded by luxury, by beauty, by willing servants from her birth on—driven by this obscure but powerful impulse to strike back through her at all the wealthy women who could never really understand the problems of the poor, he decided to be brutally frank with her.

With a scornful shrug of his shoulders, he said, "Why shouldn't it be true?"

"Oh, dear God, no!" she cried.

"Yes," he acknowledged bluntly. "I abandoned my children."

"You exposed them to die?" she gasped.

"*Exposed* them?" he retorted angrily. "Certainly not. I *deposed* them. At the hospital for foundlings. For the state to take care of them."

Greatly relieved, Madame de Francueil exclaimed, "Then nothing is lost. They can be recovered. You left identifying marks on their clothes—"

"No," he said.

"What? No note with the layette? No chain or bracelet? No initials?"

"Nothing!" he emphasized sharply.

"Oh, no, monsieur!" she cried. "No. You couldn't have been so cruel! I refuse to believe it."

"Cruel?" He laughed. "Why, I congratulate myself that I acted in the best interests of everyone. Absolutely. And I will not hesitate to repeat what I've done whenever it shall be necessary."

Overcome with emotion, Madame de Francueil could scarcely speak. "You? An unnatural father?" she finally breathed. "You, whom I've looked up to as the only virtuous man of our times."

The only virtuous man of our times, he said to himself. Yes, that's what she hungered for: to find a man of virtue. And for a very good reason. She could hardly find much virtue in her husband. The two of them were strangers in their own home. Her husband did not sleep with her. And she was thus reduced to the bitter choice of either breaking the Ten Commandments by committing adultery or else remaining unloved. As for her husband, he thought nothing of this choice. He had always had his mistresses.

Among others, he had had Madame d'Épinay.

For the rich Madame d'Épinay was another one of those women

brought to the same bitter choice. Monsieur d'Épinay did not sleep
with his wife either. Not often, at any rate. He was much too busy
with his mistresses, who were usually the best singers or dancers of
the day. With the result that eventually Madame d'Épinay, hungry
for love, went to bed with M. de Francueil, who did not so much favor
actresses as he did the neglected wives of his friends.

Unfortunately there were those rare occasions when M. d'Épinay
did go to bed with his wife. And on one such occasion he had infected
her with an ugly sexual disease. Which she, unwittingly, passed on to
M. de Francueil.

Oh, what a pus of corruption rose from this modern French society
that was so polite, so charitable, so witty and so devoted to the arts!

And he, Rousseau, was himself corrupt!

Yes. But why? Was it not because the society in which he had
lived, the society whose tone was set by the aristocracy of Paris, had
corrupted him? Had he been born with this idea of letting a midwife
take his children to the foundling home? Was it Geneva, the city of
his childhood, that had taught him such tricks? Could he have possibly conceived of it all by himself?

Obviously not.

He had merely imitated the style of living that he saw around himself. At the table d'hôte where he had eaten for years, he had heard
men laugh as they boasted of putting the children of their sins aside.
Why, almost every third child in Paris was a foundling. One of his
best friends, d'Alembert, was the child of the wealthy Madame de Tencin, the famous mistress of a literary salon. And what had she done
with her baby? Disgusted with the very idea of whelping like an animal, and long since separated from the Chevalier Destouches, who had
quickened her, she had had her maid leave the brat on the steps of a
church. Leave it there to die, which was the ordinary fate of most of
these unfortunates. In this case, however, a local official had found the
baby and put it in the care of a poor woman of the neighborhood.
And eventually the father had undertaken the child's support and
education.

While Madame de Tencin, until her death, only a year or two before,
had continued as one of the most admired women of Paris. Her salon
was frequented by such men as Fontenelle, Montesquieu, Piron. Her
brother was a cardinal!

Rousseau could not see that he had acted differently from Madame
de Tencin. But of course there would always remain this difference
between her corruption and his. For there would always be this difference between the corruption of the rich and the corruption of the

poor. When the rich were corrupt it was out of their own disposition toward evil! What else could it be? They were under no compulsion. Whereas the poor were corrupt out of necessity. Out of their grinding poverty. Their corruption was their misfortune. It was never their crime!

The poor were thus innocent. Always. Even when they were guilty. While the rich were guilty even when they were innocent.

It was the boiling up of these thoughts in him that caused Rousseau to turn upon Madame de Francueil and administer to her a lecture that she would never forget. He would show her where to lay the blame. Not on him! No, indeed. But on herself!

"If I have had to abandon my children to the foundling home," he began, "is that a crime for which you feel impelled to accuse me or a misfortune for which you've come to pity me?"

This startling opening left her dumfounded. She had expected him to fall upon his knees, show repentance, throw himself upon her mercy.

"Do you realize," he said, "that if I had shared with my children the little we have to eat, we must all of us have starved together? Is that what you would have wanted? Would that have pleased you? Would you then have called me virtuous?"

She stammered, "But—but why did you have to make children when you could not feed them? It seems to me—"

"Pardon me, madame," he interrupted her. "Nature does not ask us whether we choose to have children or not. She doesn't *question*. She *compels*. By the force of the passions which she arouses in us. But nature would gladly feed our children. For she has provided land and water and labor in plenty. But it is you, yes, you, Madame de Francueil, you and the other rich families of France, you with your flocks of useless servants, and your fountains all laid out for your pleasure, and the forests which you hold in preserves for your hunting, it is you who have stolen the land and the labor that ought to have grown the bread for my children!"

She was not steeled to find herself accused of the very crime she had come to confront him with, and she drew back, frightened.

"Yes," he said, pointing his finger at her. "If *my* children are orphaned, if *my* bowels are torn with a yearning that will never be stilled, the fault is *yours!*"

"But . . . but we would have gladly helped. We offered you a position, Monsieur Rousseau, did we not?"

"Yes," he said with a scornful laugh. "You offered me the opportunity of becoming one of the oppressors instead of one of the oppressed. So that I would be faced with the necessity of raising my children to be stupid, in order that they might bless me. For if I brought them up to be intelligent they would know enough to curse me!"

"Oh!" Madame de Francueil breathed.

"Do you imagine that I would have any pleasure from bringing them up to repeat my own miseries? To watch them ruin their health by indoor work, cripple their bodies by sitting forever at a desk, blind their eyes by endless reading and writing! I say, let them rather be foundlings! Let them be provided for by the state, as Plato wished it. Brought up to the plow and the pickax, instead of to the latest dance step and the latest witticism! Let them be farmers sooner than fortune hunters. They can only be the healthier and the happier for it."

"And so you are really not sorry for them?"

"Sorry?" He laughed. "That I have given them a better life than my own? No. If I should have another child tomorrow, I would do the same! It is only for myself I am sorry—that I will never know what it is to clasp a child of my own in these arms."

Now she was truly aghast.

But he went on, disregarding her emotions, and pounding home his advantage: "Does it disturb you that my children must grow up to be workers? Is that why you are so wrought up? Is work, then, so ignoble in your eyes? And if it is indeed vulgar to be a worker, who has made it so? Who has imposed this prejudice on the world, so that to be a poor worker is considered more shameful than to be the most vicious aristocrat in the kingdom! Answer me, you who eat and drink and wear nothing but the product of work; answer me: Who has done this to the world?"

While she remained speechless, he went on quickly, "The rich have harmed me enough already. But, Madame, it lies within your power to harm me even more. You can add a further dishonor to my poverty by spreading to the whole world the secret you have somehow obtained."

Overwhelmed, she fell upon her knees before him, and with tears in her eyes she begged him to believe that for the few months of her life that might yet remain her lips would be sealed, and she would take this knowledge to her grave.

And that indeed she did, not too long afterward. While Rousseau wrote out what must have been their conversation in the form of a letter which he set down in code, and which was found among his papers after his death.

He was rather proud of his rebuke to Madame de Francueil. And he wanted the world to know about it. Not now. No. But someday when he was dead.

And for that reason the code he used was childishly simple. The figure *1* represented the letter *A*. The figure *2*, the letter *B*. And so on. Obviously it was not meant to conceal what he had written from anyone except a person as simple-minded as his Thérèse. And only she would have immediate access to these papers. So that nothing more complicated than this cipher was required to prevent her from knowing its contents.

How bitterly ashamed he was of having to share his life in its moments of greatest passion, greatest intimacy, with such an ignorant woman! That he, with his fiery ambition, his ardent emotions, should find himself tied to a woman who after years of effort could still barely spell her way through the simplest sentences. And who would evidently never to able to learn the alphabet in its correct order!

He, tied to such a woman, he who could write in his *Confessions:* "I dreamed of nothing but princesses. My private fantasies were always of ladies of the aristocracy. I just couldn't stomach common women. Their hands so coarse from overwork. Their complexions so dingy from neglect. Lacking in every daintiness. Without taste for finery. No cunning little slippers . . ."

Yes, such was the taste that blossomed inside him. But poverty had denied him anything more than a laundress whose hands were damp and cold, whose fingers were swollen, whose nails were cracked.

And how he had suffered, when he was first meeting Thérèse, to be forced to hear just at that time so much of Voltaire's famous affair with the Marquise du Châtelet, the divine Émilie, who, while Rousseau's Thérèse was in vain trying to learn how to read time on a clock, was plunging with Voltaire into Newtonian mathematics!

"Everything pleases her," Voltaire had versified about her at that time.

Everything harmonizes with her vast genius.
Books and jewelry. Compass and trifling passementerie.
Poetry and diamonds. Gambling at cards and the theories of optics.
Algebra and late suppers. Latin and lace petticoats.
The opera. Lawsuits. Dancing and astronomy.

She had a vast fortune. Millions. She could gamble away eighty thousand francs in one evening and indeed she did once, playing at the Queen's table at the palace of Fontainebleau. A sum of money which a Rousseau, secretary or music copyist, could not hope to earn in a century and a Thérèse could not earn with her water-ruined hands in a thousand years of scrubbing.

Voltaire himself had been dismayed at the Marquise's extravagance and has whispered to her in English, "Can't you see that you are being cheated? That you are playing with scoundrels?"

Unfortunately someone had understood his English, and the resulting fury of the aristocrats at the Queen's table was such that Voltaire and his Émilie had had to flee from Paris that very night.

What adventures! What peaks of delight, of learning and of tragedy those two enjoyed! How life crackled around them! While he, Rousseau, like some mole digging in the darkness, went through his stingily paid, scribbling work along with his laundress and her brood of incompetent, impecunious relatives.

And then for his friend Diderot to reproach him for not cementing his relationship with Thérèse!

Diderot had been wooing a common shopgirl at the same time that Rousseau was getting himself involved with Thérèse. And Diderot eventually married his girl. And thereafter felt himself called upon to badger Rousseau for not marrying his love.

"I married my Nanette, didn't I?" Diderot pointed out.

"You promised to marry her, isn't that so?" Jean Jacques said.

"Yes, of course I promised her marriage," Diderot said.

"Then you did well to keep your promise," Rousseau concluded curtly.

As for himself, he had never promised marriage to Thérèse. He had said to her only this: "As long as you remain true to me, I shall never abandon you."

And indeed he never would.

Which is something that Diderot would not be able to say later of his Nanette. In spite of his marriage he abandoned her.

Corrupt? Corrupt? Who was really corrupt?

All this seethed up in Rousseau's memory one day when he noticed the new subject proposed by the Academy of Dijon for their next essay contest: *The Origin of Inequality among Men*. And once again he was fired with an irresistible desire to compete.

Who should know better about human inequality than he, who had suffered so much from it? He, who had only to think of Voltaire in order to feel the sting of jealousy, the pain and the envy that a constant comparison between their conditions had stitched into every strand of his flesh?

What caused those differences between men? Why was a Voltaire born to wealth? And a Rousseau born to poverty? Why was a Marquise du Châtelet born to "diamonds and poetry, algebra and late suppers, Latin and lace petticoats," while a Thérèse was born to wash clothes until she died?

Was it enough to say, "It is God's will"? As the priests did? Urging charity.

One must picture this passionate man Rousseau in those frantic days when his heart and his mind were thus torn between Voltaire and fame. Clad in a dingy brown suit, his shoes slashed with a razor so that his painful corns would have more room, his little round wig awry, his face with its rather delicate and feminine features left unshaven, but his eyes always savage with determination, traversing Paris in haste in order to go out into the woods, where, with paper and pencil in hand, he could relieve himself as often as he wanted and let his mind range freely (and "proudly," as he himself would put it) over the whole history of mankind, seeking out those arguments and those illustrations that he would need to prove his contentions.

On the streets of Paris he would often note the hordes of beggars. What could have driven them to such a pass? he would ask himself, his heart wrung with pity. He would watch a passer-by stop to give one of them a copper. How quickly the mob of wretches, like scarecrows brought to life, would come swarming and fluttering around the giver of alms, competitively flaunting their sores, their mutilated limbs, their rags and their crutches, each one screaming and moaning for the penny that would prolong his tortured life for yet a few hours.

But having made his modest little gift, the passer-by would calmly walk on. And Jean Jacques would note angrily in his pad, "How convenient! The charity of a single farthing, and, lo and behold, we are dispensed from the duty of concerning ourselves any further with the misery of our fellow men!"

Then he would see a rich man's carriage driving past the beggars without so much as a pause. And furiously he would add, "But even more convenient: to own a fine vehicle, and be able to roll past the beggars, giving them nothing but a splash of muck from your wheels. Right in their faces!"

What had created these inequalities?

Voltaire, for all his proclaimed belief that society must be founded on pity and justice, did not worry his head about the existence of beggars.

When he was informed that Paris had six times as many beggars as

London, Voltaire replied, "That's because Paris is six times as rich as London, and beggars must flock where there is wealth. In London they still burn tallow, while in Paris we burn almost nothing but wax. In Paris one can see a thousand times as much silverware laid out every evening as one can see in London."

As for what to do about the beggars, why, put them to work, of course. Aren't there roads to be built? Canals to be dug? Fields to be weeded? Scrubby land to be cleared?

Wealth! That was the side of it that interested and excited Voltaire. While Rousseau was forced to concern himself with poverty.

Well, if he had to, he would! And the world would know about it!

One time, for example, he came home from one of his walks and was greeted by a Thérèse in tears. What had happened? A friend in the country had promised her a pot of butter. Twenty pounds of it. The butter had never arrived. Then she had learned that the carrier had delivered the pot by mistake to a Count de Lastic, who had promptly dispatched it to his kitchen, where the butter was being consumed as needed. And when Thérèse had dared come knocking at his door to explain the situation and get back her butter, the Count had had his servants order her from the premises.

Boiling with righteous indignation, Rousseau sat down to write a letter to the Count. Not only was he furious that these few francs' worth of butter should have been stolen from him, but in addition it galled him that he had to concern himself with such a trifling sum while, just at this time, a Voltaire went to law in Prussia over a matter of diamonds, tens of thousands of francs' worth, which he claimed to have been cheated out of by a Jew named Hirsch.

DEAR SIR [Rousseau wrote]:
I am no doubt unknown to you, but when I inform you that I want not only to apologize to you, but also to pay you some money, I am confident that you will read this letter through to the end. . . .

And he had gone on to explain the circumstances of the lost butter and the incident of the Count's servants chasing Thérèse from his door. The letter continued:

I have done my best, dear sir, to explain to this poor girl the rules of fine society and the precepts of a higher education. And how it would certainly be of little profit to a gentleman to have to pay the wages of a lot of servants if he could not use them to keep the poor from his door when they come to claim their property. And that she must learn to realize that such words as *justice* and *humanity* are for use only among people of low birth. Indeed, that she ought to feel herself honored that a count should deign to consume her butter.

I have finally managed to bring her around to the light, dear sir, so that she is now convinced that it is all her fault and she is anxious to beg your pardon for having importuned you, and even to express the hope that you may have found her butter to your taste. And more than that, she wishes to reimburse you, in case you have sustained any expenses in this matter, for example to the carrier, which you must certainly permit her to do, since it is only proper.

Rousseau never sent off this letter.

Why?

Because he made the mistake of reading it to some of his wealthy friends, among others to Madame d'Épinay. And everyone had exclaimed, "My God! How shocking!"

Oh, no, they weren't referring to the Count's behavior. No. This Count was obviously a rascal. And unworthy of being the descendant of the great Lastic family that had so distinguished itself in the era of the Crusades. But that letter! As a man of honor, Rousseau couldn't afford to send out such a letter. What if people got to know about it? It violated all the canons of good taste. One just couldn't be so impolite.

Ah, well, if one can't be impolite, then what's to be done? Shall one say nothing at all and just let the Count remain undisturbed in the enjoyment of his stolen butter?

How clear the whole trick was now becoming to him. The fraudulence of it! And the cleverness of it! A conspiracy, nothing less. With all these interlocking devices of charity, of carriages, of servants, of tradition, of rich friends, all tied to each other by an intricate web of good manners, good taste, politeness, laws and regulations, the right and the wrong thing to do, and all this working intricately and ingeniously to the end that the poor should remain forever imprisoned in their poverty.

And the rich forever secure in their wealth.

And out on the streets of Paris, Rousseau could now distinguish among the beggars two varieties. Some of them were obviously imbeciles. They were born deficient. Freaks. Cripples. Sports of a cruel fate. Their bodily afflictions made them unable to earn a living and reduced them to begging for it.

Clearly these were victims of nature. Chance or accident.

But there were others. Unfortunates. Beggars merely because there was nothing else for them to do. They were born into poverty. And they would live out their lives in poverty. Digging their way ever deeper into it. Their sufferings, their lack of food, their exposure to the elements, and their despair, eventually making cripples of them too.

These were not the victims of nature. They were the victims of society. These were not the victims of chance. They were the victims of our civilization. Even though we might lump them all together as "unfortunates" in order to conceal our own guilt in the matter.

And thus, roaming one day wildly in the forest, Jean Jacques wrote down those fierce lines which would become forever famous:

"The man who first put a fence around a piece of ground, saying, 'This is mine,' and who found people so simple as to believe him, that man was the founder of civilized society. What crimes, what wars, what murders, miseries and horrors might have been spared the human race if someone had only torn down this fence, filled in that ditch and cried out to his fellow men, 'Beware of giving ear to this impostor. You are lost if ever you forget that the earth cannot belong to anyone, while its fruits must belong to everyone!' "

Voltaire read these lines one day a year or so after Rousseau had written them. And he leaped as if stung by a snake. "Scoundrel!" was the furious comment which he felt compelled to scribble in the margin of that copy of Jean Jacques's *Discourse on the Origin of Human Inequality,* a copy which can be seen today in the library of Leningrad. "Scoundrel!"

"What?" Voltaire wrote in the margin. "The first man to cultivate a piece of ground, plant it, protect it, should have no right to the fruits of his diligence? What, this benefactor of mankind was nothing but a thief? A man of injustice? Now, there's philosophy for you, when penniless wretches take to writing it!"

It was as if on that page of that book the basilisk or cockatrice of history had laid one of her fatal eggs. Here was the battle joined between the wealthy Voltaire and the poor Rousseau, this battle of philosophers of which caricatures were later to be printed and sold in the streets of Paris, this battle watched by their contemporaries with excitement, with amusement, with tolerance and with pity. Still unaware of how in time men would gradually lean to one side or the other, until finally the millions of this globe would in one way or another be caught up in the Rousseau-Voltaire conflict. And the whole surface of the earth would be split between the partisans of private property and the enemies of it.

They should, as a matter of fact, have been the greatest of friends,

Both were moved by the same sense of pity and justice. Both wished to free mankind from its miseries.

But they looked at the problem from opposite sides.

Voltaire said, "No man should be wretched. But some men must always be poorer than others. Some men must always have to work for their livelihood."

While Rousseau said, "No man should be so rich that he can buy another. Nor any man so poor that he has to sell himself."

To which Voltaire countered, "That way lies stagnation! Human beings must be stimulated by their lust for gain!"

Voltaire would always see the rich as providing the poor with the means to work and thus to earn their living. While Rousseau could never enter the home of a rich person without seeing on all sides the products which the labor of the poor had created for that rich person to enjoy.

The poor meanwhile getting nothing except the barest necessities to keep them alive from one job to the next.

9: MY MOTHER WAS NO VIRGIN

The rich, the poor! How immeasurable the gulf between them! Two nations who speak the same language and yet cannot understand a word they say to each other.

There were times, during his early poverty-stricken years in Paris, when Rousseau would pass, on the Rue St.-Jacques, back of the Sorbonne, the old Jesuit institution called the Collège Louis le Grand because Louis XIV, visiting it one day, had been so enchanted with the performances the students put on for him that he exclaimed, "This is *my* kind of school!" And the Jesuits, always at war with the Oratorians for the control of education in France, quickly called in stonemasons, and before dawn they had removed the old inscription, "Collège de Clermont," and substituted the name of the great King.

And Jean Jacques, going to and from the garret where he lived, near the Luxembourg, would sometimes find himself on the Rue St.-Jacques when it was jammed with ornate carriages, and grooms would go leaping to the cobblestones to run around and open the door for some lad in a costume frogged with gold, with plumed hat on his head, and fine lace foaming out from cuff and collar, and a jeweled sword cockily sticking out from beneath the silk-and-velvet coat.

And the grooms would go elbowing space for their master. Crying, "Make Way for Monsieur le Prince de Rohan!" or "Make way for Monseigneur le Duc de Montmorency!" And some such little master, with his name trailing clouds of French history, would descend, accompanied by a private tutor and a private valet, who would live with him in a private suite of rooms at the college.

And Jean Jacques, pushing himself close to the walls to avoid the high-strung horses, would think with envy and bitterness, Here is where Voltaire went to school, years ago. Went to school with these dukes and princes and studied philosophy and wrote poetry, when I, at his same age, was mopping floors in an engraving workshop in Geneva.

How could this have happened? Was it not somehow as if Voltaire had willed it so? That he should be rich and Rousseau poor?

Actually Voltaire had not even been Voltaire then. Still only François Marie Arouet, younger son of a wealthy solicitor who had also become head of the Royal Chamber of Accounts. And as a young collegian, Voltaire had had neither private valet nor private tutor, nor private apartments. He slept, as a matter of fact, in a room with several other boys. But there is no doubt that he was surrounded at school by all that was wealthy and powerful in France, and that he learned to feel at home on that level and made many lifelong friends there among members of the highest circles.

Rousseau could well imagine the pride these youngsters felt, knowing themselves to be the elect of the elect. Members of the first families of France, or closely linked to them. And France itself the first of all nations of the world.

A kind of pride denied to him, born in Geneva instead of Paris, and member of no special family.

All over Europe, for those who could afford it, and even for those who couldn't, it was French wigs and French laces, embroidered silks and velvets, porcelains and inlaid woods, French wines and French cooking. And, of course, if possible, French wit. So that from Moscow to Edinburgh not a gentleman could call himself cultured, who did not know France and the French. And French *coureurs des bois* and French Jesuit missionaries carried the French tongue from the Mississippi in America to the palace of the Chinese Emperor in Asia.

So powerful was the dominance of French culture in this period that the writer Saint-Évremond, exiled from France, could calmly settle in England and live out the rest of his long life there without ever bothering to learn a word of English. But the contrary, that an Englishman should settle in Paris without learning French, that was inconceivable! This was true only because French was the language of aristocracy everywhere. It was the language of almost every court of Europe. French was the language of the Russian nobility. It was the language of Potsdam, where Frederick spoke and wrote it in preference to German. It was the language of the deposed king of Poland, Stanislas. Even late in the century, Edward Gibbon would seriously debate whether he should not write his great work on the decline and fall of the Roman Empire in French rather than in English.

And it was for this world of French culture, to enable these lads to shine in it, that the Jesuit colleges trained their pupils. Trained Voltaire.

Rousseau, who had never gone to any school in his life except for a few brief months to a seminary, could only envy as he imagined what the scene might be like in August, when the school exercises were held and the prizes distributed. And when little Voltaire, as the best pupil of the institution, would be loaded down with crowns of laurel leaves.

Annually a great amphitheater would be erected by covering the college courtyard with a huge awning. The stage of the amphitheater would take advantage of the stairs and the terrace of the school building, but it would be additionally developed so that the spectators would have before them an astonishing vista of arches and columns, friezes and statues, fountains and cupolas, all done with that lavish scenic ornamentation of the period, which loved nothing so much as to create an overwhelming architectural illusion.

The school would then put on its annual theatrical representation, for which the pupils had been practicing for months. Father Lejay and Father Porée, two of Voltaire's teachers, were especially gifted in dramatic composition. Their tragedies and comedies, written in iambic verse, are unfortunately in Latin, so they have ceased to be played, but they were celebrated in their day as the work of masters and published for use in Latin schools all over the world, even as far as Boston in the New World.

This was an old Jesuit custom, these theatrical festivities. The subjects were, of course, taken either from the Bible or from the classics of Latin and Greek, with only one theme avoided as much as possible: that of love, since feminine parts would require some students to dress in women's clothes. But this was the only concession, for in every other respect the aim of the Jesuits was to impress upon the parents the Jesuit ability to form their sons into young men able to assume their proper place in society. And with the court of Louis XIV so avid for the theater and the ballet, in which the King himself loved to participate, the ability to dance and to act before an audience, to speak and to sing, gracefully and effectively, without shyness or stage fright, was considered basic.

To lighten the heavy Latin scenes, which would be incomprehensible and perhaps even boring to some of the distinguished parents, particularly the mothers, the Jesuits made it a habit to precede and to follow every one of the five acts of their tragedies with a variety of other material: songs, recitations, little pantomimes, musical numbers and the like, in the invention of which one of the Jesuit instructors of the school, Lallemand, was particularly talented.

But above all, the Jesuit fathers loved the ballet.

In the matter of singing and dancing, this royally favored college had the choice of the best instructors from the opera of Paris. And no expense was spared to make these college performances both impressive and diverting. The choreography was drilled for months and brought to as near perfection as possible.

The costuming was done with a fine taste for color and display. At times no fewer than three hundred specially made garments were ordered for a single number on the program. Boys depicting, for example, the four winds, would be clad in gauzy stuffs of changing colors, gay for the group of winds that brought fair weather, somber for those that brought storms. And one can imagine the striking costumes achieved for the lads who would do special numbers portraying forces of lightning, of hail and snow. Or, in a ballet of savages, the startling costumes that would be made of brightly dyed feathers to illustrate Indians and Africans. Or, in a ballet of the emotions, the costumes for the various sins and punishments.

All this elaborate attention to costumes was made necessary, of course, by the audience that came to these exercises, who were themselves dressed as brilliantly as any the world has ever seen. What a disaster for the faculty if the house should prove more eye-filling than the stage!

The Jesuit fathers did not think of these exercises as frivolous. On the contrary. One of the fathers of the college, Father Porée, published a study on the subject and declared that the varied movements of the body called for in the ballet were of especial value to those students who would later go on to a military career, giving them a commanding but easy posture, as well as lightness on their feet and dexterity and speed in all their gestures and physical activities.

Why, even in the year 1709, one of the darkest years of France's history, when the British had just won the battle of Malplaquet (though with tremendous losses) and no one doubted that the Duke of Marlborough and the Prince of Savoy would follow up their military advantage by racing down to loot Paris before a new ring of fortifications could be hurriedly thrown up to the north of the city, even in that year when, to make matters worse, the crops had failed all over France, and the British Navy was capturing one grain ship after another on which the French people were counting for relief, when the streets of Paris were crowded with starved-out peasants, when the rich were melting down their silverware to fill the depleted coffers of the Sun King, and the school could not serve its pupils anything but the coarsest oatmeal bread, even in that year of despair no reason was seen to cancel the annual school ballet, in which little Voltaire danced in a *Ballet of Hope,* as expensively costumed as ever.

How all this extravagant Parisian schooling, with its dancing and its music, with its costumes and its theatricals, contrasted with the sober and somber childhood of Rousseau in Geneva!

It was as if Voltaire had been born in the light. And Rousseau in the darkness. No costumes in his childhood. Scarcely even proper clothes.

Nothing could be more different from Paris than the city of Geneva, that city of which Voltaire would later make the scornful remark, "It took the violin two hundred years to batter down the gates of Geneva."

It's true that for two centuries the gates of Geneva were closed to the violin. As well as to all other musical instruments. They were forbidden. They were the tools of the Devil.

It was Calvin, the French Protestant reformer, when he was invited to rule over Geneva after that city had managed to extricate itself from the Duchy of Savoy, who had instituted these sumptuary laws. Everything that would make a man or a woman attractive—bright clothes, jewelry, cosmetics, fancy coiffures—was ruled out as sinful. Everything that might make life gayer—masquerade parties, playing cards, ballroom dancing and, of course, especially the theater, even Punch-and-Judy shows—was unlawful.

While in Paris life became an ever noisier competition for joy, in Geneva it remained a long, silent struggle for virtue.

Which caused Voltaire to say, "There's nothing for a man to do in Geneva but get drunk."

And caused Rousseau later to defend alcoholism. "People who get drunk are rarely mean or wicked."

But how could a Voltaire, with his upbringing, understand Calvin's purpose? He attributed the whole thing to ignorance and to fanaticism. "Geneva," he said, "is what happens when fanatics make our laws. Since the fanatic imagines that it is God who speaks through him, he naturally concludes that all his enemies are motivated by the Devil. No need then for any pity. That is why Calvin had no scruples in sending Gruet to the chopping block. Nor Servetus to the stake. It was all God's will!"

Actually Calvin had planned to have a state with as few inequalities between men as possible. In Calvin's Geneva the rich could not own a carriage. They had indeed little joy from their money. In Calvin's Geneva the master was required by law to sit down at table and eat with his servants. Calvin would permit only one form of inequality in Geneva: that of the more virtuous over the less virtuous. And not that of the rich over the poor. He wanted competition only in virtue. Not in money. Nor in sex. Adultery was made punishable by death. And prostitutes were ducked. Sometimes until they died.

But in the course of the two hundred years since the time of Calvin, more than the violin had crashed the gates of Geneva. The rich, grown fat on the profits of the watchmaking industry, the jewelry trade, the textile business, discovered many ways of evading the strict sumptuary laws. They owned carriages on the excuse that there was a sick member in the family. They traveled abroad and found there the theater and other amusements which were forbidden at home. And as for the rights of the citizens, they managed gradually to whittle them away, until the whole city was solidly in the grip of a few powerful aristocratic families who were members of the Magnificent Council.

But at least in one madness, the madness of the theater, Geneva still remained untainted.

And now imagine who it will be, who, after these two hundred years of Calvinistic purity, comes to establish a theater in Geneva. Voltaire, of course. Yes, Voltaire would come eventually to Geneva, would establish a splendid residence there and, disgusted with this dull town ridden by preachers shouting brimstone and hellfire, would decide to give private theatricals in his home and invite the aristocrats of Geneva to come there both as spectators and as amateur performers.

Jean Jacques should have been delighted. After all, hadn't he once gone to Paris, poor and unknown, his pockets stuffed with manuscripts of plays, hoping to put them on there and thus gain both livelihood and fame?

And didn't he love and admire Voltaire? Why, then, shouldn't Voltaire go to Geneva and put on plays?

Why should all this make Jean Jacques simply sick with fury?

Inexplicable! Unless one tears down the life of both Rousseau and Voltaire into sections. And studies each section anatomically, both grossly and microscopically, and learns what Geneva meant to Rousseau, all the hopes and the dreams he lavished on that city, and all the miseries he endured from her.

And strange, too, that of all the cities in the world where the wealthy Voltaire might have settled, it should be to Geneva, Rousseau's native town, that he would go. As if fate lay in ambush where these two men were concerned and studied how many tricks might be played upon them.

Two men so alike, and yet so different. Take as a gauge of that likeness and that difference the fact that both of them lost their mothers at a very early age, Rousseau's mother dying when he was a few days old, Voltaire's when he was seven years of age.

And that some fifty years after these women were in their graves, both men set down on paper almost the only references to them that they would ever make.

Said Rousseau, "My mother was beautiful and virtuous."

Said Voltaire, "My mother was no virgin."

Can two points of view be more at variance? The idealism of the one and the realism of the other.

Rousseau carried away by his imagination.

Voltaire armed with his cool sarcasm.

And then it is almost as if the student of these matters, to be fair to both parties, ought to split himself in two. For what can be more touching than Rousseau's statement as to the beauty and the virtue of his mother? Though he had nothing on which to base himself. Nothing but the testimony of those who remembered her from many years back. And as to her virtue, still less proof, since that might have remained her secret.

While Voltaire, on what solid ground he stands when he says that his mother was no virgin. He was simply talking common sense. After all, what was virginity? Was it not that condition in which all girls are born? And did not that condition have to be abandoned in order that the next generation might come into being? And so on, until the end of time?

Was it not, in fact, precisely because his mother had fortunately taken care of this matter and altered her condition that he, Voltaire, had the happy privilege of being numbered among the living? For it was not the virgins who saved mankind, as some people, foolishly misled by certain religions, tended to believe, but, on the contrary, the nonvirgins, without whom the species would come to an end!

But of course where virtue was so important, where perfectionism was strained for, everything connected with birth naturally bore some traces of guilt, of pollution, of shame and mystery. And it is clear now why Rousseau in his *Confessions,* describing his first hours after birth, should speak of himself as costing his mother her life, as if he had been responsible, as if he had willed his own birth and that birth had been some sort of transaction requiring payment for the damages he had caused.

Or, going back even farther, as if his mother had certainly never taken any pleasure in sex. And the whole affair was thus completely on the tragic side.

Which, as a matter of fact, it nearly was, since, as a baby, he gave no promise of living.

It was his Aunt Suzon who saved his life. She noticed that hours after delivery this puny infant still remained completely dry. Might not this be the cause of his pitiful whining? Somehow her efforts to get the baby to void its urine were successful. How she did it Rousseau does not tell us, and we are left to guess whether she used massage, or took a knitting needle to widen the orifice, or whether she employed suction.

All Jean Jacques would say was, "She saved my life."

To which he would add, "I have forgiven her for it."

"She could not know that in saving my life she was also saving my disease, my malformation, which was to grow along with me and which would strengthen itself as I grew stronger, and which would never loosen its grip on me except for an occasional respite, but then only to return and plague me all the more cruelly."

With Voltaire, sex was in no way tied up with sin. And for that reason he enjoyed nothing so much as making fun of the general Christian furor over sex. The Catholic adoration of virginity. And the Protestant habit of prying into the sexual habits of their neighbors. As if God, the Creator of a billion stars, had nothing better to do than work himself into a rage about how people behaved with respect to their sexual organs.

Once at a dinner table, when the conversation became a little free, Voltaire asked, "Why is it that when one speaks of a woman's virtue, one has only one particular virtue in mind? And that the virtue which of all virtues I would consider the least important?"

Voltaire then went on to contrast our attitude toward sex with that of the natives of Otaheite (now known as Tahiti) about whom there were recent reports by Captain Wallis of the British Navy.

The girls of Otaheite, knowing no reason why they should be ashamed of the only body which the Creator had given them, received the British sailors with open arms, to use a metonymy. "It was the British sailors," Voltaire said, "so thoroughly imbued with commercial notions, who could not conceive of not paying for the favors they craved after their long voyage.

"And since iron," Voltaire continued, "was what the islanders wanted most, because they had hitherto had nothing but tools made of stone or seashell, the payment of a nail per favor became established almost from the start as the proper tariff for this kind of commerce.

"In a brief period the ship's stores were utterly depleted of every nail. Thereupon the sailors began, surreptitiously, to rip the spikes from the ship's timbers. So that had not Captain Wallis set sail quickly, his craft would surely have disintegrated there in that harbor, before the loveliness of these island girls and the lubricity of his crew.

"But," Voltaire said, "it was particularly what Captain Wallis related of these islanders' method of worshiping the Creator that struck me most. Their Queen selects the island's most beautiful girl. Adorned with flowers, and otherwise completely naked, she is placed upon an altar—"

"Oh!" a lady interrupted. "They practice human sacrifice! How horrible!"

"It is indeed a kind of sacrifice," Voltaire returned. "But not a horrible one, as you shall learn. This beautiful girl, then, is placed upon an altar under the brilliant tropical sky. Then the most handsome man of the tribe is chosen to be her consort. He too is first adorned with flowers and is then led up to the altar. Thereupon, while music plays, these two splendid savages couple. As if in the sight of God! Is that a sacrifice more to your taste, madame?"

"Horrible!" the same lady exclaimed again. "Why, it's like dogs."

"You are difficult to please," Voltaire said. "Truly, now, can you imagine a more devout way of honoring God than in precisely that manner which the Creator himself instituted for the continuation of His creation?"

"But that's not a religious ceremony," the lady cried. "That's an orgy!"

Voltaire shrugged. "What difference? So long as the participants feel the presence of God."

"But can you really imagine that God would bring His divine presence to such infernal rites?" the lady asked, her sense of propriety outraged.

"I can!" Voltaire said stoutly. "More surely than to a church."

"Ah, monsieur, how can you say such a thing, even in jest!"

"Because it can't be otherwise," said Voltaire. "Let me ask you: What can possibly happen in a church that would demand the presence of God? Nothing. Whereas at an orgy there is always the possibility of conception, in which case God's presence is urgently required in order that He may hand out a soul to the newly conceived human being."

Such was necessarily the attitude of a Voltaire, who at the age of eleven was brought by his godfather, the Abbé de Châteauneuf, to the home of Ninon de Lenclos, one of the most notorious courtesans of history.

"I present to you my godson," said the abbé. "He is already an accomplished poet."

And little Voltaire made a sweeping reverence before the eighty-five-year-old woman who was said to have had more than two hundred lovers in her life, chosen from all that was most famous in France.

"Her skin was so thickly mottled with black and brown," Voltaire would recall many years later, "that not a particle of its original color could be guessed. And across her face, from bone to bone, stretched a skin so tight that it seemed as if the least movement of her lips must crack it open."

During almost the whole of the seventeenth century this woman had been celebrated for her beauty, her wit, her culture. So that she numbered among her lovers men such as Molière, the Great Condé, the famous scientist Christian Huyghens and even the Cardinal de Richelieu. Not to mention one of her own sons who, not knowing her as his mother, fell so madly in love with her that when she denied herself to him he shot himself.

Voltaire's godfather, the Abbé de Châteauneuf, was her last lover. When she resisted his advances and he begged her to tell him the reason why, she finally said, "You must forgive an old woman her vanity. But in a few days it will be my seventieth birthday, and it was my intention to surrender to you then."

This Ninon followed the teachings of the libertines. In her day that was still a religious movement, first preached in Flanders by the so-called Brethren of the Free Spirit. They argued that God would not have created us with such powerful desires if he had intended that the satisfaction of these desires should be considered a sin.

Surely the animals, they argued, after being created as the Bible tells us, "male and female," did not just stand around, but must have started at once to perform all their functions, such as eating, defecating, fighting and copulating. Precisely as they have been doing ever since.

And yet God did not find anything wrong in this. On the contrary, the Bible tells us, "God found it good."

If at the time of Creation, under God's own eyes, it was good, then what can be wrong with it now?

Ninon had begun life as the daughter of an impoverished gentleman of the provinces who had come to live in Paris and there managed to earn a meager subsistence by playing on the lute. Concerning which Voltaire would later remark, "It was not until Ninon brought her own instrument into play that the household began to enjoy a little affluence."

About her first lover Voltaire had this comment: "It is not certain whether the old Cardinal de Richelieu had her first—but there can be little doubt that she had his last."

The Cardinal settled a small annuity upon Ninon, and she was thus launched upon her amazing career. Her house on the Rue des Tournelles became one of the earliest salons, where in that still coarse and brutal period it was demonstrated that physical love and genuine pleasure could be had in an atmosphere of taste and refinement. Soon wealthy families began to send their sons to her, that she might form them for polite society. Indeed, her gatherings were so distinguished that an introduction to Mademoiselle de Lenclos's home was considered the key that unlocked all the most important doors in Paris.

The prudes of Paris, jealous of those who enjoyed the pleasures which they had denied to themselves, got together to have the authorities arrest her and lock her up in an institution for repentant prostitutes.

"Lock me up in a monastery, if you like," she said. "But not in a convent. For I don't like women. And don't lock me up in a home for repentant prostitutes, since I don't sell myself for money, but for love, and am therefore not a prostitute. And certainly I'm far from being repentant."

How could one ask a Voltaire, already in contact with such free Parisian spirits at so early an age, how could one ask him to understand a Rousseau who at a similar age was caught in the grip of tight Genevan minds beyond his control?

What could a Voltaire make, for example, of those scenes in Jean Jacques's early boyhood when his father would clasp him passionately in his arms and pretend that in him he could see the image of his dead mother? "It is into her eyes that I look when I look into yours. It is her lips that I kiss when I kiss yours."

Jean Jacques, as he grew a little older, came to dread those moments when he would have to substitute for his missing mother. And when he would hear his father say, "Come, my dear Jean Jacques, come and sit here with me, and let us talk about your mother," he would already know what a scene of kissing and moaning was in store for him.

"Must we weep again, Papa?" he would ask.

Nevertheless he would submit himself to his father's caresses.

"Give me back your mother," Isaac would cry. "Or console me at least for her loss. Make up for me the void she has left here in my heart. Oh, how I love you, my son, because you are all that is left to me of the only woman I shall ever love."

Actually the father had another son, seven years older than Jean Jacques. A son already learning the art of watchmaking under his father's supervision. And it would cut Jean Jacques's heart to the quick to see this older brother looking on with infinite sadness as these scenes of warmth and affection played themselves out between Jean Jacques and his father.

The brother's share was to be scolded and even beaten for neglecting his work. Once, when the father reached out to strike the older boy, Jean Jacques, falling naturally into the role of the absent mother which he had so often assumed, hurriedly threw himself between father and son. He embraced his brother, covering him as best he could with his own body, so that the blows aimed by the father fell upon him. The father, Isaac, tried to drag Jean Jacques away, but that only made him cling all the more tightly to his brother, so that eventually the father was forced to give up his desire to beat the boy.

"I can't hit you, Jean Jacques," the father said. "It would be like hitting your poor dead mother. You are so alike." And once more he opened his arms to his youngest, in order to caress and weep over him, while ordering the older boy back to his work.

This brother, feeling himself unjustly relegated to a lesser position in the family, became more and more unruly. His father had to take him out of his own workshop and apprentice him to someone else who might perhaps succeed in controlling him. But at an age when he should have still been playing with toys, this lad had already formed evil friendships on the street and had let himself in for all manner of harmful habits.

Soon he began making efforts to run away, and finally one day he succeeded. He was heard from once. From Germany. And then he disappeared forever.

There was now no rival to come between father and favorite son.

As if wishing to revive even more strongly the aura of his dead wife, Isaac took to reading out loud the books of the time of his courtship. Father and son would sit close together, and Isaac, a slow reader, would spell out the words of those unending romances of the previous century, those vast fantasies of shepherds and nymphs written by Mademoiselle de Scudéry and Honoré d'Urfé, works such as *Clélie, Astréa* and *The Great Cyrus,* which had been the amusement of the early days of his wooing and marriage.

And the little boy, wide-eyed with wonder, following his father's finger as he pronounced the words, came gradually and insensibly to know how to read, without ever having been taught.

Thereupon they began taking turns reading, so that neither ever grew tired. And their little room in the lower section of Geneva, the poorer section, would vanish in a mist of warriors and dragons, magicians and besieged castles, where there was always a princess whose life was at stake. Until, suddenly and shamefacedly, the father would become aware of the twittering of swallows under the eaves. It was already dawning.

And the father would say, "Come, let us catch some sleep. I guess I'm more of a child than you are."

The little boy would later realize that he understood nothing of what he read. And yet somehow he felt it all. And thus these great passions, these exaggerated emotions, these impossible situations and extravagant coincidences, with their still more improbable solutions, became insensibly a part of the fiber of his life.

"I had lost my identity," he would later explain. "I was instead one of the characters in whatever book we happened to be reading."

When Jean Jacques's mother's little shelf of romances had been exhausted, they borrowed the books from her father's library. He had been a preacher. And thus the nights were now passed with heavy tomes of church history, such as Bossuet's *Universal History* and old classics, especially Plutarch's *Parallel Lives.*

And the little room, once filled with amorous knights and ladies, was now crowded with the giants of classic history. Here was the unscrupulous Pyrrhus with his fabulous army of elephants, plotting war and murder in his efforts to conquer both Greece and Rome. Here was Pelopidas determined to show who was master, his money or himself, and throwing out his fortune to the poor in order to settle that question forever. Here was Pericles as a youth, going to school with the philosopher Anaxagoras, who taught him to despise the superstitions of the mob. Here was the peaceful and logical Phocion telling the Athenians that they must choose either to be stronger than their enemies or to make friends with them, and as a result eventually condemned to death as a coward and forced to drink poison at the age of eighty-three. Here was Coriolanus, thirsting for revenge against his native Rome and bringing an army to conquer it, but at the point of victory unable to resist the tears of his mother.

Such were the forces molding this little boy and tending to confuse him as to his identity, whether wife or son, male or female, criminal or innocent, a person alive in his own time or a character in a book.

But within all this confusion there grew up nevertheless an internal armature made of steel and forged in these very classic tales, so that in spite of his confusion and lack of identity he was yet somehow prepared for greatness.

So powerfully did these stories work upon the boy's imagination that one day, for example, he conceived himself as Gaius Mucius Scaevola. It was this young Gaius Mucius who, when Rome was about to be taken by Lars Porsena, sneaked out of the city at night and into the royal tent of the enemy. He intended to kill Porsena, but, ignorant of that man's appearance, he stabbed the secretary instead. Captured and brought before the royal tribunal, there to be condemned to death, he declared loudly that he did not mind execution, knowing that it could make no difference in the plan of three hundred Roman youths all of whom had taken oaths to kill Porsena or die in the attempt. One or another of these youths was bound to succeed in the end, so Gaius Mucius declared.

And lest there should be any doubt about the bravery of these Roman lads, Gaius Mucius extended his right arm over a flame that blazed upon an altar. And while Porsena stared in astonishment, Gaius Mucius held that arm there without flinching until the flesh burned, blistered, roasted and finally charred.

Intimidated by this incredible exhibition, Porsena began to wonder if he had not assumed too great a project in planning to conquer Rome. He decided upon peace, struck his tents and departed. While Gaius Mucius, acclaimed as hero and savior of Rome, was henceforth known as Scaevola, the Left-handed.

Filled with this tale, young Rousseau, barely six years old, determined to show how brave he could be, and at table one day he extended his right arm over the flame of a chafing dish and would certainly have done himself an irreparable injury if his frightened elders had not snatched him away.

That is how, all unconsciously, he prepared himself for one of the great parallel life stories of all times, his and Voltaire's, so that in spite of every disadvantage of poverty, provincialism and lack of education, he would never give up his goal, once he had decided upon it.

Misfortune was now to strike him again. He was to lose his father, who got into a brawl which made him prefer exile to judgment by the Genevan authorities.

He ran away to nearby Nyon—and got married.

Thus, the little boy who used to be told amidst tears and kisses that he was the very image of his mother found himself repudiated both as wife and as son. For years he had been overwhelmed with caresses. Now he was totally bereft. For years he had been everything: wife, mother, son. Now he was an orphan.

Suddenly, along with Bernard, a cousin of his, Jean Jacques found himself in the home of the Lamberciers, a pastor and his spinster sister, who added to their modest income by taking in a child or two to be instructed in the first principles of religion and Latin.

They were good, kind people, and their home was the usual Swiss cottage with its background of magnificent scenery. Life there might have been ideal if they had not taken so seriously their duty toward those "seeds of evil," those "abominations of God," which is how Calvin described children not yet saved by Jesus Christ. Against the innate corruption of Bernard and Jean Jacques the Lamberciers laid down strict rules of behavior which were accompanied by the warning that a painful corporeal punishment would follow the least infraction.

For Jean Jacques this was a totally new and frightening situation. Up until now he had been treated with the utmost gentleness. Now he had to dread a whipping.

Fear caused him to obey all rules meticulously. And so one day, when he had committed some slight misdeed and in a trice found himself stripped to his bare skin and laid across Mademoiselle Lambercier's knees, he was already prepared to scream from the anticipated pain.

However, when the first blow descended on his behind he was amazed to discover that contact with Mademoiselle Lambercier's firm palm did not want to make him scream. There was pain, certainly, and also fear, yes, and shame and embarrassment, but also something beyond all these, something strangely exciting and even pleasant, communicated to him by Mademoiselle Lambercier's merciless hand and more than compensating for all the suffering.

"You limb of Satan!" she cried. "I'll teach you the difference between right and wrong! So that you'll never forget it!"

This was no doubt her intention. But she taught him something more. Jean Jacques could not at once fathom this unsuspected world of rich emotion that was now suddenly revealed to him. It was still too strange. Too vague. But already it foreshadowed a future turmoil, half bliss and half torture, of which as yet he could only catch an inkling. All he knew was that when Mademoiselle's hand stopped, he missed it at once. And already his craving for this sensuous experience was so gluttonous that he wondered how he could get another whipping.

Nothing seemed easier. Now that, instead of fearing a whipping, he coveted it, all he had to do was provoke Mademoiselle Lambercier's anger by some new mischief.

But no. He couldn't do that.

He wanted to. Yes. So much so, indeed, that at times he could think of nothing else. But he couldn't.

Because that hand on his behind had not only provided him with a new experience, it had at the same time stimulated in him a strong passion of love, or at least of such warm gratitude that it extended from the hand itself to the owner of that hand. And if before that lady's word had been a warning, now it was something even stronger: an unbreakable command.

Without being able as yet to define exactly the situation he was in, he felt himself trapped. Trapped between desire and love. Desire that craved that angry hand on his buttocks. While at the same time love made it impossible to anger or even annoy his beloved.

Just so he was to discover himself one day trapped between his love for Voltaire, who had drawn him upward, and his hate for that same man, who would ridicule him.

At this particular time, he still had the pleasure of sleeping in the same room as Mademoiselle Lambercier. And in cold weather she even took the two little boys into her bed to warm their icy feet against her body, for in everything she did she had the interest of her charges at heart.

But when, in spite of his careful obedience, Jean Jacques happened once more to transgress and the longed-for whipping was finally to be his again, it was also the last time he was ever to enjoy it. Somehow

Mademoiselle Lambercier observed a physical alteration in Jean Jacques, proving that her chastising hand was affecting the lad in a manner far from corrective.

That was enough. She was through.

Abruptly she declared that it tired her to beat him. And, pushing the little rascal from her knees, she had him pull up his trousers quickly. And she added that she would never beat him again.

She went further in showing her displeasure. That same day she had the boys' beds moved into another room. She would no longer sleep in the same room as Jean Jacques.

Thus twice already in his short life Jean Jacques had found himself rejected for what nature had made him: a male. And the great confusion that was to haunt him all his life began. Lost in the world, he began to call upon his imagination for help, and as erotic fantasies began to rage through him (and in this matter he was extremely precocious) Jean Jacques felt the need of the other sex, to co-operate with him, and his imagination did not refuse it to him.

But he did not use the other sex the way nature intended.

Over many years it never occurred to Jean Jacques that women could play any role in assuaging his burning desires except that of beating him. Eagerly he would devour with his eyes all the beautiful girls that he happened to glimpse. But he did not dream of having them open their arms to embrace him. His yearning was, rather, to be laid across their knees, his bottom exposed to the smack and tingle of an angry palm.

How could he have been so blind, he would ask himself later (but when the mischief was already done), how could he have been so blind, when his blood stream, true to the laws of his physical being, swelled, stiffened and animated an organ for which, had he given the matter any intelligent thought, he would have been unable to assign any function, even in his most voluptuous dreams?

It was not that he was impotent. Or even ignorant. But, rather, that the thought of such a function, as far as he was concerned, would have revolted him at that time. For he had, naturally, seen dogs and bitches coupling. And in a slum section of Geneva, along a street that was no more than a ditch, he had seen on both sides the dark entrances to caves, and he was to learn very early in life that here prostitutes and debauchees hid from the sight of the law to carry on certain doglike practices.

He was still a mere boy, but already he had been twice emasculated. Once by the mistaken love of his father. And again by the contact of Mademoiselle Lambercier's hand with his buttocks. So that it would be years before his inner being would work itself around to the sex to which he really belonged, and to the proper contact.

Meanwhile there were other heartaches and problems in store for him. He and his cousin Bernard were now removed from the Lamberciers, and suddenly Jean Jacques was made to realize that there was a tremendous difference between himself and Bernard, a difference that had nothing to do with the quickness of their minds or the development of their bodies.

It had to do with the fact that Bernard's parents lived on the hill and were members of the Genevan aristocracy. While Jean Jacques and his father were from St.-Gervais, the flat workingclass district on the other side of the Rhone River. And thus, while Bernard was destined for further education and training in order to become an engineer, Jean Jacques's brief education was already over and he was to be apprenticed to an engraver.

He felt immediately a certain sense of degeneration. He rarely met his cousin Bernard now. And if they happened to see each other on the street, the difference in their rank was immediately apparent. Bernard wore good clothes. Even elegant ones. While Jean Jacques's were the shabby ones proper to an apprentice.

But more than that. For Bernard the world was just opening up. While Jean Jacques could already feel it narrowing around him. When, occasionally now, he would see his father, there was none of the former fondling. His father had another wife and other interests. Jean Jacques sensed that he had become just another ragamuffin of Geneva's streets.

Ballets? Jesuit professors? Gay costumes and crowns of laurel leaves? Dukes and counts? Famous courtesans?

What Rousseau had was a coarse-minded employer, the engraver Ducommun, whose favorite method of instruction was the back of his hand. And on the very first evening in his new home, Jean Jacques received a lesson in what his place was to be in this household. There was, indeed, a law that employer and employee had to sit down to table together. But there was no rule against dismissing an employee before the meal was over. Nor any rule that they had to eat the same food.

The moment Jean Jacques had finished his plate of soup, he was asked to leave the table. The roast was just then being served.

"But I want some meat," he said.

"If you're hungry," he was told, "take some bread. Or another plate of soup."

"But I'm not hungry for more soup," said Jean Jacques.

With that his hard-fisted employer gave him a demonstration of how you left the table when you were asked to leave it, and without any arguing.

Heretofore Jean Jacques had always been an equal member of whatever household he happened to be living in. He had the right to speak as often as he chose, and with only one proviso: that he must not be impolite or interrupt others. Heretofore he had always had the right to some portion of whatever dish was put on the table. With only one proviso: that his portions might be smaller. But this was compensated by the fact that as a child he might at times be given an even larger portion—for example, of a sweet.

Now, suddenly, he had no right to speak up. His opinion was not only not wanted, it was not even permitted. As for his right to share in all the dishes, that right was not recognized at all. With the meal scarcely one-third finished, and the best dishes, meat and dessert, still to come, he was excluded from the table.

Worst of all, perhaps, was his loss of the right to feel at home in the house where he lived. Hitherto he had always had the run of the house, barring one room or another. But now his presence was tolerated only where there was work for him to do. Otherwise he was not wanted anywhere except in the little room where he had his cot.

The result was a further degeneration within him. The very pressures in this house soon taught him that all the rules amounted to only one: Anything was permissible except getting caught. One could be lazy at one's work, but one must never be seen being lazy. One had a right to devour all the food one could lay one's hands on, but one must never be caught stealing any. One could think whatever nasty thoughts one pleased about one's employer, but one must never let oneself be overheard saying them.

Life thus became a matter of tricks and evasions. Jean Jacques learned to be secretive. He learned to live a private life, which he shared with no one. He learned to disguise his real feelings.

And he discovered that the best evasion of all was to lose oneself in one's imagination, where it was possible to escape into a world where pursuit was barred.

This was made all the more easy by the reading of books.

Jean Jacques's pay as apprentice was three coppers a week. And every Sunday, immediately after church services, when Rousseau's master would give him his weekly spending money of three cents, Jean Jacques would race to La Tribu, an old woman who kept a lending library of cast-off volumes, miserable dog-eared books.

But with what wild passion Rousseau would open up each fresh title! His heart would start pounding at once, in anticipation. He felt suffocated. Each still unknown volume seemed to him a ship with sails already set for another world. A world which he would enter not as apprentice but as master.

For he did not read in order to learn the story of other people. He read in order to give himself a new life. The moment the story began, he was already one of the characters, and it was about himself that he was reading. And even when the story closed, he would still remain that character, while his imagination altered the tale, played around with the cast, lived it all over again from a new angle, until he had exhausted every possibility, or until another book had come into his life to open up a different and perhaps still more exciting world.

While at his workbench, apparently busy with his engraving tools, just as soon as he felt his master Ducommun was not watching him, he would quickly sneak a look into the story he was reading. If sent on an errand, he would take his book from his pocket and read while walking. Even when going to the toilet he would take his volume along, and sometimes he would forget himself on the pot for hours.

But despite all his stealthiness, the stories were sometimes so engrossing, or at any rate his need for losing himself in them so great, that again and again he would fail to take the necessary precautions, and he would be caught at it. Caught and beaten and warned not to let it happen again.

But he couldn't stop. And his master would now and then work himself into such a fury that he would seize the book and tear it to pieces. Or throw it out into the rain. Or into the fire.

Jean Jacques would go to bed, his eyes thick with tears. Tears of self-pity. And his mind swarming with extravagant dreams of revenge. How miserable he was! And especially when he thought of the coming Sunday, and how, after church, he would have to run to La Tribu with a cravat or a shirt and bargain with her to cover the cost of the book that he was unable to return.

Thus he gradually lost every single item of his wardrobe left over from the old days. And still his debt to La Tribu mounted. Until finally he had to summon all his courage and learn how to steal. It hurt him to have to steal. But he felt crushed without a book. At first he took only the most worthless tools. Discarded ones. That was simplest. And weighed least on his conscience. He just slipped one in his pocket before going out on an errand.

Not that he didn't worry about it. Punishment and even disgrace awaited him at the first *faux pas*. It was one thing to be caught loafing with a book. It would be quite another to be found with a stolen article.

Inside himself he was now forever preoccupied. Forever troubled. Forever scheming. He knew that he couldn't steal tools indefinitely, for their loss must soon become obvious. He had to switch to engravings, which were more difficult to conceal about his person.

There were precious metals about. And money. But he never touched them. And he dreaded the day when he might be pushed to that extreme. For he was not unaware of the fact that his whole character was being undermined.

But what could he do?

It was not he who had chosen this stealthy, secretive manner of life. It had been forced upon him. Deep down, he knew, he was good. But he was being driven toward evil.

This was the first of many subtle arguments that he concocted, trying to convince himself that wrong was right and right was wrong. He reasoned, for example, that whatever he did against his master was only a kind of advance payment for the blows that would surely come later.

But no matter how clever his arguments, the load of his inner guilt grew. And here the result was just as bad as all other aspects of this sorry situation. He began to sense his own unworthiness in comparison with other people. When addressed, he found himself tongue-tied. He blushed. He stammered. He lowered his eyes.

He felt his fall from grace. Which only made him more retiring and secretive than ever.

And yet it was not licentious books that he read. His escape did not have to be into the realm of sex. Indeed, it was not until many years later, when he frequented high society as a secretary and heard a well-born lady laughingly declare that "the worst thing about off-color books is that one gets so tired holding them with one hand," that he felt curious about such literature and wondered what the other hand of this lady might be doing.

Nevertheless, he was subsequently inclined to believe that his over-indulgence in highly imaginative tales, even though devoid of licentiousness, was at the root of many of his troubles. And in his study on the proper education of children, in his famous novel *Émile,* he would argue for the total exclusion of books from the education of youngsters.

"I hate books!" he would write.

Which would make Voltaire go into guffaws of laughter, saying, "I see where that great enemy of books, Jean Jacques Rousseau, has just come out with another book. A book against books, of course!"

But in Voltaire's life there had never been a period of having only three coppers with which to run to a La Tribu and obtain some dog-eared volume.

There is no incident, for example, in all of Voltaire's life that is remotely analogous to Rousseau's attempt to obtain an apple. Jean Jacques' restricted diet had developed in him such a craving for fruit that it nearly drove him mad.

The master kept some particularly fine apples in a storeroom just off the kitchen. The door to this room was always kept locked, with the key safe in the master's pocket. And there was no window giving access. Only a wide-mesh metal grating set high in the kitchen wall to admit light and air.

These apples positively haunted Jean Jacques. To such a degree that whenever he would find himself alone in the house he would leave his workbench and pull the kneading trough over to that side of the kitchen and climb up on it in order to be able to look through the grating and feast his eyes on them.

Even through the semidark, he would see the fruit below, glowing softly in delicate greens and yellows, with here and there a fleck of ripe brown or a blush of red. The apples were laid out on tables in the coolness, so that they would last through the winter.

Oh, to get his hands on just one of them! To bite into that juicy, crisp flesh!

And then one day while he was gazing at the fruit, it occurred to him: Might it not be possible to spear one of them with the roasting spit? And pull it out through the wide-mesh grating?

Quickly he leaped from the trough and seized the spit from the fireplace. Alas! It just would not quite reach. No matter how much he reduced the part of the spit that was wasted in his grip, even to the point of raising the possibility that he might let the spit slip from his grasp and fall into the storeroom, a danger that was fraught with the certainty of discovery and a resulting punishment—even so he couldn't quite make it.

He sweated with anguish and exertion, but without effect. The apples remained, by just the length of a finger, beyond his reach.

What about the other spit—the smaller one? Would it not be possible to lash the two of them together and thus make a spear that would be sufficiently long?

He leaped from the trough once more and got hold of the shorter spit. He worked with feverish speed, for of course the danger of his master's coming home was constantly in his mind. The two spits together made a weighty affair, and some of the length was necessarily lost in the overlap. But now the fruit could be reached.

But still not too well. For what was required was not merely that he be able to reach the apples, but that he be able to strike hard into one of them so as to make it hold to the spear while he drew it up. And that was far from easy. For the fruit tended to slither away, and his spear nicked and scored them, instead of penetrating them.

But at last, success! He had an apple securely fixed on the end of his spear, and now slowly, slowly, with the utmost care, he began to draw it toward the grating.

Now he had it! No. Damnation! He had greedily chosen the biggest apple and it wouldn't go through the mesh. No amount of dexterous twisting would make that apple's odd shape conform to the oblongs of the mesh so that he could draw it through. There it was, so close that its perfume filled his nostrils. And yet he couldn't put his teeth into it. He could only lick it with his tongue.

If only he could shave off a piece, which would thus let the rest come through. A knife! A knife! But he had no knife. At least not up there on the kneading trough, with his fingers gripping the double spit and the apple.

Well, no help for it. He would have to lower the apple back to the table in the storeroom and leave it there, with the spear still in it, until he could get down and find himself a knife. And, in addition, a piece of wood, a lath or something of the sort, which he could stick through the grating and use to stem the apple while his knife worked at it.

So more effort. And more anguish, lest his master suddenly return home. But Jean Jacques went to work with a will.

And finally he had cut off a sufficiently large section to permit the rest of the apple to come through, when, malediction! both pieces slipped from his clumsy grasp, both the piece he had just cut off and the piece which now did not have enough flesh on it to support itself on the spear—both pieces dropped back into the storeroom.

Worst of all, he could hear footsteps outside. The master was at the door. In a flash he had pulled back his spear, jumped off the kneading trough, dismantled his apparatus and rushed back to his bench and to his engraving burins.

Impatiently he waited through the days until there should be another such occasion when he would be alone in the house.

That day came at last. And this time his practice paid off: he worked faster. Both spits were lashed together right from the start. And knife and lath were at hand. This time he could not fail.

Nor did he. Except that just as he drew the apple through the mesh there was a noise at the door and his master's voice: "Good work, my young friend. Congratulations on your ingenuity!"

And with that a cuff on his ribs that sent him flying from his perch, with the two precious apple halves whirling away to dark corners of the kitchen, while the sharp command was yelled into his ear: "Now let's see you apply yourself just as doggedly at your workbench!"

Ah, no, there was never anything like this in the life of Voltaire.

When the courtesan Ninon de Lenclos died, soon after little Voltaire had been brought to her home to read his poems, she left a testament one clause of which granted two thousand francs to the little Voltaire.

"For books," the testament read.

Thus this remarkable woman who had formed so many young men of the seventeenth century also formed one of the greatest men of the eighteenth: Voltaire. Starting the little Parisian boy on his way to immortality. With a sum for books which it would have required Rousseau, with his three Genevan coppers a week, thirteen thousand weeks to equal.

10: FIT TO BE FLOGGED

The more Rousseau allowed his mind to dwell on his own humble Genevan extraction and Voltaire's lofty Parisian origin, the more unfair he found everything in this world. So that not even the first smiles of fame could erase from his soul a sense of unjust discrimination. And that, walking through the outskirts of Paris while composing his second great essay, the one on human inequality, which was to become a landmark in sociological and political thinking, his ideas tended to be both wild and bitter.

What else is it but a great cry of anguish that escapes from him in those terrible lines about the savages of the Orinoco (over which generations of students have since smiled with condescension, unaware of the exquisite pain behind them), those lines in which Rousseau praises certain Indians for being unwilling to abandon their ancient practice of deforming the soft skulls of their infants by squeezing their heads between two boards.

"It's true," he had to admit, "that they thus turn them into imbeciles. But what of it? What of it, if thereby they can still preserve for them some vestige of man's original happiness?"

Man's original happiness. Ah, yes, what had become of that precious heritage?

Because it seemed to Rousseau irrefutable that once upon a time man must have been supremely happy. That the original animal-man must have slipped from the creative hands of God screaming with joy.

Alive! Alive!

Yes, of course. For to suppose otherwise—why, that would be to ascribe viciousness to the magnificent act of Creation.

No, no. It was self-evident that primitive man must have been filled with an indescribable joy. And that he must have remained so until he began to live in families and in groups of families. That is to say until love and jealousy, stimulated by so many people living so close together, began to storm through him.

And even then he must have still been happy. Until he started to fashion various articles and thus aroused in himself the first stirrings of vanity and cupidity. Then, when he went on to compete in singing and in dancing and in all the other arts, then pride, envy and disappointment began to churn in him and he fell into clans of mutual rivalry, all seeking to outdo each other. Or else tear each other apart.

But even then, yes, even then, man must have retained much of his original happiness. Those early quarrels could have resulted only in isolated murders. Or in family feuds. Never in mass slaughter. Because for war, for real war, man had first to establish his cities and his nations. And these he couldn't have until he had developed an easily stored food—that is to say, grain. And a truly deadly weapon. Which means iron.

For not until man had his grain and his iron, not until he had his agriculture and his metallurgy, those twin skills so vital to each other, since for one man to have the time to forge iron, others had to work to produce his food—not until man had his wheat, the staff of life, and iron, the stab of death, could the reign of never ending labor and never ending slaughter begin.

Now, yes, now, man could proudly proclaim himself civilized.

But tell me honestly, who would not rather be insane than participate in this frightful dance? Who would not rather be one of those flatheaded savages than one of your civilized Europeans who plunges the world alternately into blood and into wealth? In superfluity on the one hand and in misery on the other?

Try to see one of your civilized Europeans through the eyes of such a savage. What can he make of this man who sweats and snorts and agitates himself and meanwhile drives others on to equal and even greater exertions? What can he think of these men who will work until they drop dead? And, in fact, do everything they can to hasten that final hour by their fury to become important. Their insatiable itch to outshine.

Why, that savage would rather die a thousand deaths than compete in such a life. A life which hasn't even the excuse that its own lack of happiness will be of benefit to anyone, for it is all done for profit, for power, for preferment or prestige.

What does this lazy and ignorant savage care for the opinions of others? Not a farthing. He cares only for his own. He lives utterly within himself. And for the sake of no one but himself. And he cannot even begin to understand those Europeans whose existence is, so to speak, outside themselves. Bound up with what others happen to think of them.

To the mass of Europeans nothing counts so much as the envy they succeed in inspiring in others. And the moment they no longer feel themselves envied they lose their desire to live. Indeed, there are Europeans so dependent on the opinions others have of them that without those opinions they would not even know they were alive!

Which one, then, is the happier? That flatheaded savage who makes his own happiness out of nothing? Or that European who has lost control of his own happiness and is completely dependent on others?

Can there be any doubt about the answer?

Oh, there would be howls of laughter from the Voltairean circles at Jean Jacques's preference for this flatheaded South American over the cultured European. But let them laugh! He knew he was right. In fact, he had lived both lives and could talk from experience.

What experience? Where? On the banks of the Orinoco?

No. But on the shores of Lake Geneva.

Was not the city of Geneva, in its own way, just such a primitive community where they flattened your head? And was not Geneva rightly scorned by all Parisians for just that reason? For its lack of culture, its lack of music, its lack of a theater and an opera, its lack of gambling, masquerade balls, flirtations and everything else that is indispensable to the life of the Parisian?

But just the same, how often, since he had run away from there, had Jean Jacques had occasion to regret that flight! How often he had pictured himself growing old, and no doubt more stupid every day, still bent over his engraver's bench! And each time he had to confess to himself how much happier such a fate would have been than the one he had embraced by following the lure of Voltaire's brilliant mind.

For what did the scorn of the Parisians prove except that they were unable to distinguish between entertainments and happiness? Of course the Parisians had their entertainments. No end of them. But did they have happiness? While the Genevans, for all their lack of pleasures, were they not as happy as human beings could be today?

"Voltaire, Voltaire!" Jean Jacques allowed himself to dream. "Just as you went to England and made that country serve you as a vivid demonstration of how much better it was for people to live in an atmosphere of religious tolerance and useful activity than in a France of purposeless theological disputes and idle aristocratic display, so I shall go to Geneva in order to demonstrate certain other truths to the world.

"For you left out the common people in your *English Letters* of twenty years ago, didn't you? You forgot the peasants and the artisans. Your England was still pretty much of a France: a land of royalty and wealth. Whereas for my purposes I need a country where the people govern themselves and happiness is organized for everyone. Where the inhabitants all live quietly and industriously and know how to take their pleasures out of the little things of life."

But what an idea, for Jean Jacques to think of matching the enormous success of Voltaire's *English* (sometimes called *Philosophical*) *Letters*. Matching them with his *Discourse on Human Inequality*. What an idea to dedicate his essay to the people of Geneva, saying, "Everything in Geneva is prepared for the well-being of her citizens. We have nothing to do but reach out and take our joy."

Yes, what an idea! Considering all the new paradoxes this must precipitate him into. Because in the first place if Geneva could really provide joy for all her citizens, why had he ever fled from there? And in the second place what was this about Geneva governing herself? When actually she now had her aristocratic class, too, that ran the city as it pleased. And in the third place, though Rousseau might call himself a citizen of Geneva he was really nothing of the kind. Being in fact considered a traitor in Geneva. Because ordinary Catholics might come and go in Geneva without let or hindrance, but not a born Calvinist who had rejected his faith.

For such a person to show his face in Geneva meant prison!

Unless, of course, he signified that his return was for the purpose of going back into the Calvinistic faith. Then he would be brought out of prison and forced to his hands and knees before the Little Council of the Genevan aristocrats, there to crawl and beg for forgiveness.

But of course they wouldn't do that to Rousseau, would they? Not since he had become so well known. Him they would be only too anxious to bring back into the fold, so as to have a share of his glory for Geneva.

Thérèse, of course, would constitute something more of a problem. For the consistory of clergymen of Geneva was still very powerful when it came to the subject of morals. And they would want to know about this neat and lively young woman who not only lived with Rousseau, but in fact slept in the same room with him. And, if the truth be known, in the same bed.

So it was to be anticipated that lies would have to be told. That he, the first exposer of the great lies of human society and civilization, the most honest man of his generation, would have to fabricate a few lies.

But what else could he do in his effort to raise himself up to the heights of Voltaire?

After all, hadn't Voltaire involved himself in many lies in his voyage to England?

Then why shouldn't Rousseau?

Yes, but somehow Voltaire's lies were different. You could feel that Voltaire secretly gloried in them. While Rousseau had to be ashamed of his. And that consequently Voltaire did not mind very much being found out. While Rousseau must be mortified to be caught in an untruth.

Indeed, Voltaire's lies perhaps were all the more amusing for being detected. His enemies thereby all the more discomfited. And Voltaire himself was turned into an all the more interesting and exciting figure.

Never could a Rousseau write to his friend something of this sort, such as Voltaire could and often did: "If the least danger should arise from my publication of this booklet, let me know at once, so that I can disown my work with all my usual candor and innocence."

How is it that Voltaires are permitted to lie and Rousseaus not? Why is it that when a Rousseau lies it is always something dark and tragic? Or else shabby. So that neither friend nor foe must know about it. Why is it that his lies have to remain hidden until after his death, as if they were underground trap doors silently shutting off one section after another of his buried past?

While the very name of Voltaire can be a lie. Much more so than "Citizen of Geneva" had ever been a lie for the exiled Rousseau. And it makes no difference for a Voltaire. Why is that?

It was in a prison, in the Bastille, that the name Voltaire was conceived and born. Until that incarceration Voltaire had been nothing but François Marie Arouet, gifted poet and wit. Dancing around the nobility, amusing such powerful lords as the Duke de Sully and the Duke and Duchess de Sceaux.

And it was purely in the service of these wealthy patrons of his that he had scribbled some lampoons against the then Regent of France, the Duke d'Orléans. Result: an order to lock up the young poet in the Bastille. No trial. Just a sealed letter. A so-called *lettre de cachet*.

In the early morning the police came to the poet's rooms and hustled him out of bed and into his clothes. And then off to prison.

As Regent of France during the infancy of Louis XV, the Duke d'Orléans was entitled to the same privileges as a king, and that meant that he could put whomever he wished in prison. With no questions asked. And for as long as he pleased. This was considered only proper, since without that right of "sealed letters" the kings of France would have been under the law like everyone else, with nothing to distinguish royalty from subjects except wealth.

In prison, permitted no paper and only a very few books, buried behind walls of solid masonry seven feet thick, and with no knowledge of when, if ever, he would be released, François Marie Arouet found plenty of time to think about himself and the world he lived in.

His instinct was to rage. Naturally. To lash out against such tyranny. To fight for the basic human right of liberty.

But upon reflexion he did nothing of the kind.

He knew he was fortunate, even in that prison. He was still a member of the upper classes. Why, there were cells in that tower where men froze in winter and broiled in summer. Where the miserable inmate had nothing but worm-eaten rags to cover his nakedness. And that was still not the worst. Down below there were underground cells where the thick walls oozed a foul dampness day and night. Where the food that was thrown down to one would have been rejected by a starving dog. Where one's body was soon covered with boils, and one's gums became so rotten that one could suck blood and pus from them, and one's teeth disintegrated like lumps of sugar.

Yes, young Arouet knew that he was fortunate even in his misery. He was still on top. His valet came and went, bringing him fresh clothes. He ate food sent to him from the governor's table. Important people were petitioning for his freedom. Why should he cast himself head on against the powers of this world that treated him with such distinction?

Nevertheless prison, if not his innate good sense, taught him to hate tyranny. And to hate injustice. And to fight for reason, tolerance and freedom.

But how?

Only by indirection. Never frontally. If ever he got out, he would fight only from behind secure salients. He would use flattery to express the opposite. He would use deceit as strong as iron and yet as transparent as glass. He would use laughter as Joshua had used trumpets to blow down the walls of Jericho. He would entrench himself more than ever with powerful patrons and, hiding behind one big patron, would snipe with bullets of ridicule at another. But no more open warfare.

No. Never again would he let himself be caught!

Meditating thus on a new character for himself and on a new and grander destiny to result therefrom, François Marie Arouet decided that he merited a new name. Not that he had become a totally different person, no, for the new Voltaire was already formed within the old Arouet, but that now he was really setting fire to the torch of his life.

And this required a new and a flaming name.

How he invented that name Voltaire will always remain a mystery. Some say that as a child he was *le petit volontaire,* a stubborn, headstrong lad. Others say that his mother's family once owned a little landed estate with a similar name. Still others say he composed it out of the letters of "Arouet," turning the *u* into a *v,* as in the Roman alphabet, and adding the letters *l* and *i,* to stand for *le jeune,* "the younger," since there was an older brother.

This is possible, since such anagram pen names were in the custom of the times, but that would still fail to explain how—amidst tens of thousands of possibilities—he hit on *voltaire,* a striking word which somehow contains the feeling of flight from the Bastille, flight from all prisons, flight into the air and flight over the earth, and combining all this into a form that is not merely highly euphonious but also full of strength (quite unlike the soft name Molière, into which the actor Poquelin had changed his name three quarters of a century before) and at one and the same time different and familiar-sounding, so that, while clearly unusual and unforgettable, it is neither exotic nor pompous. But just right.

The name was a lie, yes, but what a glorious lie! And with what ease Voltaire would carry it off, calling himself at first Arouet de Voltaire and then just plain Voltaire.

Naturally he had to have the genius to back up his invented name with plays and poems that would become world-famous, and that would bear such a powerful imprint of his wit, of his passion, of his impregnable common sense, that even when he denied authorship everyone would still know that he had written them.

So that in the end he would force critics to say that of all the poems that he, Voltaire, had written, his best was also his shortest, his one-word name-poem: Voltaire!

Who now would dare challenge him his right to his own poem?

The only one who ever seriously tried was the Chevalier de Rohan.

That was when Voltaire was about thirty years of age and still something of a dandy, spindle-legged, clad in fine silk brocade richly frogged with gold, and with an enormous curly wig that went cascading over his sharp shoulders, shoulders that were not yet so hunched as they were later to become.

Such was the Voltaire who stood one evening in December of the year 1725, in the crowded lobby of the Paris opera house, and was holding forth with all his customary exuberance of wit and conviction. And with no more concern that his name was a lie than that his hair was also not his own. Or that in the theater the stage was not really Greece or Rome. Or that the characters on the stage were not really the people they pretended to be, or that nowhere on earth did people speak exclusively in lines of twelve syllables alternately rhyming with masculine and feminine endings. Or sing to each other with accompanying orchestra.

These accepted lies, these artificialities, didn't trouble Voltaire one bit. "Nature, nature," he would exclaim testily some years later. "What is more natural than my bare ass? And yet I cover it with a pair of pants."

The Chevalier de Rohan-Chabot, standing in a group near Voltaire, interrupted the discussion: "Now just a moment, Monsieur de Voltaire, or, rather, Monsieur Arouet, or whatever the deuce your true name may be—"

What the Chevalier proposed to say, if anything, no one would ever know, for Voltaire cut him short with a fast retort delivered nevertheless with a feline smile: "Whatever the deuce my name may be, I, at any rate, have known how to honor it!"

The press of the crowd, on its way back into the hall, broke up the situation. But neither man could forget this little interchange.

The insult, insofar as Voltaire was concerned, lay not only in the fact that the Chevalier had implied that in spite of his literary celebrity Voltaire still remained a nameless nobody, but also in the very clear inference that M. de Voltaire had no right to arrogate to himself the aristocratic particle *de*. For in France, as in Germany and elsewhere, only a special small group of people could be *from* somewhere. The rest of mankind were presumably from nowhere. They just happened, by good chance, to be around where one could lay hold of them when one happened to need them.

Thus the two letters of the word *de* had in time assumed enormous importance for some people, particularly for those who felt they had an exclusive right to the use of this little word. As well as for those who continued to covet that right.

For to have a *de* in one's name lifted one at once out of the mass, and so people tended to slip these two letters in just as soon as they felt they could live in the proper style for it. Madame Geoffrin, for example, wife of a glass factory executive, just as soon as she became a personage of importance in Paris, through her salon, was by common consent called Madame *de* Geoffrin.

After all, it was a matter of only two letters. And it was impossible for anyone to claim that he owned the alphabet. Or to consider himself robbed because someone else was also using it.

But there was an even greater insult in the Chevalier's few words. That greater insult lay in the stress he had given to his pronunciation of Voltaire's original family name, Arouet, making it sound like the words *à rouer,* meaning "fit to be flogged." Which again emphasized a differentiation between classes similar to that of the word *de*. For the rule of the baton still obtained at this time (as in most of man's history) and there was a definite pyramid of the bastinado, each tier of society being entitled to lay the stick on the tiers below, but never on the tier above.

The crude and brutal era of the stick lingered on somehow into the sparkling century, inherited from a time when kings would still beat their courtiers with their canes or kick them around with the booted point of their toes. When Frederick William I of Prussia would cane his own family, yes, even the son who was to succeed him on the throne, the same Frederick who was to become known as the Great. When the Cardinal de Richelieu would beat his minister of finances. When a courtier thinking himself caricatured by one of the characters in a Molière play considered himself entitled to take that author's head in his hands and rub his face so hard against the metal buttons of his vest as to cover it with blood. When George II would kick the backside of his minister Walpole. And the bishop of Salzburg, at an even later date, would treat the genius Mozart as if he were no better than a flunkey.

In short, when individuals would behave no better than nations, using brutality instead of reason.

Of course, there were laws everywhere against assault and battery. Naturally. But it was not deemed advisable to invoke them against the privileged classes who had so many ways of retaliating. And thus the additional implication of the Chevalier's pronunciation of Voltaire's name was "You may be a literary celebrity, but a noble Rohan can have you flogged at will."

Precisely for that reason, however, Voltaire's retort was all the more stinging, for with its "Whatever the deuce my name may be, I, at any rate, have known how to honor mine," it brought out clearly the fact that the Chevalier de Rohan had never really done anything in his life so far, and was unlikely to do anything in the future, that would add any additional luster to his name. He was therefore fortunate in having been born with a name already sufficiently illustrious.

The Rohan clan had been rulers of Brittany for hundreds of years and were so proud of their stock that when in time they were forced to join the French kingdom they insisted on retaining their princely rank in spite of the royal family. This being of course impossible, they adopted the haughty motto *"Roi ne puis, duc ne daigne, Rohan suis."* Meaning "King I can't be, duke I scorn, Rohan I'll remain."

Voltaire, the man who had built his own name from top to bottom, thus pitted himself against a Rohan who had only moved into his.

And Paris waited to see what would happen.

A few days after this first brush, Voltaire was attending a performance at the Théâtre-Français. He was sitting in the box of the popular actress Adrienne Lecouvreur, a beautiful and talented woman who had once briefly been the poet's mistress, and whom he still loved and admired now that she had become the mistress of Marshal de Saxe.

The Chevalier de Rohan entered the same box, saying, "Ah, there you are again, Monsieur de Voltaire. Or shall I say Monsieur Arouet? Or have you now some new name you'd like me to use?"

Voltaire had an immediate answer, clever as always. "Whatever name I may use, I am beginning my line. You are finishing yours," he said.

The Chevalier blushed with fury at this implication of impotence and raised his cane to strike Voltaire. The poet pulled back quickly and drew his sword. It was the first time in his life that he had drawn that weapon, which was just as much a lie as his wig, for he had only the vaguest notion of how one used it. He knew only how to wear it.

But once again a fight was avoided when Adrienne Lecouvreur screamed and fell into a faint. A false faint, of course. Lie for lie. But in the resulting confusion the issue was again left undecided, though obviously Voltaire had scored a second time.

Of course with words only.

A few days later Voltaire was dining at the table of the Duke de Sully, one of his many patrons. A lackey came up behind Voltaire's seat and informed him that there was someone at the door who requested speech with him on a matter of urgency. Voltaire had no reason to feel suspicious. He was perpetually involved in so many different directions that he was not surprised to find himself wanted at this hour. It might be for any one of a dozen reasons.

So he rose without hesitating and went to the entrance.

It was night. Voltaire peered out into the darkness and at first could see no one. Two grooms, however, came up, asked him if he was Monsieur de Voltaire and begged him to approach a hackney coach that was standing across the street.

Voltaire started to cross over, but no sooner was he out of the Hôtel de Sully than he felt himself seized by the two grooms, dragged over to the coach and there belabored on his back by a man armed with a stick. Voltaire struggled wildly, with the result that some of the blows fell upon his head and might have done him some serious injury but for his thick wig.

A sarcastic voice from the hackney coach, unmistakably that of the Chevalier de Rohan, cried out, "Careful of that head! Something good may yet come out of it!"

Voltaire took advantage of this interruption to tear himself out of the hands of the ruffians and dash back to the shelter of the Duke's door, while behind him he could hear the hackney coach driving off and the passenger inside laughing.

Voltaire, his clothes and his face showing the harrowing experience he had just been through, came running into the dining room.

"*Monsieur le duc!*" he cried. "You must come with me to the *commissaire de police*. At once!"

"*Bon dieu!*" the Duke exclaimed. "What has happened to you?"

"Can't you see? I've been attacked. And beaten. You must help me!"

"Certainly. But explain yourself first."

Voltaire thereupon related what had happened to him at the hands of the Chevalier de Rohan's men. To his amazement, however, the Duke did not appear as outraged as he ought to have been.

"Come, come, my dear Voltaire," he said. "That's nothing to get so excited about. You've had a little drubbing. That happens to many a good poet. In England it happened to Dryden. And here to Molière. And recently to Moncrif. So in a moment you'll make us all laugh by reciting a mordant poem about it."

"Am I to understand," Voltaire fumed, "that you don't mind that the Chevalier should have used your home as an ambush? And that it's quite all right with you if your guests get a little drubbing now and then?"

"Now, let's not exaggerate," said the Duke. "You haven't actually been injured. Only your feelings have been ruffled. I understand that. You're sensitive. But you'll soon forget it. Here, drink this."

"What I shall never be able to forget, no matter how much I may drink," said Voltaire, "is that the Rohans and the Sullys are cousins. That explains everything."

"Ah no!" the Duke protested. "Now you do me wrong. I had no hand in this matter."

"Of course not," said Voltaire. "But once it was done, you preferred to side with your cousin rather than with your poet—who is therefore your poet no longer."

And, bowing and thus breaking an association that was almost ten years old, Voltaire left the Sully mansion. And he never returned.

The only result of this break with the Duke was to give greater wings to gossip. All Paris soon knew about the *à rouer* pun on Voltaire's name, which had really ended in a flogging, and there was considerable laughter over the story. While Voltaire burned and began to take lessons in swordsmanship.

He swore, before witnesses, that he would yet find the opportunity for a sensational revenge and that he would wipe out the insult he had received with nothing less than the Chevalier's blood. In addition Voltaire hired himself several bodyguards, who not only surrounded him night and day with their protection, but also gave him frequent opportunity for exercising himself in the art of self-defense.

"Not that I'm afraid of the Chevalier himself," Voltaire explained. "There's no reason to be afraid of a man who boldly conceals himself in a hackney coach while his paid hamstringers do his work."

The Chevalier's uncle was the Cardinal de Rohan, and the nephew was said to be prudently hiding out at the Cardinal's palace in Versailles. Voltaire went there and pounded at the door, asking the coward to show himself. The police had to be summoned to warn the poet away.

Finally, one evening, perhaps with Adrienne Lecouvreur's connivance, there was the Chevalier once more in her box. Voltaire burst in and cried out in a voice audible to the whole theater, "Unless you are too busy cheating at cards, or too afraid to come out from behind your bodyguards, I trust you will not refuse to meet me man to man!"

There could be no evasion now. Public insults had been hurled. The Chevalier declared himself willing to fight. Any time.

Where? Porte St.-Martin? Perfect. When? Tomorrow morning at nine? Agreed.

Mutual bows, and Voltaire left.

Naturally the duel was never fought.

By midnight the police had an order to pick up Sieur Arouet, self-styled Voltaire, and lodge him in the Bastille, precisely where he had been six years before.

Voltaire, in a kind of frenzy, screamed, "But the Rohans should be grateful to me! It's the honor of their family that I have been trying to save by forcing the Chevalier to fight me."

But there was nothing to be done. The Rohans were close to the ear of the recently enthroned Louis XV, and a *lettre de cachet* had been issued.

To be sure, the Bastille was a different prison for the world-famous author than it had been for the Parisian wit of some years ago. Then it had been bearable. Now it was luxurious. The governor of the fortress came himself to Voltaire's room to beg him to honor his table with his presence.

All very well. But that did not alter the fact that he had been doubly, if not triply, insulted. First with a humiliating pun tagged to his name, then with a flogging to emphasize that pun. And finally with this: prison!

Voltaire, however, had only begun to avail himself of his best weapon: the lie.

He opened his new campaign by setting forth to the commandant of the fortress that he realized the predicament the government was in, when two men such as a Rohan and a Voltaire were quarreling. Naturally the government could not permit this duel. A Rohan killed by a Voltaire would shock all the noblest families of France. While a Voltaire killed by a Rohan would shock the whole cultural world.

"That's what the Bastille is for," said the governor. "To lock away situations that have become difficult."

"But," said Voltaire to the governor, "locking me up is no solution. For when the news gets abroad that a member of the highest French aristocracy was too cowardly to fight a poet—well, that will be even more awkward for France."

"Then what do you suggest?" the governor asked.

"Why do you not write to the Ministry and explain to them that it would be better to permit me to leave the country of my own free will?"

The governor shook his head. "You will not be trusted. It will be presumed that you will take advantage of your freedom to wreak some kind of revenge."

"The Ministry has only to delegate an officer to watch me. He will see that I shall busy myself getting letters of introduction to prominent people in England. He will see me transferring my funds to London. He will accompany me to the Channel and see me securely on board a ship."

"Why don't you yourself write that proposal to the Ministry?" the governor countered.

Voltaire did. And his proposal was accepted. Free again, though under guard, he set to work at once preparing his wardrobe, gathering letters of introduction, taking out a credit of many thousands of francs on the London Jewish banker Medina.

England, with its more democratic life, its vigorous intellectual atmosphere, the coarse satires of Swift, the barbaric dramas of Shakespeare, the healthy iconoclasm of its anti-religious writers like Wollaston, should have fascinated Voltaire at once. If only he had not had Rohan on his mind. Rohan and Sully.

It was still revenge he was after. And it had been for revenge that he had lied his way out of prison.

Secretly, in disguise, he made his way back to France. And into Paris. He knew that he was now risking his life, but his fury put him beyond such considerations. He avoided even his closest friends, having only one thought: to kill the Chevalier de Rohan-Chabot.

Somehow his presence in Paris became known, and the police were out in force to seize him. He knew that if he were caught this was his end. Never would he manage to lie his way out of prison again. His would be just another terrible story, like that of the Man in the Iron Mask.

By the skin of his teeth he managed to elude the police and get back to the safety of England.

He tried to immerse himself in work. It was particularly his great epic poem, *La Henriade,* that he wished to complete, in order to show the horrors of religious intolerance in France before the advent of Henry IV, the prince who schemed to unite France under a strong central government devoted to the general prosperity of the nation through the development of agriculture and industry.

But how could he work on a poem in which the names Rohan and Sully had to come up all the time and remind him of his flogging? In particular, the name of Sully, Henry IV's closest friend, had to be on almost every page of his poem.

Had to be?

Why did it have to be?

There!

With one stroke of his pen he could cross Sully out of his work. And if now he could make his *Henriade* the most popular epic poem of France, then every time a copy was sold, every time someone opened the pages to read it, every time someone recited a verse of it, the absence of the names Sully and Rohan would itself constitute a continuing act of revenge beyond the ability of a Rohan or a Sully to retaliate in kind!

A historical lie? Yes, but what difference? What difference if it could prove what Voltaire firmly believed—namely, that history was not made either by God or by kings or by dukes, but by the people, by inventors and artists and, in the last analysis, by historians.

And what a victory if he could show at the same time that writing was not just a pleasant pastime and that a poet was not just an amusing companion for a noble patron, but an independent artist practicing an independent and important profession worthy of any man's lifelong devotion.

Only when Voltaire saw his epic printed in a magnificent edition dedicated to the Queen of England and with a subscription list that included the most important names of England and even of France, and subsequently reprinted again and again in cheaper editions and accepted as one of the great poems of the period—only then did he begin to feel himself partially avenged, knowing how galling it must be to the Sullys and to the Rohans to have their ancestors erased and ignored.

But of what could they complain? That Voltaire had failed to sing the glory of their families after having been flogged and derided by them? No. They knew that they would succeed only in making themselves ridiculous if they should voice any chagrin at all. They were condemned to take their punishment in silence.

And they did. While poets everywhere began to feel more self-reliance and power.

Voltaire, however, carried his revenge even further. He studied the advantages that England enjoyed because of her greater civil and social democracy and her greater religious tolerance. And in letters to his trumpet Thieriot he went into eulogies over the gay, healthy, free Englanders. He pointed out, for example, how, in France, "whoever has not got a title feels himself scorned by those who have. But I ask you: Which is the more useful to his country, a powdered lord who knows the minute the King rises or goes to bed, or even when he moves his bowels, and who, because he thus plays the role of slave to a king, gives himself airs of importance, or a British merchant who enriches his country and from his offices in London sends orders to Surat or Cairo, thereby contributing to the happiness of the world?"

Let the Rohans and Sullys digest that! Let the aristocrats ponder the day when the world would belong, not to them, but to merchants and bankers.

Naturally, Voltaire would never publish such dangerous stuff. In fact, he wouldn't even write it. Only in private letters. Which somehow, when his back was turned, were filched from him and printed. In mutilated form—so Voltaire declared. With attacks against religion, added by persons who were obviously scheming to get him into trouble. This was clear.

Would Voltaire, a humble Catholic, write blasphemous material? Such as this:

Go into the Royal Stock Exchange of London, a place more respectable in its conduct than almost any princely court in Europe, and see the representatives of all nations assembled for the enrichment of mankind. Look at that Jew, look at that Mohammedan and at that Christian, all transacting business with each other as if they were all of the same religion. Which indeed they are, for the only infidel among them is the bankrupt.

And now what happens when this peaceful assembly breaks up? Why, the Jew goes to his synagogue to pray, and the Christians go to their tavern to drink. There goes a man who will have himself baptized in a big tub in the name of the Father, the Son and the Holy Ghost. While another will go to see his son's foreskin sliced off to the muttering of some Hebrew words of which he will have very little understanding. And the Quakers, meanwhile, will go off to their assembly halls and put on their hats, and wait for heaven to inspire them.

Compare this civilized conduct with that which we find in France, where there is only one religion permitted, and yet, within that religion, the Jansenist curses the Jesuit and the Jesuit curses the Jansenist.

Everyone knew that Voltaire was lying when he pretended not to have written those lines. Or claimed that, if he had, they were in private letters never intended for publication. Just as everyone knew that his elimination of Sully from his epic poem *La Henriade* was nothing less than a lie. But somehow these lies all redounded to the greater glory of Voltaire.

II: AND MORE LIES

Could it be that it was just the wretchedness of Rousseau's surroundings that made his lies so shabby? Are there poor lies and rich lies? And is it that which makes the difference?

Rousseau too had to run away from a city because of a beating. Exactly like Voltaire. Except that young Rousseau had to run away from Geneva. Not from Paris. And his beating had not taken place outside the palatial residence of a Duke de Sully. It had taken place in a grimy workshop where he was bound as an apprentice.

No swords had been drawn in his case. And no Adrienne Lecouvreur, the most popular actress of Paris, mistress of the great Maurice, Marshal de Saxe, had fainted for him at the right moment.

No, just a boor of a master, beating one with a broomstick and then handing one that broomstick to sweep out the floor of the shop. While one's eyes were still blinded with choked-back tears and one's heart swollen with a choked-back desire for revenge.

No, there had been no opera house. Nor any king to mix himself into the affair and send a poet to the Bastille. And no prisoner to run off to England and there dedicate a great epic poem to the Queen of England.

Just a young boy groping. Groping in the dark for the things he missed in life: love, money, joy, knowledge, color.

His running away from Geneva was no formulated plan. It was simply the fluttering of a frightened bird against the cage until suddenly aware that it could slip through the bars.

In those dreary days of cuffs and hard work, Jean Jacques used to find some consolation in rushing out of the city every Sunday afternoon just as soon as the compulsory church services were over. Sometimes he would join the company of other apprentices, even though their coltish play, their crude jesting at the peasant girls, irritated him.

But the wind, the sky, the sun and the space were so necessary to him that in the evening, when the trumpet would sound from the city walls, soon to be followed by the tattoo of the drums as the drawbridge was raised, the thought of having to return to his workshop would somehow fill his feet with lead. Again and again he would find himself locked out of the city for the night.

Which was no great hardship. Certainly not in good weather. One slept in the nearest barn with the farm animals. Or even under the stars, with one's back up against a haystack. No. That was no hardship at all. It was the following morning that was difficult. When one appeared before one's master and had to take his brutal blows and his coarse shouts of what he would do if it ever happened again.

How humiliating, how degrading that was, to stand there, already nearly sixteen years of age, and be forced to take this beating and this lecture. While the mistress of the house and the journeymen of the shop would stand about, either utterly indifferent or smiling with amusement, as if he were no more than a dog. And if he stood up proudly, as he remembered that a Roman would do, then it only caused the smiles to turn into audible laughter. While if he cried out in pain, then the ridicule he got was even more searing.

What had he done that he should have to endure this?

When the master was finally done with pounding him, then Jean Jacques, his eyes baking with a dry, feverish heat because of the tears he refused to let flow, would have to slink back to his bench, covered with shame, his heart so swollen with clumsy and impotent images of revenge that his lungs had no room to breathe and his whole chest ached with congestion.

He felt so miserable that he wanted to die. And yet here it was just Monday morning, with six full days yet to be suffered before he could hope to escape again.

For the next few Sundays he took good care not to stroll too far from the walls, despite the taunts of his companions. But then one Sunday, there it was again, that warning trumpet blowing retreat— and he and his companions a good half mile from the walls.

Oh, no! Not another beating! Off he dashed, at such a fast pace that he left his companions behind. Their laughter at his fears only spurred him on. Perspiration burst from his every pore. Already the trumpets had ceased, and the drums were about to go into their tattoo. And then it would be too late.

He was within a dozen paces of the walls when the drums started up. He opened his mouth to yell to the guards to wait for him. Wait! Wait! But he realized that he was making no sound. That his tortured body was snatching away all his breath, and he couldn't command the least bit of wind to his throat. It was as in a nightmare when one has to scream for help and can't.

"Wait for me! Oh, please wait for me!" he tried to shout.

But already it was too late. The horns of the first bridge were rising in the air. And the city lay locked behind those massive walls that the armies of Savoy had never been able to scale.

Now his voice came back to him. "Wait! Wait!" he cried. But of course no one paid any attention to him.

Wretched to the core, and unable to restrain his feelings, Jean Jacques burst into tears and threw himself down on the slope of the fortifications, where he dug his teeth into the earth and tore up grass, soil and pebbles by the mouthful and, panting and exhausted as he was, spat and spluttered it all out in sheer disgust with the whole world and himself.

The other apprentices, gradually drifting in, stood around in amazement, not knowing what to make of this strange exhibition of fury and despair. Some looked on with pity or tried to help him up, while others stood around giggling with a kind of stupid embarrassment.

Locked out! Locked out! That was all he could think of. The way his mother had locked him out of her life by dying. And his father had locked him out of his, by moving away from the city and marrying again. And Mademoiselle Lambercier had moved him out of her room. The way he was pushed away from the table. And locked away from the apples.

And now locked out of Geneva! Locked out until the morning, when he would have to take another drubbing from his master.

No, no. He had had enough. He would never enter Geneva again. He would run away rather.

Such was his groping in the dark for liberty.

So he fled. Yes, but not really. He was, it is true, afraid to enter the city and take the flogging that was coming to him. But he was almost equally afraid of leaving and taking the beating the world would probably give him.

So he hid just outside the city walls and sent word through one of the other apprentices to his cousin Bernard, his rich cousin, to come and say farewell to him. He was hoping that Bernard would dissuade him from running away. But Bernard did nothing of the sort. He brought him some clothes and a bit of money.

When Jean Jacques saw his cousin, he was dazzled by the bright piece of metal that hung from Bernard's side: his sword.

He must have that sword! And, unable to foresee that a day would come when he would consider a sword to be either a social lie or a weapon for murder, and in both cases a sin either of pride or of violence, Jean Jacques pleaded for that sword, pleaded so passionately that Bernard could not resist. He had to smile at this boy in such plain and even poor clothes, wanting a sword strapped to his side. He had to smile at the arguments he raised, of bandits at night, of Catholics out hunting for Calvinists. But he gave him his sword. Out of pity.

Such was Rousseau's groping not only for liberty but also for distinction. Already he distinguished between the sordid little lies and the glittering ones.

But even with a sword belted around him, Jean Jacques still could not tear himself away from the outskirts of Geneva. He still hoped that the news of his running away would reach his father's ears and that somehow he would yet be brought back into the fold. Beaten, perhaps, but at least securely fed and housed.

But his father did not come.

Soon hunger led him to knock at the door of a M. de Pontverre, one of those gentlemen of Savoy who dedicated themselves to the task of winning back Genevans to the Catholic faith.

For the first time in years Jean Jacques found himself seated at a well-set table, with fine napery, a good roast and a delicious Frangy wine.

Old M. de Pontverre did the young lad the honor of imagining that he was seeking religion rather than food and argued theology with him. A grossly unfair argument, of course, since the hungry boy could not afford to disregard the Catholic source of all this excellent food.

And thus Jean Jacques was induced to become a Catholic.

"It is God Himself who has called you to me," said M. de Pontverre. "He bids you now go to Annecy," the old gentleman went on. "There you will find a good and charitable lady, who has been appointed by the King of Savoy to rescue souls like yours from error."

Actually Jean Jacques was groping not so much for religion at this particular time as for something quite different. And on the road to Annecy he did not ruminate so much about God as about a princess. Indeed, he would stop at every pretty country home and station himself under a window and sing a song there, convinced that at any moment the casement must fly open and a princess lean out and beckon to him.

For it was also toward sex that he was groping.

He had imagined that the good and charitable lady to whom M. de Pontverre was sending him would be an ancient spinster. Instead, at Annecy, he found Madame de Warens, a still quite youthful woman, somewhat on the plump side, it is true, but for that reason perhaps all the more attractive; a dazzling ash-blonde, with eyes of such a startling blue as to illuminate as if with gems a face that was full of sweetness and vivacity. And in addition a silvery voice that murmured with compassion, "So young? And already homeless? Wandering around alone?"

All this so agitated him, so thrilled him, that he could scarcely hold back his tears. His dream of a princess in a pretty country home was right there. And beckoning to him.

But more than that. There was something else about Madame de Warens that held him spellbound, even though he had to turn his eyes away for fear that he might faint. What disturbed him so powerfully was the swelling contour of the kerchief that Madame de Warens wore at her throat and bosom. A kerchief that at one and the same time concealed and revealed the full ripeness of the breasts beneath.

How endlessly, throughout his life, Jean Jacques was to be troubled by bosoms!

Was that because he had never had his proper share of them as a baby? At any rate, with his mother dying at his birth, he could not have had the pair that nature had originally intended for him. And the substitute breasts that had suckled him must surely have been less generous, less loving, than those of his own flesh and blood.

Was that the reason he would later become celebrated for his spirited defense of a child's right to the breasts of its mother? He would assert that this was the foundation of a proper education for a child. And thousands of women of the wealthier classes of France, who had hitherto never thought that they owed their children the duty of nursing them at their own bosoms, especially when the land was so full of women of the lower classes who, because of the high death rate of infants, considered themselves only too lucky to have the added income from milk for sale—thousands of these rich women would one day worship Rousseau as the apostle of motherhood. Not knowing, of course, that this apostle had denied his own five children their mother's bosom.

For bosoms too were something that he groped for.

And perhaps the darkness that Jean Jacques had to grope through cannot be better illustrated than by his behavior with respect to Madame de Warens's breasts. And with respect to breasts in general. Alternately fainting in admiration and cruel beyond belief. Dying with desire for them, and yet unwilling even to let his eyes look upon them.

There they were, like fruit ripened by nature, inviting one's hands and one's lips. Reaching out. Offering themselves.

But no. He didn't dare.

Incomprehensible! With his insides consumed with fire, he would not cry out his longings. And five years later, when Madame de Warens finally invited him into her bed, he would still deny himself the sight of her breasts, and, with his eyes blinded by tears, he would weep over them.

Such was the darkness in which he had somehow got lost, so that he had to grope for everything. And nothing so well describes that groping as certain incidents of his journey across the Alps, on which Madame de Warens sent him in the company of a young married couple, M. and Madame Sabran, so that he could enter the hospice for converts in Turin.

What a wonderful walk that was, over the Alps in the early summer of 1728! Except at night, when, in the pitch-darkness of some cheap garret room of a village inn, Jean Jacques would be awakened by a strange noise. Not a loud noise. In fact, an almost inaudible noise. But nevertheless a noise that would somehow rouse him from his sleep and set him wondering.

What could be the cause of that almost noiseless noise? And where was it coming from?

Could it be from the other bed, on the far side of the garret, where the young Sabran couple were sleeping?

He strained his ears in the darkness, driven by an irresistible curiosity which he could not fathom.

Not that the noise really bothered him. No, he could easily have ignored it and fallen asleep. But there was something about it that intrigued him. Puzzled him. Haunted him.

There it was again.

As if someone in that other bed, either M. or Madame Sabran, were shifting about, seeking a more comfortable position for sleep. But shifting stealthily. So as not to wake anyone up.

But why should M. or Madame Sabran be so restless? Or both of them together?

Yes, now it was as if both of them were uncomfortably shifting for another spot to lie on. Both stirring together. Each unable to find the right place for sleep. Moving. Moving. But softly. As if to keep the bed from creaking.

For, just as soon as it creaked, there would be a sudden stopping of the noise. Which would resume only slowly.

Would they never settle down?

Now the noise was growing. Growing. Not louder. But somehow stormier. And now the bed did creak. And creaked some more. And still more.

But just as Jean Jacques began to be concerned to the point where he wondered if there was not something he ought to do, the noise stopped. Almost abruptly.

Silence. A silence so profound that one could hear M. and Madame Sabran breathing deeply, soundly. Both having finally and at the same time found comfort. And evidently now wrapped in sleep.

He himself would soon draw back into his own sleep again. Until some few hours later, when there it was again. The same noisy search for comfort.

It kept him awake, that noise. Puzzling out the various strands of it. And trying to give some meaning to them, in spite of the darkness. But in the end he would always fall asleep. For, as he would later phrase it in his *Confessions,* "Fortunately I was still in a state of stupidity. Otherwise that noise would have kept me awake longer than it did."

Fortunate stupidity! Not to know that which Sabastien Mercier was to express so charmingly a few years later in his book on Paris: "Thundershowers at night increase the birth rate of our fair city."

So he reached Turin. Still groping. Living in the midst of lies. And with no one to tell him the truth about either sex or religion.

There were all manner of inmates at this home for catechumens. And some, no doubt, who made a business of having themselves converted repeatedly, moving from one hospice to another throughout the Catholic world, and meanwhile enjoying the free meals and the free lodgings that were provided for the proselytes.

One of these obvious repeaters was a tobacco-chewing lad of Jewish or Moorish origin, with a complexion that was as dark and spongy as gingerbread and was rendered even more unsavory by a scar slashing across his whole face. He kept making the most insistent approaches to Jean Jacques, professing for him the liveliest sort of friendship, and even going so far as to kiss and embrace him, while Jean Jacques nearly swooned from the powerful tobacco stench.

Rousseau hadn't the vaguest notion of what this lad really wanted from him. Not even when the Moor proposed in honeyed tones that they should sleep together. Jean Jacques denied the request only because he could not have stood that heavy tobacco smell. And as the lad persisted in his pleas, Jean Jacques had to refuse him all the more energetically.

Further understanding came to Jean Jacques one morning when he happened to find himself alone with the Moor in the assembly room. The boy sidled up to him, snuggling up against him, moving closer and closer with ever more insinuating motions, and then beginning to let his hands take strange liberties with Jean Jacques, so that the latter was at first intrigued and then excited, but finally frightened.

Apparently what the boy wanted was for Jean Jacques to take similar liberties with him, and this only increased Rousseau's amazement and trepidation, which finally reached such a pitch that he disengaged himself abruptly.

But not quickly enough to prevent the boy from achieving what he wanted. In fact, it was just in the nick of time that Rousseau drew away, and then to his complete surprise he saw something white and gluey that went shooting out from the boy's organ and in the direction of the fireplace, but falling short of it and splashing to the floor.

What could that be?

Jean Jacques's stomach heaved. Certain that he was about to vomit, he rushed to the balcony.

But he didn't vomit. And from the corner of his still curious eyes he saw something that struck him most forcefully. It was the Moor's face. But how disfigured! His dark and spongy complexion was so charged with passion, so gorged with blood, that it seemed apoplexy was about to fell him.

Never, in all his life, would Jean Jacques forget the sight of that horrible visage.

"Is that how one looks at such moments?" he would thereafter often ask himself. "And I? Shall I look like that on a similar occasion? How is it possible for a human being to survive such an attack of lust and fury?"

And then he would wonder, "Is that how men look when seized with such longings? Then how can women stand the sight of them? Surely they must be revolted and push them away in disgust. And in fear."

He had to go on puzzling this out, overcome with a kind of horror at his own violent desires, which had still never expressed themselves in anything but fancies. "When I am caught up in my dreams of girls, is that how I look? Oh, no! I must never let myself look like that. No. Certainly nobody must ever catch me with a face so repulsive."

But then he would argue, "Perhaps women are themselves at times so utterly bewitched that they are unaware . . . Yes, surely they must be under some sort of spell. Otherwise they could not stand us."

And thus the feeling that had been inculcated in Jean Jacques when his father had first begun to confuse him, and which had been strengthened when Mademoiselle Lambercier had first aroused him with her spanking hand and then curtly rejected him, the feeling that there was something about sexual desires that was brutal and disgusting, something that could make one's stomach heave, something that could kill, was increasingly confirmed.

His groping persisted. For though all his being cried out for sexual expression, and he had seen the tobacco-stinking Moor obtain his satisfaction and leave the room, still he remained there, not knowing that he was both attracted and repelled by what he had seen. Not knowing that his fancies were whipping him on, even while his fears were pulling him back.

Why did he run to the institution's old housekeeper, to tell her about the Moor's behavior? Was it because, while still able to deny himself a physical release, he could not check his craving for a mental release?

But what sort of enlightenment could this housekeeper give him? On the contrary, her reaction only puzzled him all the more. She was furious with the Moor.

"The dirty dog!" she cried.

Her outrage was, in fact, so keen, it seemed that it was she who had suffered the humiliation of it. This disturbed Jean Jacques, for he could not yet understand that, old as she might be, her feminine pride was not yet so extinct that she was not put out by the fact that men should waste that precious male force of theirs upon each other and thus let the sex for whom it was obviously created and intended go hungering for it.

"Damn him!" she kept saying. "Curse him!"

Jean Jacques felt that the Moor ought to be punished and that his conduct ought to be reported to the priest.

But the housekeeper forbade that. "Let no one know about this except you and me!" she warned. And then she asked, "Are you sure you've told no one else so far?"

"Of course I'm sure," he said. "It just happened now."

"Then let me advise you: Keep it quiet. And whatever else happens, come and tell me about it. Quickly. Will you promise me that?"

Rousseau promised.

But, still too young and too inexperienced to understand that what this old woman wanted from him was precisely this secret intimacy, a dark privacy which might be expected to lead to an even closer and more exciting relationship, he did not give his promise its true value and very soon had told other inmates about his experience with the Moor, and in no time it was being repeated all over the institution.

And the next morning, when he opened his eyes, there were two ecclesiastics at his bedside.

"This is a very immoral matter, my son," one of them began.

And the other chimed in: "It is a thing forbidden."

"It was terrible!" Jean Jacques cried. "I felt sick—"

"There, there," said the first one, raising his hands with a quieting gesture. "There is no reason for you to feel affronted."

And again the other one nodded. "The sin is not yours. Not in the least."

"I tried to stop him!" Jean Jacques cried. "I never saw such a disgusting—"

The first ecclesiastic held up a finger in stern warning. "Haven't I already once explained to you that you had no reason to feel affronted? In cases where an immoral desire exists, it is the perpetrator, not the object of it, who has committed the sin."

And once more the second priest sustained the first, saying, "No man can be held responsible for the thoughts and emotions of another."

Jean Jacques was puzzled. Why all this insistence that he had no need to feel upset?

The first ecclesiastic said, "I myself was once the object of a similar desire. I would never have permitted it, of course, except that I was taken by surprise, and at a time when I could not make a protest. So I had to endure it. And look at me. Do I seem any the worse off for it?"

Once again the second priest approved, adding, "There is no pain involved."

A fact which the first one confirmed vigorously. "None whatsoever."

Jean Jacques stared in fright at the two men. Years later, when he thought he understood this episode more clearly, he decided that the institute for catechumens was nothing but an association of pederasts, of Knights of the Cuff, as he subsequently learned to call them.

It did not occur to him that they might be only testing him to assure themselves that he, Jean Jacques, was not merely seeking to cover up his own guilt by loudly proclaiming his horror.

Whatever the truth of the matter, certainly Jean Jacques soon regretted that he had not followed the old housekeeper's advice, not only because of what her intelligence and experience might have contributed to clear up his own confused notions, but also because it seemed to him that once his obstreperous hostility to this form of homosexual love, even in that passive and sinless form in which he felt it was being offered to him, became generally known, he would be subjected to all sorts of petty but deliberate annoyances intended to make his stay at the hospice as disagreeable as possible.

With the result that he decided to study hard and learn the Catholic dogma as fast as possible, so that he could secure his baptism and get out.

But as a sign of the hospice's disappointment in him, it was the Moor who got to wear the home's most resplendent white coat when they marched in solemn procession to the Church of St. John to make public abjuration of their former faith. Jean Jacques was given only a lesser coat, gray with white froggings.

Behind the new converts marched men with great copper basins which they struck with a heavy bronze key. Into these basins they invited the charity of the onlookers.

All Jean Jacques got for his conversion was about twenty francs, a mere fraction of the amount he had been given to expect, and certainly far less than the tobacco-stinking Moor received, perhaps because the conversion of this dark-faced lad brought to the minds of the onlookers stories of the Christ child and the Three Kings. So that while coins rained into his copper basin, only a few tinkled into that of Jean Jacques.

He could not forgive himself that it was for this paltry sum that he had committed the shameful act of apostasy, for which all Geneva would now forever spurn him. And he had even permitted his saintly mother to be cast into hell. A thought that often stabbed him with guilt, as if he had fouled her snow-white bosom.

And what did he have now in the way of increased knowledge? Nothing. He was, in fact, groping in deeper darkness than ever regarding the truth of religion, and as to what would happen to him and his soul when he died. And Voltaire's consoling religion was still years away.

12: I'M A PRINCE

There he was now, dismissed from the home for catechumens, set adrift in the city of Turin and practically penniless. Sixteen years old. With no home. No work. No trade.

And still several years before that evening in the home of M. de Bonac, when the name of Voltaire would begin to bring the first light and direction into his life.

He loafed about the city, eventually finding his way to the cheapest kind of hotel, frequented by out-of-work servants, where the price of a cot was only a couple of pennies a night. Now and then he would find employment as a lackey, would be fitted out with a colorful livery and would perform a variety of menial tasks, standing behind some member of the family at meals and pouring wine or water, or else clinging to a carriage through rain or shine, with dogs barking and snapping at his heels, and then leaping off as the vehicle came to a stop, in order to rush around and open the door and let down the steps.

And then, for one reason or another, he would lose his position and would be back at his hotel. He felt restless. He was absent-minded. A dreamer. By turns weeping, sighing, longing, for what he knew not. But with desires incessantly filling his mind with girls and with women, of whose true function he continued to remain stubbornly ignorant.

What urge raged through him, what struggles were fought out in his emotions, before he finally succumbed to some dark mysterious desire rising within him, we cannot know, for he refused to go into detail in his *Confessions*. Only that he suffered. That much we can be sure of. For he was not so stupid as not to know what risks he was running.

But the fancies which revolved around his buttocks, linking them in some peculiar way with his imaginary girls, were too rapturous to be denied. And one fancy would lead to another, ever wilder and ever more maddeningly enchanting, until the fever of his crazy longings would rise to such a heat that he would have the courage to go out into the streets . . .

At first only at night, when he felt reasonably safe. And along some quiet dark street, where he would quickly slip down his breeches and, with his behind naked to the cool wind, would walk along fantasying the possibility of some woman, with a longing corresponding to his own, beckoning him to her room . . .

How exciting it was!

But it yielded nothing. He was certain that women were peering at him from behind their window blinds. They were admiring him. But they were too low and too mean to betray themselves. They preferred to make him suffer.

Silence. And not a sign of interest.

Was it possible that because of the darkness he had remained unseen?

In that case he needed some place where the light would be better. Where there would be a lot of women around. Where perhaps one woman would encourage the other. Until they would join in beating him . . .

He looked for a long time before he found the right spot for exposing himself in daylight. He first watched the area carefully. Drawn to it. And yet scared. Oh, there were enough girls around. Of course they weren't letting on that they had any wishes at all. But he was on to them. The sly young things! With their mischievous eyes and their teasing smiles. As if to say, "I know something you don't know!"

And the older women, with their serious mien. They were the most hypocritical of all. Pretending that nothing mattered.

What mysterious and enticing creatures women were! He watched them in this courtyard, congregating about the fountain. Filling their pails, but in no hurry to leave. Gossiping, laughing, shouting to each other. There were times when they did not seem to him like human beings at all. Not really the female of man. But some sort of animal from the forest or the mountains who had come to live with man, just like pigeons or cats. To be man's pet. Or else like witches from fairyland. At any moment they might lift a hand and claws would spring forth. Or they would spread a wing of feathers and fly away.

How lovely they were! And yet how dangerous. Which one of them might not have some strange disease that would blow up a man's skin with deadly pustules!

But here it was safe to expose himself. On account of the dark cellars to one side. He had explored these cellars several times to make sure that they provided a safe retreat in case of a general alarm. They were endless. No one would venture to pursue him into those black caverns. And if they did he could always successfully hide from them in the branches that led off in all directions.

There was a time during which he yielded only in his imagination.

He was too frightened to do anything more. But as his passions whipped his senses to a froth, he finally found the courage to take his stand some little distance from the well, but near enough to the cellars to feel secure, and there, turning his back to the fountain, and with his heart pounding furiously, he let slip his breeches and offered the sight of his pink bottom to the girls.

How his senses swam! How his mind went through wave after wave of delicious dizziness, spiced with mortal terror. And bitten by irresistible curiosity, so that every once in a while he would twist his neck to see what effect he was creating. There were some women who humphed, throwing back their heads, as if in disdain. How he hated them! But he noticed nevertheless that they did not leave the courtyard without casting back another look at him. Oh, the sly old baggages! Nothing but pretense!

And then those girls who acted as if they saw nothing. Butter wouldn't melt in their mouths. They filled their pails and left. But he was certain that, once around the corner and out of sight, they stopped to peek.

Yes, they did!

And there were those, older women for the most part, who yelled imprecations at him and warned him to be off and behave himself. But from behind their skirts he could see the younger girls, some of them so bold and saucy that they would actually come out and giggle and would have to be slapped back by their mothers.

Jean Jacques nearly sweltered with alternate satisfaction and fright. The excitement was killing him, but he would have gladly died in such a wonderful delirium of his senses.

Until finally one girl ran away crying for help.

Jean Jacques hadn't figured on a man appearing so quickly. Almost immediately, there he was. A gendarme! He had barely time to pull up his breeches so as to keep his feet from tripping in them. And already tormented by the thought of disgrace, and the news of it carried perhaps to Geneva . . .

But fortunately the cellars were close. He quickly lost himself in them. He thought that would be the end of the chase. But he could hear it continuing. And apparently his pursuers knew these dark branching tunnels better than he did. To them they were neither endless nor labyrinthian.

The gendarme, moreover, was accompanied by some of the women and the girls, and among them was one with a lantern, so that no matter how Jean Jacques turned and twisted among the winding corridors he could not shake them. It was like a nightmare come alive. And then suddenly he found himself running into a blank wall that made further flight impossible.

He turned and saw himself confronted by a mob of women brandishing broomsticks. As for the man, he was truly formidable. A giant. With huge mustaches and an imposing hat. He carried a naked sword in one hand, while with the other he laid such a firm grip on Jean Jacques that the lad felt his knees give way.

What could Jean Jacques do before such overwhelming forces but sink down and moan the first thing that came to his mind? Which wasn't far to seek, since in his imagination he had often pictured himself in just such circumstances.

"My poor head!" he lied. "It hurts me. It's deranged. That's why my father, the Duke, keeps me locked up. But I don't like to be locked up. I got hold of these old clothes and ran away in disguise."

He could feel the stares of those all around as he mouthed these fantastic words. He trembled at the thought that he might not be believed, and he raised his voice all the louder.

"Oh, don't arrest me!" he pleaded. "Please don't arrest me. Someday I'll succeed to my father the Duke, and then I'll remember you for this. I swear I will. On my honor as a prince."

He could feel that he was beginning to move the man with the sword. He could sense his grip relaxing slightly. Oh, if only he could get out of this situation, never again would he let himself be carried away to such a dangerous pass again.

"Don't do anything to disgrace me!" he groaned. "I'm ruined forever if my father should hear of this. Oh, please don't ruin me. Please!"

Though some of the women snorted with unbelief, and others declared that even a prince with a deranged mind could profit by a good drubbing, the man with the sword allowed his hand to loosen, but before letting go completely he gave Jean Jacques a push, as if to say, "Get going before I change my mind!"

And Jean Jacques took to his heels as fast as he could. His heart thumping still with fright at what might have been.

It was subsequent to this that he groped his way to a certain lifesaving discovery, for there are maps and guideposts even in the land of confusion. He learned that it was possible to cheat nature. Somehow, while alone with his dreams, while fidgeting and fancying until he was nearly on fire, he finally brought himself to just such a moment as had revolted him so when it had happened to the Moor.

Hitherto he had avoided pursuing matters to that length. And now he was intensely disgusted with himself. And frightened at the thought that someone should by chance catch sight of him while his face was no doubt inflamed with passion.

But at the same time he noticed that, along with his flow, it was as if all the fire had drained from him. He was suddenly calm. The chaos and confusion had left him for the moment. He was content and even happy.

Still, he would never have repeated this activity, such was his hatred of it, if, a few days later, while taking a stroll with a young abbé whom he had met, he had not nearly run into the man with the sword.

He looked quickly away, trying to avoid being seen. But the gendarme had recognized him. Instead of being angry, however, the gendarme only laughed and cried out mockingly, "I'm a prince! I'm a prince!"

The abbé was startled. But Rousseau pretended that he did not know what it was all about. And the gendarme passed by without saying anything more, a discretion for which Jean Jacques thanked him silently from the bottom of his heart.

It was a long time—so Rousseau would later write in his *Confessions*—before he ever tried any similar exhibition of himself. But apparently he did try it. Only he never told anyone when or where. He had a certain control over himself now: his discovery of how to cheat nature. That was his term for masturbation: cheating nature.

In short, a lie.

How he hated himself for those lies. And how he cringed before admitting them. Even in his *Confessions,* which were not to be published until long after his death.

Some time later, being one day penniless in Lyons and sitting out of doors, hungry and with only the poorest sort of shelter awaiting him for the night, he saw himself approached by a young silkworker. After some friendly chatter, the young man proposed that they should amuse themselves together.

Jean Jacques wondered what amusement he was thinking of and waited for him to explain himself. But the silkworker didn't offer any further explanation. At least not in words. He merely moved up close to Jean Jacques and in the darkness began to work upon himself, making no demands upon the other. Apparently that was all he wanted, that each should amuse himself on his own, while sitting near the other for company.

This appeared so simple and reasonable a request that it never occurred to the taffeta maker that Jean Jacques might look upon the matter differently. But Rousseau became so wrought up by this shameless proposal that he leaped to his feet and ran away as fast as he could, fancying that the wretch might pursue him, and his heart meanwhile trembling as if he had committed a crime.

Jean Jacques's disgust—that one can understand, pretentious though it might be, considering that he was himself addicted to that habit. But why the panic? Obviously because he was suddenly forced to the realization that his face must be shouting his shame to all the world. And that anyone, even an ignorant silkworker, could read it there, plain as day: that here was a lad who cheated nature.

It was this that so unnerved him that he ran away as if he were on fire. And did not dare go back to his inn until he had taken the firm resolve never to indulge again. Never. For only total and rigorous abstention could wipe that guilt from his features.

Then why did he ever go back to this ugly vice?

Because he was driven to it. Compelled. Because self-denial carried too far precipitated him toward his other craving, which was even more shameful and even more dangerous: the desire to exhibit his rear to the other sex.

Trapped!

Yes, caught like some animal, between the teeth of one iron bar, namely the dread of being mobbed or arrested for having his breeches down in public, and the teeth of another iron bar, namely the telltale marks of onanism on his face.

What despair must have possessed him when he suddenly discovered that he had been condemned for the rest of his life to turn and twist within this trap! And no hope of escape.

How could this have happened to him? Who had laid this snare? Who had tied this noose?

And why should it be he who was singled out for this strange and cruel punishment? What crime had he ever committed?

No wonder Rousseau was to fall into a swoon on a blistering hot day years later when, on the road to Fort Vincennes, the answer came to him.

It was the century in which he lived that had dug the pit for him. It was the society of his times. And all the artists and philosophers of the day, who, instead of revealing the defects of the times, instead of correcting the evils of their day, coated the society of their times with a wonderful luster that only made it all the more deceptive and all the more deadly.

It was because they covered over the pit instead of revealing it that he finally came to hate them. And particularly—in time—Voltaire.

Voltaire, who more than anyone else might have changed the century. Voltaire, whom he would call upon later to write the "Catechism of the Citizen." For who but Voltaire had the talent and the power to fix new ethical values for the world?

But Voltaire only laughed and refused to understand. Voltaire liked the world he lived in. Yes, of course he saw its faults. And he pointed them out for everyone's scorn and ridicule. But he saw no reason to destroy the society in which he had his wonderful existence, merely because there was evil in the world.

Man was evil. Voltaire admitted it. But for that very reason any society which men might form would also contain evil. There were no short cuts to Utopia. One could only hope that gradually there might come about some improvement in the affairs of men. It would take time. That was certain.

Voltaire! Voltaire!

How far apart they were, these two men. Voltaire so much at ease on every level of society. And Rousseau so nervous and so ill at ease.

On what basis could they ever meet? Merely because they had both been exiles? Yes, but how could you even compare Voltaire's exile from France to Rousseau's sense of exile from the whole human race of his times? Besides, Voltaire's exile was but a matter of years, while Rousseau's exile must be for his whole life.

And Voltaire's single and short flogging by Rohan-Chabot. What was that compared to the never ending flagellation that Rousseau had to endure from his conflicting inner drives, from which, he knew, only old age or death could release him?

And as for Voltaire's numerous enemies, all of them together, no matter how many and how powerful, even when Frederick of Prussia turned against him, and Louis XV and later Louis XVI too—how could they possibly constitute as much of a menace as the single enemy that Rousseau had? For Rousseau had Rousseau for an enemy. And the stronger he became, struggling against this enemy, the stronger that enemy became struggling against him.

And no hope of escape. No running away. Dogged by his enemy all day long. To bed with him every night. And waking every morning only to face another day with him.

How far apart! Voltaire flitting from one mistress to another, so readily and so often that Nicolardot, his most vicious critic, would later write an almost book-length essay with the title "How Voltaire all his life had Mistresses that cost him Nothing."

Whereas Rousseau—ah, Rousseau . . .

Being once in Venice, years later, as secretary to the French envoy there, for one of Jean Jacques's brief moments of modest affluence he was tempted to behave like all the gay Venetians of that era and devote himself to the goddess of love, who perhaps never reigned anywhere so completely as she did there at that time, when, as Cardinal de Bernis was to write, the convents of the city would vie with each other as to which could offer the papal nuncio the prettiest nun to be his mistress. And since Jean Jacques was hearing on all sides the praise of a certain girl from Padua, he was determined that he too would enjoy her favors.

He was graciously received and found a young lady whose freshness of complexion and liveliness of spirits were a delight. But Jean Jacques's resolution to possess this beauty vanished quickly at the thought that there might be serious consequences. Was it really possible that a girl so universally admired and so readily accessible to anyone who had the price could fail to be diseased?

True, she did not look diseased. Indeed, her eyes sparkled and her skin glowed with health. She seemed as fresh and as clean as a water lily.

Nevertheless Jean Jacques was stricken with terror.

For convention's sake he had to sit down and order a glass of sherbet and carry on some sort of conversation with her, but he had made up his mind to leave in a half hour without taking the risk of contamination.

So in a little while he rose, put a ducat on the table and would have left, except that the Paduana could not comprehend such actions. She considered herself an honest girl, and as such she had scruples about taking money that she had not earned.

Jean Jacques was therefore compelled either to acknowledge himself lacking in manhood, a matter which might shortly be the gossip of the whole town, or to give the girl reasons for thinking that she had not wasted her time.

How he managed to perform any kind of act is a mystery. Perhaps he had some contact, but surely of the briefest nature. Then, leaving her as fast as he could politely do so, he had himself conveyed in his gondola to his lodgings, and there he threw himself at once into bed and had the doctor fetched with all possible speed.

When this gentleman arrived, Jean Jacques flung himself at him as if he were at death's door. "Save me!" he cried. "Save me!"

"But from what?" the bewildered doctor asked.

"Surely you know of some powerful brew that will prevent the pox!"

"Let me examine the symptoms," the doctor requested.

Jean Jacques had to explain that as yet it was too early for the symptoms to show.

"Ah, you have just been with a diseased woman," the doctor said.

"Yes, yes," said Jean Jacques.

"Well, tell me, what were her symptoms?" was the doctor's next question.

Again Jean Jacques had to explain that he had seen no symptoms.

"No boils? No exudates? No sores?" the doctor inquired.

"None."

"Then what makes you so sure she had the pox?" the doctor wanted to know.

How could Jean Jacques explain to the doctor his feelings about women, which were such that he was certain he could not go unpunished from the arms of such a person as the Paduan girl? That in any relationship with women Rousseau expected to be beaten. Had to be beaten!

For three weeks Rousseau suffered the torments of hell, feeling himself again and again devoured by the pox, which he was convinced must be fermenting within him. And again and again the doctor had to come to reassure him, and to tell him that this or that pain which he happened to feel, this or that little skin discoloration that he happened to observe, was not a sign that syphilis was breaking out on him.

In the end the doctor succeeded only by arguing that a man such as Jean Jacques, with his difficulty in urinating through his narrow orifice, was better protected from a sexual disease than most men, and that it was highly unlikely that he would ever catch the pox, no matter how severely exposed.

This idea that he was possibly immune to sexual diseases was a great comfort to Jean Jacques. He need no longer fear. He could be like other men. And so when, a little later in Venice, a young courtesan was suddenly and madly infatuated with him and invited him to her chambers, he was delighted.

He had never seen anyone so utterly bewitching as this Zulietta. So much so that years later, when writing his *Confessions,* he would be at a loss to describe her perfections, declaring that she seemed to him fresher than a virgin in a cloister, more seductive than a harem beauty and more radiant, surely, than the houris of Paradise.

When she received him, clad in the Venetian *vestito di confidenza,* an almost transparent robe of silk, decked out with ruffles and bows of pink ribbon, he felt as if he had entered the shrine of some goddess and had come to worship there.

And scarcely had Zulietta welcomed her Zanetto, kissing him, embracing him, with all manner of frolicsome cries and caresses, than straightway he was inflamed with lust for her. And yet at the same time with revulsion.

After all, what was she but a slut?

With beauty and charm such that kings ought to be happy to lay their scepters at her feet. Yes. But how could this utterly lovely creature fall in love with him, who was poor and unknown?

Obviously this filthy streetwalker was making him her dupe! She had some secret defect. A pox or something. That was the answer. Otherwise she would have nothing to do with him.

All unconscious of the turmoil going on in her Zanetto, the girl threw aside her robe and pressed Jean Jacques's head to her bosom, which was so cool and shapely that it seemed no man could ever have violated its purity.

And then he noticed that she was, so to speak, one-eyed.

Yes. One nipple was missing. No, not exactly missing, but not at all like the other one. How horrible! One imagines that one is holding in one's arms the most beautiful creature on God's earth, and she is nothing but a sport of nature, a miscarriage, an outcast! A monster!

Carried away by the trend of his thoughts, Jean Jacques, with his strange fear and love of bosoms, could not resist asking her how this had happened, and whether she had always been so or had suffered some injury.

Zulietta took it as a joke, teasing him back in such a manner that if he had not been so completely possessed by his madness he would have died of love. But instead he continued to betray his uneasiness and even his distaste, until at last he made the girl so self-conscious that she blushed and covered up her bosom.

She rose from the couch where they had begun their disports and went and sat by the window.

Immediately his arms missed her warmth, her softness and her sweetness. He rose, too, and went to sit by her side. But that irritated her. She left her seat and returned to the couch. And when he followed, she rose and went about the room, fanning herself vigorously.

Finally she said, "Zanetto, give up ladies. Study mathematics."

This stung him. For it was as if she had said very plainly, "Stick to masturbation."

He felt he had to leave her now. He had ruined everything for the moment. But he begged her to give him another appointment for the following day.

She smiled ironically. "Better make it three days from now," she said. "You will need a little time to recover from your exertions of today."

And with that she pushed him out.

"In three days, then," he said.

"In three days," she repeated, and closed the door on him.

For three days he could think of nothing else but her graceful, adorable playfulness, which he had so crudely interrupted. For three days he could do nothing but regret the moments with her which he had so stupidly wasted when he might so easily have turned them into the most memorable of his life.

And when the three days were over he flew to her apartments.

She was gone! She had left for Florence the previous evening. And he was never to see her again. So that throughout his life he would be stuck with his failure, and the memory of those last contemptuous words of hers: "Three days. You will need a little time to recover from your exertions of today."

You see, he was somehow doomed to remain blind. Doomed to feel himself prodded by his confused and violent desires. Doomed to grope his way forward with the conviction that nothing lay ahead except precipices.

And yet his yearning to find truth, order, purpose in life never left him.

13: MAMA

Eventually Jean Jacques was to be saved by two people. A man and a woman. Both of whom would give direction to his life. The man was Voltaire, whose works he gradually began to discover from his eighteenth year on, and the woman was Madame de Warens, she of the ash-blond hair and the ripe bosom.

Madame de Warens was, like Jean Jacques, also originally a Protestant. She had been married when very young to a nobleman of Vevey and had brought him a considerable fortune in dowry. But she was reckless. She had a taste for gay company. And she loved excitement. Speculation in all sorts of projects, from mining to manufacturing. And she was not unwilling to introduce her own beauty into these ventures, offering her body as a further inducement to bring others to invest their money in her schemes.

With the result that one day she faced not only the ruin of her reputation, but also some sort of official investigation into her financial affairs which would surely have terminated in a most unfortunate way.

She chose to tell her husband that she was not feeling very well and that she had seen her doctor and he had advised her to take the baths of Evian, across the lake, in Catholic Savoy.

Somehow she had played her game so skillfully that her husband was not suspicious of her and even agreed to lend her his fine walking stick with its golden pommel so that she might make a more dignified appearance. And it was only later, when she had already crossed the lake, that he discovered that she had taken not only his cane, but every other piece of jewelry that she had been able to lay her hands on, as well as all the silverware they owned, all their lace and every other easily portable article of value.

In addition, the superintendent of their estate, Claude Anet, a man who was very able in the preparation of herbs for curative teas, had gone along with her and was obviously her lover.

That all this had been a cleverly arranged affair was evident when she arrived in Évian precisely when the King of Savoy was also there; and just as he was about to enter church to hear Mass she fell at his feet and cried in Latin, "Into your hands, O Lord, I commend my soul." From the twenty-third chapter of Luke.

The Archbishop de Bernex had been behind the whole business, having coached her, and the resulting conversion was the sensation of the entire lake area and a mighty victory for the Catholics. Protestant Vevey was so aroused that its citizens threatened retribution, and the danger of armed raids was such that the authorities had to provide Madame de Warens with a bodyguard of fifty men until the passions aroused by the affair had died down.

The King of Savoy was not overly generous with Madame de Warens. He granted her a pension which was rather skimpy, considering her former style of life. Still, she was able to mount a fairly decent household, with cook and maid and cleaning woman, plus a gardener and the use of two porters to carry her chair. In addition there was Claude Anet to superintend her business affairs. For she continued to engage in all manner of activities, sometimes undertaking confidential voyages in the service of the King, and at other times trying to produce a superior kind of soap or a new kind of chocolate, or to distill some specially valuable elixir from herbs that Claude gathered in the Alps.

She was still young and attractive, and her home was often gay with the coming and going of guests, the intellectual elite of the region. And Jean Jacques, vagabonding around Savoy, would somehow always find his way back there, floating in and out, now living with her, now gone again, sent off, perhaps, to a seminary to become a priest, and then to study music, changing his mind again and again, but never varying in his feelings about Mama, and always finding his way back, and gradually getting to be more and more at home with her. As if that was where he rightfully belonged.

Now, finally, he had what he wanted. A mother. And a country home. And whether he went off to work in the land survey office or elsewhere, eventually he would always return to Madame de Warens and find his room and his books, and resume his studies, whether chess, philosophy, music, Latin or Greek.

If his dream of a home in the country, inhabited by a princess, had come true, why not another dream? Why not his dream of someday being worthy to stand beside Voltaire? All it needed was application. He tried his hand at everything. He struggled to write a play. A poem. He was determined to master mathematics. Sick or well (and how often he was sick!), he would invariably open his books, spread out his notes and read or write all night long. And often all day too.

Interrupting himself at night, only to run into the garden to study the stars, for he wanted to know how to locate all the constellations—to find, for example, Aldebaran in the constellation of the Bull, and all the other major heavenly bodies, too. He wanted to observe what had so struck all the ancient people: the manner in which the planets weave their incomprehensible way among the fixed stars, a path that no one had been able really to figure out, not until Kepler had discovered that if one imagines it to be an elipse, then all observations will check.

And interrupting himself during the day only to pursue his duties, give music lessons, take care of the dovecote and a certain part of the garden, or else run to kiss his Mama and to beg her to sit with him for a moment at the piano and sing songs. And then back to work again.

But not really knowing how to work. Not even knowing where to begin. And in addition troubled by his attention, which would constantly wander off and leave his empty eyes following the words while his mind was gathering fancies.

And so much he didn't know. So much! And he couldn't bear not knowing, not with Voltaire obviously knowing everything.

So that if on page one of a book he encountered a reference to Scholastic philosophy, or to Pico della Mirandola, nothing could make him go on until he had consulted a treatise on philosophy or looked up Pico. And if in the course of looking up these matters there would be references to Duns Scotus, or to Abélard, or Saint Thomas Aquinas (with Pico it would surely be references to Castiglione's *The Courtier*), then off he was again, tracking down these matters.

It seemed to him that he would never get back to that page that he had left because of one word which he hadn't quite understood.

"What I need is a storehouse of solid ideas," he often said to himself, "a strong base for my research." And for months and months he worked acquiring such a storehouse. But there again he had trouble. What were these solid ideas? Was there any notion in the world that did not have its critics who opposed and derided it? Which "authority" was right? Instead of acquiring a storehouse of ideas, he found himself sinking into a morass of arguments.

At any rate, he must know history. And he started a huge "General History of All Times specially compiled by Jean Jacques Rousseau for his own use," as he wrote on the title page of one of his notebooks. And he copied out from history books passages which struck him and which he felt he ought to keep available for future use. Thus, from Fénélon: "I must love my family more than myself. My country more than my family. And mankind more than my country." The last was, of course, the hardest, for all the patriots then called you a traitor. But it was the highest form of earthly love.

History? Yes, he had to know history. But meanwhile what about chemistry? What about physics? What about mathematics?

He studied Father Lamy's *Geometry*. And Father Reynaud's *Science of Calculus*. And the same author's *Analysis Demonstrated*.

But there was also geography. There was botany. Biology.

And languages. Latin was, of course, indispensable. Many important works were available only in Latin. And almost every important book of his time was studded with Latin phrases and quotations. And there were the classics, which somehow must be read. And even memorized. Horace. Everyone had to know Horace. And Ovid. And Virgil. And Lucretius.

In his eagerness to read the Latin authors before he had the requisite grammatical foundation and the necessary vocabulary, he overreached himself and found himself stumbling through works too hard for him, so that he had to double back and forth between his text and his grammars and dictionaries.

And that was only Latin.

What about Greek? That too. And perhaps Hebrew.

And so he worked on, sometimes so sick, perhaps from sheer despair, that he would say to himself, "This is surely my last day on earth." But he would open his books anyhow. "Perhaps I shall survive. In that case I will regret having wasted a day." And somehow his youth would pull him through.

He still labored against his miserable memory, as if rowing upstream against a current that was sweeping him downstream almost as fast as he worked himself up. How discouraging it was! With only the thought of Voltaire to sustain him!

One of his music students was a M. de Conzié-des-Charmettes, a Savoyard gentleman who didn't have much talent for scales. But he had a fine library. Together they discovered each other's admiration for Voltaire. So that soon the music lessons turned out to be anything but music. They read out loud to each other from the latest publications of Voltaire. For example, from the *Philosophical Letters*.

And Rousseau would wonder, "Shall I ever be able to write so elegantly? Shall I ever be able to think so cogently and keenly? Shall I ever correspond with kings?"

He felt himself still locked up. Still confused. Still stupid in society. Madame de Warens knew of his embarrassment and would give him bits of advice about how to behave when he went out to give lessons to the daughter of Madame Lard, wife of the town's wholesaler, or when he went to teach the daughter of the Countess de Menthon. Advice which he did not know how to follow, so that Madame de Warens became afraid of all these young and pretty girls and of all these scheming ladies into whose homes her young man had to go. She trembled lest he commit some social blunder that would either land him into a bad marriage or disgrace him and force him to leave the district.

She decided that she must guard Jean Jacques from such a fate.

And now young Rousseau gradually became aware of a new attitude on the part of his Mama. No longer would she race him through the house, her fingers smeared with her latest elixir, black, sticky and disgusting, and gleefully force him into a corner, where he would have to lick the stuff from her fingers and, while choking with laughter and a heaving stomach, declare that it was the best elixir she had yet produced and that he already felt himself cured of all diseases.

What gay times they used to have!

But now her attitude had turned sober. Her utterances all serious. Her advice grave.

So that one day when they were alone together he burst into tears and threw himself at her feet.

"I've offended you!" he cried. "You're going to send me away. Oh, punish me! Yes, punish me! But don't be cold to me. Don't turn away from me."

She raised him up and kissed him. "Don't be silly, little one," she said. "You've done nothing wrong. But it's time we had a serious talk, you and I. Tomorrow we'll have a walk in the garden. Is that agreed?"

Of course it was agreed. But meanwhile he was utterly lost. What were they going to talk about? Wild fancies surged up in his heated brain. Tomorrow the servants would be out. And Claude Anet would be up in the mountains gathering herbs. In short, they would be all alone, he and Mama.

Was that what she wanted? To be alone with him?

How he dreaded that interview, aware of his secret vices and wondering if by chance he had been discovered. If his face had not perhaps betrayed him.

And indeed her first question the next day seemed to indicate the worst. She asked him how old he was.

"But you know that I'm past twenty-one," he said.

"That means you're a man," she said.

"Yes," he mumbled.

"And it's time you assumed a man's place in the world."

"Yes, yes, of course," he breathed.

"I too must learn to think of you as a man."

He didn't like this conversation. Why did things have to change? He liked their playful, teasing, frolicsome relationship. In which, in spite of the laughter, he was all worship and devotion and respect. And she was all kindness and motherliness.

But she talked on, and he had to admit that yes, he was ardently inclined. Indeed, his passions were quick to boil over. And yes, there was a thirst in him for every feminine body that he saw. But as yet, he swore, his face blushing furiously, he had never touched a single one intimately.

Did he realize, she wanted to know, how dangerous such a period was for an inexperienced young man? There were women who laid traps for just such youths as he. And there were others who were indiscriminate, and who might even be diseased.

He stammered, his mind wandered. He suffered every kind of torment.

"Nevertheless a man has a duty here on earth," she said. "The two sexes complement each other. No woman is really a woman without a man. And no man is truly a man until he has a woman."

He nodded, still wondering, still dreading.

And finally she said, "Amidst these dangers and these duties, a young and inexperienced man may well go astray. And that is where I feel that I must be of help to you. Perhaps I can teach you your duties as a man—and at the same time spare you the dangers that you might otherwise encounter."

Was he hearing correctly? Was his beloved Mama really offering him her body in order to protect him from the snares of other women?

His knees turned to water. With difficulty he continued to pace beside her in the garden. He thought of her body. And in particular of her bosom. And his heart seemed to interrupt its beating.

"There will be certain conditions," she went on. "I shall have to exact a promise."

Of course he promised. What else could he do?

"I demand discretion," she said. "The lives of people are their own private affair," she explained. "But there is such a thing as gossip. And we have to take precautions. Outwardly we must remain as we have always been. The change will be only for ourselves. For the world at large we shall remain as before. It is only in the privacy of our rooms, in the privacy of our hearts, that I shall from now on think of you as a man. And you will think of me as a woman."

He accepted everything. So overwhelmed that he could only stammer.

"Of course this is a great change," she continued calmly. "A big step in your life. And no doubt you are still too shocked to frame an answer. I understand. Take a week to think it over."

He assured her that he did not need a week. That such a thought was an insult to the deep passion he had always had for her. His heart, he told her, had always been hers, since the first moment he had laid eyes on her.

But she would not have his immediate acceptance. "Take a week," she insisted. "It is a bigger step than perhaps you realize." And before concluding her walk with him, she cautioned him again to be discreet.

Discreet! Discreet!

Oh, he knew exactly what she meant by discretion. She meant lies. She meant, above all, that Claude Anet would have to be lied to.

When Jean Jacques had first begun to live with Madame de Warens, he had had no suspicion of any more intimate relationship existing between her and Claude Anet than that between any employer and an employee of confidence. Mama was always charming and cheerful toward everyone. And Claude, in his neatly combed iron-gray wig, his carefully brushed black coat, was always retiring, prudent, serious and respectful.

But one evening they had had a little disagreement at table. Nothing serious. But Madame had let drop a belittling remark. Claude's face had darkened slightly. He had risen from his seat, bowed correctly and excused himself from the room.

That night Jean Jacques had been awakened from his sleep by cries of distress. Mama! Mama! He had stumbled through the dark toward the source of the noise and had found himself in Claude's room. And there was his Mama struggling to bring Claude back to life.

On the floor lay a little phial that had contained laudanum.

The two of them, working together, had managed to rally Claude. They had forced him to vomit the poison. And Madame de Warens, with tears in her eyes, had begged Claude to forgive her. She had assured him that she had never meant to wound him. That she loved him as much as ever. And always would.

From then on Jean Jacques knew.

And now Mama was offering to make a man of him. That meant that she would be giving herself to both of them. Only Claude mustn't know.

Discreet. Another name for lie.

That disturbed him. Not that he held it against Mama for thus being willing to distribute her favors. He knew that it was not out of an irresistible passion, not out of concupiscence, that Mama was offering herself to him. She herself was obviously not particularly sensual. Though seemingly designed for love, it was more out of kindness of heart that she went to bed with a man.

Oh, if only he were sufficiently master of his own passions, as she was of hers, so that he might go to her and honestly say to her, "Mama, my dearest Mama, there is no need for you to sacrifice yourself for me. I can promise you that I will be on my guard against all temptation. You need not worry about me. I will answer for myself."

But could he do that? Could he honestly do that? What about his cheating nature? Did Madame de Warens suspect him of this vice? Did his face betray it to her, as it had certainly done to the silkworker? Surely she knew. Or suspected. And surely she would want him to promise her to free himself of that ugly habit. No longer live a life of lies.

Could he? Dared he? Was he not likely, if he attempted to stop, to fall back into his old proclivity of exposing his naked bottom? Imagine the disgrace he would bring upon himself and upon her house if he should be caught at it. Here, in this small community. What a scandal! No matter how great her affection, Mama would find herself compelled to cast him out.

No. There was no escape for him. Not if he wished too continue to live with his Mama. He would have to accept the sacrifice she wished to make and even pretend that he wanted nothing else so much in the world.

But the word "incest" kept hammering itself into his head, and he was convinced that the affair would be an utter failure. That too would be a disgrace. He had to prove that he was a man.

And thus the days of that week of waiting passed, hour by hour, until the dreaded moment was upon him and he found himself lying naked beside her nakedness.

And there—at last!—were those beautiful breasts which he had so often guiltily admired and so often virtuously denied to himself. But did he caress them? No. "I wetted her bosom with my tears," he would later write in his *Confessions*.

For a moment he lacked all manly power. He could have died of shame. But then his imagination came to his rescue. It was no longer his Mama who was lying there, opening her arms to receive him. It was one of the princesses of his dreams. And as he imagined her chastising hand coming down upon his rear, the spell of incest faded. His passions rose, and he was able to accomplish his role with every manifestation of joy which the situation required of him.

And Mama was very satisfied. She had shown no particular awareness of his facial expression. Indeed, she had not shown any particular passion at all. She had remained her usual gay and carefree self, taking her joy out of the feeling that she was giving joy to another. Her partner's ecstasy was her fulfillment. That was all she craved.

And somehow this very lack of passionate participation preserved her from any sense of sin. After all, the lust was not hers, was it? She merely surrendered to the lust of others. Willingly. Because of the sweetness of her character.

Thus the three of them lived for a while in a kind of discreet idyllic bliss. To Jean Jacques it was a succession of wonderful days when all his problems seemed solved. He had a woman. He was a man. He had his books. And all the out-of-doors. And whether he worked in his study or in the garden or at his music, he was happy.

But suddenly Claude began to suspect. Then the days of happiness were over.

Evening meals became ugly affairs, with heavy exchanges of bitter looks. Over a nothing, vicious arguments would flare up. Over a trifle, the fiercest hatreds would explode.

Madame de Warens would wring her hands and weep.

"Don't you see that you are both necessary to me?" she would cry. "Can't you see that both of you hold my happiness in your hands?" And she would challenge them, "Which of you wants to break my heart?"

She would shame them into a reconciliation. But that did not wipe out the bitterness of Claude, who saw himself as the older man being pushed aside. Nor did it erase the sense of tragedy that was always just barely beneath the surface in Jean Jacques.

How much better we enjoy in the imagination than in reality, he would think.

Then one day Claude announced that he was going up into the mountains to gather the rare *Artemisia glacialis,* the plant from which the sweet *génépi* liqueur is distilled, a plant which grows only on the highest slopes, close to eternal snow.

It was not the right season for such an expedition. But Claude went anyhow, and apparently he found the flower he was looking for: a mortal pleurisy that now was dearer to him than the arms of his mistress.

That was his vengeance: to have them stand by his bedside, unable to stop the course of the disease, compelled to watch him die of a poison that this time they could not force him to vomit. And even forced to be grateful to him for choosing a way of dying that would provoke no scandal in the village.

When it was over, Jean Jacques had a moment when he rejoiced. He thought of Claude's possessions, his fine clothes and so forth, which he would now have for his own. He could not forgive himself for this guilty thought. It worked havoc in his spirit. He was responsible for Claude's death. And now he coveted his possessions.

One day he went to lift a small table. It should have cost him no effort at all. But a disturbance arose in him, like a storm suddenly developing over a lake. His blood seemed to mount in waves. All his limbs shook. Every beat of his heart, every pulse of his arteries, resounded through his body like the drums of a regiment.

It was as if it thundered and lightninged inside him.

Of course no storm could be perpetual. It must eventually subside. Only it didn't.

Alarmed, fearing for his life, he took to his bed and begged Mama to have a doctor fetched. The physician drugged him mercilessly. He suffered from the ferocious medication, but he got neither better nor worse.

As he had been afraid of dying, so now he began to be afraid that he would not die. Was it possible that he might have to go on living with this endless tumult within him? He was so young, and already he had to have everything repeated to him. It was not that his hearing was bad. If only the noises inside him would stop, he was certain, he would hear as well as anyone.

But the noises wouldn't stop and hung around him like a dirty curtain, obscuring his life.

He could not conceive that his condition might get even worse, when it was already beyond endurance. But he was wrong.

Since Claude's death he had been managing Mama's affairs, there being no one else to keep order in her accounts. But now that he was ill, he fell behind in his work. Mama was distraught. She had no head for figures. The situation was growing daily more tangled and impossible.

He had to agree that another man should come into the house.

Thus Vintzenried. A journeyman wigmaker. Tall, handsome, full of energy. Jean Jacques considered him pretentious and stupid. But he certainly went about his duties with all the noisy enthusiasm that a man could muster, that is to say a man who wanted to put himself on display. One never saw him without an ax in his hand, or some other tool. And always on the run, hustling the help, shouting, as if he were taking not just the place of a Jean Jacques, but that of ten other men besides.

And particularly when Jean Jacques was dragging himself around the garden, barely able to move—that was just when Vintzenried would put on the most elaborate exhibitions of his strength and energy.

So that Jean Jacques was not surprised to discover him one morning coming out of Madame de Warens's bedroom, having obviously spent the night there.

He was stricken with a sense of humiliation so corrosive that he could no longer stomach food. He had to keep to his room.

Mama came rushing to his bedside.

"But my dearest little one," she said, "there is nothing changed between us! Nothing at all. I love you just as dearly as ever."

This only made him suffer all the more.

He wept. He threw himself from his bed to the floor, in order to kiss her feet and to beg her not to degrade herself by distributing her favors.

"But none of your privileges shall be touched," she insisted, bending over him, weeping along with him and trying to get him to go back to bed. "Our pleasures together shall not be curtailed. Not in the least. I promise you that, my little one. Believe me, you are just as precious to me as ever."

Such scenes had their momentary effect. But they could not permanently reconcile him to sharing his Mama with another. He knew now every bit of pain that Claude must have suffered when he had to stand by and see his beloved passing into the arms of another. He understood now why Claude had preferred death. No wonder! He was beginning to prefer death himself.

And he often said as much to Madame de Warens. But still without extracting any more from her than her old assurances that she loved him the same as always and would go on loving him to her final hour.

"But don't you see that you only sully yourself?" he argued. "Don't you see that if I seek further enjoyment with you, the person I love more than anything else, I am myself guilty of degrading you?"

Mama resented such talk of sullying and degradation. All she could gather therefrom was that Jean Jacques was rejecting her.

Both of them began to feel that their many years together were drawing to a close.

And how painful this separation was! With what tenacity a thousand strands of memory, of gratitude, of affection, resisted being pulled apart. His love, his devotion were still so alive in him that all it sometimes took was a glance from his Mama for his passion to flame up anew.

Then they would drown their thousand mutual reproaches in tears and in kisses. But the reconciliation could only be short-lived. Nothing more than a half-smile or an incomplete sentence passing between her and Vintzenried the wigmaker would rip up all his wounds again, and once more he would feel himself bleeding to death.

He had to leave. And he did leave. But it was like all his separations. He left only to come back. And then to leave again. Finally, however, the break was made. He drifted ever farther. He went to

Lyons to be tutor in the home of a M. de Mably. Then he went to Paris, to live in wretchedness. But always studying, always striving. Always dreaming his dream of someday meriting the esteem of the great Voltaire.

Can it be any wonder that his thoughts would subsequently tend to be both wild and bitter? And that he would counsel parents, in his book on education, to take their sons to visit a hospital for syphilitics so that they might see faces ravaged by the pox and bodies wasted by this most frightful disease?

"Take them on such visits," he would advise, "to purge them of every bit of lust for women. But be careful," he would add in warning, "that you do not take them to such places more often than necessary, lest you inure them to the very thing you wish to guard them against."

Can it be any wonder that he wanted children to sleep on the hard floor of cold rooms and have no books at all, lest their bodies become overheated and their minds too, and they be seduced into lustful imagery?

It was with his own life in mind that he issued these warnings, recalling all the sufferings he had been through and wishing that he might himself have been brought up in such a wholesome Spartan fashion.

14: THAT TIDBIT VIRGINITY

Think of a Voltaire, born, so to speak, on a mountaintop, and having nothing to do except stretch out his arms toward the sun. And think of others struggling along the slopes of that mountain, far from the peak. And others still, who haven't yet reached the slopes, wandering more or less lost in the valley below.

And still others caught in a swamp in that valley.

And who knows? Some still more unfortunate, buried in a peat bog beneath that swamp.

How different Rousseau's life might have been had he been free from those lewd desires that were perpetually traversing his mind, distracting him, upsetting him, compelling him.

Early in his Paris days, trying desperately to find some means of livelihood, he went to the home of Madame Dupin to apply for a secretarial position. Madame Dupin, one of the wealthiest women of France, heiress to the colossal fortune of the financier Samuel Bernard, happened to be in dishabille and thought nothing of receiving a nobody in that condition.

But Rousseau's starved senses swam at the sight of her bare arms, her loosely tied hair.

He fell upon his knees before her, seized her ankles and vowed her his eternal fidelity.

Naturally, she showed him the door. And it took a letter containing the most abject and fulsome apology to repair the damage.

And yet, what else could he have done, trapped as he was in his poverty, between his fear of the pox and his hatred of masturbation, while his senses nevertheless drove him on with a too vivid imagination and too easily aroused desires?

But finally, by good fortune, he found a solution to his woman problem.

One evening, at his hotel near the Luxembourg, a little laundress hitherto confined to the rear, where she battled with dirty linen, was put to waiting on the tables. Hard work from childhood had endowed her small frame with grace, liveliness and a beautiful posture which made her firm little breasts strain against her bodice. But at the same time it had left her ignorant, shy and awkward.

The habitués of the table d'hôte began to get some good-natured entertainment out of a competition to see who could bring out the most furious blush on her face by multiplying lewd gestures and remarks with obvious double meaning.

Embarrassed, in terror of failing at her new work, poor Thérèse was on the verge of giving up in tears, when Rousseau suddenly exploded. Was there no respect here for the innocent? he demanded. No honor for womanhood? No pity for the poor? Could they not at least whisper their filthy remarks to themselves, to spare the feelings of a girl forced by circumstances to wait upon them? A girl who was striving so hard to please them, while they were striving so hard to make her feel miserable?

Shamed into silence, the men at the table finished their meal without any further horseplay.

As for Rousseau, with his taste for daintiness in women, with his love of finery, of well-kept hands with slender fingers, of tiny slippers, the last thing he desired was a relationship with this slum girl who in all her life had never known anything but labor.

And yet he was drawn to her. Except for her total lack of education, so that she could not even tell *A* from *B* or read the face of the church tower clock, was she not his feminine counterpart? Condemned by her position in society to slave for the rest of her life?

But for all his pity and his sympathy, he studiously avoided closer contact. After all, there could be only two possibilities: Either she was a virgin, in which case she had a right to a man who would marry her, and that he did not propose to do, or she was not a virgin, in which case she was probably diseased.

As for Thérèse, she, for her part, could not but conclude that this gentleman took her for an innocent virgin. How else could he have interpreted her blushing? And since she did not know how to confess to him that she was no longer a virgin, she also avoided her champion.

It was their separate loneliness that finally drove them together. And one evening, in the dark courtyard, she revealed to him her story of having been deceived by a lover who took her virginity and ran off without marrying her. Since then she had been on her guard against men, for, while she no longer had her virginity to offer, at least she still had her cleanliness and her good health.

Liberated at one and the same time from his fear of having to marry the girl and his fear of getting a pox from her, the starved Rousseau opened his arms to Thérèse with a cry of joy.

"My darling Thérèse," he said, "I cannot begin to tell you how happy I am to discover in you a girl who is both modest and healthy."

He made it immediately clear to her, however, that if she could not expect him to marry her, she might rely upon him to do everything he could toward her comfort.

Thérèse, in her simple way, was happy to accept his offer. Only she could not understand how it was that he took her lack of virginity so lightly.

"Virginity, virginity!" he cried with contempt. "Let Parisians and boys of twenty make a fuss about that tidbit. As for me, I am far from being disappointed at not finding in you what I was never looking for."

In fact, she fitted his needs to perfection. She was clean and devoted. She proved that she could cook, keep house, wash clothes. And at night, in bed, she could drain off his desires far better than Madame de Warens. And he, with his imaginative power, could transform her in the darkness into whatever woman he wished to possess.

How wonderful to have a Thérèse! No longer to be afraid or lonely! And yet there were times when Rousseau would rage. Why should he have nothing better than this stupid serving wench, while a Voltaire found everywhere such glamorous mistresses? Especially later, when Jean Jacques began to acquire his fame and was able to meet fine ladies on a more familiar footing; then his disgust with Thérèse would sometimes mount in him so powerfully that he would compile lists of her incredible blunders in order to amuse the guests at the rich homes to which he was invited. The Duchess de Luxembourg, for example.

Love her? How could he? He despised her. And yet, almost before he realized it, he had forged between himself and her a bond far more powerful than love: he had adopted her.

She was like some household pet whom he now caressed and now kicked around mercilessly. The butt of his every emotion. No matter how contrary. She was like a household animal before whom one need not blush for one's crazy desire or feel ashamed of any signs of lust on one's face. Before her he could be shameless. Confess and even exhibit his urinary problem. She was his thing.

But it was different when this thing undertook to whelp.

The idea!

He did not intend to have her litter cluttering up his small apartment.

How could he? Where would he find room to work? What would become of his dream of Voltaire, with the home atmosphere steamy and sour from milk and soiled diapers? Where would he study? How could he write, with squawling babies underfoot? Why, he wouldn't be able to concentrate for even a second.

Ah, no! Let her take the brat to the foundling home!

Don't you dare bring one of them into the house! To be got rid of before you come back from the midwife! Do you hear me?

Thérèse wept and clutched her aching breasts, already swollen with milk. She pleaded on her knees. Let him at least wait until the baby was born. Then let him decide. Surely his heart would melt when he saw the little Rousseau, the little Jean Jacques or the little Jacqueline.

Fine! And where would the money come from? The money for layette, and the money for doctors?

She promised to ask for nothing. She declared that she would herself go out and work for whatever money might be needed. And not a single comfort of his would be sacrificed.

He refused even to listen. He had sworn never to abandon her. And he never would. But that did not include her children. Still, if her children were more important to her than he was, well, then the matter was easily solved. Let her pack up and leave.

Yes. Let her get out! Hurry! Make up your mind!

Very well, then. But now not another word. Hush! No more tears. He was busy. He had work to do. Silence!

Such was the Rousseau who, after more than a quarter of a century of vagabonding, was proposing to return to Geneva and have his citizenship there restored to him. After all, he was a somebody now. His return should be welcomed by Geneva. Was it not he who had startled the lighthearted world of Parisian luxury with his sensational attack on the arts and sciences? An essay that had captured the coveted gold medal specially struck by the Academy of Dijon?

And gone on from there to compose a highly successful operetta, *The Village Soothsayer,* that had delighted the King of France at a command performance at Fontainebleau?

What other Genevan had the like to say of himself? Indeed, what other philosopher of Europe could compose an opera? Was it Diderot? Or d'Alembert? Or even Montesquieu? Or the great Voltaire himself?

Or, on the other hand, where was the composer who could also turn out a prize-winning philosophical essay? Rameau, perhaps?

No. Rousseau stood unique. And was proud to call himself a citizen of Geneva. And Geneva should be proud of him, too.

Of course, when it came to certain kinds of notoriety, he couldn't yet pretend that he was a match for Voltaire. That kind of world-wide fame was not yet his. But for the little republic of Geneva, whose inhabitants did not add up to twenty thousand souls, Rousseau could consider himself a personage of real distinction.

So that when he arrived by stagecoach at the little village of Eaux-Vives, just before Geneva, and let the word spread that he wanted to regain his citizenship, he was amazed at the total lack of any sort of official reception. Only the local pastor, Maystre, and some other clergymen got in touch with him, but on a purely personal basis.

Pastor Maystre, who queried the Little Council in Rousseau's behalf, had to inform him that, much as Rousseau was admired in Geneva, the authorities were determined to make no exception in his case and insisted that he should enter the city and there let himself be arrested for treason.

"What?" Rousseau exclaimed angrily. "I must be thrown into jail like a common criminal?"

"It will of course be only for the shortest time," Pastor Maystre assured him. "Just long enough to satisfy the custom and impress on the minds of our citizenry that to abjure from the Calvinistic faith is still the most heinous of crimes. Then the Little Council will call you into one of their sessions."

"And have me crawl on my knees before them, I suppose," Rousseau cried.

"That is the custom," said the pastor. "That is the rule for all those who have gone back to the abominations of papism. There's no other way."

Rousseau was indignant. If he consented to this, might it not eventually get around to the knowledge of all Europe, and he be laughed at everywhere? Just as the enemies of Voltaire never let it be forgotten that the great poet had been flogged, would not Rousseau's enemies keep reminding the world that Rousseau, the great democrat, the author of the *Discourse on Human Inequality,* the man who had scorned the King and the aristocrats of France, had nevertheless gone down on his hands and knees before the provincial aristocrats of Geneva?

Rather than face this eventuality, Rousseau preferred to lie. "How can one speak of a return to the abominations of papism in my case," he argued, "when it was as a mere child that I was taken to Paris? Could it be expected that one so young would protest to his guardians against being raised as a Catholic?"

"It does seem," said Pastor Maystre, "that in your case there should be some exception."

"You must work for me, my dear Pastor," Rousseau pleaded. "You must assure the members of the Little Council that just as soon as I was of age where I could use my own faculties for thinking, I immediately recognized the errors of my ways. And ever since then no one has been more assiduous than myself in his attendance at the special services for Protestants held in Paris under the auspices of the Dutch envoy to France, in the palace of the Holland embassy."

There was, of course, not a word of truth in all this. Nevertheless, Rousseau continued, "Surely Their Magnificent Lordships cannot wish to hasten my end. And in view of my grave physical state, I cannot promise that crawling on my hands and knees will not be more than my poor frame can stand."

Pastor Maystre, thus coached, felt himself honored to work for the celebrated Rousseau, and he performed his part so well that the Little Council not only excused Rousseau from these preliminary humiliations, but went further and excused him also from an appearance before the consistory to answer on matters of theology, contenting themselves with the appointment of a small committee to go themselves to Rousseau's rooms and there interrogate him on his religious principles.

Which, of course, required some additional lying on Rousseau's part. For he had to affirm that he believed that God had actually revealed Himself to man. Which Rousseau emphatically didn't believe, except insofar as the wonders of the universe may be considered a manifestation of God's reality.

He had also to declare that he believed firmly in the divinity of Christ. Whereas, on the contrary, Rousseau followed Voltaire's belief that nothing robbed Jesus of his greatness so much as this folly of deifying him. For what is there to admire in a God who speaks in beautiful parables? Or performs miracles? Or rejects the dominions offered to Him by Satan? What is there to admire in a God who shows such wonderful courage in His "spurious" death on a cross.

For a God who created the universe, such displays were silly trifles.

No. The greatness of Jesus lay precisely herein: that, being but a man, he nevertheless had the faith that could move mountains. And the courage to face death with dignity, while forgiving those who were murdering him.

But naturally, before these convinced representatives of the Calvinist faith, and with his citizenship at stake, Rousseau did not dare express his real ideas. He lied and lied again.

The committee was finally satisfied with everything except the matter of Thérèse. And nothing now lay between Rousseau and his desire to be admitted to Holy Communion in Geneva except this woman who occupied such a suspiciously anomalous position in his household.

"Gentlemen," said Rousseau quietly, sadly, "if you were but fully informed concerning the state of my health, you would realize how incapable I am of justifying any suspicions you may be entertaining regarding my relations with Mademoiselle Levasseur."

The committee expressed their sympathy for their distinguished visitor's affliction, but they would nevertheless have to insist on questioning the lady in person.

With what trepidation Jean Jacques must have rung for the inn servant and asked him to please find Mademoiselle Levasseur and beg her to come to his room! For though he had been coaching her for weeks now on every detail and aspect of the story he had invented concerning their relations, and though he had threatened her with the direst consequences for the least false step, how could he be sure that —whether out of stupidity or out of spitefulness—she would not let drop a word that would explode his whole scheme?

But there was no way out now. Thérèse had to appear. She had obviously fortified herself with a few glasses of wine, but for all that she was still tongue-tied and frightened.

It seemed for a moment that anything might happen. And Jean Jacques trembled at every word she uttered. But as she answered question after question, and as her whole story came out, then, despite blunders and corrections, she gave the impression of being honest, all the more so because of her lack of glibness.

She told of how she had first met M. Rousseau. He was then a patient, occupying a bed in her mother's apartment. Her mother, Madame Levasseur, had, at Madame Dupin's request—Madame Dupin was a very wealthy Parisian lady . . . M. Rousseau was her secretary, and he had come down with an incurable illness, requiring constant care. For which reason Madame Dupin had engaged Madame Levasseur to nurse Monsieur Rousseau.

Then, one day, Thérèse happened to walk into a street brawl. Innocently, unaware of what was going on. She tried to push her way out, but received such a kick that she fell unconscious. She was transported to her mother's apartment, and it was not expected that she would live.

It was then that M. Rousseau generously insisted on surrendering his bed to her and denying himself all the comforts he was so much in need of, in order that she might be restored to health. And only when she was herself out of danger would he permit himself to be put back to bed.

What could she do in return, poor and ignorant girl that she was, to show her gratitude? Except vow that as long as she lived she would not abandon M. Rousseau, but would do everything in her power to alleviate his troubles. She really owed her life to him. And now there was nothing—no, nothing—that could move her from his side. That is to say, unless he himself dismissed her. Which God forbid!

With that she threw her apron up over her face and sobbed.

The entire committee was deeply moved. And Jean Jacques, lest this wonderful impression be dispelled by some unfortunate remark, quickly found some errand for his devoted nurse and ushered her out of the room.

But now what? Was he not going to be the recipient of some sort of honor? Was not the community of Geneva aware that he must earn his living in some way or other? Did they not realize that in this city where music was quasi-forbidden he was likely to starve to death as a music copyist?

What would they do for him, their famous citizen?

It seemed for a while as if they would do absolutely nothing. And then the famous Dr. Tronchin came forward with a plan to make Rousseau their city librarian. Just so that he would be able to settle down and pursue his studies and his literary work.

The one drawback was that at the moment there was no such post provided for in the city ordinances. The Council would first have to create it. And then funds would have to be found to take care of some sort of modest salary. It was even suggested that some one of the wealthier inhabitants might be able to spare a cottage for Rousseau.

But day after day passed and still nothing happened. And Rousseau became more and more impatient with this town which didn't seem to remember who he was. A man mobbed by the aristocracy of Paris, a man who had turned down a fortune as cashier of the House of Dupin and even snubbed a royal pension.

And now here he was, left cooling his heels for a miserable job with a pittance for pay.

No wonder he finally decided to return to Paris and see to the printing of his *Discourse on Inequality,* and wait for word of the ratification of his post as librarian.

He delayed his departure for only one reason. De Luc, one of the prominent pastors of the city, an admirer of Rousseau, invited him on a week-long excursion by boat around the shores of Lake Geneva. It was fall, the weather was well-nigh perfect, the company took their meals picnic style on the banks and slept each night at a different waterfront inn.

It was just the sort of life that Rousseau loved most. Away from the affairs of men. Out in the open. Nature at its grandest all about him. Silence and sunshine and water. Raising once again the permanent question of his whole being: If this was the best that life could offer, why did men insist on packing themselves into cities, there to engage in a deadly struggle for values that were as nothing in comparison?

And so at last he came back to Paris with his Thérèse. And nothing else. And waited for word from his ungrateful Geneva.

And that was when the big blow struck him.

15: MONSIEUR LE DUC DE VOLTAIRE!

Voltaire was in Geneva!
What? Voltaire in Geneva?
Yes. And received with acclamation by the noblest dignitaries of the town.

Of course Voltaire hadn't arrived by ordinary stagecoach, as had Rousseau and his Thérèse. No. Voltaire owned an impressive vehicle. Specially constructed for a man who happened to be the most celebrated poet of Europe.

A coupé. Superbly hung. Commodious. Upholstered in blue silk. Abundantly furnished with pockets and compartments for manuscripts and books. Two enormous trunks in the rear. And ahead six spanking horses. And on the box Voltaire's coachman. As well as his valet, who could also function as a copyist.

And inside Voltaire. Voltaire and his plump little niece, Madame Denis. Both bundled in furs. For it was cold on the road, in December of the year 1754. But cold or not, Voltaire occupied himself with reading or dictating. While Collini, his Italian secretary of the moment, took notes as best he could in the swaying coach.

And at Voltaire's feet lay a strongbox. Polished rosewood, heavily brassbound. Containing not only gold for out-of-pocket traveling expenses, but Voltaire's and Madame Denis's collection of diamonds and other jewelry. But, most important of all, that box held Voltaire's business papers. For example, his bonds on the city of Paris, and his investments in the Compagnie des Indes. Together these yielded him some twenty-five thousand francs a year, worth more than seventy-five thousand dollars of today. Constituting, however, only a fraction of his total income. For he speculated heavily in shipping from and to the Spanish port of Cádiz, making thirty per cent and more every year in cargoes of cocoa, sugar, indigo and tobacco from the Americas, as well as in wheat imported from the Barbary states of Algeria and Tunisia.

Here were also the certificates of his heavy loans to the Duke de Richelieu, the Duke de Bouillon, the Duke d'Orléans, the Duke de Villars, the Marquis de Lézeau, the Count d'Estaing, the Prince de Guise, and so on. And in particular the just recently concluded loan to the Duke of Württemberg, secured against the Duke's personal revenues and constituting the largest transaction in all of Voltaire's business life.

No wonder innkeepers in France and Germany bent themselves double when they saw this splendid equipage pull up into their courtyards, and the millionaire Voltaire, clad in black velvet, his fur cape draped over his shoulders, descended with his niece, his secretary and his valet. And no wonder they exhausted themselves in addressing him as "Your Excellency" and never called him anything less than Count or Baron de Voltaire, titles that Voltaire accepted with a smile in public and with laughter in private.

For over a year and a half, ever since his quarrel with Frederick, Voltaire had been traveling through various German principalities on the border of France, wondering where he could settle now that he was welcome neither in the Prussian states nor in France.

With the threat of war in the air (the Seven Years' War, which was to break out soon), Voltaire was afraid that if he settled in some country and it turned up on the wrong side in the coming conflict, his debtors would use this as a good excuse to confiscate his bonds, while the French nobility would find it their golden opportunity to cancel their obligations to him, on the pretext that he was now an enemy and perhaps even a traitor.

It was for that reason that Voltaire had given up his plan of moving to Pennsylvania, much as he admired the Quakers and respected the scientist Benjamin Franklin, who had just drawn electricity from the clouds. And decided to go instead to Geneva.

So there he was on a cold night in December. With the city gates shut. And the drawbridges up.

But did the guard keep him out?

Did he have to scream, "Please! Please!"? Did he fling himself on the slope of the fortifications and bite dirt and grass?

Of course not. It was not every day that a coach-and-six drove up to the gates of Geneva. Particularly one containing the great Voltaire. Voltaire's coachman simply said, "Monsieur de Voltaire."

Monsieur de Voltaire? Yes, that's all. And almost at once torches began to flare in the darkness, and the guard turned out as if for a parade. The drawbridge came down and the gates were flung wide.

It was a festive evening, anyhow, in Geneva. It was December 12, anniversary night of the famous Escalade, when the Catholics of Savoy had attempted a surprise scaling of the walls of Geneva and had been bloodily repulsed.

"But I succeeded in scaling your walls," Voltaire smiled, as the members of the best families hastened to greet him. "You didn't repulse me."

Did they ask him now to crawl on his hands and knees, as they had done to Rousseau only a couple of months before? Did they insist on questioning him about his religion? Did they want to know about Madame Denis, Voltaire's niece, who certainly occupied an equally suspicious role in the Voltaire ménage? What a strange story of incest would have come to light if they had! That is, if Voltaire would not have lied his way out.

But nothing of the kind. Naturally not. Not for the rich and successful. Not for the man who could hold his own against Frederick the Great.

Instead, on all sides invitations to occupy this château or that. And hopes that Voltaire would be pleased to settle in their community.

"But where would I live?" Voltaire wanted to know. "Your laws forbid selling property to Catholics."

"Oh, laws, laws," he was told. "Whatever property may be for sale, whatever house may be to your taste, a way can be found for you to acquire it."

The foremost citizen of the town, Councilor François Tronchin (brother of the Dr. Tronchin who was trying to get Rousseau the post of city librarian), declared himself willing to buy any estate that might interest Voltaire, and lease it to him for life, on terms that would not make it any more expensive than outright purchase.

Of course Voltaire was welcome in Geneva!

Indeed, Rousseau, waiting patiently in his Paris apartment for news of his appointment, was almost forgotten. Geneva was now full of families grown rich from industry and banking, families that made as many trips to Paris as they decently could, in view of the sumptuary laws. And coming back, what a frightful nuisance it always was for the ladies to have to put away their bright dresses and change back into the prescribed coarse and durable stuffs, all dull browns and blacks, which were the only ones allowed by the Calvinistic rules.

And erase the last vestige of cosmetics. And remove their jewelry too. Because even earrings were strictly forbidden. And, finally, no escape from that deadly routine of rising at four o'clock in the morning, except during the very cold months of the year, when one was permitted—just think of it!—to laze in bed until six o'clock. As if there were any reason to get up at all in this city without theater, without opera, without concerts, without balls! Where even a flirtation was a crime!

Why, Voltaire was a breath of fresh air! A promise of gayer times.

With all the aura of forbidden things about him. Those mistresses he had had in his time. The censored poetry he had written. And of course above all, most recently, that incredible feud he had fought with Frederick of Prussia. The famous duel between the scepter and the pen!

To say nothing of the fact that Voltaire was good business too. The Geneva publisher Cramer was after him at once, proposing a fine new edition of his complete works. The city was noted for its fine printers who had fled France during times of religious persecution. Moreover, Cramer didn't intend just another publishing venture. Not still another one of those omnium-gatherums of everything that could be attributed to Voltaire, of which there were already so many. But this time a really first-class edition. With every page revised and annotated by the author himself.

Voltaire was delighted with this proposal and ready to sign contracts at once. And indeed, with his usual energy, he got to work on it immediately.

Oh, by all means Voltaire must be persuaded to fix himself in Geneva! He must be assured that there was no likelihood whatsoever of Switzerland's becoming involved in the new war that was brewing. Never. What with Genevans so heavily invested in France, and Frenchmen so heavily invested in Geneva. Confiscation? Not the slightest danger of it!

Why shouldn't he move at once into the magnificent Château de Prangins, which just then happened to be vacant?

Voltaire did. But he and Madame Denis found the huge rooms terribly drafty and almost impossible to heat. Bundled in their furs, they hugged the fireplaces, stared out the windows at the snowy landscape and shouted for Collini to put on more wood.

Many Genevans who could afford to had winter homes in Lausanne, up the lake, where the climate was distinctly milder. There was, in fact, a place at Monrion where Voltaire would have all the comfort he required. And then, for the better season, there was available a place across the river from Geneva which Voltaire would find extremely pleasant.

Voltaire leased both places and found them both extremely livable and attractive. In particular the spot just on the other side of the Rhone was so ravishing that he renamed it Les Délices.

No, there was no comparison possible between Rousseau, waiting for the creation of an ill-paid job as librarian, and Voltaire, busy establishing himself in his two fine estates (he was later to acquire several more) and to whose supper parties all that was wealthy and distinguished in Geneva was already beginning to intrigue for invitations.

The women craving a glimpse of stout Madame Denis's superb Parisian toilette (on which she sometimes expended such extravagant sums that Voltaire, bills in hand, would pursue her through the house with screams of fury, while she would coldly berate him for a doddering old miser and threaten to pack her bags and go back to Paris). And the men craving an opportunity of conversing with this wit, this poet, this playwright, this philosopher and historian, who was also a man of the world and easily ranked among the twenty wealthiest Frenchmen of his day.

Indeed, one might well ask if ever before there had been a figure who so bestrode his era as this philosopher who at various periods of his life had been made welcome at almost every court of Europe. At the Palais-Royal by the Regent. At Buckingham Palace by the late Queen Caroline. At Lunéville by the former King of Poland. At Versailles and Fontainebleau by Madame de Pompadour. And who right now was being entreated to the court of Vienna by Empress Maria Theresa, a call which he surely would have heeded if there had not been this threat of war in the air.

Nor was that all. Dukes and duchesses made him welcome at their lesser courts of Gotha, Kassel, Mannheim and Stuttgart. The Pope wrote to him from Rome. And Empress Elizabeth Petrovna from St. Petersburg. Indeed, his mail was so enormous and the charges (generally, in those days, paid by the recipient) so onerous that in a fit of retrenchment he once had a huge board made bearing all acceptable seals, and his secretaries and copyists had orders to accept no letter whose seal did not have its match on the board.

Supper parties? Never in all his life did Rousseau give a supper party. Oh, he might now and then have a friend in for dinner. Yes. But only because that friend happened to be there just when Thérèse would be wanting to spread her checkered tablecloth. Which would, so to speak, force Rousseau to grumble, "You may stay and eat with us," in a tone that implied one would do better to leave at once. But if the friend remained nevertheless, then Rousseau would add, "I warn you, you'll have to take pot luck." So keenly conscious was he that he could not mount a fine household, with the necessary silverware, the lackeys and the customary number of courses. At one and the same time both proud of his poverty and bitter about it.

Supper parties? No. And besides, if he had ever given any, never could he have made them as lively and amusing as Voltaire could.

Never would he have been able to tell such a sensational story as Voltaire might tell, for example, about the sexual habits of Frederick the Great.

In that department, so it would seem, the King was far from demonstrating any greatness. Every morning he would play a game of, well, call it drop the handkerchief, with his officers. And the lucky young man thus distinguished would have the privilege of a, well, let's call it tête-à-tête, with His Majesty. Only that the King, in this situation, was not likely to behave according to his station, for he seemed to prefer the, well, let's say secondary role.

Oh, no, Rousseau never gossiped. Mindful of his own touchiness and how readily painful memories of his own sexual perversion might be aroused in him by a careless word from some guest, he even went so far as to ask, "How dare people talk? How dare they so much as open their mouths? Should one not know everything about a person's life before speaking in his presence? As for me, if you want me to come to one of your supper parties, then let me bring my cup and ball and play quietly. And let the others do the same. Rather than risk wounding even a single guest with our idle chatter."

No wonder Madame d'Épinay called Jean Jacques her "bear." That's how he was. Silent and surly. Just grunting now and then. And yet she dearly loved him. But of course he wouldn't have anything to do with her. In the way of an intimacy. For not only had he heard it whispered that she had once had a sexual infection, but, what was even more criminal in his eyes, she had no breasts to speak of.

"Her chest was as flat as the back of my hand," he would later write in his *Confessions*. And one can visualize that thin, bony chest of hers in which all the ribs could be counted.

A woman without breasts! Well! There's nothing more to be said. Scratch her from the human race.

Yes, that's how he wrote of her in his *Confessions*. For though he never gossiped in his life, that didn't mean that he would go out of this life without having delivered himself of the whole accumulation of his long-suppressed feelings. He let it all out in one grand blurt of gossip. His *Confessions*.

Whereas Voltaire, who gossiped incessantly, has left us no memoirs to speak of.

Because Voltaire, for all his deviousness, really lived an open life—or at any rate a transparent one. While Rousseau, for all his determination to get at the truth of society and speak it out, lived a dark and secretive life.

So that one feels that at the end of his life Voltaire had just about spoken his last word. That he was finally as dry and empty as an old husk. And that, picking him up by one ankle, you could have shaken him for an hour and not another syllable would have tumbled out of that exhausted throat.

While as for Jean Jacques, one feels that he went to his grave still bursting with things left unsaid.

Ah, Rousseau, Rousseau. Yes, he was already a somebody. Except in comparison with that permanent European sensation, Voltaire. Voltaire, fresh from his arrest in Frankfurt. Fresh from his triumph over Maupertuis. Fresh from his feud with Frederick the Great.

And everyone wanting to hear the most intimate details of that feud. What had really started the fight between King and poet?

Literary jealousy?

No. Though that might not have been an unimportant factor. For there was nothing this German King so much desired as to be a great French poet. And he was not without talent. Indeed, just to be a monarch and at the same time have such an ambition was in itself a distinction. He was an earnest student of science and philosophy. An accomplished flautist. But it was not easy for him to forget that he was a king, and that though he might do what he pleased with his 150,-000-man army, he couldn't change the word *fragment* into *fraguement* just because he happened to need a three-syllable word at that particular point of his poem.

No, poetic rivalry wasn't the start of it. Nor was it the Jew. Though the King did feel himself besmirched and demeaned when his favorite writer and courtier was caught dabbling in forbidden speculations with Saxon bonds. And, what was worse, along with a Jew, with whom Voltaire soon had a falling out, so that the matter had to be dragged through the courts, with both men yelling "Cheat!" at each other.

A shabby business. Yes, so it was. The great Voltaire and this rascally Jew. Caught in the act of financial skulduggery. And the King was properly indignant. And gave Voltaire notice that so long as this foul matter was being aired in the courts Voltaire would kindly refrain from showing himself at their literary suppers.

Whereupon every European gazette cried in its columns, "Voltaire in disfavor!"

And at least one of the guests at the King's suppers, Algarotti, murmured, "A supper without Voltaire—it's like a ring without a diamond."

But as for Voltaire, he shrugged. More time for his own work. What difference what stupid stories about his miserliness were being circulated by his enemies? He had nothing to be ashamed of. Prussia had conquered Saxony, and Saxon bonds had fallen to a fraction of their original value. The King had decreed that Prussians ought not to suffer a loss from the victory of their own country over Saxony, and that therefore all Prussians owning Saxon bonds should have their paper cashed at its face value. Well, Voltaire was now a Prussian, wasn't he? Only he didn't happen to own any Saxon bonds. But maybe that could be remedied. Maybe the Jew Hirsch could find some Saxons who owned such bonds and, unable to cash them, would be happy to transfer them for little money to Voltaire.

There would be some quick money in it. For all concerned. And who didn't want quick money? After all, when it came to speculation, what about Frederick's going to war? The war for the conquest of Silesia, for example. Or Saxony. What do you call that if not a speculation? And which, pray, is really the shabbier—the speculation of a Voltaire with some bonds or the speculation of a Frederick with the lives of so many young men, whose only crime was not to be able to see the bullet coming at them? Now, there was a crime that merited death!

Ah, yes, gradually, after many months, one begins to learn the ways of kings. And it turns out that kings—yes, even philosopher-kings—have a vocabulary all their own. When they say "my friend," what they really mean is "my slave." And when they say "my very dear friend," then depend on it, they mean "Your life isn't worth a tuppence to me." And when they say "Come up and sup with me to-night," then they mean "Come and let me rag you, let me make a fool of you for as long as I happen to please."

Thus, you see, the question becomes: How can one give a king a lesson in good manners? Because if the King felt that he had to give Voltaire a lesson in the proper behavior of a philosopher, then why not the other way around?

That's where the feud really started.

One evening, when Voltaire had been forgiven and was once again being expected at the suppers, and when, as sometimes it had to happen, everybody was proving himself cleverer than the King, Frederick lost his good temper and began to make some cutting personal remarks, all the easier since his exalted rank protected him from retaliation.

That was when Voltaire suddenly rose to his feet and said sharply,

"Gentlemen! The King!" as if indeed His Majesty had just entered the room. As if up to a certain moment they had been a group of wits and savants, but now they were a group consisting of King and courtiers.

The King's face darkened. His eyes blazed. And he looked around as if to see who else dared rise. Or even dared to look as if he wanted to rise. Or so much as approved of Voltaire's rising.

No one rose. But it was plain where the sympathies of these writers lay.

And Voltaire, thin, with that eternal underlayer of smile that always somehow lurked and trembled in his face, stood there. Hunched. One shoulder higher than the other. Waiting for the King to give him permission to sit. Stood there in respectful attention. But with that mocking smile just under the surface.

So that the King had his choice: either to leave the party, so that the guests could be at their ease again, or to recognize the existing situation, abdicate his misplaced assumption of royalty and invite Voltaire to be seated.

Why not? They had so often been just good comrades. And all of them speaking their minds so very freely that La Mettrie could rise and leave the table with no more than this comment: "Sire, my physical machinery wants to pee." And on another occasion they could speak of the King as "the foreigner," because he was the one German among all these French and Italian wits. Which was all the funnier because this German King didn't have a single German book in his entire library!

Yes, but now the King had to give in. Beaten. For one couldn't deny that Voltaire had exhibited an extraordinarily clever and at the same time courteous way of suggesting that Frederick had no right to invite them to a party as a philosopher and then suddenly turn king on them.

Yes, the King had to give in. But naturally the resentment of a military man against defeat remained. And in the back of his mind there grew up a desire to wring everything he could in a literary way from this genius. And then get rid of him.

In fact, one day he said as much openly. In the presence of La Mettrie, who straightway went to Voltaire and reported it with tears in his eyes.

The King had said, "One more year. Then I'll no longer need his damned literary guidance."

"And then what, Your Majesty?" La Mettrie had asked.

The King had made an eloquent gesture with his hand. "You squeeze an orange and then throw away the rind."

It was that comparison with a squeezed orange that really stuck in Voltaire's craw. That skinny craw of his. Well, yes: rind! That's all he was. Skin and bones. The rind of his former youthful and handsome self. Nineteen teeth he had lost—every one counted and mourned over—since he had come to Prussia. The loss causing the skin of his face to cave inward. So that indeed he did look like a squeezed orange. His nostrils too. Shapeless and flared from endless snuff taking. His lips ridged from endless coffee drinking.

But before he would let anyone throw him away . . .

Well, what else can one expect from a potentate accustomed to throwing away lives on a battlefield? As if life were not the most precious thing in the world. But of course, once you've overcome your scruples against throwing away the lives of soldiers, why stop at philosophers?

There never was, in Voltaire's thinking, a just war in history. Except the resistance against an invader. Or the effort of slaves to throw off their masters. Against chains only did man have a right to kill. Never otherwise.

16: DR. AKAKIA

After that phrase "You squeeze an orange and then throw away the rind," Voltaire could no longer abide life in this land of military ambition with its huge army. And he began to show it more and more. Once, when he was staging one of his plays and needed some supernumeraries, he asked that some men be put at his disposal. But after he had struggled with them for a few days and was unable to whip them into any kind of shape for his play, he finally shouted, "Hereafter when I ask for men, send me men! Not Germans!"

And, again, when General Manstein came to Voltaire's study one day to beg him for some help with the memoirs he was writing, Voltaire gesticulated at the mass of papers on his desk, poems from the prolific King, which he was struggling to turn into something resembling verses. "Can't you see that I'm in the midst of laundering the King's soiled linen? Bring me your dirty clothes later!"

But it was the Maupertuis affair that finally revealed the ever widening distance between poet and King. Maupertuis was that pompous scientist, head of the King's Royal Academy of Sciences, who had chosen to have himself painted and engraved with his hand flattening the poles of our earth, because he had been the leader of an earth-measuring expedition to Lapland which had demonstrated the truth of Newton's theory that our globe must be an oblate spheroid. That was actually neither a discovery nor an invention, but Maupertuis certainly exploited it as if neither Columbus nor Galileo had done as much.

Voltaire had helped him reach his present position by recommending him to Frederick, but at the same time had poked fun at him (in *Micromégas*) for his pomposity and had not been surprised to see him marry into one of the most ancient and noble families of Prussia. Just like Maupertuis! The ambitious climber. Taking every advantage. Of science. Of women. What difference, so long as the way was up?

Recently he had proudly enunciated a new theory of least action, according to which nature always works with the most economical expenditure of material and forces.

König, a mathematician and a member of the Royal Academy, opposed the president in this matter, declaring that he had already argued against this same theory when it was propounded many years ago by Leibnitz, who had since died. König opposed it now on the selfsame grounds: Such a theory of least action was backed up by absolutely no experimental evidence. How, indeed, would you go about proving it?

Maupertuis felt himself affronted in his dignity, not so much because his theory might be invalid as because his theory was declared to be old and already once rejected. He challenged König to produce evidence that Leibnitz had anticipated him.

König thereupon displayed a letter by Leibnitz wherein the theory was in fact discussed.

"This letter is not an original," said Maupertuis. "How do I know it is genuine?"

"It is not the original letter," König admitted. "But it is a true copy of a letter by Leibnitz. A letter since lost or destroyed."

"An obvious fraud!" cried Maupertuis. Though nothing was really less obvious in this era when the letters of great thinkers were often spread around in copies. Nevertheless, Maupertuis declared that if the original could not be found it was for a very simple reason: there had never been any such letter. The supposed copy produced by Kö-nig was a falsification.

Thereupon, exerting the power he had as president of the Royal Academy, he had König denounced as a forger. A motion to expel was proposed and quickly voted upon and passed.

König, an old man, suddenly found himself pilloried before all scientific Europe as a charlatan.

Surely the King will remedy this matter, thought Voltaire. For certainly here was a matter causing more ugly gossip in the gazettes of Europe than ever did his speculations in Saxon bonds. Besides, far more was involved. Not just money, but the life and reputation of an honest man. Furthermore, Voltaire admitted he was a speculator, but König denied he was a forger.

Why, then, wasn't the King angry with Maupertuis, as once he had been with Voltaire, for overstepping the boundaries of good taste? Was it because Maupertuis was now allied with the best blood of Prussia? Was it because Maupertuis was the president of the Royal Academy of Sciences? And everything Prussian must be defended, just like the fatherland? Right or wrong.

As the King continued to remain silent, Voltaire wrote a little anonymous piece for a local periodical, defending König. The result was an anonymous reply attacking the anonymous Voltaire, but with such poor arguments that it was given short shrift by the critics, whereupon it reappeared as a pamphlet, still anonymous but with a scepter, an eagle and a crown so prominently displayed on the title page that there could be no doubt as to who stood behind Maupertuis. This time the critics kept a respectful silence.

And supposedly Voltaire would also know enough to keep his mouth shut.

So this is the land that boasts of freedom of thought under a philosopher-king, Voltaire said to himself. He wrote to his niece, then still in Paris, "Unfortunately I'm a writer, too. And the King and I now find ourselves on opposite sides in this Maupertuis matter. He has his scepter. But I have my pen. And the goose quill I sharpen is such that I could make even Plato ridiculous."

Ridicule, yes, that was the weapon that was required in this case. And the whole massive army of the house of Hohenzollern was going to prove powerless to stop Voltaire from killing Maupertuis with laughter.

Maupertuis had recently published a volume of letters, where he advanced all sorts of seemingly bold scientific suggestions. Voltaire, perusing it, was struck not only by the stupidity of these suggestions but also by the feeling that he had run across these same foolish ideas before. Sure enough, they were also to be found in Maupertuis's *Collected Works*. Except that there they were not in the form of letters.

That was all Voltaire needed in order to let the air out of this bombast who copied from his own works to make a series of letters written to no one in particular, and then put the letters together in a volume just for the sake of having his name on still another publication.

Voltaire's *Diatribe of Dr. Akakia,* physician to the Pope, was the result.

Says Dr. Akakia: "Not for one moment do I accuse the president of the Royal Academy of having written these letters. One can tell at a glance that they were written by some student impersonating him. Because the president is also the well-known author of the theory of least action, according to which nature always works with the utmost economy, and he would therefore certainly want to economize the time of his few readers, sparing them the ordeal of reading the same stuff twice, once in his *Works* and then again in his *Letters*."

News of Voltaire's writing a diatribe under the name Dr. Akakia, a diatribe against Maupertuis, soon spread, and the King summoned him to warn him that he would not permit any attacks upon the head of his Royal Academy.

"Then into the fire it goes," said Voltaire lightly, and with a careless gesture he cast his manuscript into the fire of the hearth. And stood there smilingly watching the flames lick at it.

"Oh, but I must read it first!" Frederick cried. Because his avidity for Voltaire's works was still as strong as ever. Quickly he snatched the pages from the flames, singeing his cuffs in the process.

And almost at once he started to laugh. And as he read on into the enumeration of all the pseudoscientific follies proposed by Maupertuis, his laughter increased.

There was, for example, Maupertuis's scheme for establishing a city where nothing but classical Latin would be spoken, no other language even permitted. For Maupertuis had noticed what everyone notices, namely the facility with which foreigners coming to Paris pick up French and are soon proficient in it. With such a Latin city in Europe, those who wished their sons to have a good education would simply send them to live for a year or two in the new Rome. They would come out fine Latinists.

Says the *Diatribe* in this connection: "When we made the proposal

211

that a Latin-speaking city be established, we realized, of course, that even washwomen and street cleaners in that town would have to become proficient in Latin. And we also realized that once these men and women had perfected themselves in the Ciceronian tongue, they would then object to remaining mere washwomen and street cleaners and would feel themselves entitled to be professors. Yes, we realized all that. But who cares about clean shirts? The Romans didn't wear any shirts at all. And who cares about cooks and so forth? Our pupils and professors will get along without."

"No, this must never be printed!" Frederick cried, laughing until the tears rolled down his cheeks. "Maupertuis is destroyed if this ever sees the light of day."

And he went on reading.

Among other Maupertuis suggestions was the one for a hole to be dug to the center of the earth to learn the nature of our globe.

Says the *Diatribe:* "With respect to the hole that we wished to dig to the center of the earth, we must hereby renounce this project. For we can't find a single sovereign in all of Europe who will let us open up such a hole within his boundaries. This is because the hole would have to be quite big around to accommodate the hundreds of thousands of workmen required to push the job to completion, four thousand miles deep. And the dirt that would be dug out would naturally have to be put somewhere, and if it were spread around it would bury the kingdom in which it was situated. All Germany for example. And with Germany buried, what would become of the balance of power in Europe?"

And, still laughing, Frederick went through to the final "scientific" notion of Maupertuis, his recent strange conclusion that if the original of a copy couldn't be produced, then it must, ipso facto, be a forgery.

Says the *Diatribe:* "Even though we have posited that whenever the original of a document does not exist the matter must evidently be a forgery, it goes without saying that in maintaining this we do not mean to cast any doubts upon those other well-known copies the originals of which also do not exist—I refer to the foundations of all our sacred religions—and that anyone presenting the Bible as true ought therefore to be expelled as a forger . . ."

This really shook Frederick with such laughter that his bones threatened to become dislocated.

"Oh, never, never," he said, "must this infamous thing appear in print."

"Your Majesty is so right," said Voltaire, and, taking his manuscript back, he threw it once more into the flames. Still smiling.

"Ah, but that doesn't mean you should destroy it!" the King cried. And once again he snared it out of the fire. "I'll keep this with those other unprintable works of yours," he said. "With your *Virgin*. And your *Essay on Manners*."

And he put it into the drawer of his desk.

"Your Majesty honors me," said Voltaire. He let the King imagine that this was his only copy. But of course he had another one. Naturally.

And he intended to get the King's signature for printing it. Because without the King's signature nothing could be printed in this land of freedom of thought. "You can think what you like," said Voltaire. "And write it down too. But print it? No."

Recently Lord Bolingbroke, favorite of Queen Anne and statesman of the peace of Utrecht, had died, and on all sides priests and ministers were belaboring his memory because of his antireligious views. Voltaire felt called upon to defend a man who had shown him many favors in years past. So he wrote a *Defense of Milord Bolingbroke*.

There was no problem in getting the King's signature to that. It was the kind of attack on religion that Frederick admired. Nor was there any great problem in slipping the *Akakia* into the approved pages in such a way that the printer would print both works without realizing that the signature of the King applied only to one of them.

Somehow Frederick found out and had the whole edition seized. And immediately summoned Voltaire. Who, of course, played his usual role of astounded innocence.

"Who would dare do such a thing?" Voltaire cried. "One of my miserable copyists, no doubt. The scoundrel shall suffer for this!"

Frederick stared at Voltaire with cold contempt. "Don't lie to me," he said sternly. He opened a door, and in stepped the printer.

Voltaire, seeing that everything was discovered, threw himself on his knees and pleaded for mercy.

But the King spurned him with his foot. "There's only one thing I want to hear from your lips, and then I want to hear no more. And this time I want the truth."

"The truth! The truth!" Voltaire promised.

"Have I got every copy this time?"

"Every copy! I swear!"

"You have not a single copy? Printed or manuscript?"

"Not a single copy!" Voltaire cried. "My honor."

But he said nothing of the fact that he could sit down and write the whole thing from memory. After all, it was only ten thousand words or so, which Voltaire had written once and could write again.

Besides, that wasn't even necessary. He had already smuggled out copies to printers in Leipzig and in Amsterdam.

And before long printed *Akakia*s were actually on sale in Berlin bookstores, sneaked in from abroad.

It was as if Voltaire were saying, "Wouldn't it have been better, Sire, if you had not tried to stop ideas? If you had adhered to your bold program of freedom?"

But the King now really lost his head. He stooped to the methods of the Inquisition.

One morning, Voltaire, who, in disfavor again, was living at the time in Berlin, saw certain remarkable proceedings taking place out on the street. With his weak eyes he could not quite make them out.

"What is that?" he asked his secretary Collini.

"Why, that's the hangman," said Collini. "There's a crowd gathered around him. He is about to perform an execution. But there's something strange about it. The victim is not a man. It's a book. A slender pamphlet. The hangman is now ripping up the pages. There's a fire being built. Evidently they are going to burn the culprit after they are through torturing him."

"I'll wager they are burning my *Akakia*," said Voltaire.

And he wondered out loud, "Will the next step be to burn the author?" No. That would be entirely too humiliating an end to Voltaire. Imagine! Voltaire burned at the stake, in Prussia, the land of freedom of thought, under a philosopher-king.

"Such a death would be a disgrace I could never live down," he said. And he recalled how eighteen years before, in Paris, his *Philosophical Letters* had been ripped to pieces and then burned by the public hangman at the foot of the great staircase of the Palais de Justice.

Burned in effigy. That shouldn't have struck such fear into Voltaire. But only thirty years ago, in Spain, when the fourteen-year-old daughter of the Duke d'Orléans had gone to Madrid to become the bride of the future King of Spain, Don Louis, nine heretics had been burned alive in her honor while the Princess looked on.

Voltaire might say in jest, "That black smoke now rising from my *Akakia*, that must be the nasty soul of Maupertuis taking wing," but he could not forget how recently men had really been burned at the stake, and how little it might take to provoke the authorities into a return to this practice.

How far might even the liberal Frederick go in his attempts to frighten his subjects away from those *Akakia* pamphlets that continued to flow in from all the foreign presses?

As Frederick saw himself losing this battle, he sent an angry note to Voltaire: "So you think you have pulled the wool over my eyes? That is an impudence which I certainly never expected from you. Your works may still merit statues of you in every land of this earth. But your conduct is such that chains for life would not be enough!"

And immediately upon the note came Count von Fredersdorf, the King's personal adjutant, with a demand that Voltaire surrender his chamberlain's golden key and his cross of merit, those decorations that Frederick had bestowed upon Voltaire with his own hands.

Voltaire immediately removed the golden insignia from his caved-in chest and handed them to the Count. But then he said, "One moment, my dear Fredersdorf."

And he sat down and, with that talent of his which was always at his immediate command, wrote this bit of verse:

> Je les reçus avec tendresse,
> Je vous les rends avec douleur;
> C'est ainsi qu'un amant dans son extrême ardeur
> Rend le protrait de sa maîtresse.

Voltaire wept as he wrote those lines, and Frederick must have wept when he read them. For it was exactly as the verses said: a lover was returning the portrait of his beloved. The long romance between the King and the poet was over. Frederick had proved himself too much of a poet. Voltaire, too much a king.

For many months the King was unwilling to let Voltaire leave. Was there not a chance for a reconciliation? The King even sent back Voltaire's decorations. But still the poet asked for his permit to depart. Eventually, forced to recognize that if they could not live together, it was only right that they should be permitted to live apart, the King gave him permission to leave.

That's when that rascal of a Voltaire committed his final treachery toward the King. But what else could Voltaire do? Could he say to the King of Prussia, "Look here! I don't trust you. You have in your possession certain dangerous manuscripts of mine. If you should have those published I might be declared a traitor in France. And my fortune there might be confiscated."

No. You can't say that sort of thing to a king. And if the King himself will not think of the matter, then you have no other recourse but to steal from the King something that the King would not want to see published.

What Voltaire stole—or forgot to return when he packed to leave—

was a volume of poetry by Frederick. Perhaps that monarch's *Palladion*. Or else a collection of verses. In any case, a volume that had been specially printed in an edition of only two or, at the most, three copies. For the work of a reigning monarch is not generally meant to be tossed out into the public arena for the raging lions of criticism to tear to pieces. Frederick's writings might too easily be parodied. His verses were sometimes atrocious. They were often loaded with tactless political allusions.

With this volume hidden in one of his crates of books and sent out of the country, Voltaire felt that he held the same club over Frederick that Frederick held over him. The King would not dare publish Voltaire's bold *Essay on Manners,* nor his obscene *La Pucelle*.

Both men thus had the right now to feel themselves safe in a truce of equal strength.

Except that a Frederick, King of Prussia, the conquering monarch of his era, was not disposed to permit himself to remain in the power of a Voltaire.

Voltaire himself seems to have been unaware of Frederick's fury. At any rate, he felt that once outside Prussia he was secure. He failed to realize just how dominant Frederick had become in all the little principalities of Germany.

Frankfurt, for example, was a free city. Its freedom was guaranteed by the laws of the Holy Roman Empire, which Voltaire had said was neither holy nor Roman nor an empire. Still, the Empire did exist, and Francis I was its Emperor. And Frankfurt was a free city within that Empire. But the local authorities felt themselves powerless compared to the Prussian resident there. Who behaved as he pleased and thus was the real ruler.

And thus, one morning, when Voltaire awoke in his room at the Inn of the Golden Lion in Frankfurt, he found himself a prisoner in the hands of Prussian Resident Freytag. He had to surrender the Prussian decorations once again. And then he was asked for the book of poems.

Poems? The Devil only knew where the King's poems were. In some crate or other of his books. They were packed and waiting somewhere. A man like himself, with a great library, didn't travel with all his books.

Despite Voltaire's protests, the resident took eight hours to go through every bit of baggage that Voltaire had, examining every scrap of paper. And when the poems still couldn't be found, the resident declared that they would wait until Voltaire produced them.

Voltaire wrote a violent letter to the Emperor. With no result.

He was guarded so closely that even when he went to use his chamber pot he found himself surrounded by German guards. Watching him sharply from every side.

Voltaire exploded at such indignity.

When his niece, Madame Denis, arrived from Paris, she was included a prisoner along with her uncle. And even when the guilty crate finally arrived from Leipzig and the book of poems was surrendered, the two were still not released.

"I have to send the book to His Majesty," the resident said, "and wait for his orders."

Voltaire screamed to the authorities of Frankfurt, "What, here on free soil the King of Prussia rules?"

The authorities shrugged.

"These hands," Voltaire mourned, "that the King has kissed a hundred times over in admiration of their talent, he has now loaded with chains!"

At length Frederick's order arrived. He had no further reason to detain Voltaire.

And still they couldn't leave!

What now?

"Your bill!" said the owner of the Golden Lion.

Voltaire jumped. What? He must pay for his prison? No, that he would never do! Let the King of Prussia pay for it. Or the local authorities who had refused to interfere with his illegal imprisonment. Let them pay.

But in the end he had to pay. He left Frankfurt, his mouth full of curses.

And still the scepter was not satisfied. Now that Frederick had his poems and was safe, he was ready to deal his antagonist a really punishing blow. He had Voltaire's *Essay on Manners* published in Paris.

At once there arose from Church and State in France an outcry of rage against Voltaire. An outcry so violent that Voltaire realized that any notion of going back to Paris was finished for the time being. And perhaps forever.

Even his fortune stood for a while in danger of confiscation.

What was so terrible about this *Essay on Manners*—this book that Voltaire had written years ago as instruction for his mistress the Marquise du Châtelet?

Nothing. Nothing at all. Except that for the first time in history the story of mankind had been told by one to whom kings and conquerors were no more than brigands and receivers of stolen goods. To whom the only thing that counted was the advance of mankind under the leadership of its discoverers, scientists, artists and poets. An advance to which popes and priests and military leaders had contributed little, if anything, according to Voltaire.

Voltaire's enemies took care that a marked copy of this work should be put before the eyes of Louis XV. The King read a few lines and was outraged. The business of historians was to tell the glory of kings, and not to trace the history of the human mind!

The Queen went so far as to tear a copy to pieces with her own august hands.

There was no telling what might have happened if the French authorities had been able to lay hands on Voltaire at this moment. It was, to be sure, an era of caprice. An era in which much was forgiven if only one went about it with grace and wit. Even the Chevalier de Rohan-Chabot had cried out when his men were beating Voltaire, "Careful of that head! Something good may yet come out of it!"

Cleverness was respected by all.

But the danger was always there. Long ago an important official of the French police had written a secret memorandum on Voltaire: "This man must be locked up where he can never have pen, paper, ink for the rest of his life. Voltaire is capable of bringing down an empire in ruins."

Twice already he had gone to the Bastille. And twice had managed to get out. More fortunate in this than his lesser-known contemporary Lenglet du Fresnoy, who went to the Bastille four times, for a total of eight years, generally for the most oblique derogatory references to the government.

Or Imbert. For daring to say that the King of Spain was a poor huntsman. Because Louis XV was convinced that, in saying this, Imbert was only taking a roundabout way of implying that it was the King of France who was a poor huntsman.

Or the Abbé de Saint-Pierre, who for a modest criticism of Louis XIV was expelled from the Academy. His life ruined. And the same with La Bletterie, for a single word in praise of Julian the Apostate.

And yet in general nothing much happened to most men of letters. Some short incarcerations, a bit of exile, or even nothing at all.

Why?

Because, as Abbé Galiani put it, "Eloquence today is the art of saying everything without going to the Bastille."

There was an art to it.

Voltaire's play *Mahomet* was certainly not a criticism of Mohammedan fanaticism. And people everywhere quickly pointed out that the three syllables of "Jesus Christ" could be substituted in all lines for "Mahomet" without injury to the rhythm. Montesquieu's ridicule of France was supposedly the work of Persian visitors to Paris. Others wrote of China or Peru.

It was all sleight-of-hand. A battle of deviousness. A tangle of pseudonyms. Voltaire used over a hundred and fifty of them. Works printed in Paris were marked "London." Or "Amsterdam." Or "The Hague." The government knew it. To stop it would throw too many printers and binders and publishers out of work. But lest the practice become too flagrant, a printer or two would be packed off to prison. Or a couple of professors. To warn the bigger names that there was a limit to the government's patience.

And so the battle went on. All the ancient practices of man gradually coming under the light of reason. And the public watching with excitement this process of enlightenment.

In this game of cat and mouse, everything was forbidden to the mice. And yet everything was said. One only had to know how to say it.

"Let's talk about an elephant," said Duclos one day. "It's the only big subject that's safe." He had said nothing and yet everything. And the phrase was quoted by everyone.

Everybody was telling stories about highwaymen one evening after dinner. Came Voltaire's turn: "There was once a government tax collector . . . Sorry, but I've forgotten the rest." He had said nothing and yet everything. And the story was repeated everywhere.

What could the government do? To attack such squibs was to render its authority ridiculous.

Before publication Voltaire would always claim to have heard of this or that priest, or some other completely respectable person, who had written a book about this or that. He would write letters asking that a copy be sent to him as soon as this author published it. And upon receipt of his own work he would attack it mercilessly.

Then he felt safe.

Diderot had for a while worked the following trick. Before publication he would run to the police, crying, "I've been robbed!"

It was already an old story to the magistrate. "What, again?"

"Yes, your honor. Again."

"And once more all your manuscripts stolen?" the bored magistrate would ask.

"Yes, yes. Everything."

And when the offending work appeared, Diderot could claim, "Thieves did it. My manuscript was stolen and was printed in mutilated form. My enemies are trying to get me into trouble." While at the same time taking bows for his book in private.

Finally the police magistrate had to say to him, "I forbid you ever to be robbed again!"

"How can you forbid me?" Diderot spluttered. "Tell that to the thieves!"

"That's an order!" the magistrate shouted. "I'll see to it that you go to jail if you are ever robbed again!"

Diderot had to think up a new scheme.

If Voltaire spent so much time accumulating wealth, it was because he knew that financial independence was the best protection of all. With so many men in high places occasionally in need of his money, he could always count on support somewhere whenever he was in hot water. And for that reason he was generally the most daring of all.

But at the same time the most easily frightened. For he trembled not only for his personal safety, but also for that of his huge fortune.

But as reason began to penetrate into more and more minds, the government itself became honeycombed with traitors working for enlightenment. And such an important man as Malesherbes, for example, censor of books for the government, himself managed to protect a whole clique of philosophers.

To Diderot he once whispered, "Hide everything. Your place is about to be ransacked by the police."

"But where can I hide my things? I have no room," Diderot said.

"Bring everything to my home," said Malesherbes.

Yes, it was a game. And a matter for laughter to see the big cat seemingly unable to catch the little mice. But Voltaire never forgot that behind the velvet paws were the claws of steel.

And every once in a while the government became irritated and reminded its subjects that, reason or no reason, the century-old laws were still in force. And an author who stirred up the people might be burned along with his book. As for the Church, it not only could still execute people for lack of proper respect for religion, but it was shortly to have a young man's head cut off for failing to remove his hat when a religious procession went by.

The fist of fanaticism still ruled.

No wonder Voltaire was sick with fright when his *Essay on Manners* came out in Paris. The repercussions were so great that in Colmar, where Voltaire happened to be staying, he was threatened with imprisonment, the Jesuits being very powerful there.

As quickly as he could lay hands on a copy he compared it to what he claimed was his true manuscript. He called in notaries to observe that his version was twice as long. And that many passages had obviously been mutilated by the printer.

The notaries drew up a list of such mutilations and Voltaire spread copies of it far and wide. It showed that where he had, for example, written, "Historians resemble those tyrants of whom they write, in that they sacrifice the human race to an individual," a perfectly innocent sentence criticizing no one but historians and tyrants, someone had substituted the line "Kings sacrifice the human race to a caprice."

"See?" Voltaire was crying to the world. "My enemies are trying to make it appear that I am the enemy of kings. But it isn't so."

He even went to church in Colmar. Confessed and communed. And sent a gift to the monks who had assisted him. And made sure that the news was spread throughout Europe.

"See?"Voltaire cried to the world. "I have nothing against the Church. It is my enemies who wish to make it appear so."

Voltaire expected that his *La Pucelle,* of which Frederick had a copy, would also be published soon. And indeed it was. But already Voltaire had anticipated it by spreading around a hundred or more different manuscript versions filled with the crudest obscenities in bad versification, which no one with any sense could attribute to such a polished writer as Voltaire. With the result that to this day no one knows for sure the true version of the poem. But at any rate in his own day no one could legally accuse him of being the author of the printed one. There were too many different copies around.

Voltaire thus managed to protect himself from financial ruin. But he was not allowed back in Paris. Madame de Pompadour did her best, but Louis XV said curtly, "I do not wish to see Voltaire in Paris." And that was that.

Thus Frederick had amply demonstrated who was the more powerful of the two. Who had deprived Voltaire of his office? Who had deprived him of his honors and decorations? Who had had him arrested, even in a free city beyond the boundaries of Prussia? Imprisoned him there and held him for as long as he chose? And then barred him from France? Or, at any rate, from Paris. Who had put Voltaire in jeopardy of life, liberty and fortune?

And yet, for all that, no one was fooled. Everyone knew who had won the battle between the scepter and the pen.

The proof of it was Maupertuis. In spite of the King's protection, he was a destroyed man. Haunted by that Voltairean invention Dr. Akakia, physician to the Pope. Maupertuis's authority as a scientist was finished. He was unable to ascend the rostrum of the Royal Academy of Prussia, because in front of him he could read on every face the strain of a suppressed smile.

It was clear that, secretly, they were all laughing at him.

For a while Maupertuis raved about murdering Voltaire. Which evoked from the fleeing Voltaire (for even while he was running away from Frederick he did not stop his duel) some humorous advertisements that ran like wildfire through the periodicals of Europe. Voltaire offering a reward for the capture of this would-be maniacal assassin, recognizable by his scalpel (because another of Maupertuis's unfortunate notions was that the giants of Patagonia might be dissected in an effort to locate the seat of the human soul), the reward to be paid in diamonds and gold (because still another one of Maupertuis's scientific notions was that comets might be composed of diamonds and gold and might someday shower the earth with these minerals).

In the end, surrounded on all sides by ridicule, Maupertuis was stricken with a congestion of the chest. He went to recuperate at a health resort, but, finding no alleviation, he soon retired to Bern, to live with the famous mathematical family of the Bernouillis, turning very pious and expiring a few years later in the arms of two monks.

In a sense he had been killed. By nothing but a feather. The deadliest feather in Europe! Voltaire's goose quill.

17: ADAM AND EVE
WITH DIRTY FINGERNAILS

Such was the famous and dangerous Voltaire whom the Genevans were now welcoming into their city. Rejoicing as the Trojans had done when they had dragged in the wooden horse. Geneva, that city which so recently Rousseau had hoped to preserve as an exhibit of primitive happiness, as a model and a lesson to all the world. And which Voltaire had now captured without even half trying.

But at last, after months of waiting, came the news that Rousseau had been hoping for: Dr. Tronchin had succeeded in having the Council approve Jean Jacques for the post of librarian. Along with a very modest honorarium. Twelve hundred francs. A pittance, really. And at the same time a gentleman of the city was willing to let M. Rousseau occupy a little villa which was on the border of the lake.

So they were now giving him that post! Wasn't that just too wonderful for words? A bit of a villa and a modest little salary. Had they given it to him months ago, yes, gladly would he have accepted it. But now? What did they expect him to do? Rush to Geneva and underline for all the world the vast inequality between the reception they had accorded him and the one they had given Voltaire in that city of equality? And he a citizen and a Calvinist, Voltaire a foreigner and a Catholic!

What did they imagine he would do now in Geneva? Go and crane his neck, perhaps, along with other gaping simpletons, watching the notables of Geneva flocking to Voltaire's supper parties? Notables riding in their carriages despite the ban against the vehicles proclaimed by Calvin?

Did they imagine he would join in the crush of coachmen, lackeys and footmen gazing from the outside through the windows of Voltaire's château at the brightness and gaiety within, so that he could eavesdrop on Voltaire passing out flowery compliments to his rich Genevan guests? Lauding their politeness and their culture. Telling them that all they lacked was just one single thing to make their city as attractive as Paris: the theater.

Too bad, wasn't it, that ancient laws should still prevent Geneva from having a theater. There was really nothing like the stage to give men and women that final polish, that grace and that tact, those little elegancies of style that are the last word in artistic refinement and that in the end mark off your truly metropolitan person from the provincial.

Something of that sort, from Voltaire, would no doubt be the cue for Madame Denis to say that surely no one could refuse her uncle the privilege of a little theatrical in his own home. At least the recitation of some lines from his most recent play, *Orphan of China,* about to open in Paris, along with a reprise of his *Alzire.* Or some lines from his *Mahomet,* which he was dedicating to the Pope. Or from that perennial favorite of his, *Zaïre;* Voltaire loved especially the role of old Lusignan, the ancient Crusader, and could recite this part so movingly that he never failed to draw tears from his audience.

Wasn't it too sad for words that this great playwright who had enriched French literature with so many masterpieces should now be barred from ever seeing the production of his own plays? Forced to live in a city without a theater? Was it not like the fate of Belisarius, who, after conquering Italy for his Emperor Justinian, was punished by having his eyes gouged out and being forced in his old age to beg for a living?

And as Voltaire recited his verses, many Genevans wiped away tears.

While Madame Denis would find this an appropriate moment to slip away and come back with a couple of lackeys loaded with colorful costumes, which she would spill out in front of the guests. Theatrical costumes. Just arrived from Paris. Have you ever seen anything more resplendent? And another shipment still due!

In a moment she would have picked out some elaborate robe right out of *The Thousand and One Nights* and, wrapping it around herself, would begin to play opposite her uncle. Interrupting herself, however, to beg her guests not to be shy, but to select whatever costumes they preferred for themselves and make suggestions as to what parts they would like to play. And then, later, they would lay plans for a real theatrical evening.

The young Genevans would be dizzy with the prospect. But the elders would find it proper to look severe. While Madame Denis would go on prattling, telling what delightful times they would have, especially when the greatest French actor came to visit them and joined in the festivities.

What? The greatest French actor was coming to Geneva? To visit Voltaire? Not the great Lekain?

Why not? Who had put Lekain on the stage if not Voltaire? Hadn't Voltaire seen him once displaying a snuffbox, and, struck by his gracefulness, hadn't he cried out, "What? You sell snuffboxes when there is not a single actor on the French stage who can put such beauty into his gestures?" Yes, Lekain himself was expected. And of course they were all invited to meet him.

Such amiability! How could one resist it? And before one could tell how it had happened, the Calvinists were ready to succumb to the corruption of the stage.

But what would the ministers say?

"They'll be against it," Voltaire could assure them. The church may at times tolerate the theater, but it can never really approve of it. Why not? Well, imagine a man who sees, let us say, ten plays a year. And in

224

that same year hears twenty or even fifty sermons. How many plays will he be able to recall at the end of the year? And how many sermons?

Is there any doubt that he will easily recall every play he has seen? And have trouble remembering even a single sermon?

"With my plays," Voltaire felt that he could assert, "I have preached better sermons, and to more people, than any minister or priest. Why, then, shouldn't Calvinists see my plays? Am I so evil compared to Calvin? Have I banished people for daring to disagree with me, the way Calvin banished Bolsec, banished Okin, banished any number of people? Tell me, whose head have I cut off, the way Calvin had Gruet's head struck off? Whom have I burned at the stake, the way Calvin had Servetus burned, the way he had Berthelier executed? And how many others?"

And he would add quietly, as if not wishing to be overheard, "I'm a better man than your Calvin." And he would smile maliciously.

Really, he threatened to twist Geneva around his little finger.

Yes, wild and bitter must have been the thoughts of Rousseau when he gave up all his plans for Geneva, turned down the librarianship and wrote in his notebook, "The rich! They hold the law in their well-filled wallets! While the poor man must sell his freedom for a crust of bread."

Not that Rousseau himself wanted to be rich. Oh, yes, he dreamed of it now and then for a moment, his imagination conjuring up mythical millions. Only to reject them almost immediately.

"Suppose I could have bougies made of gold," he once wrote to a correspondent in Geneva. "Could I piss any better?"

He was once and for all destined to be poor. But why did he have to be defeated too? And defeated by a man who was not even trying to defeat him. A defeat so humiliating to his pride that he would not even acknowledge it.

He pretended that it was Madame d'Épinay who was preventing him from going to Geneva. He pretended that it was her entreaties, her friendship, her assiduities, that were keeping him from going to the city of his birth, where he longed to be, where happiness awaited him.

He pretended that in order to hold him near herself she had remodeled a cottage on her estate into a commodious home, with five rooms with kitchen, pantry, cellar, vegetable garden and orchard. As well as a forest in which to stroll. And had offered him all that as an inducement.

And that he had succumbed.

After all, he had often spoken of something of this sort. A retreat. A hermitage. Where he could enjoy solitude and work hard. Where he would be surrounded by nature. And yet not too far from Paris, so that his friends, Diderot, Grimm and so forth, could visit him now and then.

And there it was. Conjured out of the ground for him.

And for that he gave up Geneva.

Lies! He gave up Geneva on account of Voltaire. But he refused to say so. Only later, much later, in his *Confessions,* would he write:

I sensed at once that that man would cause a revolution in Geneva. And that everything I hated in Paris, everything that was surely driving me out of that city, its dissipations and its shallow pretences, its airs and mannerisms —all that would soon pervade my native country.

But what could I do about it? Engage in a struggle with Voltaire? How could I? I, such a poor speaker, so timid and, furthermore, so alone. Against that man with his brilliant eloquence, his wealth and his arrogance, and backed up as he was by all the notables who had welcomed him with such spontaneous enthusiasm. Already he was the idol of the younger set of the city.

I did not even dare go near Geneva again. I knew that if I went there I would be forced to choose between two equally disagreeable and, indeed, for me impossible courses. Either I would have to resign myself in the most cowardly fashion to this Voltairean revolution and thus convict myself of bad citizenship or I would have to put up a fight, which would exhibit me as an insufferable pedant.

And that wasn't entirely true, either. For Jean Jacques still so admired and worshiped this man whom he hated that no sooner was his *Discourse on Inequality* off the press than he hastened to send a copy to Dr. Tronchin in Geneva, begging him to convey it, with his respects, to M. de Voltaire.

Voltaire accepted it with a smile. When he had a spare moment he would open it up and have another laugh at that idiot. But when he did, he found himself in no mood for laughter. This was really going too far. This was beyond laughter. Here was dangerous and fanatic nonsense!

And the nerve of him! To send such stuff to him, to Voltaire, who had just published two volumes called *Essay on Manners,* which, no matter how mutilated, still expressed his abiding conviction that there was nothing that man had done on this earth of which he had any right to be proud except this one thing called civilization.

Did this little Rousseau really expect to persuade Voltaire that, on the contrary, it was civilization that had been the ruin of man?

In his *Essay* Voltaire had lauded man's power to reason. "He who thinks," he had written, "makes others think." And now Rousseau dared write, "The man who meditates is depraved." What? Thought was a depravity for which man should blush?

Voltaire's anger rose to such a pitch that he seized his pen and made a violent slashing stroke across the page.

And then he began racing through the rest of it. Scribbling a furious comment in the margin: "Rotten logic!" And again: "Fool! How you blow up and distort everything!" And then: "Pitiful!" "Absurd!" "Abominable!"

And where Jean Jacques declaimed against our modern "eagerness to get ourselves talked about," Voltaire wrote, "Why, you monkey of a Diogenes! It's yourself you condemn!"

And so it went, down to the place where Rousseau accused the first man who ever put a fence around a piece of ground of being the cause of all wars and subsequent miseries of mankind. It was there that Voltaire wrote the words "What? The first man to cultivate a piece of ground, plant it, protect it . . . this benefactor of mankind was nothing but a thief? Now, there's philosophy for you, when penniless wretches take to writing it!"

Voltaire was about to toss the offensive little volume to his copyist, to have it flung back by mail right in the face of Rousseau. But he hesitated. He recalled another Rousseau: Jean Baptiste Rousseau, the poet. Now long dead.

How viciously Voltaire had attacked *that* Rousseau. Yes, viciously. But rightfully too. Imagine a hypocrite like that, pretending to break off his friendship with Voltaire because Voltaire had dared read to him a poem that offended his deep religious convictions! Religious convictions! What a lie! As if Jean Baptiste Rousseau had not himself written any number of irreligious poems!

And besides, Voltaire's poem, *For and Against*—that was not an irreligious poem, but, on the contrary, a very religious one, full of love and reverence for the Creator, only trying to clear away the tangle of superstitious nonsense that the Church insisted must be believed in as a precondition for any belief at all.

That was tyranny! Tyranny of the mind and the heart. The Church had no right to be a tyrant.

But of course it was rather devilish on Voltaire's part to revenge himself by adopting Jean Baptiste's own favorite style of versification, one in which Rousseau considered himself supreme, the style of Marot, and in that style write a poem against Rousseau: *La Crépinade,* a really damnable bit of poetry.

And a naked challenge to J. B. Rousseau: There! try and surpass that! Try even to equal it! Go ahead. Let's see how good a poet you are—you, supposedly the foremost poet of our day. Go ahead. Attack me. And I'm using your own favorite weapon. Your own preferred style. So as to make it all the easier for you to answer me.

J. B. Rousseau couldn't reply. But surely he must have tried. Oh, how he must have tried! How many sheets of paper he must have covered with his attempts to write a better poem than Voltaire's. He, the old and recognized Rousseau, who used to come as honored guest to the annual school exercises of the Collège Louis le Grand and give the poetry award to a thin, pathetic little boy with nothing but a pair of startling black eyes.

And now to have to admit to himself that he didn't have this boy's talent. And that until he could come up with something better than *La Crépinade,* he would have to publish nothing, lest everyone recognize his inferiority. Yes, he had to keep quiet. And die, choked up with the bitterness of his failure.

And so there the poem was. It existed. It was printed everywhere. And forever unrecallable now were those lines about Satan envious of God and determined to create a being, too. In his own image, "out of sulphurous mud, the water of the Styx, and gutter garbage."

> *Rien n'épargnait: il vous remplit la bête*
> *De fiel au coeur, et de vent dans la tête.*

"With bile in his heart and flatulence in his head." That's how Satan made Rousseau.

Nothing for Voltaire to be proud of, that poem. No, indeed. He himself had put a footnote to it in one of many collected editions, saying, "Too bad that M. de Voltaire, who until now could pride himself on never having used his talents to crush anyone, should have been willing to forgo that glorious distinction."

Sad. In particular that he should have gone so far as to title his poem *La Crépinade* and thus recall for those who knew the meaning of the word, or who knew the Rousseau family, that the poet's father had been nothing but a shoemaker, Crispin and Crispinian being the patron saints of the shoemakers' guild. That had been a foul blow.

But he was not to blame. It was the fault of those idiots who knew nothing and yet insisted on enraging him! There lay the blame! This new Rousseau, for example. This imbecile of a Jean Jacques Rousseau, known as "the little." Glorifying the good old days. Imagine! That old, old error revived. Hadn't Voltaire settled that stupidity years ago, in his poem *Le Mondain*—The Worldly-minded Man?

And how furiously the theologians had turned on him when that poem began to circulate. How they had castigated him. As if they could know any better than he did how Adam and Eve actually looked in Paradise. All Voltaire had done was use his reasoning powers. How do men and women look who for years are exposed naked to the sun and to insect bites and to dirt and bramble bushes? How do they look when for years there isn't a barber or a comb or a cake of soap or a pair of scissors around?

Of course Adam and Eve were dirty. Sticky with dirt. Smelly. And with long black fingernails, crooked and broken. And with their matted hair in disorder. Beasts. Despite all the old poetry and all the painters of pretty pictures.

And love? That first love between man and woman? Well, just imagine it for yourself.

> Sans propreté l'amour le plus heureux
> N'est plus l'amour, c'est un besoin honteux.

Who can doubt it? Where there's no cleanliness the most beautiful love is not really love, but just the satisfaction of a gross and shameful craving.

Oh, how the priests howled with rage at having their fanciful Paradise invaded by reason and logic. Not all the priests, of course. For their ranks were just as varied as those of any other group. Enlightenment had come to them too. And there were many of them who had had the courage to brave the fury of their ignorant parishioners by doing as much as, for instance, Bishop de Noailles, who had cast out of his church its most precious relic, the navel of Jesus Christ. Priests, in short, who, as much almost as Voltaire, believed that the Creator would not have given man the power to reason if He had not meant him to make good use of it.

And now here was this Jean Jacques, daring to say that thinking is a depravity! His kind of thinking—yes, *that* certainly was. Where, for example, was the merit of our ancestors in not knowing either mine or thine? It was neither unselfishness nor generosity on their part. Lacking all the bounties of useful articles that the arts and sciences have since given us—houses, furniture, clothes, foods, delights and comforts and joys of every kind—they had nothing to be selfish about.

But now it was different. And against the efforts of those who were always trying to get us to live as meagerly, as ascetically, as possible, as if there were some special merit in being poor and learning to do without, Voltaire had boldly proclaimed, "The superfluous, what a necessity it is!"

"Let others praise the age of gold," Voltaire said in his poem. "As for me, I love this age of iron." And he concluded with the forthright line, "Paradise, for me, is where I am. Here and now!"

Well, of course it was. Where else should Paradise be but here? And what era should one love if not one's own? How can one be alive today and yet be in love with some other time in the distant past? Why, that wasn't being alive at all. And a man who went through life dreaming of other times, that man might be said never really to have lived.

"Whoever is not of his own century is of no century at all," Voltaire had said. One had to love our today. One had to love it and at the same time work for a better tomorrow. So that our children might have even better reasons for cherishing and enjoying the world they would then live in.

Yes, to straighten out this stupid Jean Jacques, the kindest thing to do would be to send him back his book, with all of Voltaire's virulent marginal comments. That would shut him up! At any rate, it would warn him of the fate that was reserved for him if he didn't mend his ways. It would remind him of the fate of that other Rousseau. The fate of Maupertuis. And of how many others!

Still . . . And Voltaire hesitated again. There was such a thing as pity. . . .

Besides, this Jean Jacques—he couldn't really be that bad. Wasn't he, after all, the friend of both Diderot and d'Alembert, the editors of the big *Encyclopedia?* Wasn't he, if only in a minor capacity, associated with that great enterprise? In charge of the articles concerning music, and in addition writing on certain other subjects, such as political economy?

The man was obviously no utter idiot. In spite of his two essays. Or else he couldn't possibly be connected with that little band of men putting out this first great compilation of all human knowledge, with particular emphasis on the advance of the arts and sciences, a compilation being pushed out in the teeth of the fiercest opposition from every reactionary theologian and aristocrat in France. And indeed in the whole world.

No. There must be some good in him. And it would be a mistake to antagonize even a single member of their tiny group. And particularly he, Voltaire, who might be considered as the chief of the little army of the Enlightenment—he had no right to waste a single man.

And so, instead of sending back the book, Voltaire tucked it away on his shelves. To remain there until after his death, when, along with his books and papers, it became the possession of Empress Catherine the Great of Russia.

In its place Voltaire composed one of his gently malicious letters. Strewn with only enough pinpricks of irony to make his position clear. But otherwise full of the respect that one writer owes to another.

"I have received, my dear sir," Voltaire began, "your new book against the human race. Please accept my thanks for it."

Impossible to describe the mixed feelings with which Rousseau must have received this letter. Just think of it: a letter from Voltaire! At last. At long last. A letter waited for, dreamed about, schemed and prayed for, during all of twenty-five years. A lifetime given for a letter. Yes. And here it was finally, a long, full letter, not just one of those miserable scrawls such as he had twice received before.

But now? *Now* a letter from Voltaire, when his heart was so full of envy, rancor, hatred and contempt for that man. And still, in spite of it all, somehow his heart was ready to burst with joy. In the midst of his bitterness he felt like singing.

More disturbing than the receipt of the letter were its contents. Once again this elegant Voltairean mixture of flattery and irony, this clever concoction of respect and derogation. Flattering him with one hand while scorching him with the other. Treating him to ridicule and to admiration at one and the same time.

But still, there it was! A letter from Voltaire! And never, the master wrote, "never has a writer painted the horrors of our society in more powerful colors than your pen has achieved. Never has a writer employed so much intelligence in an effort to render us all stupid."

Yes, a letter from Voltaire. But perhaps it would have been better if it had never come. For these were words that Rousseau would have to answer. And how could he? He had no talent for this sort of thing. He did not know how to play this modern game of wit and counter-wit. He could not match this sort of cleverness with a cleverness of his own.

The best he could do was write, "It is, on the contrary, I, sir, who must thank you for your letter. Indeed, in offering you the rough draft of some of my sad reveries, I could not imagine that I was mak-

231

ing you a present worthy of your attention, but, rather, acquitting myself of a duty, rendering you the homage which all of us owe to you as our chief. The man who has pointed out to us the path to glory."

How heavy that was. How labored and pedestrian. While Voltaire's prose barely skimmed the paper. Like swallows darting over a pond. And nowhere in his paragraph a line that could equal Voltaire's "your new book against the human race," or his "never has a writer employed so much intelligence in an effort to render us all stupid." Thus pinking him with another paradox.

"Reading your work," Voltaire went on, "one is tempted to drop on all fours. But alas, it is sixty years since I gave up that habit, and I feel myself incapable of taking it up again. So I leave this more natural gait to those to whom it would be more fitting than either to you or to me.

"Nor can I set sail to join the savages of Canada. In the first place because my ill health keeps me chained here, near Europe's foremost doctor [Tronchin], and I should hardly be able to enjoy his like for professional assistance among Missouri Indians. And in the second place because there is now a war among those savages too [the French and Indian War, offshoot of the Seven Years' War of Europe]. For we Europeans have without doubt set those barbarians a bad example, turning them into creatures as wicked as ourselves. Grant me therefore the privilege of remaining a peaceful savage, here in this retreat that I have chosen, so close to your own country. And where you yourself ought to be."

The sarcasm of that "where you yourself ought to be" was not lost on Jean Jacques, who realized that Voltaire must know everything about his return to Calvinism and was taunting him now with still another paradox, that he, the lover of the simple life, was nevertheless remaining in Paris or near it, while he, Voltaire, the man of the world, had to take refuge, as a peaceful savage, near the walls of straight-laced Geneva.

But he could only reply, "I beg you to adorn the asylum you have chosen, M. de Voltaire. And since you know so well how to depict virtue and freedom, teach the Genevans to cherish these qualities within their walls. As all of us must cherish them in your works."

Once and for all. He was simply not of this century. This cat-and-mouse game was not for him.

While Voltaire continued in his sweet way, complaining gently of his travails, travails such as so many men who have worked for the betterment of mankind have had to endure—Descartes, Bayle, Galileo and so on.

"Nevertheless," Voltaire wrote, "we must continue to love literature, in spite of the abuses to which it is subject. Just as we must continue to love society, for all that the wicked may spoil its sweetness. As we must continue to love our country, even though it may treat us unjustly. And never stop loving and serving the Supreme Being, no matter how much our worship of him is dishonored by those who promulgate and enforce superstitions and fanaticisms."

It was in this delicate way that Voltaire hinted that Rousseau's hatred for the civilization of his day might arise from the long-standing envy of a neglected talent, turning in its chagrin against every aspect of his times.

Rousseau could only argue back that all our troubles came from "this fury that possesses us to know everything," such knowledge becoming like a "sword in our vitals," with which we must henceforth learn to live, since "to pull the sword out would kill us." But surely M. de Voltaire must realize that if this fury to know had never arisen, then "those who pretended to know that the earth didn't turn would never have punished Galileo for saying that it did."

But there was still Voltaire's final pinprick. Not so gentle, this one, as the others.

"M. Chappuis," Voltaire wrote, "informs me that your health is far from what could be desired. You must come and restore yourself in your native land. Come and enjoy our atmosphere of freedom. Come drink with me the milk of our Swiss cows. Browse on our good herbage."

The sting was in that word "our"! That really hurt. *Our* Swiss cows! *Our* good herbage! *Our* atmosphere of freedom!

Yes. It was true. He had a right to the word "our." It did all belong to him. To the rich Voltaire who would soon buy up one big property after another, until he would have four big estates in or on the borders of Switzerland. And now, as a kind host, inviting Rousseau to come and share with him.

Ah, no! This was more than one could bear.

And yet, what could he possibly say? It was an invitation. And it would never do for Voltaire to be able to show the world a gross and uncivilized answer from Rousseau. "I am sensible to your invitation," he was forced to write. "And if this winter should leave me still capable of traveling, I shall, this spring, go to live in my native country and there profit from your kindnesses."

And so their letters closed in that polite and lying form that Rousseau so despised: "I am, very philosophically and with my tenderest esteem, your most humble servant, Voltaire." Compelling Jean Jacques, despite everything, to subscribe himself as Voltaire's most humble servant, too, "with all my heart and all my respect."

Worse was to come! Voltaire was to ask Rousseau for permission to have both letters printed. What, the whole world was to be invited to see how poor a match he was for the master?

But how could he refuse?

It happened that Voltaire was about to publish his recent big success *Orphan of China,* a play that had created a sensation (was there anything this man ever did that was not a sensation?) because for the first time a French dramatist was drawing upon a Chinese source for his tragedy (the thirteenth-century *Orphan of the Chao Family*), and Chinese characters in startling costumes were walking the Paris stage.

The play being short, Voltaire suggested to the publisher that he round out the volume with his letter to Rousseau and the latter's reply. And a few days later the November issue of the *Mercure de France* also carried the letters.

The contrast between his own cumbersome and humorless prose and Voltaire's sparkling style oppressed Rousseau and seemed to him to call for some sort of excuse or explanation, which he thought to furnish by writing a tirade against the editor of the *Mercure,* accusing him of having turned his letter into a meaningless jumble by incompetent proofreading.

But now the unexpected: the letters were a startling success!

Voltaire's, with its delicate malice, of course far more so than Rousseau's. But still, there they were. Together. Rousseau's beside that of the master. Sharing the honors. Voltaire showing his minuscule rival the greatest respect. And even extending to him the courtesy of an invitation to his château in Switzerland.

So that suddenly, and for the first time, people were speaking of Voltaire and Rousseau together, coupling their names, as if these two were actually on the same level of achievement. With their letters printed and reprinted over and over again, and obviously destined to become classics in French literature.

It was as if all at once—after these many long years of effort—Rousseau had finally proved himself worthy of Voltaire's esteem.

True, it was not quite the way he had imagined it. Nor the way he would have wanted it. But there it was, nevertheless—as if he had thrown himself at the feet of Voltaire and the latter had raised him up kindly and presented him to all the world. Saying, "Gentlemen. Allow me to introduce to you Jean Jacques Rousseau, whose remarkable essay against the human race you've all read. Never has anyone painted in more striking colors the horrors of our society. Never has anyone employed so much intelligence to render us stupid."

Voltaire and Rousseau! Really, it was amazing. Only a few months before, had you wished to indicate the two greatest names in French thought you would have had to say Montesquieu and Voltaire. But Montesquieu had just died. And now Rousseau had slipped into the conveniently vacant place. Before anyone else could claim it.

What had he done to deserve it? Very little indeed. Two booklets and an operetta. Which had received considerable attention, no doubt, but hardly entitled him to occupy the shoes of Montesquieu. To say nothing of ranking him beside Voltaire. Voltaire, famous for a dozen times as much work. And in a variety of fields totally outside Rousseau's range.

Still, for all that, it was somehow right that these two men should be coupled. In a general way people realized that society was breaking up. That the two old powers, Church and aristocracy, were about to retire, however unwillingly, and however slowly, from the scene of the struggle. While two new powers were trying to disentangle themselves from ancient ways of thinking and stand forth on their own.

Two new powers. The Voltairean group of the rich and successful, those who could fight for and secure their own independence and happiness, irrespective of the state of society. And the Rousseauan world of the downtrodden, the poor, the unfortunates, who could never win independence on their own, and whose happiness and prosperity would always be that of society as a whole.

Thus top and bottom of the coming world, individualist and socialist, the man of property and the man of nothing, met here for the first time in these two indecisive and in many respects even misleading letters. Foreshadowing their temporary alliances and prolonged battles, their mixed feelings of love and hatred that would disturb the world for the next two hundred years.

Voltaire and Rousseau! How wonderful that was!

Yes. But who had done it? Who had written the first letter? Who had exacted a reply? Who had planned the publication? And whose letter was it that had made the exchange so popular?

The bitterness of it! The humiliation of it. It was Voltaire who had made him. Voltaire who had picked him up and carried him aloft.

Suggesting the opposite: Might he not with equal ease cast him down?

Could one forget the Sullys, the Rohans, the Desfontaines', the Crébillons, the La Beaumelles, the Fredericks and their Maupertuis', and that other Rousseau, Jean Baptiste?

Across the years Rousseau recalled that dark bedroom in the home of M. de Bonac, the candlelight falling on the works of Jean Baptiste Rousseau. And M. de La Martinière saying, "So you really intend to be a writer. Well, well. Then you'll have to beware of Voltaire. Especially with that name Rousseau."

18: THE SPORT OF JEW-STICKING

Yes, a dangerous man. And so vicious in a fight that to this day Rousseauan scholars have not forgiven him for his brutal attacks on Jean Jacques. Particularly during their so-called Battle of Geneva.

Apparently there was nothing Voltaire enjoyed so much as clawing at his enemies. Fréron, for example, the literary critic. Of whom he wrote:

> *L'autre jour dans un vallon*
> *Un serpent piqua Jean Fréron.*
> *Que croyez-vous qui arriva?*
> *Ce fut le serpent qui creva.*

The idea of a serpent biting Jean Fréron—and then what do you suppose?—it was the snake that went into convulsions!

Of course Fréron was himself no mean enemy. But the gentle, psalm-writing poet Le Franc de Pompignan! Just because in his acceptance speech before the French Academy he had the nerve to refer to Voltaire as a menace to society.

Well!

Voltaire literally fell on him. All the way from Switzerland he rained his derisive pamphlets on him. Going so far as to have the latest catchy tunes printed up and distributed free, along with music for the guitar, and with irresistible lyrics lampooning Pompignan. Songs already popular in Paris, but now, with Voltaire's new verses, the rage. So that

Pompignan could hear them whistled day and night through the closed and shuttered windows of his rooms. Almost driving him out of his mind, and certainly out of the city and back to his former provincial obscurity.

And this Le Franc wasn't such a bad writer, either. Only opposed to Voltaire's philosophy. Need one say any more?

La Harpe, sometimes credited with having been the first professor of French literature, managed to trick Voltaire into admitting Pompignan's ability. He read Voltaire some verses, but without mentioning either the name of the author or the title of the poem.

"Well?" La Harpe asked when he had finished. "What's your opinion?"

"Magnificent!" Voltaire exclaimed. "Absolutely magnificent. And who did you say was the author?"

"I didn't say," said La Harpe. He was a dwarfish fellow, and he felt it prudent to retreat a few steps before he ventured, "They're by your friend Le Franc de Pom—" Which was as far as he got.

"Liar!" Voltaire stormed at him.

La Harpe held up his hand as if to ward off a blow before he added, "Worse than that, it's from Pompignan's eulogy to another good friend of yours—Jean Baptiste Rousseau."

For a moment Voltaire looked as if he would have to burst. Then, grudgingly, he conceded, "It's magnificent. Yes, it's still magnificent."

La Harpe was able to relax. As for Voltaire, he was willing to confess that perhaps he might have been a trifle unjust to Pompignan at times. "But you know," he said, "I don't really feel well unless I've got a fight on my hands. Something to stir up my blood. My doctor has actually advised me to do a little Pompignan-sticking every morning. Just for the sake of exercise, so to speak. Warm me up for my real working day."

Apparently he had to have an enemy around. Big or little. Guilty or innocent. No matter. Just so he had a target for his spleen.

The Jews, for example.

How he loved to lash out at them! Calling them "that wretched little tribe" or "those miserable and ignorant people." And making endless sport of the fact that among the laws codified by Moses was one that forbade the Jewish women to indulge in sexual intercourse with goats.

"Imagine having a special law to stop that!" Voltaire would gloat. "The Jewish ladies must have really been extremely partial to this singular form of gallantry."

It's impossible even to imagine Jean Jacques Rousseau jesting in this abominable fashion about an oppressed people such as the Jews. A rootless folk, everywhere either exiled or despised. And so squeezed into their stinking Alsatian ghettoes that whole families, crawling with naked and dirty children, had to make their home in the corner of a storeroom packed to the ceiling with whatever rubbish and discarded clothes the Jews (barred almost everywhere by law from the practice of any trade or craft) could manage to buy, beg or steal.

A people so abused and degraded that in France, where they were tolerated in only a few towns, many of them were not even listed as human beings in the census, but were lumped with the cattle of the land. And as such actually forced to pay the annual tax levied on all *pieds-fourchus,* that is to say on all cloven-hoofed animals such as sheep and swine.

But did that give pause to Voltaire in the exercise of his cruel wit? Not for a moment.

He continued to speculate about that law against intercourse with goats. "Of course, with those Jews wandering for forty years in the desert," he said, "without a drop of water for a bath, and with their God working a miracle for them so that their clothes somehow never wore out, the goats themselves must have conceived a certain fondness for the Jewish women, mistaking them—because of that forty-year odor—for their own kind."

That was really going so far that even a few Christians had to protest. And challenged Voltaire on his free interpretation of Jewish history.

"Well, find me another ancient people whose laws had to take special notice of the inclination of their women for intercourse with animals!" Voltaire cried. "No such people exists, except the Jews!" he declared with finality.

Certain wealthy Jews, for example M. Pinto from the Portuguese colony at Bordeaux, addressed themselves directly to Voltaire, pleading for a cessation of his attacks on a defenseless people already so misused. Which only roused Voltaire to a new line of attack.

"Tell me, Monsieur Pinto, why is it that you Jews never had anything but murderers for your kings? Your King David assassinating Uriah. Your King Solomon killing his brother Adonijah. Your King Jehoram killing all his brothers. And your King Herod slaughtering not only his wife and his brother-in-law, but all his children too, leaving not one of his kindred alive. Tell me, why is that?"

M. Pinto stood nonplused before this avalanche of accusations. While Voltaire pressed home: "Is there any other people that has a record of violence equal to yours? Surely yours must be just about the bloodiest of all mankind."

Voltaire had him there. For, as usual, he had taken the trouble to make sure of his facts. He had had the patience to go through every verse of the Old Testament, making a list of all the crimes of violence.

"And this is called Holy Writ!" he screamed. "This—this blood-spattered volume!" And he held it up as if it were something that could soil.

Moreover, he wanted you to know that he hadn't attempted to swell the total figure of Biblical murders by including the innumerable battle casualties. No. That was warfare. Cruel and ugly, no doubt. But sometimes necessary, and not to be put in the same class as wanton murder.

Nor was he including the vast numbers of people slaughtered by God Himself. Inexcusable. And cruel too. The countless victims of His change of mind—for example, when He drowned all the earth's inhabitants in a universal deluge, in an effort to annihilate His own creation. Nor those hordes whom He struck with the plague at the behest of Moses. Sacrificed in a struggle for power between two religions. Nor the first-born of Egypt, whom His angels killed. Nor any of the other divine murders, for example the seventy thousand innocent men whom God slew in Israel because David disobeyed the prophet Joab. Which, for some unfathomable reason, didn't include David himself, the actual guilty party.

No. Voltaire counted only human murder. One human being killing another. Beyond the call of warfare. And having nothing to do with God.

Though how Voltaire managed to reach a precise figure in cases where he had only such vague indications as are to be found in the books of Judges and Kings, where the chroniclers speak again and again of the "ripping up of all the women and the children" and the killing of all the men so that "none that pisseth against the wall" was left alive—how he could add up these mass slaughters of indefinite size, it is impossible to say.

Nor how he managed to estimate the number of men in Shechem, for example, that town whose men, for love of the Jewish maidens, consented to figure in a grand circumcision fest and then, being confined sick to their beds, with bandaged organs, were set upon by the Jews and poignarded down to the last one.

And yet, despite those foggy figures, which could only be guessed at,

239

Voltaire somehow arrived at an exact number, 239,020, for the total of cold-blooded murders committed by Jews in the Old Testament.

Fantastic! Causing Voltaire to crow with glee, "Now there's a Chosen People for you! Two hundred and thirty-nine thousand murders recorded among that tiny folk, in one book. And imagine God picking out that dangerous region, inhabited by those insatiable assassins, for the birthplace of His son, Jesus! Hahaha!"

And he would add gaily, "The moment Jesus appeared among that bloodthirsty people, it was a foregone conclusion that he would come to no good end. Indeed, it can hardly be a surprise, for anyone who looks at the facts, that Jesus should have ended up on the Cross."

But of course for Voltaire the cream of the jest, in this Jew-sticking, was to see himself labeled as a Jew hater. Yes, and if only he could have lived another century, he would have roared with laughter to see any number of historians of the Jews—Heinrich Graetz, for instance—solemnly berating and belaboring Voltaire as an anti-Semite in page after page of the most virulent invective.

Imagine! The man who had written in his *Essay on Manners,* "At bottom we Christians are only uncircumcised Jews"—this man was himself taken to be an enemy of the Jews!

This man who certainly explained himself clearly enough when he said to M. Pinto, "Agree with me, sir, that you Jews were monsters of cruelty in Palestine and I shall be compelled to admit that we Christians have been monsters of cruelty in Europe." For he had had the same patience with the Christians as with the Jews and had figured at 9,468,800 the number of victims of Christian religious fury.

Ah, but no! The Jews were no more willing to confess their misdeeds than the Christians were to acknowledge theirs. Each would have it that they were somehow better than other human beings. And for that reason preferred by God. Above all peoples.

Of course Voltaire couldn't fool the Christians as easily as he fooled the Jews. The Christians knew this crafty man of old, and they suspected that nothing he did was really honest. No, this Voltaire couldn't possibly be an honest Jew hater.

His attacks on the Jews could be nothing but a sneak assault against the Christians! An attack from beneath.

And indeed he was to show his hand eventually very clearly in his *Questions of Zapata,* where he presented a puzzled Catholic priest asking his theological superiors, "Why, if our God is the same as the God of Abraham, do we despise the children of Abraham? Why do we continue to recite prayers written by the Jews, even while we are burning Jews at the stake? Why is it that on the one hand we must revere the book of Jewish laws, while on the other hand we must torture those who follow that law?"

Ah, the merry sight it was then for Voltaire to see Christians rushing to the defense of the Jews, those Jews whom they had been cheerfully mistreating for fifteen hundred years! Realizing finally that as Voltaire shook the foundations of Judaism he was bringing the whole structure of Christianity, built upon the very same foundations, into peril of collapse.

Not that Voltaire had ever really taken any great pains to conceal his purpose. Just that people had been too stupid to understand him. After all, hadn't he written, "When I see Christians beating Jews, it seems to me that I see children beating their parents?"

In the end the whole battle degenerated into a kind of masquerade. With, for example, one Christian priest taking up the cudgels against Voltaire with such pro-Jewish fervor that he couldn't think of signing his own name to it, but felt compelled to disguise himself as "Six Jews" (whose names he actually listed). Publishing the volume under the title *Six Jews against M. de Voltaire*.

Which made it a sheer delight for Voltaire (himself brought up in a Jesuit college, and therefore quickly detecting the hand of the Catholic theologian behind those six spurious Jews) to write a delightfully witty reply under the title *One Christian against Six Jews*. Which was an additional laugh for all those who knew who this brave Christian was who dared to tackle six Jews singlehanded.

Voltaire hate the Jews? How ridiculous.

"Jews," he cried in his *Philosophical Dictionary*, "do not reproach me with not loving you! On the contrary, I love you so much that I wish you were all back in Hershalaim. Better you there than those despicable Turks who now ravage that bit of land that was once yours. With your bare hands you would once again scrape earth up to the tops of your arid mountains. You would never have much grain, but what excellent vines! Together with some palm and olive trees and a small amount of pastureland."

Does that sound like an honest Jew hater? Of course not. In fact, there was never a more fraudulent one.

To M. Pinto, Voltaire even said, "What a remarkable people you Jews are!"

"Thank you, sir," said M. Pinto, "but pray, in what way do you mean that?"

"I mean that your insignificant tribe should have somehow become the mother of two of the greatest religions of the world. Destined to envelop the globe."

Pinto asked, "Then why do you continue to heap scorn upon us? You should honor us instead of despising us."

Voltaire smiled. "Shall I tell you truthfully what I've got against the Jews?"

"Please do," Pinto begged.

"Very well, then. It is you Jews who forged the heaviest chains that man has ever been burdened with. Yes. Your Bible. Do you realize that I may disbelieve the miracles, the oracles, the legends and the superstitions of the Egyptians, and no one will ever dream of taking it amiss? Do you realize that I may disbelieve the mythology of the Greeks, the Romans, the Norse, the Hindus, the Chinese, and indeed all the other fairy tales of all the peoples of the world, and not a soul will fight me on that?

"But *your* legends! Ah, that is another matter. *Your* superstitions, *your* miracles, *your* oracles—these I *must* believe. I *must,* on pain of death in this life and the threat of hell in the next.

"Have you any idea," Voltaire went on, "how many people the Christians have excommunicated, tortured, burned at the stake, in order to force *us* who are not Jews to believe in *your* damned Jewish superstitions while at the same time denying *you,* the real Jews, the right to remain exclusively true to them?"

So you see what it was? The Jewish Bible. That book not written by Christians, but with which the Christians had nevertheless kept Europe enslaved to superstition and ignorance for fifteen hundred years. *That* was really what Voltaire hated.

Someone once asked Voltaire, "But if you hate that book so much, why is it that I see you reading it all the time?"

Voltaire was caught without an answer. But of course for only a fraction of a second. Then he cried, "Am I not the lawyer for the opposition? And this, isn't it my opponents' brief? Isn't it therefore my duty to read it, so that I may know in detail this entire record of ignorance and fanaticism?"

In this connection, one of the parts of the opponents' brief that Voltaire perhaps studied more intently than any other was the story of Adam and Eve.

How is it, Voltaire asked himself, that no other people of the world knew anything of those first parents of the human race except that wretched little nation of the Jews?

List, if you please, all the great and populous nations of the ancient world: Greece, Rome, China, India, Egypt. How is it that not a single one of them had ever heard of Adam and Eve? Isn't that unbelievable —that only the Jews should have preserved this memory?

But of course no more ridiculous than any other part of that weird book. That incomprehensible God of the Jews, for instance. That God who, over the triviality of a piece of stolen fruit, condemns Adam and Eve to pain, hard work and death. Which might perhaps be justified, however severe, had it limited itself to the actual culprits, but never when that same punishment was extended to include all their offspring for countless generations to come!

And then just notice how upset this cruel Deity becomes when Cain kills Abel. Just one little murder, but what a fuss God makes over it. Saying to Cain, "Thy brother's blood crieth unto me from the ground."

The impertinence of it! The hypocrisy! That this God who has just sentenced millions and billions of people still unborn to suffer the horrors of life and death should now pose as the refuge of the afflicted! What a laugh!

Voltaire could never get over this. "Our tormentor takes pity on us!" he would sneer. "But naturally without interrupting His torture."

"And note too," Voltaire would point out angrily, "that Adam and Eve, the original guilty pair, are permitted to live nearly nine hundred years after their crime. While I, today, who had nothing whatever to do with that misdeed in Paradise, I am to be killed off in a fraction of that time!"

Hate the Jews? Whatever for? Weren't they condemned to death too? Just as much as Voltaire? Weren't they as much to be pitied as all other human beings?

But that God! That brutal Jewish God!

The flagrant injustice of it was such that it would arouse him from his sleep at night. Voltaire condemned to die! Yes, and already, so to speak, lying in his death cell. With the date of execution still undetermined, but no matter. For it was just as certain as the waxing and waning of the moon. And not too far off, either.

Why? For what? What had he done? Where was his crime?

The horror of it screamed to high heaven. He, Voltaire, the most harmless of men! Angrily he would grab his stick and poke at the ceiling over his bed. Whereupon his secretary, Wagnière, who slept above him, would hastily wrap a robe around himself against the chill, open the trap door and let himself down into his master's room, where he would strike light to a candle and wait for Voltaire to dictate.

And the poet, his nightcap making his caved-in, toothless face look more grotesque than ever, would brood in mingled fury and pity on the fate of man.

And on his own fate, too.

For in truth the dangerous Voltaire was the most frightened and timid of men. And the most religious too, some of his contemporaries suspected.

Building a church on his estate of Ferney. And bursting with anger at anyone who dared deny the existence of God. So that the bolder spirits of Paris, men like Diderot, d'Holbach and Helvétius, who were beginning to see that all the various plant and animal forms, including man himself, might be readily explained by slow processes of growth and gradual change, with no need for God whatsoever, began to refer to old Voltaire as "that canting bigot."

Imagine anyone of real intelligence in this day and age still believing that God existed and that man was His special creation!

Which caused Voltaire once to stoop and grab up a handful of soil. "You say that this created man?" he cried.

And his critic answered calmly, "Certainly. Given enough time. By gradual evolution."

"This!" Voltaire exclaimed. "This dirt made Michelangelo?"

"Why not?" the critic maintained. "Given millions of years in which to unfold itself. Producing creatures ever more perfect."

"But in that case," said Voltaire, "on some of the other billions of planets of our universe, where this dirt has had not millions of years, but billions and trillions of years, this dirt must have evolved forms so perfect as to be God!"

And he thrust the dirt he held in his hand at his critic. "Here, you worship this dirt for creating God, while I go on worshiping God for creating this dirt!"

No. He wasn't religious. Just deeply aware of the nothingness of himself and the vastness of the universe. Man's incredible ignorance.

As a youth Voltaire had been taken to see the King's own library, a great collection of books which His Majesty Louis XIV had graciously put at the disposal of scholars, and which was eventually to become the Bibliothèque Nationale of Paris.

Voltaire stood in a kind of state of shock before these endless shelves, where two hundred thousand volumes crowded row upon row.

"Who reads all these books?" he wondered, as he looked in vain for a familiar author among the names he saw stamped in gold on the spines of the scarlet bindings.

The librarian told him that of the two hundred thousand volumes upwards of one hundred and ninety thousand would almost never be called for.

Then this isn't a library! Voltaire cried within himself. This is a cemetery. A cemetery of books. A graveyard of dead hopes and dead reputations, where a million dead thoughts lie embalmed in pages that no one will ever turn.

Voltaire ran from this necropolis, and for a brief moment he lost all desire to write. Why add another dead thought to this vast mausoleum? What for? For fame? To hand his name down to posterity? What made him imagine that he, Voltaire, could write books that would have a different fate from these? Wherein did he differ from others? Was he not just another drop of water lost in the ocean of humanity?

By what right did he flatter himself that he might be just that one particular drop of water that an oyster would swallow and that would thus be turned into an imperishable pearl? And as such would be taken from the sea to become the principal ornament on the throne of the Grand Mogul? He, Voltaire, the one fortunate drop out of billions! While all other drops continued to be lost in the immeasurable seas.

And even fame? Was that enough? Suppose he should become that pearl of a writer, how long would his reputation last? How long could it possibly last, seeing that the centuries must inevitably succeed each other, and the millennia accumulate, until his name must in time become as illegible and as meaningless to the inhabitants of that distant future as the hieroglyphs of the Egyptian temples are to the peasants who cultivate their little plots of ground along the Nile.

If that was the best that man could hope for, why struggle? Who could wrestle with time?

Once, during Voltaire's first exile from France, when he was in London, he found himself in a crowd gathered thickly about the entrance to Westminster Abbey.

The day was March 28, 1727. The body of Sir Isaac Newton was being laid to rest.

Never would Voltaire forget that day. Nor that scene.

Imagine! Six of the highest peers of England: two dukes, three earls and the very Lord High Chancellor, the most powerful official of the realm, functioning as pallbearers to carry Newton to his crypt. Moving slowly and with dignity. With solemn music playing. Out of respect for Newton, a rude farmer's boy, who to the end of his life had not been able to rid himself of the coarse speech of his father.

The crowd wept to see English nobility of the proudest ancestral blood humbling itself before this professor of mathematics whose only distinction had come from his talent.

And Voltaire wept, too. Thinking of how this scene, so unusual even in semidemocratic England, was well-nigh inconceivable in an almost totally aristocratic France.

Surely if it was at all within the power of man to grant some measure of protection against oblivion, it must lie in such an impressive burial. Surely for at least as long as men of our kind inhabited this earth this abbey would stand here and this bronze-and-marble memorial would continue to proclaim to all people the magnificent feat that Newton had accomplished when he had snatched the moon from the skies and demonstrated that the same laws of physics that hold true on earth also rule in the heavens.

This funeral ceremony would not give Newton immortality. No. Not by far. But it was the best imitation of immortality that man could fashion. Only God could make the real thing.

And suddenly every fiber of Voltaire's being that craved life, and still more life—and even life eternal—cried out for a funeral like Newton's.

How wonderful that would be! Yes, no doubt. But by what right dared he hope for it?

When his time came, what equivalent service—compared to Newton's—would he have rendered to his generation that would entitle him to equivalent honors? Would it be for his struggle in behalf of reason against fanaticism? Common sense against superstition? For an end to disputes about matters which were beyond proof? Matters which must forever remain either myth or speculation?

Nonsense! That was more likely to get him burned at the stake. Besides, how could he manage to convince the people of France that man could live and die without the aid and comfort of superstition?

How could he convince people that the entire subject of religion and theology was nonsense, except for perhaps a few dozen words: Adore the God who gave you the precious gift of life, even though He also gives you death; and be just to your fellow creatures who share the same fate of life and death that you do.

How could one hope to spread such a simple religion in a world crawling with preachers and dervishes, monks and nuns, professors of theology and fakers, churches and holy shrines?

How could you spread it in a world where millions of people had died to prove or disprove this holy book or that, and whether it was right to drink wine or eat pork, or whether man should keep his foreskin on or cut it off, and which one of the seven days of the week was really the holy one?

How could one preach a religion so simple—adore God and be just—in a world filled with soldiers and cannon, with warships and fortresses, with jails and instruments of torture?

Once, when Voltaire was already settled in Switzerland, at his estate of Ferney, he received a visit from the Duke de Villars, son of the famous general. As he was showing him around the extensive acreage of the place, the sky suddenly became overcast and great rolls of thunder rumbled overhead. Voltaire, who up to that moment had been chatting gaily, stopped in alarm.

"Good God!" he cried. "What shall we do? We're so far from shelter!"

Villars tried to calm him. "Oh, it won't pour for a while yet."

"Yes, but don't you hear the thunder!" Voltaire screamed.

"Don't tell me that our great philosopher is afraid of thunder," Villar laughed.

Voltaire, however, began to run as fast as his old legs would carry him, crying to Villars, "Help me! Hurry!"

The puzzled Duke gave Voltaire his arm and hustled him as quickly as he could back to Voltaire's château. No sooner were they inside than Voltaire wiped the sweat of fear from his brow and collapsed into a chair.

"Thank God!" he breathed.

Villars was both shocked and amused. The great philosopher behaving like a child! "I give you my word of honor," he assured Voltaire, "that not one word of this episode shall ever pass my lips. No one shall ever learn through me of the great Voltaire's fear of thunder. Nor of his thanking God for his safety."

"What's the matter with you?" Voltaire asked, still trembling and in a sweat. "Can't you see that I might have been killed by lightning? Does that mean nothing to you?"

"Nothing except that I would imagine you would do your best to conceal such unworthy fears."

"Ah, you may well say that!" cried Voltaire. "You who have the privilege of dying as you please. Or as fate may dictate. But what about me? Don't you realize that even since the earliest ages of man, the gods are presumed to speak in syllables of thunder? And that their favorite weapon is a bolt of lightning? Have you never seen representations of Zeus and Jupiter? Or of the Norse god Thor? Have you not read in your Bible how God gave Moses the Ten Commandments amidst thunder and lightning? Doesn't David say in the Psalms, 'The Lord thundered in the heavens'? Didn't God speak to Job out of the tornado?

"If tomorrow," Voltaire continued, "the news should spread that Voltaire, the great reprobate, the mocker of the Holy Word, had been struck by lightning, can you imagine what would happen? A hundred thousand priests and preachers would rush to their pulpits to preach a fiery sermon on how God had finally grown tired of my blasphemies and had stopped my mouth with heavenly fire.

"Yes, and what's more, millions would believe it. And my lifelong battle against superstition would be lost. The fanatics would triumph."

"You frighten me," said Villars. "And to think that I was taking it all so lightly. And even presuming to laugh at you."

"Ah, my dear friend," said Voltaire, "everyone has to die in one way or another. Everyone except Voltaire. He has not that precious privilege of meeting his death in whatever way it happens to strike. For, you see, people will not so much mourn my passing, or pity me for it—they will judge me thereby. Yes, they will accuse me of it. They will hold me accountable.

"Can you imagine the talk, the arguments, the conclusions that will be drawn, if for example, I should commit suicide? And have you any idea of how often my recurrent fevers, my painful colics, my inflammations of the eyes, my endless toothaches have almost driven me to the point of wishing to be rid of this miserable frame of mine?

"But no. No suicide for me. I must go on living and suffering. For if I killed myself, it would be not just me but my whole philosophy that I would be murdering. I would be canceling out the work of decades.

"La Mettrie, with his mechanistic philosophy—did he not make himself and his ideas ridiculous when he died from eating too much of a venison pasty into which an eagle had been cooked? One cannot read his works without scorn and pity, thinking of how his machinery gave out from gluttony.

"True, in pagan times Anacreon, for example, could die from a grape seed that got stuck in his throat. Aeschylus, so it is related, died when an eagle wishing to break a turtle's shell dropped it on his head, mistaking it for a rock because of his baldness. And that other philosopher—what was his name?—could die of laughter from seeing a toothless hag trying to eat a juicy overripe fig. And the works of these men did not particularly suffer because of their strange decease.

"But it is obvious that mine would.

"Think, my dear Villars, of the dreadful sermons that would be preached if I should perish in some loathsome manner. Chained up as insane. Or leprous, so that I had to be locked away from other men. No. At whatever cost, I must die old. And with all my mental faculties as nearly intact as possible. My talents still discernible. Of some ailment which can only be described as normal to an advanced age.

"And I must meet my end philosophically. Calmly staring into the horrors of the tomb. Demonstrating all the courage of Socrates with his cup of hemlock, or Jesus on his Cross.

"And in public. Preferably in Paris. In the midst of my enemies. So that there can be no doubt of just what my last moments were like.

"For you see, I am, in a manner of speaking, a soldier. Fighting in the endless war against the fanatics, that is to say those who hold a gun at your head and order you to think as they do. And I have no choice but to die on the field of battle. My followers are counting on me. And you may be sure that I know my duty, and that I shan't fail them."

Voltaire reached over and softly touched Villars on the arm. "Do you understand now why I run for shelter when I hear thunder?"

19: THE BEST
OF ALL POSSIBLE WORLDS

But there was to be a day when, run as he would, Voltaire could find no shelter against God's thunder. When no house could hide him. For this time God's thunder grumbled underneath his feet.

Voltaire! Voltaire!

That was when he was really frightened.

It was on November 1, 1755, on All Saints' Day, in the morning, precisely at that hour when the churches of beautiful and wealthy Lisbon, in Portugal, were most crowded with the faithful. It was then that the earth began to growl as if from deep caverns below. And at the same time the ground shook and shuddered, as if it were the deck of a ship on a stormy sea.

Church towers leaned and toppled. Columns of masonry gave way. Roofs disintegrated into beams and stones and rained down upon worshipers, crushing them like ants. Amidst wild screams the living trampled over the dying and the dead, fighting to get out of the portals of God's temple, into the open air.

And while mobs of people headed for the safety of the countryside, the disturbed ocean in the harbor slopped back and forth like water in a basin and three times came washing over the ruined city. Waves forty feet high swept additional thousands to their death. Beams and furniture were torn away by the rush of the water and carried out to sea, along with coffins unearthed from cemeteries and floated away, as if God wanted the dead to die again.

And then, in the abandoned city, fires broke out and raged unhindered.

Half the globe felt this mighty stirring of its crust, which continued to shudder now and then over the ensuing weeks and months. In Africa, in Ireland, its effects were noticed. Across the Atlantic, in Boston, over a thousand chimneys had to be repaired.

And in Geneva, one day Voltaire watched in horror as a bottle of muscat fell clattering from the table to the floor. Then pride succeeded horror as he felt himself still safe. God had killed thousands of good Catholics. While they were praying in churches! And spared him, the blasphemer.

Did that mean that God approved his battle for truth against superstition? Or did it mean nothing except that God didn't even concern Himself with such trifling matters as what men happened to think?

Meanwhile all Europe was gripped by a new fanaticism. Everywhere the end of the world was being preached. In London thousands were so convinced of it as to sell their goods and order themselves shrouds. In Lisbon so many mad monks screamed of greater cataclysms to come that the Marquês de Pombal, in charge of reconstruction, had to hang the wildest of them in order to stop the feeling of uselessness that paralyzed his workers.

Printing presses in Edinburgh, in London, in Madrid, in Paris and elsewhere poured out pamphlets and books by the hundreds, drawing the direst conclusions from the great earthquake. From every pulpit preachers and priests united in declaring that it was man's wicked ways that had roused God's anger. Lisbon was but the warning finger, they cried. Mend your ways, sinful man! Or else worse, much worse, will follow! Close your theaters! Burn your evil books! Stop your frivolous lives!

Even Madame de Pompadour, the King's mistress, was frightened into locking the door of her bedroom against her royal lover. She reformed and went so far as to solicit the post of lady in waiting to the Queen.

And one night, in Geneva, Voltaire reached with a trembling hand for his pen.

A flood of questions assailed him. Could one really believe this nonsense, that the earthquake was God's vengeance upon wicked mankind? Then what about all these hundreds of infants crushed to death upon the battered and bleeding bosoms of their mothers?

What wickedness had these babies committed?

No, it was ridiculous to imagine that the earthquake could be God's punishment for man's sins. Then perhaps it was somehow meant for the best? After all, since man is born to die anyhow, what difference, in the light of eternity, can it make when or where that death takes place? So what if Lisbon be destroyed in the process? Isn't that perhaps even to the good? May not a more beautiful Lisbon rise from its ruins? And will there not now be work for thousands of carpenters and masons who might otherwise have gone unemployed and hungry?

In short, is this not after all the best of all possible worlds? As the philosopher Leibnitz declared.

Oh, undoubtedly! Though you yourself, killed in the disaster, are not going to get much satisfaction out of this best of all possible worlds, don't forget that a million maggots will be eating your rotting corpse! Maggots that otherwise would not have a bite to eat.

Can you ask more of God but that He should take care of the needs of worms too? The Creator must safeguard His whole creation, must He not?

O God, is this really Your law? Is man born so sinful that You must punish him throughout his life?

Or are You in fact so far away that, as ruler of the universe, You look at Your creatures with unpitying eyes, satisfied that Your original decrees are working themselves out according to an immutable but mysterious plan?

What other explanation can there be? Unless it be true that You try men's souls here on earth in order to see which of us merits an eternity of pleasure and which an eternity of pain.

Ou l'homme est né coupable, et Dieu punit sa race,
Ou ce maître absolu de l'être et de l'espace,

Sans courroux, sans pitié, tranquille, indifférent,
De ses premiers décrets suit l'éternel torrent;
Ou la matière informe, à son maître rebelle,
Porte en soi des défauts nécessaires comme elle;
Ou bien Dieu nous éprouve, et ce séjour mortel
N'est qu'un passage étroit vers un monde éternel.

How many quills Voltaire must have ruined that night when he cried out his ignorance and his anguish. How many times he must have bruised his forehead against his desk! His groans are crystallized forever in the lines of his poem.

But there was no answer from God.

No answer to the great questions: Who am I? Where am I? Whence do I come and where am I bound?

And the only certainty: that there was evil in this world. And that we, tormented atoms living on a ball of mud flung somehow into space, must all experience death.

And yet, God, we are Your thinking atoms! Our eyes have looked deep into Your space. We have measured Your heavens. Though we may know nothing about ourselves, we have assaulted Your infinity.

And we still have hope!

That everything is fine today, that is our illusion.
That everything will be fine someday, that is our hope.

Such was the poem *On the Disaster at Lisbon,* which Voltaire wrote shortly after settling in Geneva, and which he begged his Parisian trumpet Thieriot to distribute to Diderot, d'Alembert and Rousseau.

Jean Jacques had just recently moved from his little Parisian apartment on the Rue Grenelle St.-Honoré out to the country estate of Madame d'Épinay, wife of the millionaire tax farmer. She was that woman of whose chest Rousseau would later make the disparaging remark that it was as flat as the back of his hand; but, for all that, she cherished her surly "bear," and she had put at his disposal a lovely cottage of five rooms, completely furnished, plus kitchen and wine cellar, plus orchard and vegetable garden, and with the whole surrounding forested countryside for him to roam around in.

It wasn't Geneva. No. But considering how that city had treated him, or, rather, mistreated him, compared to the enthusiastic reception they had given Voltaire, there could no longer be any question of his going there. Later, perhaps, but not now, when he was still smarting from his defeat.

Rousseau's friends, Grimm, Diderot and others, had been concerned about Jean Jacques's going off to live in the country not just for the few warm months of the summer, but for all year round. Thus isolating himself still further from the society of man. And they pressed him to reconsider his decision, warning him of the dangers involved in living away from people.

"What dangers?" he challenged them. "You, of course, would find life impossible without your Paris."

"Man was not made to live alone," they told him. "But in society. Alone, he falls into evil."

"That's ridiculous!" Jean Jacques cried. "Answer me this: What evil can a man commit who lives alone? On whom shall he commit it?"

"Perhaps upon himself," Diderot said.

"Nonsense. To commit evil requires society. How can I commit evil upon myself?"

"Perhaps through loneliness," Diderot repeated.

Lonely? He? Amongst all the gifts of nature? Amongst his books and his writings? And all the treasures of his imagination?

Early in the morning, after his first night in his new home, he rushed out of doors to feast his eyes on the beauties of nature.

It was spring. But winter still clung here and there to the ground, in small patches of snow. As if it would take more than violets and primroses to force her to surrender.

How could one be lonely with all that? He spread out his arms and drank it all in!

Listen! A nightingale. The first to arrive. Hear it? Is there a more beautiful sound in all the world, than a nightingale when a low note throbs and slowly dies in its throat?

And here a brook! And there a ford! Why, it was the twin of the one he could never forget. The one in Savoy, where—it was now all of twenty-six years ago—he had stopped to watch Mademoiselle de Graffenreid and Mademoiselle Galley, both on horseback, trying in vain to get their mounts to go into the water.

How lovely they had been, those two young girls! But even lovelier now in his recollection of them. For then their beauty had been of a day. While now, in his mind, it would be preserved for as long as he would live.

"Surely you are going to help us, aren't you, Monsieur Rousseau?" they had cried. Without their invitation he would have wandered away. But thus specifically requested, he took the bridles of their horses and compelled the animals to follow him into the water. He would have forced elephants or tigers, had a charming girl demanded it. The water had come up over his knees, but he hadn't minded. And he had brought the two young ladies safely across the brook.

And then once more he had made as if to leave. And would in fact have left if the two girls had not exclaimed, "Oh no you don't! You can't escape us now!" And Mademoiselle Galley had declared, "You are now our prisoner of war! Up with you, prisoner!"

Their destination was an uninhabited château owned by Mademoiselle Galley's mother, and they were determined that he should keep them company. He wanted to climb up behind Mademoiselle Galley. For she was much the more beautiful of the two. But there was that damned timidity of his again: he climbed up behind Mademoiselle de Graffenreid instead.

And would have promptly fallen off if Mademoiselle de Graffenreid had not cried, "Hold on!" Whereupon he had found sufficient courage to clasp his arms around her waist.

But that was all. Around her waist. And nothing more.

For those three or four inches that separated his hands from the paradise of her breasts, lying just above, those few inches constituted a forbidden territory that he did not dare cross.

Oh, but just the delicious proximity of her breasts—that was more than enough to make his head swim. So that even now the very memory of having once been so close, so warm, to them still dizzied his head, a head already growing gray with age.

And never once, not even for a second, not even as if jogged upward by accident, did he let his hands shift from her waist.

He could still remember how he had cursed that shyness of his! And how eagerly, when they had arrived at the château and the girls were busying themselves preparing a meal, he had looked forward to a drink of wine that he hoped would give him the courage he wanted for the return trip. He wasn't going to miss his opportunity twice. No, indeed!

But alas! the girls had forgotten about wine. They themselves never touched it. No need to. Their young blood was wine enough. But what a calamity for him! He had run out, desperately searching for some wine in that tiny village clustered about the old castle. But not a bottle to be had.

After lunch, however, they had gone out into the old orchard, where the cherries were just ripening. He had climbed a tree and thrown down cherries to the girls. And somehow, half hidden there in the foliage, he had been bold enough to aim the cherries for that gap in their bodices, that gap widened by their stance, their breasts rising as they looked up at him. Oh, if only his lips had been cherries, how gladly he would have cast himself down there!

Ridiculous. Yes, to cherish such an unsubstantial romance. Nothing but imagination. When he might so easily have pressed his advantage. Enticed these two girls to heaven only knows what intimacies, uncovering perhaps their most hidden charms, arousing them to the most daring caresses.

Alas, what a throng they were, those girls with whom he had not dared to sleep. That mocking Zulietta, above all. And La Paduana, with her truly frightening perfection, which he had scarcely more than touched. And so many others! Gentle Madame Basile, who used to permit him to curl himself up at her feet while she sewed. And that Mademoiselle de Breil in whose home he had been a lackey when he lived in Turin, and of whom he had once caught a glimpse as she was being dressed for presentation at court, which, in the décolleté fashion of the day, required her breasts to be pushed into such prominence that her nipples had for a moment been forced out of her corsage.

Just the glimpse of those proud nipples of hers bursting into freedom had been more than enough to make him enamored of her for the rest of his life. Not that he had ever been able to tell her. No. He wouldn't have dared. But someday he would write about it, and then she would know. She would be able to say with pride, "Jean Jacques loved me. Loved me with an undying love. Loved me as no other man in the world could possibly love. Innocently. Eternally."

Yes, what a throng of women there had been in his life! Not all of them in his real life. No. Only in his imaginary life. Often they had just, so to speak, brushed past him. But that had been enough. An odor. A softness. A curl of hair caught by the wind. And they were his forever. And he forever their slave.

Ridiculous. Yes, was it not? For a man to cherish such visionary romances. But then, why not? The realest love, did it not in the end become nothing but a memory? It stood to reason then that it was not the person who had the most experiences who was in the end the greatest lover. No. It was he who had the most vivid imagination.

And who in all the world could surpass him with such a remembered throng of beauties? Who else could gather them at will here in this forest? Who could give them life as he did now, by the grace of his mental powers? Tell me, then, what lover surpasses me?

For all these remembered creatures belonged to him. Utterly. Without reservations. To do with as he pleased. And no question now, here in the privacy of his own brain, of any shyness or lack of courage. Nor any need of wine. He intoxicated himself.

His blood boiled with mad desires. At will he bent his beauties to his wildest desires. No sultan ever had a harem to equal his. His body was inflamed with passion. He reeled as he walked.

People who happened to catch a glimpse of him as he strode through the forest stood still and wondered. What could be the matter with that man? Was he ill? Was he out of his mind?

As for Jean Jacques, he had no eyes for anyone else. He scarcely heard the "Bonjour, Monsieur Rousseau." And he only made some annoyed grunt of a response.

Who were these people anyhow who dared interrupt his dreams? What right had they to poke their noses into what was none of their business? Strangers! Foreigners! Barred forever from the land of his imagination. Inhabitants of another world—a lesser one. The prison-world of reality, where facts were like iron chains.

And as if to leave these clods farther behind he let his imagination soar still higher. Climbing from one extravagant vision to another. Until his desires were so rarefied that no woman on earth could have satisfied them, and his walks were now in the company of creatures so fabulous that they could have existed nowhere except in that feverishly inventive mind of his. It was as if he had left the earth for good. And was alone now in a universe of which he was god.

Day after day, scarcely pausing to take a little breakfast, he would head straight from his couch to the groves, and into his world of magic. Woe to Thérèse, woe to anyone who dared speak to him of trifles. He silenced them with a glare.

Occasionally he still copied music. Occasionally he still worked at various projects. One for world peace, for example, to be extracted from the papers of the unfortunate Abbé de Saint-Pierre, who had been expelled from the French Academy because his hatred of war and his desire for universal peace had led him to criticize Louis XV. A gentle madman, the abbé. Basing his whole philosophy on two words: *give* and *forgive*. . . . But for Jean Jacques all this was just an occasional momentary interruption to his long walks and his wild dreams.

Even Madame d'Épinay, his benefactress, and his friend Grimm, when they came out to the estate, got short shrift from him. He realized that Grimm was cleverly working himself into the good graces of Madame d'Épinay and would shortly find his way into her bed (and would soon in effect possess himself of the château, while Rousseau would have only the cottage). But for the moment this did not bother him.

Only later would he realize that while he had been pursuing disembodied fancies Grimm had been seizing the real thing. That château could have been his! It was he, Rousseau, who had introduced Grimm to Madame d'Épinay. It was he, Rousseau, whom she had really wanted for her lover!

But of course she, with her flat chest—how could she compare with the resplendent creatures which his imagination manufactured for him?

He could have gone on thus to the end of his days. Filled with indescribable joys. Asking nothing of existence beyond these interminable intoxicating dreams. But, as he was to say in his *Confessions,* "Everything seemed in league to tear me from my delightful and foolish reveries."

It was, in the first place, the organs of his very own body. Overstimulated by these endless Babylonian indulgences of his senses, certain parts of him eventually became so engorged with blood and humors that they could no longer perform their humdrum but more necessary earthy functions.

Suddenly he found himself unable to urinate at all. His bladder was as if locked up. His kidneys began to weigh him down like lumps of hot lead dragging at the small of his back.

The poisons which he could not void began to swamp his system, distending his body and making him dull and feverish. So that finally he had to take to bed and beg Thérèse to boil his bougies again. And once more he had to face the hell of prodding pieces of metal up his urethra in order to coax the waste out of his system trickle by trickle.

Who, under such handicaps, could conjure up ethereal creatures? And yet never was it more important to him than now to prove that he could do it. For if the body could drag down the imagination, if pain in the groin could kill the flights of human fancy, then this was a world where matter reigned and not thought. Where the body ruled and not the mind.

And it followed then that the soul was nothing but an organ of the body!

Which meant that when the body died, everything died.

His salvation was at stake! It was just as years ago when he had been throwing stones at the trunks of trees and had said to himself,

If I hit the next tree I shall be saved. How he had trembled at the thought of missing! All eternity would be the price he would have to pay.

And now too, all eternity hung in balance as he tried to hold on to his dreams. . . . But in the midst of this struggle to make his mind independent of his body, Voltaire's poem reached him. And never did anything come less apropos.

Still under the sway of Voltaire, Rousseau could not help but groan out loud when he read that litany of man's ignorance: "Who am I? Where am I? Whence do I come and where am I bound?" And he groaned out loud again when he read Voltaire's description of men as "tormented atoms living on a ball of mud flung somehow into space" and sure of only one thing: that they must experience death.

"Voltaire, Voltaire!" he cried. "What do you want of me now? Is it not enough that you have robbed me of Geneva? Must you now deprive me of the only comfort that a dying man can have: the hope for survival?"

But in the midst of his outcry, it occurred to him that if he suffered so much while reading this poem, how much more so had the writer while penning it. And suddenly he was filled with pity for poor Voltaire. And with that came the realization that in spite of everything, in spite of his poverty, in spite of his sickness, in spite of his lack of genius, he was nevertheless the more fortunate of the two.

Yes, he was! And it was therefore his duty now to help Voltaire. As Voltaire's works had so often helped him. But the old dream of casting himself at the feet of Voltaire was over. For how could Jean Jacques cast himself at the feet of a man who was groveling in the dust?

Perhaps now it was his turn to raise Voltaire from the ground! Embrace him and talk to him.

For in the same way that Jean Jacques could use his imagination to bring life to scenes of love with his inamoratas, so he could conjure up a talk with Voltaire.

Intimate. Two philosophers, sitting by the fireside. Voltaire taking his snuff and his coffee. Rousseau drinking his wine. And talking. The pupil Rousseau, with all due deference, showing the master where he was wrong.

And Voltaire grateful . . .

Electrified by this reversal of roles, himself playing the leading part and Voltaire the humble one, Rousseau suddenly roused himself from his dreams and shouted for Thérèse to prop him up with pillows. Quick! His writing board and pen and paper. For in spite of the sound sticking deep into his vitals, in spite of the fever emanating from his still distended bladder, he meant to rescue Voltaire from his false doctrines.

Yes indeed. For as Jean Jacques began to muster his arguments and to polish them into their most telling form, he became aware, as he had often done in the past, that there were times when his reasoning was sounder than Voltaire's, his points more convincing. Whereupon his mind leaped forward to a shining possibility: that once again he might appear in print along with Voltaire in an exchange of letters.

But this time it would be Rousseau taking Voltaire by the hand. This time it would be Rousseau who would have the approval of the majority of mankind. So that Voltaire might even appear slightly ridiculous. Getting a taste of his own medicine for once.

And then—yes, yes, and then it would be Jean Jacques who would emerge as the greatest name in French literature.

Greater even than Voltaire.

20: THE GIFT OF SYPHILIS

In his *Confessions*, Jean Jacques would later describe the mixture of emotions that caused him to write his letter on Providence to Voltaire. "Shocked to discover this poor man declaiming so bitterly against the miseries of this life and declaring everything to be bad, while himself overwhelmed with fame and prosperity, I formed the bold plan of bringing him to himself again: proving to him that, on the contrary, everything was good in this best of all possible worlds. . . . For the absurdity of his doctrine was all the more glaring coming as it did from a man loaded down with blessings of all kinds, who, from the bosom of happiness, yet seeks to reduce his fellow man to despair by a fearful and cruel picture of human calamities from which he himself is largely exempt."

Bold plan, he calls it. And indeed it was, for Jean Jacques to attempt to teach Voltaire. Making thus his sly bid for the topmost place in French thought. While he was in fact still so intimidated by Voltaire that he could not rid himself of his usual deferential style of address:

Never would I dare oppose you, my dear master, if it were not for the fact that I have found so much support for my position in your former works. Certainly I need not be afraid, when I find that you yourself are really on my side. . . .

But even with the feeling that he had the backing of Voltaire, it was only with the utmost trepidation, only "loving you as a brother, honoring you as my teacher, and remembering the many lessons which I absorbed from you," it was only thus that Rousseau dared to make his advance against that mighty man, who, however prostrate, was still formidable.

. . . But, dear sir, I have suffered too much in life not to expect another. And all the subtleties of the metaphysics in your poem will not budge me.

I hold that there must be immortality for man. Yes, there must be. Otherwise, with so many people living only short and truncated lives, there would arise an ever swelling burden of injustice in this world which nothing could cancel out. So, if there is a God—and which of us, beholding creation, can deny the existence of a Creator?—then that God must be wise, all-powerful and just. Otherwise He would not be perfect. Otherwise He would not be God.

And since God is wise and all-powerful, then the world He created must be the best of all possible worlds. His wisdom would dictate nothing less for man, and His power would immediately call it into being. And since God is just and all-powerful, then our short lives cannot be the end. His justice would not brook it. And His power would immediately provide the remedy.

In short, we are immortal.

And I ask you then, Monsieur de Voltaire, since my soul exists in eternity, what difference can it make to me whether I die now, as a result of some Lisbon disaster, or live another thirty years?

No, nothing in your metaphysics will ever make me doubt the existence of a beneficent Providence, and the consequent immortality of my soul. I feel it, I believe it, I want it, I hope for it. And I will defend that hope to my last sigh.

But it was not this theological argument, which, after all, was familiar to Voltaire, since he himself had employed it in previous works (and it was, in fact, older than either of the two men)—no, it was not this argument that roused the anger of Voltaire when he received the letter. It was a certain comparison that Jean Jacques had dared to draw between himself and Voltaire:

Reading your beautiful poem, M. de Voltaire, I could not prevent myself from observing what a striking contrast there exists between you and me.

You, satiated with glory, bored by the empty honors that are daily heaped upon you, living as best pleases you, in the midst of abundance, and philosophizing at your leisure on the nature of the soul, in complete confidence of the world-wide fame that is yours; able to rely, too, on the talent of your good friend Dr. Tronchin to heal you of whatever bodily pain may strike you . . . yet, for all that, it seems, you find nothing but evil on this earth. Whereas I, obscure, penniless, tormented night and day with a disease for which there is no remedy, I nevertheless, here in my country retreat, meditate with pleasure and find that everything is good.

What can be the cause of this sharp contradiction between us? Your poem explains it: you enjoy, sir. But I hope. And my hope embellishes everything.

Voltaire was beside himself when he read this. "Why, the insolent dog!" he exclaimed. But of course that was how it had to be; when one picks up a puppy one must be prepared to be licked on the mouth. Faugh!

Why, the whole impertinent letter was nothing but Jean Jacques measuring himself up to Voltaire! And everywhere finding himself ahead of his master. In spite of a superficial show of the greatest humility. Yes, the whole letter seemed to be saying nothing but "Note my arguments. Are they not more logical than yours? Observe my conduct. Is it not more dignified than yours? Consider my character. Are not my virtues . . ."

Well, damn it, yes! The man had not passed up a single slip on Voltaire's part. For example, in the course of dashing off his poem Voltaire had left in a phrase suggestion that if earthquakes had to happen, then why not in the desert instead of the city?

To which Rousseau now retorted:

But earthquakes do happen in the desert, sir. They must. Deserts cannot be any more exempt from the shaking of the earth than any other part of our globe. But who lives in the desert? Only savages. Only poor people. And what happens to them is not worth writing poems about. For it has been established once and for all that only when something affects the cultured gentlemen of our great cities is the matter worth reporting. . . .

Yes, that was well argued. And Jean Jacques continued even more tellingly:

. . . Moreover, in their ignorance of architecture, those poor savages who live in the deserts build their tents or their huts close to the ground and far apart, so that earthquakes can cause them but little damage; whereas we have the skill to crowd 20,000 six- or seven-story buildings close together, and in fact that is exactly what we do in order to extract all the more gain. And then, of course, when a temblor dares to level our investments we cry out against the laws of nature and even against the laws of God.

But surely, sir, you are not asking that the earth should change her behavior according to our caprices, and that all that should be required in order to keep an earthquake from happening in a certain spot is for us to decide to build a city there?

"Pestilence!" Voltaire cried. Or, more likely, to evaporate the hot emotions that flared up through his dry frame he must have used some more violent profanity, such as "You *chiure,* you *crotte* drenched in corrupted blood!" For it was obvious that here was a potential enemy far beyond a Pompignan. Or a Maupertuis. Or even a Fréron or a Jean Baptiste Rousseau.

Indeed, there was more than just a measuring up to Voltaire here. There were certain hints that Rousseau was on to Voltaire. That he had ferreted out Voltaire's secret terror of dying. His fear of oblivion. His eventual need to face death philosophically so as to earn for himself a glorious funeral.

An early death in a disaster may be a kindness [Rousseau wrote as if in answer to Voltaire's unspoken thought]. It's done and over with. Can you, M. de Voltaire, imagine any end more to be pitied than that which confronts so many of us these days—where a dying man is overwhelmed with irritating and suffocating attentions? Lawyers and hopeful heirs crowd about a man's bedside, scarcely allowing the poor victim room for his last sigh; and meanwhile doctors unload their useless drugs upon him, not only killing him all the more surely, but expecting to be well paid for it; while priests cannot be prevented from throwing in those barbaric rites of theirs that serve only to make the moribund taste the bitterness of death down to its last acrid dregs.

Devil take this Jean Jacques!
But even more harrowing was this:

So what if my body must die and be eaten by worms and go to manure the soil? Must there not be a circulation of nutritive substances? It's all in the order of nature. My children and my brothers will eat of the produce of the soil, and they will live and die as I have lived and died.

The body manures the soil, does it? And the next generation will enjoy the produce of it? Well, that's fine. Voltaire knew as much about agriculture as Rousseau, if not more than he. But if the human body was so important for manure, then a brute of a king who squanders the lives of tens of thousands of young men on the field of battle is really a friend of humanity! What a great manuring he has done for the soil! Far better than any one of us could manage individually.

And in that case why not let people die like dogs? Throw their bodies out on the town dump with the carcases of horses and cats.

So much for your wretched philosophy of nature!

And between a Frederick the Great who says, "Squeeze the orange and throw the skin away!" and a Jean Jacques who says, "Die and manure the soil!" there's really little to choose. The big tyrant and the little tyrant. That's all.

Take death lightly? Ha! Yes, your own death, if such be your pleasure. Voltaire himself loved to jest at death. He liked to say, "I want to die laughing." That was every man's privilege: to think of his own death as he wished.

But take no one else's death lightly! Throw no one else's skin away!

Why, even for the life of a dying bird Voltaire once wept, and he could have killed a maid who made light of the matter.

That was the time he kept an eaglet as a pet, an eaglet which he had bought from some mountaineer, and which, chained by one leg, perched on the crossbar of a pole in Voltaire's courtyard.

Not that Voltaire liked that eaglet. On the contrary, he hated it. What was it but the incarnation of regal scorn and aristocratic lack of pity? A razor blade come alive. A thing with a heart of steel and blood of ice. No wonder that kings all over the world took the eagle as their symbol.

And yet even for this implacable creature Voltaire had a genuine affection. And one day when from his upstairs study he heard a commotion in the yard and looked down to where two roosters were attacking his eaglet, he was shocked by the cruelty of it.

But before he could get down to the yard the combat was over and the eaglet lay bleeding on the flagstones. Anyone else would have said, "That thing is done for." But not Voltaire. So long as there was a vestige of life left, he would fight for it. He called to one of his servants, "Quick, Blaise! Saddle my fastest horse. Go to Geneva and bring me back a good veterinarian."

In the meanwhile Voltaire helped the wounded eaglet back to his perch and watched it take a shaky hold there. And afterward went up to his study and resumed his work. But only to jump from his desk every few moments to look down and see how the eaglet was faring, and to peer along the road to Geneva to see if Blaise was back yet.

When finally Blaise came into the courtyard with the veterinarian mounted behind him, Voltaire hastened down to greet the doctor, pull him off the horse and rush him over to the eaglet.

"Assure me that he will recover," Voltaire begged. "Ask me for any reward you like, only heal the poor thing."

The veterinarian poked his fingers under the bird's plumage, endeavoring to estimate the extent of the injuries. But he could offer little hope. "Let us see if he responds to my first dressing," he said. "Then we'll be able to say for sure."

The dressing was applied, and now the eaglet looked truly forlorn, with its feathers stained with medicine and plastered over with wax to keep the healing extracts pressed up against the wounds. Voltaire tried to tempt the big bird with a choice piece of meat, but it only blinked its lackluster eyes and hung its head.

And a few days later the veterinarian was able to deliver his opinion. "Very doubtful," was how he put it.

Voltaire's eyes moistened. "Surely there's some way to . . ."

The veterinarian spread his hands. "Nature alone can cure that bird. And it would surprise me very much if nature did."

But still every morning Voltaire woke with hope. And when his buxom maidservant Madeleine came to his bedside, the first thing he would say, even before getting out of bed, was: "How is my eaglet this morning?"

And Madeleine would have to reply, "Not too well, monsieur."

One morning, however, she entered the room, her stout face wreathed in smiles, and declared, "Well, your eaglet is no longer sick, monsieur."

Voltaire threw back the covers, crying, "Healed! How wonderful!"

Whereupon the maid saw that she had gone too far and she said quickly: "I mean, sir—dead."

Voltaire froze. "Dead?" he repeated.

Then he exploded. "How dare you make such a dreadful announcement to me as if it were a laughing matter?"

"But, monsieur," Madeleine defended herself, "that poor eagle was just skin and bones. I thought he was better off dead."

"Just skin and bones, was he?" Voltaire cried. "Now, there's a fine explanation!" He rose in his nightclothes. "Skin and bones, did you say?"

Madeleine drew back a step or two in fright. While Voltaire, opening his robe, continued to shout at her, "Look at me! What am I but skin and bones? And will you say that I too would be better off dead? Ha? Answer me! Is that what you think? Better off dead? And would you announce it with laughter some morning if you found me done for?"

"Oh, monsieur . . ." Madeleine pleaded, tears coming to her eyes.

But Voltaire was not to be assuaged. "Why, you waddling slut, you! Is it your idea that only people with lard in their behinds have a right to live? Is it to be nothing but a world of fat arses? Well, I say to you, get that blown-up rump of yours out of here before I kick it off!"

The poor girl ran out of Voltaire's room covering her face with her hands and sobbing loudly.

Meanwhile Madame Denis, hearing this commotion in her uncle's room, had come huffing and puffing up the stairs to find out what it was all about.

But Voltaire would only mutter darkly, "Skin and bones. Ha! So I must be killed just because I'm not fat." And for quite a while that was all he would tell his niece. She herself was a ball of suet and might also be convinced that the world belonged to the fat.

But finally Madame Denis got the story out of him. "Get rid of that girl," Voltaire screamed in conclusion. "Get her out of this house, I say! I never want to see her again! Do you hear me?"

"Yes, yes," Madame Denis said. "I hear you."

Some weeks later, however, Voltaire suddenly asked his niece, "That girl—Madeleine. What about her? I suppose she soon found herself another place."

Madame Denis said, "Another place? Can you imagine! When all Geneva knows that you threw her out of your home? No, I hardly think she'll manage that easily."

"Serve her right!" Voltaire cried. "The fat tub! Let her starve a little and see if *she* would like to die just because she's skin and bones." He muttered on for a while and then said, "Still, I wouldn't want her to die of hunger. In fact, you might ask her back. But only on condition that she keep out of my sight. Find her some work to do about the place. But warn her that I never want to lay eyes on her again!"

It is of this extremely touchy man, where it concerned the subject of death, that we must think, when we try to picture Voltaire's reactions to Jean Jacques's letter—on learning from it, for example, that it should make no difference whether Voltaire died now in some disaster or lived another thirty years.

No difference, eh? Thirty years of my life means nothing to you? How cavalier can one be with other peoples' lives?

And telling him that the best thing Voltaire could do was to give up the ghost and let his body manure the soil. Altogether in the order of nature, if you please. Indeed, Voltaire might feel honored that his corpse would grow turnips to feed his descendants. Rotate the nutritive substances! That was man's sole purpose.

Well, of course where Jean Jacques's nature was concerned what did it matter whether one man was a poet and made books, and the other just munched turnips and made manure? Jean Jacques had no use for books. Except of course when they happened to further his own career!

And to cap it all, this brutal scheme of things, believe it or not, constituted the best of all possible worlds. Take Jean Jacques's word for it. He happened to know more about God, and about God's plans, than did this ignorant fellow Voltaire, who stubbornly refused to manure the soil with his body.

Voltaire worked himself up into a rage. How stupid he had been to have spared that fool so often. But not again. No, sir. This time he meant to crush him. Crush him with a pamphlet that would make Desfontaines, Maupertuis, Jean Baptiste Rousseau, all his former enemies consider themselves as having got off lightly. Now Europe would see a real bit of pig-sticking.

But wait a moment . . .

What if that was precisely what this rascal was itching for? The man was said to be a remarkable chess player. What, then, if this letter was nothing but a gambit intended to draw Voltaire into a fight, where Jean Jacques Rousseau would represent the case of the common man and his optimism while Voltaire represented the rich and their pessimism due to a surfeit of the good things of life?

How would that look to the eyes of Europe? That poor, sick, still inglorious Rousseau fighting the rich and pompous Voltaire. Why, obviously, Jean Jacques would get all the sympathy. Voltaire would be laughed at.

This thing was really more dangerous than it had seemed at first sight. Amazing! That this tiny splash of a Rousseau, who so far had published only two brief essays, both of them silly, and one operetta, of which those who were in a position to know could swear that half its tunes were stolen from melodies long popular in Venice—this insignificant worm could actually threaten to overthrow Voltaire, whose reputation had been acquired by more than fifty solid masterpieces?

And if he should succeed? What then became of one's dream of a Newtonian funeral? Jean Jacques would get it. And Voltaire's corpse would be thrown into the sewer.

Well, Voltaire could play chess, too. Instead of the crushing reply which he had been ready to give, suppose he should change his move. *J'adoube,* Monsieur Rousseau. I decline your clever gambit.

That made sense! And a trickier revenge too.

Voltaire replied to Jean Jacques in one of his sweetest and briefest of notes.

What a beautiful letter from you, my dear Rousseau. A pity, really, that I should have to deny myself the pleasure of further philosophizing with you. How amusing it would have been, even if it should have led us nowhere. Unfortunately I have with me one of my nieces, who, for the past three weeks, has been close to death. So dangerously close that, much though I myself am in need of bed and doctor, I must nevertheless be up and about to nurse her.

There! That first paragraph should stop all this nonsense about the "striking contradictions" between poor M. Rousseau and rich M. de Voltaire. The one might be indigent and the other affluent, but what difference did that make in the face of the great facts of life and death, where we are all afloat in the same leaky craft and adrift on the same angry seas?

While, in addition, for the wise who might someday study the matter, there was the hint that we succor our dying instead of being content to let them perish in accordance with nature, even though it makes no difference whether life be short or long, God being always there to even things up with his eternal justice (according to His prophet Rousseau).

And then one more little paragraph, overflowing with kindness, so that if there should linger the least suspicion of a sting in the first paragraph, it must be more than wiped out by the following:

I hear from Dr. Tronchin that you might after all decide to return to your own country. Ask M. d'Alembert, who was just here on a visit, what a quiet philosophical life we enjoy here in my retreat. I call my place The Delights, a name that it will never so truly merit as when it will have finally had the privilege of sheltering you. Please believe me, my dear Rousseau, that though I may often be guilty of jokes and sarcasm of questionable taste, of all those who read you none is more disposed to love you tenderly than your ever humble servant Voltaire.

No, none more disposed to love him tenderly than his ever humble servant Voltaire. Well, why shouldn't he say that? It was true, wasn't it? Of course he loved Rousseau. Certainly as much as he loved the Jews. Or the Christians, for that matter. Was not this Jean Jacques condemned to death like everyone else? But of course that didn't mean that so long as life still flowed in Voltaire's paper-thin veins he would permit this dog of a Jean Jacques to get ahead of him.

That, never!

And Rousseau? He too still revered his master Voltaire. But he boiled with indignation to have received no more than this short letter. Letter? Call that a letter? This two-minute scrawl in answer to the days of work that he had put in writing his own, which was practically a complete essay on divine Providence?

Outplayed again! As always when he tangled with Voltaire. Still another one of those flowery notes. A bit of paper tossed off in less time then it takes to blow one's nose. And the result not worth wiping one's behind with.

And worse than that: Voltaire remaining in possession of Jean Jacques's letter. For this was the cruel custom of correspondence. And that sly fox had obviously scented Rousseau's aim of eventual publication and had deliberately written him an answer not worth printing, while at the same time retaining possession of Rousseau's letter, which was clearly ready for the press.

Short-changed! And by this rich man. This rich man whom he had taken pity on and tried to save. Short-changed, because a letter, once sent, ceased to be one's property. It became the property of the addressee. Not, indeed, for him to palm off as his own, but still his private possession. Which now could not be published except by mutual consent. In just the same way that their previous exchange of letters had required Voltaire's request that Rousseau grant him permission to publish.

But he, Rousseau, had agreed! While it was so obvious that Voltaire did not intend to return the courtesy. Oh, it was enough to make one weep tears of blood! The poor forever defrauded! And all because he had wished to bring Voltaire into a better frame of mind.

Too furious to trust himself to write a calm letter to Voltaire, Rousseau begged a correspondent in Geneva to approach the great man for the right to publish. Wasted effort. Exactly as Jean Jacques had known it would be.

"A letter from Jean Jacques Rousseau?" the great man asked, obviously relishing the fact that he had outguessed his little opponent, but nevertheless having his additional fun by pretending that he had some difficulty recalling the matter. "Oh, yes, of course. *That* letter. An excellent letter, by the way. And really, I owe Monsieur Rousseau an answer. Please tell him that I shall get around to it as soon as possible."

Naturally, he didn't get around to it. But Rousseau controlled his anger and waited yet a while. And then, to make doubly sure, he wrote to another correspondent in Geneva to sound out Voltaire again.

And Voltaire had his fun again. Deliberately pretending to misunderstand the situation. "Please assure Monsieur Rousseau," he said, "that I am a man of honor, and that I would never dream of releasing to the press a letter which I must obviously regard as a very private communication from Monsieur Rousseau."

What could Jean Jacques do? Prostrate himself for the hundredth time before this jeering man? Oh, someday he should pay for this! But meanwhile Jean Jacques could only rage secretly, still afraid to come out openly, and going so far in concealing his real feelings as to boast to his friends (who, of course, were all admirers of Voltaire) that he had just received the most charming and "obliging little note" from the great man.

But in his *Confessions,* later, he would write, "Voltaire promised me an answer, but he never sent it. What he did was publish it instead. It is nothing else but his novel *Candide,* of which I am unable to say anything, since I have never read it."

Never read it? What? Can this be believed? Of Jean Jacques, who only a few years before had been able to speak of himself as "never letting the slightest word written by Voltaire escape his attention"? But now would not even glance into this *Candide, or Optimism,* with which Voltaire was making such an international sensation?

But really, what need did he have to read that book when he could gather from all the excited comments he heard around him how wonderful it was, how witty, and with what a mad pace it held you spellbound in a world of burlesque violence, while ripping to pieces the old Leibnitzian notion that this was the best of all possible worlds.

No, he had no need to read it, and indeed he could not possibly have read it through the tears of rage that would have blinded his eyes. This was the answer that Voltaire should have sent to him. Had in fact promised him! This was the Voltairean piece that should have been published with his own. It was due him! For it was he, with his letter on Providence, who had roused Voltaire to write this immensely popular tale. Popular already in manuscript form, popular before the first printed copies came from the presses. And after that a Niagara. Printed and reprinted, translated and devoured everywhere. Thus adding yet another crown of laurel leaves to a brow that was already overloaded.

And Rousseau meanwhile left without so much as his own letter.

No. This was one volume by Voltaire that Rousseau need never read.

Couldn't he guess from the comments he heard all around him that the book was nothing but a vicious attack on himself? What difference if he wasn't mentioned by name? This Candide, the hero, was obviously a caricature of Jean Jacques. Presented to the world as a simpleton who was still willing, in our day and age, to hold to the Leibnitzian belief that this was the best of all possible worlds.

No. He didn't have to read that book. He would hear often enough references and derisive laughter from those who had read the episode of Candide in the Bulgarian war, where "nine or ten thousand rascals were removed by musketry from this best of all possible worlds."

He would hear often enough the booming laughter of those who admired the stomach-upsetting encounter in Holland of Candide with his old tutor, now a victim of syphilis, "his face covered with sores, his eyes half dead, his nose eaten away, his mouth distorted, his gums rotten and his teeth so black with decay that as he spoke through his throat, tormented by spasms, he came near ejecting a tooth with every word."

And still the tutor would not have Candide lose his faith in this, the best of all possible worlds, on account of syphilis. "If I had not tasted the delights of Paradise in the arms of Paquette," Voltaire had the tutor say, "I would not have received the torments of hell. Paquette got this disease from a Franciscan monk, who had it from an old countess, who had acquired it from a cavalry captain, who owed it to a marquise, who had taken it from her page, who had got it from a Jesuit, who, when a novice, had been infected by one of the sailors of Christopher Columbus, who had brought the disease back from his voyages of discovery in America. But if we got syphilis from America, we also got chocolate," the tutor concluded, in order to show the bright side of disaster.

And so it went, through every kind of violence from rape to burning at the stake, through every kind of catastrophe from earthquake to tornado, and through every manner of absurdity. All served up with the speed of slides going through a magic lantern. And with all the shrieks and mayhem of a Punch-and-Judy show.

What rude shocks the world provided for poor Candide, who had to protect his optimism through every trial! Even an encounter in South America with a Negro slave who had had his hand cut off in a sugar mill and his leg cut off by his master for trying to escape. "Such," says the Negro, "is the price that must be paid so that Europe may have its sugar."

No, Jean Jacques did not have to read that book. Its contents seemed to float in the air around one, so popular was it. And everyone knew that only one man could have written it, even though that man denied it, and even though the book itself was issued as "translated from the German papers of Dr. Ralph."

As for Voltaire, he wrote again and again in letters to friends, "One must be insane to attribute such stuff to me." And went so far as to appeal to his publisher, Cramer, to find him a copy of this *Candide,* "which, I understand, was first circulated in Lyons, a scandalous work which people brazenly accuse me of writing, when, as a matter of fact, I have still to lay my eyes on a single copy."

Naturally the cowardly Voltaire would lie about his authorship, considering that the authorities everywhere were ordering the public executioner to burn it and churchmen were everywhere condemning it. The Seven Years' War was on, which Voltaire had fought so hard to prevent, and almost every government in Europe was involved, and no king on his throne could approve of a book in which one of the most famous episodes was that of the carnival in Venice, where six deposed monarchs found themselves by chance seated at the same table.

And no statesman sending his troops into combat for the glory of the fatherland could enjoy such Voltairean scorn for war as in this sentence: "Rest assured that of the young men lined up for battle, on both sides, twenty thousand out of thirty thousand have the pox. And it is these young diseased men who will decide the fate of nations."

Rousseau should have applauded such statements. He hated kings and wars as much as Voltaire, if not more so. He had far more complaints to make about the condition of man than Voltaire. In fact, it was he who should have written this book, not Voltaire. All this success should have been his! Voltaire had stolen Rousseau's earlier thesis, that the world was all wrong.

In the bitterness of his deception Jean Jacques began to write letters such as this to his admirers in Geneva: "Don't ever talk to me about Voltaire. Never let the name of that clown soil your letters. I could only hate that man more if I could learn to despise him less."

And to another correspondent: "Geneva will yet have to suffer for harboring that godless braggart, that genius without a soul!"

Voltaire had beaten him just once too often. Now he was sustained by nothing except the hope that someday he would have his revenge. Someday, somehow, he would bring Voltaire to his knees.

And then? Why, then, of course, Jean Jacques would raise him up and embrace him.

Antipodes. That is how one critic described these two men who were a world apart. And yet so close.

Once, for example, Voltaire was visited by an elderly countess wearing a daring décolleté. Seeing the great man staring at her bosom, she remarked coyly, "Oh, Monsieur de Voltaire, you mustn't keep looking at my two little kittens."

"Your two little kittens?" Voltaire exclaimed. "And I was just thinking that I had never before seen such a pair of hangdogs."

Afraid of breasts? Voltaire hadn't the slightest fear of them.

It was only that which reminded him of the end of life that disturbed him.

Whereas Rousseau was disturbed by everything that reminded him of the beginning of life.

21: HOT MEDICATED CLYSTERS

How does one get the better of a man to whom nothing is really serious? Nothing really sacred. A man who can jest about everything except his own death. And even about that too at times.

"I'm amusing myself with the construction of my tomb," Voltaire informed his friends when he was in the process of rebuilding the little church on his Ferney estate. And he carried his little tomb joke so far as to have the contractor come up and measure him for the job, so that no money would be wasted in overbuilding. After all, he wasn't going to be much of a corpse. "The services of two little boys," he wrote, "will be all the pallbearers I'll need."

But the tomb, when finished, caused considerable amusement, for it was seen to be only half inside the church, with the other half projecting through the side of the building out into the open air. A joke preserved for the ages in brick and mortar. Indicating, no doubt, that even when he was dead there was no church that could really hold Voltaire.

He had laughter for every occasion. And for every mood. So that, from the Homeric *haw-haw* to the derisive *hoo-hoo,* from the *hay-hay* of malice to the *ho-ho* of boisterous good fellowship, there was not a vowel in the alphabet of laughter that Voltaire did not possess.

All except the timid *hee-hee* of nervous children and of reluctant adults. Which, one suspects, must have been the nearest thing to laughter that Jean Jacques could manage.

But then, what could Rousseau do? Suspended as he was between love and hate. Sawed back and forth between loathing for the man he was nevertheless compelled to admire and affection for a man whom he could only despise. So that no matter what emotion might well up in him, he found himself cut to the quick.

And now, in addition, under his little round wig, an ever increasing stubble of gray. Old age! Old age approaching, and with it the inevitability of death. And still no sign that he would ever once get the better of that man.

Good Lord, must he die without ever having brought off a single coup? No, no! At least once before his grave, Voltaire must be soundly humiliated.

But how? That was the question. How does one beat the unbeatable? Who had ever succeeded in downing that slippery wrestler?

Frederick the Great? Well, yes. But for how long? All too soon after his revenge on Voltaire at Frankfurt, even that mighty monarch had been forced to humble himself before Voltaire, before that man whom he had once intended to cast aside like a squeezed-out orange.

It was the Seven Years' War that did it. When the three powerful petticoats of Europe, Maria Theresa of Austria, Catherine the Great of Russia and Madame de Pompadour of France, united to crush the Prussian woman hater. And when the Austrian general, Kaunen, opened the military campaigns of that war with the battle at Kolin, where Frederick's troops were so badly beaten that it seemed the end was already in sight, what with Swedes, French, Austrians, Russians all pouring down upon defenseless Prussia. So that Frederick, despairing, decided that suicide was the only honorable way out.

That was when he wrote his farewell poem beginning *"Ami, le sort en est jeté . . ."*

Friend, the die is cast. And of course the friend he had most in mind was old Voltaire.

Old Voltaire, who had tried so hard to keep this insane war from happening. Old Voltaire, who thought of war as nothing but murder done to the sound of trumpets and the fluttering of flags. Old Voltaire, his good teacher through so many years, on whom he had always depended for the correction of his poetry. And who must now correct this one above all—the last poem of his life. For the thought of leaving behind him a wretched poem at which connoisseurs would snicker, that was intolerable.

And though it ought to have been unthinkable that a monarch should make the first move toward reconciliation with a commoner (an upstart who had invented his own ennobling particle *de*), still Frederick resolved himself to it. Writing out his poem in his own hand and dispatching it to Voltaire by special messenger, along with a letter pleading for a speedy reply.

And Voltaire?

Though he spotted in this poem many a line plagiarized from other writers, to say nothing of several lines stolen from his own works, and though he found far too many references to such convenient symbols as roses and myrtles, as well as some rather incoherent chains of thought, he concluded that for a king it was not a bad poetic effort. No, not really bad at all. Just too long and repetitious. But then, how many kings in the history of man have ever written anything worth while in the way of poetry? The Jewish kings Solomon and David, yes. But a German king?

And so Voltaire (according to those all-too-brief *Mémoires* of his which he had ordered destroyed, but of which La Harpe, the dwarfish professor of French literary history, managed to filch a copy for posterity) forgave the King and rushed into hasty prose in order to dissuade a ruler who had taken the lives of so many soldiers from taking still another one, namely his own.

For to Voltaire death was still the only enemy. And it made no difference whose death. He could laugh at the rites with which man surrounds this appalling disaster. But at death itself, *la camarde,* the snub-nosed one, he could not really laugh. No matter how much he might pretend to.

"I argued," Voltaire says, "that Europe needed Frederick. Needed him to restore that ever teetering balance of power which alone could give Europe those wonderful moments of respite from war, when once again the arts and commerce could flourish and the people be enriched."

And besides, even with the loss of Prussia, will he not still have Saxony and Silesia? Is not that enough for a philosopher-king?

Thus Voltaire saved Frederick's life. For which some Frenchmen cannot forgive him to this day, since the Prussians would soon manage to gather their strength again and crush the French at Rossbach, while Prussia's ally, England, would take advantage of France's weakness to steal away her colonial empire of Canada and India. The two men, however, were friends again now, and correspondents ever after.

Now how could a Rousseau even dream of getting the better of such a man? A man whom even kings failed to overcome?

By his talents, perhaps?

But men of talents far beyond Rousseau's failed to break Voltaire.

Piron, for example. Piron, who seemed as if created by a special act of nature in order to outdo Voltaire.

"An intellectual machine," is the way Grimm would describe Piron in his secret literary correspondence. "A machine that flashes wit."

Even Voltaire, whose wit was legendary, couldn't match that machine and could think of nothing better to do than just keep out of Piron's range. For almost every time they collided it was Voltaire who got scorched.

For instance, at the opening of Voltaire's *Zulime,* which was admittedly one of the dramatist's poorer efforts, when, at the end of the first act, with the fate of the play still somewhat in doubt, Voltaire made the mistake of asking Piron, "Well, what do you think of it, my dear Piron?"

And Piron replied, "I think, my dear Voltaire, that before this evening is over you'll be wishing that I had written it."

There was laughter from everyone within earshot. Which of course put it up to Voltaire to make a suitable reply. One that would steal the laughter from Piron's side. But Voltaire couldn't think of anything brilliant at the moment. He could only mutter, "I really love you too much to wish my play on you, my dear Piron." And he scurried to efface himself in the crowd, obviously determined that it would be a long time before he would let himself get involved with that dear Piron again.

Piron, on the other hand, was gradually becoming convinced that he far outweighed the redoubtable Voltaire, and he began to want nothing so much as a real duel of wits in order to put himself on top permanently.

At Fountainebleau, where the two poets happened to be one summer, both busy preparing entertainment for the court, Piron tried repeatedly to corner Voltaire and have it out with him. But Voltaire remained prudently out of reach.

Piron was a towering man, built like a barbarian, ruggedly healthy, barrel-chested, and with a booming voice. So that Voltaire had no difficulty spotting him from afar, which gave one just enough time for quick excuses from whatever company one might be in, and for rapid ducking down some convenient corridor. Almost before Piron could be quite sure whether he had just glimpsed his rival or not.

"Where is he?" the flabbergasted Piron said time and again. "What is he? A man that walks? Or just a little green pea that keeps rolling around?"

In the theater it seemed for a while that they would each hold his own. But in somewhat different fields. Voltaire at the official theater, the Théâtre-Français, which leaned to tragedies in the classical style, and Piron at the unofficial theater of the Foire, where the dramatic rules were somewhat relaxed.

In the rivalry between these two theaters, the official theater once tried to crush its competitor by forcing through a law prohibiting the other from having more than one speaking actor. It was then that Piron, with a series of extremely clever three-act monologues, kept the Théâtre de la Foire from going under. Monologues so witty that at times all the theatergoers of Paris were drawn to the Foire, leaving the official theater to play its classics (even its Voltairean classics) to an empty house.

The result, of course, was that eventually the official theater got such Draconian laws passed that the unofficial theater was driven out of business altogether.

Piron always claimed that no one else but Voltaire was behind this dirty business. He also claimed that Voltaire, by scribbling poems of love to all the actresses, was able to have his plays so scheduled as to work out to his own advantage. Putting, for example, on the boards of the official theater his own masterpiece *Zaïre* just ahead of Piron's *Gustava Vasa,* so that all Paris would still be talking of the Voltaire play when Piron's opened, and the latter would never get the attention it deserved. And again, swamping Piron's *Fernand Cortez* with his *Mérope.*

Of course there's no doubt that Voltaire did make love to all the actresses. And furthermore that by his habit of distributing among the actors all his theatrical profits he enjoyed an ascendancy over less moneyed writers who couldn't forgo their share of the box-office returns. With the result that the company preferred to put on Voltaire plays and extended itself to give them longer runs.

"There's no trick too dirty for that man to stoop to," Piron concluded. "Not where his reputation is at stake. A man like that would cheat his way into heaven."

Piron thereupon wrote a biting dramatic satire on Voltaire, *La Métromanie*. Presenting him on stage as a fop perpetually tossing off bits of versified compliments to all the ladies.

La Métromanie was a hit. And everyone waited for Voltaire's riposte, which would naturally have to be a crusher.

But the crusher never came.

"He can't touch me," said Piron scornfully. And this would have clinched the matter for Piron, except that Voltaire claimed that he hadn't had a chance to see the play, that he had been out of town and extremely busy and didn't know what the play was about.

"Excuses!" roared Piron. "The man's just too frightened to pick up my challenge. But he'll not escape me forever. Someday, I swear, I'll get him at a dinner table. And before witnesses I'll flay him alive. So that he'll never be able to deny my victory to his dying day."

Despite Voltaire's wariness, such an encounter finally took place. In Brussels. Where Voltaire had to go on business. But where, learning that Piron was in town, he kept himself very quiet. For obviously it was going to be pretty difficult for two such prominent Parisians as himself and Piron to avoid bumping into each other at some home to which both of them would be invited.

According to Piron, Voltaire changed his hotel and gave out the story that he had already left town. "But I kept seeing apothecaries running through the streets," Piron would later relate. "They were rushing hot medicated clysters to some important client. That was obvious. And what could that mean except that Voltaire must still be lurking around? For that man can't live, you know, without his hot medicated enemas. Has a veritable passion for them. Actually quivers with anticipation."

With huge gusto Piron would tell how he tracked down Voltaire by following the spoor of these apothecaries. Until finally he came pounding on Voltaire's door.

"Voltaire! Voltaire!" he cried. "This is Piron. Your apothecary!"

Piron was, as a matter of fact, the son of a well-known French apothecary.

"Don't come in!" Voltaire screamed from some distant room. "Don't come in!"

In his most seductive voice Piron sang out, "I've got a clyster for you, Monsieur de Voltaire. A fresh hot clyster. You'll love it!"

"Excuse me!" came Voltaire's voice, shrill and frightened. "Excuse me, my dear Piron. But no jokes, please. Not now. Please come some other time. I'm confined to my bed with a terrible headache."

Voltaire's valet tried to prevent Piron from entering, but the massive Piron just brushed him aside and penetrated into the poet's bedroom.

"Confined? Yes, that he was!" Piron would admit. "But not to his bed. And not with a headache. He was confined to his *chaise percée*. And the terrible ache, if he had one, was at the opposite end of his anatomy. Ah, my friends, what a sight! The great Voltaire, the glory and the light of our century, sitting, all crunched up, on his potty chair!"

One can imagine how Voltaire must have hated Piron, this man of superabundant health, for making fun of a person such as himself who had to practice every kind of ingenuity to wring another drop of energy, another hour of well-being, from his wretched body.

"Just think!" Piron would crow, his big face steaming with the sweat of satisfaction. "Only four days in Brussels and already our Voltaire had got himself involved in six colonic irrigations and one lawsuit."

To be sure, it was no particular novelty to make fun of Voltaire because of an addiction to enemas. As well as to lawsuits. For the son of a lawyer, and himself compelled for a year to study law, the one came naturally. And the other because of his devotion to the old Egyptian theory of internal cleanliness as the basis of good health. Voltaire always claimed, for example, that but for five hundred glasses of lemonade that had washed all the poisons out of his system, he would never have recovered from an attack of smallpox which he had had at the age of thirty.

While in exile in England Voltaire had written Thieriot a letter that many people had been privileged to read: "Oh, the delicious British invention! Conceive, my dear Thieriot, a machine with which one can administer oneself an enema, and this machine so perfectly contrived as to fit into one's watch pocket. Imagine the convenience of it! Always available, no matter where one may happen to be. If ever my exile to England should come to an end, I shall make it a point to bring you half a dozen of these incomparable devices."

Well, be that as it may, it was there, in Brussels, that that decisive Piron-Voltaire encounter was to take place. One fine evening, just as Voltaire had feared, he arrived at a dinner party confident that Piron was elsewhere, and instead there he was, just waiting for him. And all the dinner guests too, sitting on the edge of their chairs to see how the situation would resolve itself between these two champions of the world of wit.

Voltaire paled and declared that he was indisposed. Which Piron recognized as just another old trick: it would make Voltaire's victory all the greater, if he should obtain it, and diminish his defeat if he should suffer it.

But Piron didn't mind. While Voltaire scarcely did more than nibble at his shirred eggs and barely moistened his lips with the wine, Piron, already relishing victory, downed a couple of goose legs, explored some of the more elaborate dishes and tossed down glass after glass of wine.

Exactly what was said has never been recorded. Voltaire, for his part, never so much as whispered a word about any of this. As for Piron, he would only gloat and say, "Huh! I made the discovery that your great Voltaire is nothing but a pygmy! Mounted on stilts. And did I have fun cutting those stilts down for him! *Rasibus!* Flush to the ground! I tell you, the end was pitiful."

As far as Piron was concerned the matter was now settled. Your Voltaire was a fraud. A skeleton, an Egyptian mummy, come alive. Good for nothing but to be exhibited at fairs.

But dangerous. Oh, yes, still dangerous. Like a wounded viper. For the more this Voltaire failed in an open fight, the more he was to be feared in a hidden one. There would be dirty work soon, Piron was convinced of that.

And an opportunity was to present itself some years later when Piron, in bad financial straits, was hoping to get himself elected to the French Academy, principally in order to enjoy the pension of six hundred francs a year to which he would be entitled. This would relieve him of his worst embarrassments. His election seemed, as a matter of fact, a certainty, after Louis XV was heard to express surprise that Piron, the cleverest wit of the day, was still not a member.

That's when something happened that Piron would always lay at the door of Voltaire. The very fact that the main cog in these machinations should be the bishop of Mirepoix, a dedicated clerical enemy of Voltaire's, only added further confirmation to the suspicion that none other than Voltaire was behind it. It would not be the first time he had hidden himself behind ecclesiastical garb. Notorious was the dedication of his play *Mahomet,* a play fundamentally anti-Catholic, to the Pope.

In any case, this bishop, who had been the King's tutor during the Regency, appeared now before Louis XV, crying, "You must listen to this, Sire! A poem by Piron. Piron, who is about to become a member of your Academy of Immortals."

And despite his gray-haired tonsure, despite his churchly robes and pectoral cross, he read out loud Piron's unprintable *Ode to Priapus,* a poem that not only starts out with an absolutely unprintable word, but goes on from there, for two hundred lines of the most unbuttoned language ever used, to glorify that fertilizing fluid upon which, in the last analysis, all animal and human creation depends for survival, namely the spermatic fluid, a liquid which not even in nature can be said ever to have spurted, gushed and geysered as it does with such shameless exuberance in this infamous poem.

Who could have slipped the bishop a copy of this old poem of Piron's youth, except Voltaire? And what could the King do, thus facing his old tutor? Except pretend to be terribly shocked, even though he was himself notorious for his addiction to the deflowering of virgins.

In ringing tones of outrage he declared, "Such an immoral writer must never sully our Academy!"

Nothing more was needed to convince every member of the Academy to turn thumbs down on Piron's application.

That was that. And Piron was left without resources. Cursing Voltaire. The viciousness of that man! And the hypocrisy too. For hadn't Voltaire himself written a lascivious poem? In fact, many. In particular his notorious *La Pucelle.* And got into the Academy in spite of it?

But shortly afterward the King made it up to Piron by granting him a special pension of double the one he would have received as Academician. So Piron, delighted, could boast, "More money—and no Academy sittings to attend! And Voltaire smashed again!"

Voltaire, to be sure, denied that he had had any hand whatsoever in this Piron matter. To which Piron retorted, "Naturally. Since he was beaten. But now watch out for some new trick even more malicious!"

But nothing happened. So that finally Piron was led to conclude that Voltaire was just waiting for Piron to die, in order to unleash his fiercest attacks. "The coward!" Piron cried. "Waiting to besmirch my memory after I'm dead. Because alive I'm too much for him."

For some time Piron cherished the hope that he might survive his perpetually ailing rival. But finally, nearing eighty-four, he realized that it would be he who would have to go first. Whereupon he began to make certain preparations.

In his will he wrote, "I shudder to think of what Voltaire will do to my reputation, when I am dead and he need no longer fear me. It is for that reason that I have prepared one hundred and fifty epigrams against Voltaire and have left them in a little box. So that if ever Voltaire should start any new machinations against me, my literary executor can fire off one epigram a week in the direction of Switzerland. That will soon put a stop to him."

The three years' supply of epigrams was, however, never put to use. No need to. Because Voltaire never made the least attempt to besmirch Piron.

Why should he?

All Voltaire said, when he learned of Piron's death, was, "I didn't really know him too well. But my friends often told me that in his play *La Métromanie* the principal role was intended to hold me up to ridicule. I never paid him back for that. But don't you think I could have? And well too? Have you any idea how really wicked I can be? When I want to be. But you see, I've been too busy. He spent his life drinking wine and writing clever lines, odes to Priapus and that sort of stuff. Really a sad waste of his great talents. And not the sort of occupation on which a writer can look back with satisfaction when it comes time to die."

No, a man of Piron's talents, who had spent his life in trivialities (a hundred and fifty epigrams against Voltaire, for example), was not likely to feel satisfied with himself when it came time to die. True enough. But was it proper for Voltaire to be saying that, when it was he who had always encouraged Piron to imagine that those spicy little epigrams of his were so terribly important? When it was he who had always behaved as if Piron's wit frightened him to death, so that at Fontainebleau he had had to duck out of sight like a little rolling green pea?

Why all this pretense? Why all this show of inability to compete with Piron in this field? And particularly in Brussels, where he had put on such an elaborate performance of falling into Piron's trap? And then purposely giving such a miserable account of himself at that dinner that Piron was led to denounce him as a pygmy on stilts.

Granted that Voltaire was no match for Piron's wit. But neither was he a pygmy. That was overdoing it.

Why? Why all this rigmarole?

Was it not because Voltaire had recognized in Piron a more than usually menacing rival to his own fame? A physical giant with talents to match his physique? The kind of rival with whom one must be deucedly careful? No place here for a head-on attack. That might be just the thing that would spur Piron to come back at one with twice his usual strength. For there was no telling how much these people who never had to exert themselves might accomplish if they really extended themselves.

No. Here was the spot for the wounded-quail trick. The simulated retreat. Let Piron keep on imagining himself the champion. Why not? While we pretend to cower on our little potty chair. Where's the harm? Just so long as that continues to satisfy him, and he drops all fight for fame and settles back into the pleasures of life. Drinks his wine and writes his odes to Priapus.

Oh, yes, if one could be absolutely sure that *La Métromanie* was Piron's best, then one might answer it with a crusher. But suppose he came back at one with a still stronger satire? The struggle might eventually reach a point where one would have to acknowledge a real defeat. In the field of drama, not just in table talk. One would have simply egged the man on to the very greatness one intended to deny to him.

So why give fame to a man who is willing to defeat himself if only one will let him? It's sad, of course, to see such a talent wasting itself. And expecially sad to see him waking up too late to learn that not innate gifts, but only perpetual application, can guarantee permanent literary success.

This is no doubt the thought that Goethe must have had in mind when he later reviewed the literary rivalry between Voltaire and Piron and summed it up in the following succinct fashion: "Piron was always the Voltaire of any given moment. But only Voltaire was the Voltaire of all times."

Piron himself, in his old age, must have suspected that it was Voltaire who had won those encounters of wit after all, for he left a series of bitter epitaphs about himself, all of them revolving around the notion that he was *"rien."* Nothing. Nobody. The most famous being his couplet

> *Ci-gît Piron, qui ne fut rien,*
> *Pas même académicien.*

Here lies Piron, who was nothing,
Not even an Academician.

Yes, sad. Very sad.

22: THE GAME OF FRIVOLITY

And it was this trickster of a Voltaire, who did not shrink from cheating a man out of his life's career, whom Jean Jacques proposed to beat?

Was he mad?

Yes, in a way he was. To be sure, all of this Piron story had not yet played itself out by the time Rousseau began to burn with a fury to crush Voltaire. But in any case there was no lack of other Voltairean victims around to warn the foolhardy.

But what could Rousseau do? He was never the kind of man who could select his passions by a process of reasoning. Indeed, he can't be said ever to have taken thought. It was the other way around. Thought took him. Thinking and writing, with Rousseau, was a kind of intellectual seizure. A feverish sweat that at times would burst from his excited pores.

He himself had not been at first aware of it. For years, for example, he had tried to sit down and work the way other writers did. Voltaire, for instance. But he was lazy. He couldn't. And when he forced himself nevertheless, what a struggle it was. And then, after all, how little accomplished.

And then one day he had discovered that, not forcing himself down to a desk, but, indeed, at times running away from all desks, going out into the hills, was the only way he could write. Renouncing all duties and just letting his heart swell with whatever emotions might come to it.

That was when ideas would really occur to him. Tumbling down on him like pellets in a hailstorm. So thick and fast that he could not hope to jot them all down.

That was when he would become creative. While his feet went uphill and downdale, and his mouth raged or mumbled, his lips sneered or whispered and his eyes were either dry with scorn or wet with pity.

At times he wasn't even sure what all these emotions signified. Only that he was gripped by them. Only that he could feel their power over him. While their meaning still escaped him.

His mind, he would later say, was like backstage before the production of a play. With pieces of scenery lying around in disorder amidst lumber and tools and pots of paint. Costumes, armor, wigs, drapery, piled up hit or miss. And stagehands rushing here and there, lugging this or that and laughing or cursing. While actors wound their way amidst this confusion, mooning or declaiming their lines, gesturing insanely to a nonexistent audience. And the director shouting and pleading, tearing his hair—so that only a madman could imagine that out of this jumble there would ever come anything intelligible.

And sometimes he wondered if anything intelligible had ever come out of him. Sometimes his own books, after they had poured out of him, seemed to make no sense whatsoever. Brought up on Voltairean clarity of thought, he found himself condemning his own works when his seizure was over and he could contemplate them coldly.

"Trash!" was his verdict when he tried to read his novel *La Nouvelle Héloïse* after it had become the sensation of Europe.

And when an admirer went into raptures over his *Social Contract* Rousseau said, "Yes, but what does it mean? Nothing. I should have torn it up and started fresh."

And the same with his *Émile* when another worshiper declared, "I've read your masterpiece, and I intend to bring up my son according to your *Émile*."

"God help the poor lad!" was Rousseau's comment.

"Anything to call attention to himself!" So certain critics would say about such moments.

But actually these were only further illustrations of how torn Rousseau was. Voltaire too repudiated his works, denied his authorship, but his reason was always clear: He had his financial investments to protect. He had his life to protect. But Rousseau? He signed his name to everything and had no money that might be endangered. And the only reason he repudiated his own words at times was because, brought up as he was in admiration of Voltaire, there had to be moments when he would look upon his own works precisely as his great opponent would.

For right down into the very depths of his being this battle for and against Voltaire went on.

Why, for example, would he be drawn one day to a certain manuscript which he saw in a Paris bookstall? This was shortly after his return to Paris, when Voltaire had just gloriously established himself in Geneva, the city where Rousseau had hoped to live and to shine.

The manuscript was entitled "The Siege of Orléans and the Trial of Joan of Arc."

Rousseau couldn't resist it. He had to have that manuscript.

Why? It was expensive—one louis. Which for a man of Rousseau's pocketbook was not insignificant. If he had been just then entirely dependent on his income as a copier of music (which is what he wished to be) it would have taken him many weeks of hard work to save up enough beyond his household expenses, in order to pay out that much. He happened, however, just then to have a little ready cash from his operetta.

In any case, he bought it.

What for?

To read? No. For he immediately inscribed it "From Jean Jacques Rousseau, citizen of Geneva," and sent it off as a gift to the library of his native town, where at the time there was still a question whether he might not take the position of librarian.

Was he, then, in the habit of making gifts like that to libraries? He certainly was not. Or was he a student of the life and martyrdom of Joan of Arc? Not at all. And furthermore, was this history of a Catholic girl who claimed that she was led by Catholic saints, and, indeed, that she conversed with them, quite the proper gift for a man like himself—only recently put to the test of the sincerity of his return to Calvinism (with its opposition to saints and the like)—to make to the Geneva library? And particularly if he intended to head it soon?

It would be then as if he intended to mutter, *"Eppur si muove"*—like Galileo claiming that, for all this ecclesiastical decision, the earth did move. "And I am still a Catholic at heart. And will stock your library with Catholic books if ever I'm in charge."

Which must have been far from his intention.

No. But this gift was nevertheless singularly appropriate. Because in that city of Geneva there now lived Voltaire. Voltaire, author of a humorous poem about Joan of Arc, *La Pucelle,* a poem so coarse that Voltaire cringed lest it find its way into print. And so it was only right that Geneva should have in its library the true and serious record of the virginal Joan of Arc to stand there as the antidote against Voltaire's poisonous burlesque.

It was of this poem that a lady once exclaimed, "What a shocking poem! Oh, Monsieur de Voltaire, how could you have written it? Mocking a girl so pure and so gentle, who gave her young life to save France."

"My dear lady," Voltaire countered, "tell me first how many murderers you are personally acquainted with, and then I shall explain to you why I wrote my poem."

"Murderers?" the lady cried.

"Yes, how many do you personally know?"

"Do you imagine I know any murderers?" the lady protested.

"Assassins, then. Why, history is full of them. Surely you must know some. Or at least some highway robbers, some rapists or traitors. Tell me how many you know."

"I'm sorry," the lady insisted. "But I really don't know people of that stripe!"

"Ah? You don't? Then perhaps you will agree with me that the average human being is a pretty decent sort of person?"

"With all my heart!"

"Minor vices he has. Drinks too much, perhaps. Runs after every skirt. Little lies. Petty thefts. But in general hard-working, reasonably honest. The father loving his family. The mother cherishing her little ones. The sons ready at a moment's notice to sacrifice their lives for their king and their country."

"Yes, indeed. Such, at any rate, are the people I happen to know," the lady declared.

"Then why is that we are all such miserable sinners? Why are the priests forever exhorting us to repent? To reform? To throw ourselves on our knees and beg for forgiveness? How is it that we must all go to church and beat our breasts and pray and confess? What is it that we have done? Where is our crime?"

And as the lady could only stare in amazement, dumfounded by all these questions, Voltaire went on, driving home his point: "Don't you see that we have all been turned into sinners only because we have been led to think of our frivolities as though they were crimes? When it comes to sex, which one of us has not sinned?"

"I begin to understand," the lady said quietly.

"That is why I wrote my *La Pucelle*," said Voltaire, "I was not ridiculing Joan of Arc, but only the veneration of her virginity."

Indeed, Voltaire was so incensed at the everlasting battle of the churches against frivolity that he wrote in another of his poems, "When God saw the terrors of this life which man would be forced to endure, He took pity on His creation and invented frivolity, in order to make life more bearable."

And that there should be men so stupid as to condemn God's mercy!

But not Voltaire. He was, in fact, so grateful to God for this gift that there was a time when he kept for himself a *sottisier*, that is to say a kind of bible of frivolousness, a little notebook in which he entered brief reminders of witticisms, salty stories and the like that occurred to him, or that he happened to run across in his reading or conversation and wished to remember for suitable occasions.

With the result that he had no difficulty keeping a tableful of guests in stitches.

"Would you like to hear the favorite risqué story of Sir Isaac Newton?" Voltaire would ask. "It's one I picked up long ago, during my exile in England. About a young man, a Protestant, who married a Catholic girl, but soon had her converted to his own religion. In time, however, this woman died. Whereupon the widower married again. And once more took a Catholic girl to be his wife. But this time he did not succeed in converting her. Which he would explain in this fashion: 'I'm afraid my arguments are no longer so convincing.'"

Oh, the delicious *double-entendre!* "I'm afraid my arguments are no longer so convincing!" How the table would rock with laughter. Not the least exquisite part of such stories being the discomfiture and the blushing it would bring to the ladies, who always felt that they had to pretend not to understand too well, making the evening all the more amusing for the men.

Only a Jean Jacques, only a Jean Jacques who in Venice had tried so hard to be frivolous and had so miserably failed, only he, when he heard such stories, would not laugh. Could not laugh. Where was the humor? he would ask. Really, now, what is there to laugh about? Is it perhaps this picture of mankind caught between two great religions, both threatening each other's millions of faithful with eternal hellfire? Is it that which you find so funny?

While poor lads such as Rousseau have to change their religion in order to have a bit of bread. Or is it perhaps the death of the first wife that amuses you no end? Yes, that's really rollicking, isn't it? And you do not even know, or care, how she came to die. In childbirth, perhaps.

Leaving behind her a little boy, just born. A Jean Jacques, who would never know the meaning of the word "mother."

Or is it the part where the man grows old? Now, there's high comedy for you. A man's stubble of hair turning white under his wig. His vital powers beginning to fail him.

Ah, if that is so funny to you, then why listen to stories around a dinner table? Why don't you go to executions? To cemeteries or battlefields, and have yourselves a really good laugh!

Oh, those stories of Voltaire! The men would vow not to forget them. And in order to make sure, they would surreptitiously mark them down in their own little *sottisiers.*

"Have you heard the one about the Parisian couple who were so anxious to have a child of their own?" Voltaire would ask.

"The wife especially," he would tell his dinner guests, "yearned for a pregnancy, like Sarah of old. As for the husband, he was not unwilling that his wife should have the assistance of another man, since he seemed unable to accomplish the task himself. But the thought of gossip if ever the story should get out, the possibility of the real father afterward claiming certain rights over his offspring—such fears prevented them from attempting this solution.

"But one day they hit upon a plan. The husband waited until dark and then went into a distant quarter of town and picked up a blind beggar from where he customarily stood in front of a church, drove him home in a roundabout way, washed him clean and put him to bed with his wife. Fed him afterward. Rewarded him with money and clothes. And drove him back by a similar circuitous route to the church where he had been found. Left him there.

"The happy couple were soon able to look forward to a child. But many years later," Voltaire would conclude, "one might still see a blind old beggar standing before a certain church in Paris and crying out in vain, 'Doesn't anyone else need me?'"

Now, there was really something to laugh at: sterility. Or if that should fall short of exciting your risibilities, take blindness. Even funnier, isn't it? And then there are the problems of a man and a woman living in a world of malicious gossip. And for a truly ribtickling climax, that finale: the old blind beggar still recalling over the years the one fulfillment of his life.

Oh, Voltaire, Voltaire! Is that really you? Clown! First frightened to death over the hazards of life, as in your poem about Lisbon. And then laughing at man's afflictions. And in the end caring for nothing except yourself. Just posturing shamelessly, determined that one way or another the world should be forever occupied with you.

No wonder Frederick the Great maliciously assigned you to a room in his palace the walls of which happened to be decorated with green monkeys!

"Do you know the story of the unmarried girl who went to confession and admitted that she was pregnant?" Voltaire asked, dipping again into his vast fund.

Good God! Was there nothing safe from this Voltairean mockery? Was the whole world, under the leadership of the Voltairean philosophers, rushing toward endless frivolity and corruption? Disgracing man instead of honoring him? Stooping to his lowest instead of reaching for his highest.

Right here on this estate, Jean Jacques could feel this disgrace of mankind. On this beautiful spot amidst trees and rolling hills. And when, late at night, after dinner at the château, Jean Jacques would take his lantern and make his way across the dark grounds to his little cottage, he could, if he cared, turn around and see the various bedrooms upstairs lighting up behind their shutters and their curtains.

How well he knew those bedrooms. He himself might now be occupying one of them, had he so chosen. The one which would be occupied by Grimm instead, right down the hall from the bedroom of Madame d'Épinay, mistress of the château.

And beyond, there was the room assigned to Madame d'Épinay's sister-in-law, Madame d'Houdetot. And next to it, the room given to the Marquis de Saint-Lambert.

How very proper!

With each person in his own private room. But of course only until maids and valets had done helping their masters and mistresses to undress.

Then, when the servants had retired, the interconnecting doors would begin to function. Jean Jacques knew all about those doors. Knew that when the candles winked out, and the great house lay in complete darkness, then those doors would open.

Gently, of course. Oh, very gently.

But why? Why gently? What difference would it make if the doors were slammed? Was there any servant in the house who did not know exactly what was going on? Or any servant who did not consider himself or herself entitled to imitate the frivolity of his betters?

And yet, suppose for just a moment that a door should be slammed. What a commotion! Upstairs and down! The whole house awakened.

Yes, a single door-slamming in the night could do that which no amount of quiet adultery could accomplish.

Was it not as if the rule of life read: "Be as corrupt as you please, but open and close doors gently—discretion is more important than any and all of God's Ten Commandments"?

And so the doors were opened gently into the darkness. And then would come a little rustling of bed curtains, pushed aside by sweet-scented, impatient arms, arms reaching out into the gloom to welcome a longed-for visitor And then a single whispered cry quickly muffled under a kiss.

And after that the curtains rustling back into place again.

And now everything very still indeed.

Except for those mysterious sounds, those vague little noises that used to keep young Jean Jacques awake at night, in the inns where he slept with the just married Sabran couple when he crossed the Alps to Turin—those noises whose meaning he used to try so hard to unravel . . .

But in the morning not a sign of all this nocturnal activity. Each person back in his own bed, and all interconnecting doors closed.

As if nothing had happened. And therefore no need for anyone to feel guilty or ashamed. Nor any particular need for hypocrisy either. Just a little smile of satisfaction on people's faces. And no sign of either virtue or sin. No sign of either boasting or denying.

What? Two people are in love? They thirst for each other's presence. They hang on to each other's words. Their bodies crave to join and to melt in the fury of sexual passion. And it is all nothing? Just a moment of shared frivolity? An amusing escapade?

And afterward the pardonable trace of just a smirk of pride in a secret shared.

Is that how this cold and calculating century knows love? Is that how it understands passion? What? Does no one's blood boil up in his veins? Then who really knows love, genuine love, today? All that these people can know is the comfort of the flesh. Each partner fortunately equipped to provide for the other's physical satisfaction.

A great convenience. Yes. But devotion? Where is that? And adoration? And yearning and sacrifice and madness?

This love is only a pastime. The game of concealing your own pranks while spying out the adventures of others. So that you can gossip without being gossiped about. A game decorated with suitable bits of quickly composed verses. A sport tricked out with little winks of the eye slyly suggesting concupiscent pleasures. And double-meaning words that must be caught on the fly, or else the shepherd's opportunity will have vanished and another partner been chosen.

Why not? It is nothing but the changing figures of a dance. It is nothing but a game. A sport.

For others, no doubt. But not for Jean Jacques, who refused to understand these games and, in fact, despised them. No, not for Jean Jacques, who felt within himself the pain and the passion of a love that was deeper and grander. And, for all that, saw himself forced to stand aside and see men who had not a fraction of his fire capture all the ladies. Cold, scheming hearts such as Grimm. Gossipy and flighty characters such as Diderot. Small parlor talents such as Saint-Lambert. And artful, agile climbers such as Voltaire.

All of them successfully indulging themselves in one excitement after another. Only he growing older without ever having actually lived. Or really loved.

Ah, if only somewhere there could be found a woman who would really understand him! Who would appreciate him at his true worth. What violent emotions would flare up between them! What a world-consuming passion!

But was there such a person in real life? Could there be any in this world already so degenerate, which even geniuses like Voltaire did nothing to correct?

Would he have to invent her, because there were none such on earth?

And so, as Rousseau rambled through the forest of the d'Épinay estate, he began to dream of such a woman. She would be living on an estate, too. But nothing like this d'Épinay estate. So near to Paris, for one thing. And so artificial, for another. Consisting as it did mostly of park and hunting preserve.

No. Rousseau's ideal woman would live on an estate that was not just an expense, but also an income. An estate in Switzerland. A piece of land near the village of Clarens, on the shore of Lake Geneva. A region more beautiful, because more natural, more picturesque, with its wild brooks rushing down from Alpine mountain crags. An estate rooted in honest toil, in farming, in vineyards and in husbandry. With no bronze nymphs spouting water amidst flower beds laid out in designs inconceivable to nature.

And on this estate a young girl, Julie d'Étange, nothing at all like that Parisian Madame d'Épinay who was enjoying a series of adulteries on her side while her husband explored the night life of Paris on his side. No, but a girl who was virginal and unspoiled and at the same time beautiful, intelligent, sincere.

And then himself.

For Jean Jacques did not intend to leave himself out of his own dreams. He saw himself as still poor. Always that. But younger. More handsome. Saint-Preux his name. The preceptor of the household.

Yes, poor, and of common birth, far beneath the d'Étange family in the matter of pedigree, but redeemed by an inner nobility that came out of the elevation of his thinking and his feeling. Out of his soul. An aristocracy of the spirit.

Naturally, the tutor would fall madly in love with his beautiful blond pupil Julie d'Étange. But never a word would pass his lips. Never a sign of passion would sully his face. Never a hint would he give of the love that burned so violently within him that it must soon consume him.

Until finally one night, what an effusion on paper! All the volcanic heat of his emotions exploding suddenly in a letter which he left where Julie would be sure to find it. And then he waited with a trepidation that he had to struggle to conceal.

But from Julie, nothing. Not even the most fleeting expression on her beautiful blond face that might have hinted that something new and disturbing had come into her life.

Jean Jacques tramped the woods, waiting. But still no answer from Julie. Meanwhile he himself copied out the tutor's love letter, finding it so beautiful, so moving, that he felt impelled to transcribe it in his best hand, on the most expensive gilt-edged paper that could be bought, and using an azure-and-silver sand to dry the ink and give it a bit of glitter. And finally fastening the sheets together with a narrow blue ribbon.

He read it and reread it. And he knew: Here was love!

Day after day Jean Jacques wandered about, taking down notes for two more love letters from the tutor to Julie. And still no answer. The tutor wept. And Jean Jacques with him. On paper he cried out his swollen heart to Julie. He begged her to relieve him of anxieties that must surely cost him his life. How, he asked, was he to go on living, so close to her, knowing that his love had made no impression upon her?

And then, finally, a note from her. But cool and philosophical. Imbued with that very philosophy of stoicism that he had been trying to teach her. And which she had apparently learned only too well.

"If you, sir, were really as virtuous as you pretend to be, you would either overcome your passion or else keep silent," she wrote.

Not that her letter was short, for she was as nimble as he in minutely dissecting her innumerable ideas and emotions. And the letters which Jean Jacques had now to transcribe at night, while his Thérèse cooked dinner, served it and washed up the dishes, quickly grew into a sizable sheaf. And while Thérèse fussed and gossiped and was annoyed at the little attention her man gave to her, he went on living in the exciting story of his imagination.

"Very well," he wrote to Julie. "Then the matter is settled. I must leave. And carry my passion, which will never quit me, into my tomb. Goodbye."

And now another letter from Julie. With feverish hands he tore it open. What did it portend? Lifelong happiness or eternal misery?

"If your love is really so great as you have described it," she wrote, "I wonder how you can possibly find the strength to leave."

She was absolutely right! He was impaled on the horns of his dilemma. If he could really contemplate leaving and imagine his life going on without the sight of his beloved, then obviously he had much exaggerated the power of the passion he felt.

In short, there was only one way to prove the strength of his love: suicide. He wrote, begging her for only twenty-four hours. In order to arrange a few matters. "Tomorrow," he said, "you shall be satisfied with my conduct."

Ah, that finally roused her! "Beware!" she cried. "Beware, you madman! If you can feel that *my* life is precious to you, how dare you dispose of *your own* so long as you have still the least doubt as to how precious yours may be to me?"

Now it was all out in the clear between them. They were overwhelmed by their mutual passion. But only for a moment. Then he perceived the new danger for himself: seduction. For the law everywhere in the eighteenth century was that a servant who seduced a girl in the house where he worked was punishable by death.

"Protect me!" he pleaded with her in his next letter. "Your virtue will have to be so severe that it will not only save your innocence, but save my life at the same time!"

In the little cottage on the d'Épinay estate there thus began a fight for a woman's chastity. Not the chastity of Thérèse, long ago vanished. Nor the chastity of Madame d'Épinay, which went on its usual adulterous way. But the chastity of two imaginary characters, Julie d'Étange and Saint-Preux, who loved each other as never two souls had done before.

Jean Jacques was deft at double living, forced as he was to accept the corrupt world he lived in while dreaming of a better one. Thus, in spite of his life's going on as usual, the problem that obsessed him was that Julie was daily becoming more beautiful. Daily becoming more gay, more lively, more charming, more healthy.

While he, living in daily propinquity with the imaginary creature of his greatest desires, whom he did not dare touch, he soon found himself worn out by endless struggle.

"How little it has cost you to swear eternal love!" he wrote, with both envy and reproach.

"So my good health tortures you, does it?" she wrote back almost gloatingly. And she tried to explain to him the difference that existed between them: "For me it is only the heart that needs a lover. And my heart has one. But as for my senses, as for my body, they can do without. Whereas you, you let yourself float away on dreams of vain desires. You permit yourself to get drunk on them . . ."

But suddenly Julie's philosophy, too, was shown to be insufficient. One day her family introduced her to the man whom they had selected to be her husband. A worthy gentleman. The Baron de Wolmar. Kind and well-to-do. But long past fifty years of age.

Now it was Julie's health that was shattered. It was her turn to despair. And waste away. And whom could she look to for support but to her lover? It was no longer just her heart that needed love. Her body needed that proof, too.

And thus the battle for chastity was lost. Julie herself arranged an assignation. . . .

It was the culmination of happiness. And at the same time the beginning of an even more difficult situation. For in time Julie found herself pregnant.

What now? Run off together? But where to? And what if they were caught? Might it not mean death for her lover?

And even if they were not caught, would it not still mean disgrace and disaster for her aged parents? Besides, how would they manage to live? She eventually to become a mother, and he utterly without resources.

Something must be done, however. For the wedding day was fast approaching, and she could not go to the altar to marry one man while bearing in her womb the child of another.

And then suddenly, unexpectedly, it seemed as if every problem of their lives was solved. As a result of a slap given to her during an altercation with her father, who was a hotheaded former military man, Julie suffered a miscarriage. Secretly, of course. So that no one in her family knew anything about it. And she herself told no one except her lover and her cousin, who was her closest girl friend.

Now there was nothing to prevent Julie from marrying the man intended for her—thus satisfying her parents. Nor from indulging herself subsequently in a secret adultery with Saint-Preux—thus satisfying herself and her lover.

All problems solved.

Yes, for the world of frivolity. On the d'Épinay estate, this might be the end of the book. They would all live happily ever afterward, in a life of guarded adultery. Not, to be sure, that Julie's husband might not eventually get wind of his wife's little escapade. He was even bound to. But he would naturally be discreet about it, for presumably he would have his own little romantic moments to conceal.

Nor would this mean that Julie would have no other lover but Saint-Preux. At any rate, not permanently. Nor that he would necessarily continue to adore her eternally. At least, not exclusively.

All such matters would have to be left to take care of themselves in their own good way, and in their own good time, according to whim and frivolity. With the participants of course exercising the usual good taste of opening and closing all doors with a minimum of noise. Saving all the conventions.

Such indeed might be the pleasant solution for Paris. For the world of Voltaire. But never for the environs of Geneva. Never for Jean Jacques, nor for his alter ego Saint-Preux. Nor for Julie either any question whatsoever of a discreet adultery. Not when she was wedded to the Baron de Wolmar and heard herself promising, before God's altar, to love and honor her husband. At that moment she knew that she could never break the word she had given to God.

23: DIRTY LITTLE LADY-KILLER!

Could anything be more startling by way of contrast than this book which he was writing and the life that Madame d'Houdetot and the Marquis de Saint-Lambert were living (and which Rousseau could observe when they were the guests of Madame d'Épinay and as such occupied the other two bedrooms, with interconnecting doors)? Theirs was so obviously one of those typical examples of the French frivolity which Jean Jacques despised that he could entertain little but cold contempt for them.

How, then, did Jean Jacques ever let himself get involved in an affair so utterly at variance with the ideals which he was then consigning to paper?

As in the case of the manuscript gift to the library at Geneva, the answer is Voltaire. And again in the most complicated and roundabout way.

For what could there possibly be about the Countess d'Houdetot that should make Jean Jacques fall in love with her?

Was she pretty?

On the contrary. He himself had to admit that she was ugly. And some of her contemporaries went much further.

Take her complexion, for example. Jean Jacques maintained that he loved nothing so much as a well-cared-for skin. Petal-fresh. Pearly.

"That's how I am," he was to say truculently in his *Confessions*.

But if that's how he was, what about Madame d'Houdetot? As a girl she had had a severe attack of smallpox. With the result that her normally sallow skin became choked with pits. And at the bottom of each pit there was left an ineradicable brown spot. So that her face never afterward looked clean. Always as if unwashed.

Take her nose next. Covered with the same kind of pits. And, in addition, shapeless. As if crushed upon her face.

But most unfortunate of all: her eyes. Small and round. And more than that: crossed. And so nearsighted that, as she peered to see, she blinked incessantly.

Explain, then, how this person could have become the great love of Jean Jacques's life. Unless it be because he saw in her a way of reaching out toward Voltaire.

Not that the little Countess didn't have certain qualities. Indeed she had. For example, she was genuinely witty. But wasn't wit something that Rousseau positively detested? Especially in women?

She was also rich. And of noble birth. But to how many women of the upper classes had not Rousseau said that he wished they were poor and without titles, so that he could find a friend amongst them?

And what else was she? Accessible? That is to say married for some ten years, with three children and a husband, and yet at the same time so neglectful of her family duties that she was willing to sleep with another man? Yes, but once again that was something Rousseau loathed. And, just then, was in fact staying up nights excoriating in the most virulent attacks.

What, then, one asks oneself, did this young woman have to atone for all the attributes about her that Jean Jacques couldn't possibly stomach? Her masses of curly black hair? Yes, that she had, but his own taste ran to blondes. As well as an infectious gaiety. And that's all.

The Marquis de Saint-Lambert, however, when the war began, found himself under the necessity of going into the field against the Prussians (as did also Grimm and the Count d'Houdetot), and, being of a rather jealous nature and concerned lest his mistress, who was so much younger than himself (just about half his age, in fact) and gay and rich besides, should now find solace in the arms of some other man (as, after all, she had found solace in his own when neglected by her husband), he advised her to seek out, during his absence, the company of that philosopher of virtue Jean Jacques Rousseau, who was anyhow so conveniently at hand in his cottage on the estate of her sister-in-law.

After all, where else could Saint-Lambert conceive her to be more safe? Where else could she be better armed against the temptations of the flesh than in the company of Jean Jacques? Who would no doubt instill in her some of his own philosophy of austerity. For the Marquis de Saint-Lambert never for a moment doubted that Jean Jacques actually practiced the rules of living which he promulgated.

Grimm and Diderot, Rousseau's old friends, who had known him when he was younger and still without fame, might indeed have recalled that some dozen years ago Jean Jacques had lived something of a Bohemian life, or at least had tried to, and even that he had confided in them the secret of his putting away an illegitimate child or two. But what person who had known Rousseau during the period when he was making one sensation after another as he sold his sword, sold his watch, tore off his gold frogging, got rid of his curly wig, what person, having witnessed such a man resign an extremely lucrative post and then throw away the opportunity of a lifetime by refusing the King's pension and insist on earning his living by the labor of his hands, could possibly doubt for a moment that the Citizen of Geneva was anything but a paragon of virtue?

And above all Saint-Lambert. Saint-Lambert, who knew himself to be the very opposite kind of man, having lived off practically nothing but sinecures and mistresses all his life. Who dreamed of the King's pension for himself and meanwhile thought nothing of asking the women he slept with—Madame de Boufflers, for example—for fifty louis after a night of love. He was indeed now very devoted to Madame d'Houdetot (and would remain so for nearly half a century), but it was obvious that her wealth had not been a matter of little consideration in this choice. Since he was otherwise practically penniless. And she not having much to offer except that wealth, aside from her youth and her good spirits.

And Madame d'Houdetot, in obeying Saint-Lambert's instructions and coming over to see Jean Jacques in his cottage, had had nothing further from her mind than seducing the philosopher. She had arrived once muddied from head to foot as a result of sudden showers and bad roads. And another time dressed as a page boy and straddling her horse.

That was scarcely the way to seduce Jean Jacques, who demanded that women should always be womanly.

If ever indeed there was a creature who was unlikely to attract Jean Jacques away from his imaginary Julie d'Étange, it was this skinny and flat-chested frivolous woman, of whom the most charitable thing one could say was that the gentleness of her character, the inner serenity of her temperament, was not truly mirrored in her face.

And again, looking at it from Rousseau's side, what could have predisposed him toward this woman? When roused to animal heat by his imaginary love affair, didn't he always have his Thérèse to drain off his ardor? His faithful, always available Thérèse, guaranteed free from disease.

And if he wanted a change, were there not all the idle and rich women of Paris who were forever showering him with gifts and forever begging him to copy out their music? And whose advances he was forever nipping with some frosty answer.

Or as a last resort, why not Madame d'Épinay? In whose cottage, on whose estate, he was living. And who was alone now in her château, with her lover Grimm gone off to war, and with far more title to Rousseau's attentions, since he was deeply in her debt. A much more exciting person than her sister-in-law. More talented, certainly. Leaving behind her memoirs crowned by the French Academy when they appeared and still read and studied to this day. And herself so striking in appearance that even Voltaire would be impressed and would describe her as "an eagle in a cage of gauze." To say nothing of her being more accessible than Madame d'Houdetot, having had a much more extensive history of adulterous affairs. And, finally, being so close a neighbor.

Yes, of all the women with whom he might have had an affair, why did it have to be Madame d'Houdetot?

Was it not because no other woman could have meant so much to him? No other woman could have stirred him so profoundly in every aspect of his life.

But why?

An affair with Madame d'Épinay? That would only have been cuckolding Grimm. (Cuckolding, because within each infidelity there had to be, of course, an area of fidelity, an area of minor vows, so to speak. An area of fidelity which, in Catholic France, where divorce and remarriage were so difficult, often constituted a more or less permanent union, any violation of which could be considered a betrayal of the adulterer.)

No. An affair with Madame d'Épinay would touch only Grimm. But an affair with Madame d'Houdetot—that involved Saint-Lambert. And Saint-Lambert involved Voltaire.

Not that Rousseau ever explained his falling in love with Madame d'Houdetot in that fashion. As a matter of fact, he never offered any real explanation at all for this strange choice that certainly seems to cry for an explanation. Nothing except the rather cryptic phrase to be found in his *Confessions:* "Love is contagious."

Which he elaborated only to this extent: "I heard Madame d'Houdetot speak of her passion for Saint-Lambert, who had left her to go to war. Listening to her, I was seized with a delicious shiver. I took deep draughts of that poisonous drink, of which at the moment I tasted only the sweetness."

That's all. And never a word about Voltaire.

Not a word. As if it were possible not to think of Voltaire in connection with Saint-Lambert. As if Rousseau, with his eyes fixed on Voltaire over so many years, had somehow managed to live in Paris without being aware of what a burning curiosity Parisians of the frivolous set had manifested regarding Saint-Lambert when he had arrived in the capital some years back. All the women wanting to meet this man who had intruded himself—with such fateful consequences—into the long-standing romance between Voltaire and the Marquise du Châtelet, a romance so splendid and exciting that it had reminded many of the love of Pericles and Aspasia in the days of Athens' glory, so gifted and famous was Voltaire and so learned the Marquise, especially in philosophy, in mathematics and in physics.

As if, in short, it had never once occurred to Rousseau that if he could now cuckold Saint-Lambert as Saint-Lambert had cuckolded Voltaire, then it would be he, *le petit* Rousseau, the scorned little Jean Jacques, who would be on top of the heap. And not just in a dreamed-up novel, either. But in reality.

And Voltaire at the bottom of the heap. Yes, at the very bottom!

It could only have been a wild thought crossing his mind for just a flash. But still enough to arouse his first interest in Madame d'Houdetot. A wild thought, immediately rejected. For it was too mean, too contemptible. But, for all that, fully in keeping with Rousseau's desire to distinguish himself in the field of love. Evinced so strikingly a few years later, when his *La Nouvelle Héloïse* was published and people everywhere presumed it to be the true story of his very romantic life.

"I was careful to say nothing that would undeceive them," he would later admit in his *Confessions.* A startling admission from the man who had pledged his life to the truth.

But no matter how far Rousseau meant it, or how clearly he envisaged his purpose, in any case the meaning could not possibly be lost on Voltaire. That his most ambitious literary rival should now be involved with that very same Saint-Lambert once so intimately involved with him—what a coincidence! If coincidence it really was. Why, the little bastard! Was he trying to match himself against Voltaire not only in literary productions but also in the matter of women?

"The dirty little lady-killer!" Voltaire exploded. *"Sale petit corps à bonnes fortunes!"*

Which has caused Rousseauan scholars to cry, "For shame!" and to point out that never once did Rousseau indulge in such ugly language against Voltaire.

But what old and painful wounds all this must have opened up for Voltaire. All the anguish of that terrible day when the Marquise du Châtelet had died, and Voltaire had gone stumbling out of the palace at Lunéville, blinded by tears, to throw himself down on the cobblestones outside, before the astonished sentry in his box, and beat his head bloody against the pavement.

While Saint-Lambert, hurrying after him, had tried to pull him to his feet, pleading with him to control himself.

And Voltaire had turned upon Saint-Lambert, crying, "You killed her! Yes, you! You did it!"

Not that he had minded so much that Saint-Lambert should have had an affair with his Marquise, his learned and beautiful Émilie. No.

For, unlike Rousseau, it was not adultery that disturbed Voltaire. It was, on the contrary, the slamming of doors that upset him. Never did adultery do anyone any harm. Not really. But the fuss, the gossip, the furor, the recriminations. These were your killers!

After all, it would have ill become an experienced adulterer such as Voltaire to have condemned adultery. He could not conceivably fight an inclination in others to which he was himself addicted. And this was only one of the reasons why Voltaire would later so vindictively pursue Rousseau's *La Nouvelle Héloïse* when it came out. Declaring, "It is the disgrace of our century to have applauded this wretched and immoral novel! A book in which the hero gets a venereal disease in a bordello and the heroine has an aborted baby from the hero before she marries an old sot. All this dished out with lectures on Jesus Christ, divine grace, original sin, and so on and so forth."

There's hypocrisy for you! Jean Jacques striving to dissuade others from a style of living to which he was himself attached! And the vulgarity of that book of his that turns the Deity into a snoop and a gossip, deeply concerned about the trivial concupiscences of men and women!

How that diminished God!

As for Voltaire, he never saw any reason why his Marquise du Châtelet should not be having another love affair. Despite their many years of close association and affection. As a matter of fact, wasn't he just then carrying on a little private affair of his own, very quietly, with his niece Madame Denis, a young and pretty widow, lively and amusing (although on the plump side and eventually to turn quite stout, if not, in fact, corpulent) ?

Why, then, shouldn't his Marquise be doing the same? Either with Saint-Lambert or with any other person of her choice? And that despite the fact that she was the mother of two grown children and had a living husband too, although on garrison duty at Dijon. And she, with Voltaire's encouragement, was meanwhile undertaking the vast project of writing a book on Newtonian mathematics.

Yes, why not? In the busiest life there is not only time but appetite for such things. All that one can therefore ask for is discretion. Especially in his particular case, because he had so many enemies. And gossips were forever looking for something with which to attack him.

He and his niece, therefore, practiced such discretion that it would be two centuries before scholars would discover, in hitherto carefully concealed letters, the evidence that would prove the intimacy of uncle and niece. Letters in which Voltaire would sign himself "Yours forever with a thousand kisses on your sweet little bottom," or with similar endearments that could leave no doubt about his more than avuncular warmth, and that Madame Denis would try to disguise as best she could by scratching out, for example, "your bosom" and writing "your wit" above, or by covering "your bottom" with the words "your soul." Thus lifting her uncle's affection to a more spiritual plane.

That was her innocent mania. She wanted to be loved for her character and her talents rather than for her too abundant flesh.

But both of them taking care to give the gossips nothing to chew over. Not even during an exciting period when Voltaire had hopes that his niece would give him a little Voltaire. This too being a matter that would have been handled, in due time, with all necessary adroitness, since any publicizing of this affair could only have resulted in wounding the feelings of his more legitimate mistress, the Marquise.

To whom, incidentally, Voltaire remained just as devoted as ever. Except that for some time he had no longer been sleeping with her. But he had made that quite clear to her in a poem the first lines of which expressed the situation very concisely:

Si vous voulez que j'aime encore,
Rendez-moi l'âge des amours . . .

If you wish that I should still make love to you,
Then give me back the age of love . . .

Not that Voltaire was entirely played out as a male when he composed that poem, at the age of forty-seven; but the Marquise had a passion that was now beyond his ability to cope with, while he had found in his niece a person considerably less demanding. Perhaps because what her uncle lacked in that respect she pieced out with the virility of others.

Corruption? Or human necessity? That depends on how you see it.

Voltaire had made his position in this matter abundantly clear in that couplet which he had inscribed under the statue of Cupid in the palatial wing he had built especially for his mistress and himself at Cirey in Lorraine:

> *Qui que tu sois? Voici ton maître.*
> *Il l'est, le fût ou le doit être.*

> Whoever thou art, thy master he!
> He is, or was, or ought to be.

And to make his meaning more plain, Voltaire had this statue of Cupid, with its inscription, placed in front of the stove that heated the room, as if to say, "From this comes our fire."

What had shocked Voltaire in the Saint-Lambert matter was not that his Marquise should fall desperately in love with this forty-year-old officer, which was certainly her right, but that they should surprise him with this information in the most upsetting fashion.

It was at the court of Lunéville, the miniature Versailles of King Stanislas, that the Marquise became involved with Saint-Lambert. And one day when the court had moved for a summer holiday to the King's château at Commercy, Voltaire happened to go to the apartment assigned there to the Marquise.

The door was wide open. One could see that the antechamber was empty. Nevertheless Voltaire knocked, but, getting no answer, walked in. Seeing the door beyond also open, he entered the Marquise's bedchamber, and traversed it to an alcove, where suddenly he saw that which the eyes of no lover, no matter how liberal, ever could wish to see: the Marquise du Châtelet so deeply engaged with the Marquis de Saint-Lambert that neither Voltaire's knocks nor his entry had been able to distract them from their athletic embrace.

What could Voltaire do except scream out his fury?

"Betrayed! Betrayed!" he bellowed with all his might.

It was not that he really felt himself betrayed, but that with such careless conduct it was obvious that every servant in the palace already knew what was going on and was already laughing at him behind his back. And it was necessary for him now to arouse everyone and demonstrate that he was not the kind of person who would stand for this.

The Marquise, at last recalled to earth, quickly disengaged herself and attempted to calm Voltaire. While Saint-Lambert, hurriedly adjusting his uniform, began to bluster about giving Voltaire every satisfaction.

Voltaire, naturally, ignored him. He had no intention of being cuckolded and then killed in a duel, too. That would really be too much. And when his servant and secretary, Longchamp, arrived, Voltaire shouted at him to pack his things and get him a post chaise ready for immediate departure to Paris.

"You can't leave me!" the Marquise cried. "You can't! You know that I love you and will love you forever!"

"If this is your proof of eternal love," Voltaire exclaimed, "I must say that I find it very unconvincing."

And he bolted from the room.

But the Marquise was able to reach Longchamp and bribe him to go to Voltaire a couple of hours later and pretend that he had looked for a chaise everywhere and could not find one for hire.

"Here's money," said Voltaire, still fuming. "Get on a horse early tomorrow morning and go to Nancy, and buy me a carriage there. Any sort you can find!"

But before that happened, the Marquise came to visit Voltaire. She had waited until he had retired for the night. Waited until two o'clock in the morning. And then she came to sit at the foot of his bed, and to recall to him stories of all the years of their association. Until both of them were in tears.

"I have drained my strength and my wealth," Voltaire sobbed, "to make you the wisest woman of our times and to house you like a princess, and you have deceived me."

"Did I not love you too?" the Marquise wept. "And as long as your health was good, did we not share our life? But for a long time now you have been complaining of illness. Of losing your energy. And that you can no longer work as you used to. Can you blame me, then, for sparing you? Surely you don't imagine that I want your death. No one can care more for your health than I do."

She went on to remind him that he himself had recognized that her hot temperament was such that her body required frequent physical expression.

"When I spare you from damaging your health," the Marquise concluded, "is it fair of you to be outraged when you discover that I have chosen a friend to supply your omission?"

And thus, though she had played fast and loose with his reputation, so that all Paris soon knew the whole story, Voltaire not only forgave her but also forgave Saint-Lambert when he came humbly to plead for the continuance of their friendship.

"You are still young," said Voltaire. "And I am getting old. It is not for the aged to set limits in this matter."

He was as sensuous as anyone else, or even more so. But he had no wish to play pasha. No desire to see himself surrounded by eunuchs or semi-eunuchs in order to prolong for a few more years his own decreasing sense of masculinity, puffing up his self-esteem by crushing that of others.

Indeed, he carried his philosophy of tolerance so far as to remain, in the eyes of the world, at least insofar as possible, the lover of the Marquise. But six months later he noticed that the Marquise seemed unusually melancholy. Not merely languid, but upset. And less actively devoted to her great work on the mathematics of Newton.

On Christmas Eve, uneasy, he finally questioned her. And was startled to hear her say, "I'm afraid I'm pregnant."

Voltaire's first reaction was a jest: "Well, here's a baby that you will not be able to publish among your scientific books. I'm afraid you'll have to include it among your miscellaneous works."

There it was: more careless slamming of doors. This would really cause a scandal. What now? Flight? So that the Marquise could bear her child in some obscure country place where the event would remain hidden from the world?

Impossible. It would fool no one. All the people—by this time legion—who knew of the events at Commercy would be able to account for the mysterious disappearance of the Marquise. No. Some better solution would have to be devised.

For years now the Marquise du Châtelet and her husband had been living their own separate lives. But the birth of a child—that was something he would not be able to take without protest. He would have to refuse to let himself be stigmatized thus, openly, flagrantly.

But in that case, why not make the Marquis du Châtelet feel that the child was his own? Then everything was solved.

It was necessary only to write to him at his garrison at Dijon under the pretext that certain business ventures on his properties at Cirey were turning out unexpectedly well and that his presence at home would be desirable. And then, with the additional excuse that the season was that of the New Year, hastily to improvise a series of dinners at which the Marquise glittered in seductive décolleté beside her husband, whose plate she kept heaped with food and whose glass she kept filled with wine.

With the result that he fell in love all over again with the wife of his youth, and she, a few weeks later, could blushingly whisper to him that he was about to become a father again. So that he could return to his garrison at Dijon proud as a barnyard cock.

Deception? Fraud? Yes, but why not? This way everyone was pleased. Everyone had had a gay old time. And the ancient military man was in fact delighted. (And that irrespective of whether he was completely fooled or not. He was in any case protected.) While the Marquise was saved from a most embarrassing situation that would have robbed her of the peace of mind which she needed to finish her *Mathematical Principles of Natural Philosophy.*

And the Marquis de Saint-Lambert could continue on his usual uninhibited course of life. Along with the Marquise.

And Voltaire the same.

In short, no one really cheated except the gossips. And not even they permanently.

Voltaire had anyhow few scruples about what some people would have called cheating. He would have gladly defrauded God himself if he could have found some way of postponing his death forever. Instead of just for a few years.

In his day, for example, certain forms of disease were considered to be the scourge of God, and when Voltaire fought for inoculation against smallpox he found himself attacked by various theologians who raged at this effort to contravene the will of Heaven.

As if it might not also be the will of Heaven that man should discover a way of preventing smallpox! A disease that killed millions and caused thousands of hopelessly disfigured girls, convinced that they could never marry, to bury themselves alive as brides of Christ in provincial convents.

Besides, why not cheat the will of Heaven? What difference if inoculation was first discovered by greedy Circassian mothers who wanted to find some way of protecting the complexion of daughters whom they hoped to sell into Turkish harems?

Man's business was precisely that: not to submit himself to every whim of nature, but to outwit her, compel her.

And that was why he was eventually so furious with Saint-Lambert.

At first it had seemed as if there would be no trouble for the Marquise and her expected child. Indeed, the pregnancy and the birth were so uncomplicated that the pangs overtook her while she was at work at her desk and she had barely time to call her maid, who spread out her apron and received the baby in it. A girl child, who was quickly placed in the trough of a huge open book, while her mother lay down and went to sleep.

It had all seemed so wonderfully easy. But a few days later both mother and child were dead. It was then that Voltaire staggered like a drunken man, falling to the cobblestones outside and there beating his head as if he would smash it.

And Saint-Lambert rushing to pick him up. Restrain him from doing further injury to himself.

But Voltaire turned on him with fury, screaming, "You killed her!"

"I? No. Never!" Saint-Lambert protested.

Voltaire, however, cried him down. "Yes, you! Did you have to get her with child? Did you?"

There was Voltaire's point! What do human beings have brains for if not to devise precautions? What do we have doors for if not to close them quietly when we cannot resist the urge to do things which others ought not to see us doing?

What are we, anyway—beasts? savages?—that we should take each other with squeals and with grunts, careless of all possible consequences?

24: I WILL NOT DEFILE YOU

To Rousseau, however, the matter was just the other way around. Away with hypocritical precautions! Away with efforts to gloss over the truth. Away with lies! He had done enough of that under the compulsion of the rotten morals of his time. Now he was through.

Besides, what did he and Madame d'Houdetot have to hide?

The fact that they loved each other? Or at least that he loved her? What was there to conceal about that?

This was the real thing. And he did not intend to besmirch it with lies. Real love, such as he had never experienced before. Neither with Madame de Warens nor with Thérèse. This was love in all its elemental force and frenzy. A succession of moments of agitation, of shivering, of palpitations and faintness of the heart, of sudden floods of words broken by meaningless sighs and strange convulsive motions.

But innocent. All of it utterly innocent. And therefore nothing to hide. No precautions to take. No tricks to be practiced. On the contrary, let the world see and admire.

Here was a great, a beautiful, an innocent love.

What else could it be with a man like himself? And a woman like Madame d'Houdetot? He a man of honor, a citizen of Geneva. And she a woman unique in the world.

That summer and fall they met almost every day. It was almost as if they lived together, so indispensable had they soon become to each other. She had rented a house at Eaubonne, some miles away, and they would meet either there or halfway between. Or else she would have herself driven over to her sister-in-law's estate.

And then they would walk together.

She loved to talk about Saint-Lambert, who had brought happiness into her life. And he would urge her on to this topic, even though every word of praise for Saint-Lambert that dropped from her lips fell upon him like a hot coal. And yet he enjoyed the tenderness that the subject of Saint-Lambert would bring to the timbre of her voice, and the way her body would slowly melt towards him, the longer she talked.

Then he would finally reach for her hand and slowly twine his fingers among hers, feel their softness and their warmth, and press them gently, sympathetically. While she would gradually respond with a gentle pressure of her own.

And thus they would walk along in silence for a while. Until he would sigh and begin to talk about his work. About his Julie d'Étange. And the hopeless love that bound her to Saint-Preux.

And, little by little, opening up to her his whole new way of thinking. Of the great pity of man, everywhere born free and yet everywhere in chains. In chains to bad governments, bad laws, bad religions, bad systems of education, bad customs.

Children ruined almost from their birth. Mothers refusing them their breasts. Tutors then stuffing them full of knowledge which they didn't need.

Oh, what a task there was to be done in this world! To heal it!

What suffering, what bloodshed man might have to undergo before things were bettered.

When Jean Jacques spoke to Madame d'Houdetot thus, in disconnected sentences, it was apparent how many years of thought he had given to the condition of man. And how great was his love for people. And how great his hope for their future perfection.

His earnestness would bring tears to Madame d'Houdetot's eyes. And he too would weep. And they would both walk along, weeping, their bodies moving ever more closely together, their arms holding each other ever more tightly.

Love?

Adultery?

Who spoke of such things? It was the furthest topic from their minds.

But slowly their steps would drag to a halt. Beneath a tree, perhaps. And there they would stand, their faces so close together that it was if they could mingle both their smiles and their tears. Their lips would touch, and their hands would stray . . .

Until she would heave a great sigh and would cry out, "Oh, never did a man love like you!

"But Saint-Lambert . . ", she would add quietly.

"Yes, Saint-Lambert," he would repeat. And if ever he had had the slightest desire to eliminate Saint-Lambert, he certainly had none now.

So why hide?

And as if to exhibit the utter innocence of their relations, they would sometimes stroll up and down the terrace of the d'Épinay château. For hours on end. So that no one could fail to see them. All the servants of the house, in the first place. And thus, eventually, the whole village.

And of course in particular Madame d'Épinay herself, who seemed to keep out of the way, but whose presence could almost be felt, lurking in her empty château hour after hour behind her curtained windows, consumed with rage and envy as she watched her "bear," her "savage," walking hand in hand with her sister-in-law.

All of which made no difference to Rousseau. Not even that reports should eventually be spread around Paris, and that all the salons should talk of little else but that the austere philosopher Jean Jacques was in love with Madame d'Houdetot. "Our little Jean Jacques in love. Fancy that! And imagine with whom! You'll never guess."

And that visitors should even come down from Paris to satisfy their curiosity with their own eyes. The Baron d'Holbach, for instance, that very wealthy atheist and philosopher, who came to gaze upon the spectacle and then stayed to dinner with Madame d'Épinay and Rousseau, and during the course of the meal made a hundred bantering remarks, one funnier than the next, or so it seemed, for Madame d'Épinay had to hold her sides lest they split with laughter.

While Jean Jacques just sat there, with a kind of stupid smile frozen on his face, for he was apparently missing all the finer points of the Baron's wit. Asking himself, What was really going on here? What was really so funny about his love?

What an amazing sense of humor everyone seemed to have. Only he . . .

Strange, wasn't it, that he should be the source of all this amusement and yet not be able to take part in it. Unable to understand it. And still another source of wonder: that despite all these fireworks of wit, the Baron's eyes seemed to be lit up with a malignant joy.

All Rousseau knew was that he was gloriously in love. And that instead of laughing people ought to be congratulating him.

But what, he had to ask himself, if that were precisely what was funny? Namely, that he should be so gloriously in love with Madame d'Houdetot, while she was so gloriously in love with someone else. Two people madly smitten—but not exactly for each other.

But no. That should have occasioned tears, should it not? That is to say, from truly sympathetic people it ought. From people who were really his friends.

Or perhaps they were laughing at him because he was in love with a woman who was an adulteress. In love with her, but not sleeping with her. Yes. Now, there was a spectacle for you: a scrupulous man caught in a situation that called for unscrupulousness. Too utterly precious, wasn't it? Yes, that might be considered excruciatingly funny.

Not by everyone. No. But by these Parisian wits it might.

No. However he turned it around in his mind, Jean Jacques couldn't see the humor of it. There was nothing to laugh about. Did they expect him perhaps to be preaching to Madame d'Houdetot that she should return to the husband whom she had sworn fidelity to before God? But that man had long since established himself with his mistress, hadn't he? And suppose Jean Jacques were successful in breaking up both these relationships, bringing wife and husband together again, where would that leave Jean Jacques? Jean Jacques and his great love?

Was it because of these impossible situations that they were having their sport with him? Well, let them laugh. So long as Madame d'Houdetot did not laugh at him. That was all that mattered.

But suppose that she too . . . Ah, no! That he could not bear. The very thought . . .

The first moment he caught a sign of gaiety in her face, he demanded an answer. "You're laughing," he said accusingly. "Am I, then, so ridiculous?"

"You? Ridiculous?" she cried out, apparently completely taken with astonishment.

"Answer me," he begged. "Answer me, please. Why are you laughing at me? Tell me!"

"But, my dear Monsieur Rousseau," she exclaimed, "why should I laugh at you?"

"I don't know," he burst out wildly. "I'm just asking if you are. I must know!"

"But how could I possibly laugh at a friend who is as dear to me as you are?" she argued.

"Perhaps because I am . . ." He hesitated. "Because I'm—well, decrepit."

"Decrepit? You don't mean that. In the first place, you're not decrepit. And in the second place, who would laugh at you for that? Do you think I would do such a thing?"

"I mean, because I'm old," he corrected.

"But you're not yet fifty," she pointed out.

He was evidently going to be compelled to make himself absolutely clear. "In short, because I do not force you to a stronger proof of your affection for me. Because I do not insist on the proof that would be positive."

"Is there anything that I could refuse you?" she asked. Tears came to her eyes. And her voice was so gentle and so sweet that he could not doubt for a moment that she would sacrifice even Saint-Lambert for him.

"Ask," she whispered. "And it shall be granted."

"There's nothing I want!" he cried. "Nothing! I may die of the fury of my passion," he told her. "I may suffer from those who laugh at me. But one thing I will never do. I will never make you vile solely in order that I may shine in my own self-esteem."

Even while saying this, he had to think, Had she not already made herself vile, with another? And yet he could not budge from his position. "Remember this," he said to her. "If you permit yourself the least

310

feebleness toward me, then I must inevitably succumb. But I will hate myself for it. For I intend you to return to Saint-Lambert as pure as he left you."

And yet, somehow, he had to test that willingness of hers to grant him whatever he might ask. And though knowing that he did not want her to commit adultery, he had to see how close he could bring her to it.

Now, alas, they became secretive. They hid. Yes. Precisely that which he did not want. Compelled to it by the world's laughter.

She did not resist. Her body lent itself to his desires, as sweet and supple as he could possibly hope for. And he gradually drew her into an exploration of all that broken and dangerous coastline of rocks and violent surfs that separates chastity from unchastity.

"She refused me nothing that the most tender, the most affectionate relationship would not grant," he would later explain. "But she permitted me nothing that would actually make her unfaithful."

A perilous intoxication seized them both. In spite of which he would hold himself in check.

"My own duty, yes, that I could forget. But it is yours that I refuse to forget. Ah, if only there were some way in which I could sin while you did not. For I care nothing for my soul, provided only that yours shall not be lost."

He lived and breathed this madness. And yet somehow he went on working, dreaming of new books, continuing to write his novel and copying out the whole work as a present for her.

And all the while as if enveloped in some kind of rosy fog. So that when he was actually on his way to her it would be as if the kiss with which she would greet him were already glowing through that fog, as hot as the rising midsummer sun. Her imaginary lips clung to his like burning branding irons. And long before he was able to take that kiss in the flesh his blood was so inflamed that he would feel dizzy. His eyes swam. His knees refused to support him. He had to stop. Rest.

He would let himself sink to the ground, feeling his whole body machinery out of gear, like some clockwork sprung asunder.

What could he do? He couldn't get up. The moment he did he was ready to tumble back to the ground with faintness. There was only one way out: resolutely to fix his mind on some other chain of thought. That helped. But only for a few minutes. Twenty steps later his mind was once again lost in another anticipated caress, and his body ready to go to pieces again.

Nothing, not even cheating nature, emptying the reservoirs of his virility, would enable him to get hold of himself.

"Never," he would later recall, "did I reach her place at Eaubonne without having paid a terrible price. I was so exhausted that I could scarcely stand upright. And in spite of that, the moment I caught sight of her I felt myself completely restored, reinvigorated, filled with all the importunity of an inexhaustible and utterly useless sense of masculinity."

Sometimes when they had agreed to meet on a plateau about half-way between, if he arrived first the pain of expectation, the longing for her presence, was so keen as to be almost beyond endurance. He would try to compose a letter to her, but he could scarcely achieve more than a note, and that note so scribbled that it was hardly legible.

"It would have cost me less," he would subsequently declare, "if I had dipped my finger into my heart and written my note with my lifeblood."

Naturally his body began to suffer from this endless storm of emotions. And there were times when, in addition to his nervous attacks, he would feel actual physical pain—for example, a sharp stab in the groin, a stab so vicious that he would find himself suddenly doubled up and giving vent to a scream.

There was something happening without his being aware of it just yet. It was the strands of muscles in his lower abdomen gradually yielding from the ceaseless strain of his animal desires. But it would not be until some of his madness for Madame d'Houdetot had dissipated that he would realize the extent of the damage: a double inguinal hernia. A double rupture, right and left. If micturition had so often been a torture to him, now it was to become even more: a puzzle that had to be solved every day anew. Some form of manual milking being the only way he could void his urine, and this to the eternal accompaniment of pain. And supporting bandages would remain a necessity through the rest of his life.

"A falling of the gut"—so he would write in his *Confessions*—"which I would take to my grave. Or, rather, which would take me there."

Meanwhile, however, his elation continued so great that he remained oblivious of the changes going on within him. He felt trapped, yes, and dizzy too, but still wonderfully stimulated. Indeed, as never before in his life.

Why?

Could it really be that precisely this mixture of compulsory innocence and fleshly lust was what his nature had always craved in a woman? And was this, unknown to himself, perhaps exactly the situation in which his deepest feelings were somehow most thoroughly gratified?

That is to say, love for a woman whom it was permissible for him to adore but forbidden him to sleep with?

Noli me tangere.

But was this not logical? The woman whom he had missed more than any other in his life—had she not been just such an untouchable? His mother. And if she had lived, would he not have caressed her, worshiped her and never dared defile her?

Madame de Warens—she too fell into that category. In fact, he had even called her his Mama. And deliriously happy they had been together. Until she had broken the magic spell of their relationship by inviting him into her bed. Turning love into incest.

And the girls in Venice. And elsewhere. Girls whom he had certainly desired. Or thought he had. But had they not remained his most delightful memories precisely because he had never possessed them?

So unlike Thérèse. Nothing but a utensil—that's all she was. A household convenience. And for that very reason, perhaps, the idea of her as a mother was something he had never been able to stomach. No, not his Thérèse, this woman he used and abused and misused. She, a mother? Why, it would be a desecration of the word.

But Madame d'Houdetot! It seemed as if all the longings of his life had finally found their fulfillment in her. A woman made for worship and not for lust. And about her an aura, a mysterious radiance, a glow cast upon her by linkage to a man for whom he had similarly yearned over so many years: Voltaire.

No wonder Jean Jacques describes these few months of love as the happiest of his life. All his profoundest desires stirred up and satisfied and again stirred up. If only people could have let him alone! If only they had not insisted on scrutinizing him, talking about him and laughing at him. Everyone putting a hand into what was nobody's business.

With a result that might have been anticipated:

One day Madame d'Houdetot met him with tears of consternation in her eyes. "Saint-Lambert!" she cried. "He knows everything."

"But how? What has happened?"

"An anonymous letter," she sobbed. "We must no longer see each other. At least not so often."

In vain Rousseau tried to persuade her that if Saint-Lambert knew everything, then surely they had nothing to be afraid of. He himself had to recognize that the danger was that Saint-Lambert would not really know everything.

And that danger threw them both into such a fright that at once Jean Jacques began to write to her a series of very different letters, letters respectfully headed *"Chère Madame"* and referring to their trysts as "occasional walks" where they would converse of "every subject that honest hearts may freely discuss."

Oh, God! There he was, closing doors softly. Manufacturing evidence for her, so that she could show Saint-Lambert that the love letters they had supposedly been writing to each other had been nothing but friendly correspondence, such as is surely permissible.

Yes, he too was opening and closing interconnecting doors quietly. But it was not his fault. He was driven to such subterfuges. Just as he had been driven to craving frantic embraces from Madame d'Houdetot. Because of the Baron d'Holbach and Madame d'Épinay, with their endless jokes and their raucous laughter.

He, the truest man of his age, was corrupted into the falsest, by the machinations and the humor of these atheists and philosophers.

Of course they were all at the bottom of that anonymous letter to Saint-Lambert. And who else but Madame d'Épinay would have actually penned it?

Quickly, while his rage was at its peak, Jean Jacques sat down and flung a defiant note at her. Thérèse must rush it at once to the château. Leave it there.

Soon a lackey came running from the château over to the cottage, bearing an answer from Madame d'Épinay.

"Obviously in a hurry to defend herself!" he thought scornfully.

But when he read her letter he was amazed to see how cleverly she had taken advantage of the fact that he had not spelled out her misdeed. She claimed she was terribly puzzled and would not permit herself any emotion, one way or another, until he had enlightened her.

Well, he, for one, had no intention of falling into that trap, which would give her, on paper, black on white and in his own handwriting, something to show Saint-Lambert. Had she not often enough tried to lay her hands on one of his letters to Madame d'Houdetot? Even to the point of badgering Thérèse, and actually pushing her curiosity so far as to feel for a concealed letter in her bosom. No, he would not fall for that, but instead would let her know at once, and in the most withering language, that he was aware of all her conniving methods.

This roused her, of course. She came back at him, answering fire

314

with fire. And the news of the quarrel spread, so that Grimm and Diderot were soon involved.

And thus began that tangle of notes, letters, interviews, expostulations, arguments, kisses and oaths of eternal friendship, a veritable blizzard of explanations and accusations, which dozens of scholars have tried in vain to unravel.

All Paris was soon gossiping of nothing but this fight. So that the Marquis de Castries exclaimed, "Good God! Wherever I go, people are talking of no one but Rousseau and Diderot. Fancy that! Nobodies! People who don't even own a house of their own. Who have difficulty paying rent for a couple of garret rooms. What's the world coming to? There will be no living in it!"

He was, in fact, seeing the end of his kind of aristocracy of birth and the beginning of a new one: the aristocracy of being talked about. Of living in the public eye. Reserved for actors, writers, artists, politicians and so forth.

All these discussions and quarrels would end in passionate reconciliations, which, however, might be turned into violent enmity almost before the ink was dry on the last exchange of notes. But what hurt Jean Jacques most was that Madame d'Houdetot saw in each such flurry a new reason for meeting less frequently, for writing less often.

Until they were almost strangers again. And his great love, born in the spring, seemed doomed to die before the snow flew.

Then one day Madame d'Épinay sent for him to see her at the château. She seemed, according to Jean Jacques, to be in an unusual state of agitation which she was doing her best to conceal.

"My friend," she began, "I am leaving for Geneva."

"Geneva?" he exclaimed.

Quickly he gathered himself together and tried to appear calm, though a thousand questions were suddenly flooding his mind. Geneva? Of all places! Geneva—which meant, of course, Voltaire. What could be the meaning of it?

He said, "But of course you do not intend to leave immediately. Not with the cold season almost upon us."

"Unfortunately I must leave at once," she declared. "My chest is bad. My health is breaking down. I feel that I must consult Dr. Tronchin."

Dr. Tronchin! Now things were becoming clearer. All the Tronchins were intimate with Voltaire. Councilor Tronchin had facilitated Voltaire's acquisition of a house in Geneva. Banker Tronchin was handling a share of Voltaire's funds. Dr. Tronchin attended him as his personal physician.

Despite all these thoughts, Rousseau continued to make conversation, showing all the sympathy that the moment required. "Your chest? I'm grieved to hear of this. Of course Monsieur d'Épinay will be going with you. For surely you cannot be planning to go alone."

"Alas," she replied, "he is too busy. But I will take my son. And his tutor." And then she added, as if offhand: "Unless you too, my good bear, should do me the great kindness of keeping me company on this wretched trip."

Now it was out of the bag! She wanted to drag him to Geneva, not only in order to put a finis to his relations with Madame d'Houdetot, but in order to disgrace him in his home town. So that the people there might see their famous citizen in the train of a notorious adulteress. What a show! The stern Jean Jacques, the enemy of wealth, of aristocracy, the enemy of loose morals and of oppression, here consorting openly with all of them in one person, as if he were after all nothing but a *cicisbeo*, the lapdog of a Parisian whore who was married to a tax farmer.

What a triumph for Voltaire! And how that great laugher would laugh.

But still Jean Jacques dissembled. Pretended she must be jesting. "Your bear is a very sick bear," he said. "Now, wouldn't that make for a good journey—two sick travelers nursing each other en route?"

She did not let herself be dissuaded quite that easily. "I thought that you, with your strong desire to return to Geneva . . . This would be just the opportunity you were looking for."

"At any other time," he hastened to agree. "But now? So close to winter? I'm afraid that I, at least, would never complete the trip."

"I'm sorry to hear you say that," she remarked quietly. And did not refer to the matter again. And after some small talk, which Jean Jacques found as embarrassing as always, they parted.

It was only when he got back to his cottage that the full viciousness of her maneuver was exposed. It was Thérèse who was able to supply the missing link:

"So she has chosen to have her brat in Geneva?" She laughed.

"Are you telling me that Madame d'Épinay is pregnant?" Jean Jacques exclaimed.

"There isn't a servant in the house who doesn't know all about it," Thérèse declared.

Oh, that bitch! Sick, was she? Going to consult Dr. Tronchin because of her chest! And M. d'Épinay too busy to go along. "But you, my good bear, won't you do me the great kindness of keeping me company?" And all the while the truth was that she was running away to conceal the birth of an illegitimate child.

Grimm's, of course. Couldn't be anyone else's. Naturally M. d'Épinay would not go along.

Ah, but now the whole plot was becoming clear. Voltairean in its concept. Yes, truly Voltairean. Another case of making an innocent man play the role of father to a bastard. Just the sort of hoax that they were all so clever at concocting. And he, Jean Jacques, selected for the buffoon's part. Which would be a howling success, of course. For who could doubt that he was the father, when all Geneva would be witness to the "good savage" appearing there in her company. It was as plain as the nose on your face.

And of course Voltaire on hand to enjoy the comedy more than anyone else. In on it from the very beginning, if the truth were ever known.

Yes, and if any slight doubt might linger in Jean Jacques's mind as to the scope and purpose of this invitation to Geneva, a letter from Diderot now came to remove it.

Diderot! His good friend Diderot. From the days of their garret poverty! Now lending himself to this sordid scheme. And here was the proof! This letter! Written and signed by his own hand. And to remain in his files forever, as incontrovertible evidence of how low a man can sink.

Diderot wrote: "What is this I hear, my dear Jean Jacques? Madame d'Épinay must go to Geneva for reasons of health, and it seems you will not go with her? But have you thought of the obligations you are under to this generous woman? Here, then, is your opportunity to discharge this debt. Consider it well, my friend. She is ill. She will need distraction on the long and tiresome journey. It will soon be winter, too . . ." And so forth.

Boiling with indignation, Rousseau sat down to compose a blistering answer: "When I came to live in Madame d'Épinay's cottage it was a sacrifice made out of friendship. Must I now make one out of gratitude too? Must I pay double rent? Obligations, you say. Have you any idea what discomforts I live under here? With twenty servants at my beck and call, and not one who will brush my shoes. Forced to eat dinner at her overloaded table, and regretting the simple fare I might have had at home—and the good service at home, too, serving myself instead of being served by a dozen contemptuous lackeys who neglect me purposely because I do not have the money to tip them. I ask you, who is under obligations to whom?"

At once the letters began to fly again. Until Diderot would finally write to Grimm, "I tremble at the thought that I might ever have to see that wretch Rousseau again!"

And Grimm, from the field of battle, would write to Jean Jacques, "If I could ever forgive you for the affront you have perpetrated against Madame d'Épinay, I would have to consider myself unworthy of ever having a true friend. I have only one wish with respect to you: never again to see you in my life."

Only Saint-Lambert refused to break with him. Was that because an open break would only have confirmed what the public suspected, namely that Rousseau and Madame d'Houdetot had really had an affair? In any case he wrote to Jean Jacques, "The austerity of your character is too well known for me to entertain any unworthy suspicions."

But at the same time Madame d'Houdetot deemed it advisable to beg him to return her letters.

With a heart as if touched by the bony finger of death, he brought her precious letters back to her. Letters almost illegible, so often had he covered them with kisses. As he handed them to her, he was under the impression that she would give him back those he had written. In order that they might both be quits.

But she explained, "I burned your letters."

For a moment he stared at her. Was it possible that she too was, in some strange way, a part of the conspiracy to ruin him? That she had perhaps the intention of making some nefarious use of his letters?

No. It was only that she was human. That she was all woman. And that he had written to her love letters greater even than those he had written in his novel for Saint-Preux and Julie d'Étange. No woman on earth could have burned such a testimony to the love she could inspire. So she lied. In order that she might keep them forever.

25: THE RIGHT TO BURIAL

But as for the rest of his friends, Rousseau was soon convinced that they were all parties to an intricate plot against him. And if any thought that he might be unfair to them occasionally haunted his mind, it was finally and irrevocably removed when the capstone to the whole monstrous structure was suddenly unveiled.

D'Alembert was the author of it. Yes, the gentle d'Alembert. And it took the form of an article in the just-issued seventh volume of the great *Encyclopedia,* which Diderot had prepared with his staff under the editorship of d'Alembert.

It was the *G* volume, and the article was on Geneva. And written by the editor himself, d'Alembert.

That in itself was already a public insult. For had not Jean Jacques collaborated in the preparation of the *Encyclopedia?* Then should not he, the Citizen of Geneva, have been requested to do this article? Why, then, had d'Alembert taken it upon himself? And this without even consulting his friend and associate Rousseau.

But perhaps it was best so. For now it could be seen who was the master plotter of them all.

In that article on Geneva one could read: "The theater, the drama, is not permitted in Geneva, out of fear lest a passion for finery, for diversion and for levity be propagated. But against this, might not strict laws be enacted and enforced, and the people of Geneva thus not be denied the good influence of the theater in the refinement of the public taste?"

Who could have inspired d'Alembert to write those lines? For d'Alembert himself, whose specialty was geometry and after that philosophy, could not have thought of them.

The article went on to urge Genevans to construct a playhouse in their city, so that it might be said of Geneva that it "united the civil virtues of Sparta to the grace and urbanity of Athens."

A theater in Geneva! Imagine! And presenting whose plays, do you suppose? Yes, just guess whose. To the wild applause of the young Genevans. And the whole town acclaiming guess whose favorite actress? The whole town talking of guess whose latest play? And speculating about his next one.

Could anything be clearer? He, Jean Jacques, was to be disgraced in the eyes of Geneva, at the same time that Voltaire was to triumph there. Geneva was to be turned into a little Paris.

With Voltaire presiding.

Nevertheless Rousseau hesitated for a moment before letting his righteous fury dictate a blow. A terrific blow. He hesitated because the *Encyclopedia* was just then going through another one of its endless moments of danger, when the whole enterprise seemed about to perish from the united attacks of theologians, Jesuits, aristocrats and paid pamphleteers.

Nothing was lacking but the word of the King, and indeed that would soon come to crush the enterprise, with d'Alembert resigning and Diderot carrying on through all the remaining volumes in secret, gathering the necessary material through twenty years of endless work, waiting for the moment when publication would be permitted again.

Sickness too delayed Rousseau's coup against the *Encyclopedia*. For he had to get out of the cottage on the d'Épinay estate. Madame d'Houdetot, it is true, had begged him to wait until the warm weather before moving, but he had written for Madame d'Épinay's permission. Written to her in Geneva, to which city she had gone with M. d'Épinay, since Rousseau would not go with her. Yes, with her husband, which was indeed strange—that is, if she was really preparing to give secret birth there to an illegitimate child.

But Rousseau no longer had that subject on his mind. He wrote, "I know it is my duty to move out of your cottage. But a friend urges me to remain until spring. What shall I do?"

She replied coldly, "When I see my duty clearly, I do it and never find it necessary to consult my friends. Nor will I advise you now as to whether you should do your duty or not."

The implication was so obvious that he began packing at once. An admirer, hearing of his difficulties generously offered him a very small house at Montlouis, near Montmorency, overlooking Paris. There he felt so low, from the end of his love affair and from the conspiracy of his oldest friends, that he had to take to his bed.

As Thérèse busied herself with his comfort, he wept to think how much he owed this faithful woman, and he had a notary summoned so that he might make out his will, acknowledging that he had not paid his servant Thérèse her wages for thirteen years, and that in return, if he died, she was to have everything that he owned.

But the very moment he could rise from his bed, he had a table moved into a nearby ruined tower that was on the property, and there, despite the lack of windows and doors to keep out the cold and the wind of winter, he wrote in a matter of three weeks his *Letter to d'Alembert on the Theater*.

It was not a letter to Voltaire. Oh, no! He could play at that game of the indirect attack, too. Just as Voltaire had hidden behind d'Alembert, so would Rousseau. Indeed, Jean Jacques specifically exempted Voltaire from his strictures. Voltaire's *Zaïre*, for example, was still a bewitching drama. And indeed, "if Geneva should insist on having a theater, then let it be only if M. de Voltaire will consent to fill it with his genius. And to live as long as his plays, which will endure forever."

But after that, what an attack!

Yes, for a corrupt people like the Parisians, perpetually intriguing, gambling or visiting bordellos, the theater, of course, saves them from what would be far worse. But for a pure people such as the Genevans, the theater can only be a corrupting force. Just imagine Geneva with actors and actresses living there, in the style that actors and actresses always affect—a perpetual business of costumes, entertainments, dinner parties, love affairs, chatter and factionalism.

After all, what is an actor? A person without personality. A character without character. A human being without humanity. Isn't that what his craft demands? Can he hope to succeed otherwise? Would not beliefs, if he ever had any, get in the way of his ability to say the things he doesn't believe in, but which the part he is playing demands that he say?

Is not the talent of an actor, and his power, just that? That he can say anything with force and conviction, whether it be lies or not? And that he will gladly do so for money and for glory? How, then, can he be anything but false? What has he got but the ability to deceive? It is his living. And for that he takes his bows. And merits his applause.

Does it not follow, then, that if a man's greatest ambition should be to realize himself, the actor must be the greatest degradation of a man that there can be? For he can never be himself. That great role is denied to him.

But even worse are the actresses. For what can one expect from a woman who would as lief play whore as virgin, Messalina as Joan of Arc? Can she help but carry over from the stage into her life this utterly demoralized point of view, contaminating everything she touches? Licentiousness must be the very breath of her being. If she can sell herself to appear on the stage in any part whatsoever, why should she scruple to sell herself off stage, for any role whatsoever?

No wonder that in almost every land where theaters have been permitted, the profession of actress has been considered a shame. And the Church to this day feels itself justified in refusing her the right to be buried in consecrated ground. For it is inconceivable that a woman should be able to play the role of any woman, no matter how evil, on the stage and then go home and be fit to play the glorious role assigned to her by God: that of wife and mother.

And what of the much vaunted power of the theater to lift our emotions? Her power to instill in us the knowledge of the highest passions of life? Lies! Nothing but lies! A transparent attempt of the theater to pass itself off as serving a useful function in society.

On the contrary! The theater is the betrayer of the very highest purpose of man. Because an audience that has experienced in effigy, so to speak, all the beautiful emotions that the human heart hungers for, that audience goes out and feels completely satisfied with itself. It has already felt pity and charity, in the theater. Why, then, go out and practice them in real life, where they are so difficult to exercise? It has already felt the surge of patriotism, the heat of love, the sacrifice of devotion, while comfortably seated. Why, then, experience them all over again with all the discomforts that real life entails?

Thus it is that without ever having done anything for either his God or his country, for himself or his fellow man, each member of the audience of a theater nevertheless considers himself as having fulfilled all his duties as a man. And so it is that the natural hunger of the human heart for real emotions finds itself endlessly deceived with food that does not feed, with emotions that are nothing but a simulacrum of emotions, until, gorged with emptiness, the heart is astonished to find itself dying of starvation.

And all of us are thereby diminished. All of us! Both man and mankind. Defrauded, every last one of us. Of our very lives. Which we haven't really lived at all, merely watched being lived, on a stage, in other people's stories. As if we had spent our years before a mirror, deceiving ourselves with facial contortions, while actually experiencing nothing. And dying at last without ever having lived at all. Cheated out of everything that God created us for. Our lives nothing but a dream. A puff of smoke.

And in spite of all this, are we still to be told that Geneva must have her theater? Who would dare tell us that? What can we need a theater for? To drain away our money and our time?

Have you ever seen those citizens whom you propose to benefit with a theater? Go look at them! See if they need a theater in order to unite "the civil virtues of Sparta to the urbanity of Athens." Go see those craftsmen who build their own houses, both comfortable and elegant, and furnish them with their own cabinetwork and in addition earn their living from constructing and repairing clocks, or from weaving beautiful stuffs that are in demand all over the world. And who, besides that, serve in the militia and bear arms in defense of their country—and often in the defense of other countries. While their womenfolk keep house, cultivate their little gardens and raise their children to be as upright and as hard-working and as thrifty as their elders.

And such a people, busy living their own lives—they need a theater? Who is it that dares claim that?

Voltaire must have leaped as if struck by a snake when he read this violent tirade against the theater, his favorite activity. Rousseau's eulogies of Voltaire and his plays didn't deceive him for a moment. This was obviously aimed at him, the foremost playwright of his time. And naturally from the pen of that same Jean Jacques Rousseau who had only recently tried to seduce the mistress of Saint-Lambert.

"Why, you bastard dog of a Diogenes!" Voltaire screamed. "You incompetent playwright, you petty librettist! You spent your life trying to get your own miserable plays produced, and, being finally booed off the stage for good, you saw no other way to ease your envious heart except to drape yourself in the robes of a moralizer and condemn as immoral the art that rejected you!

"That's the truth, isn't it? Confess it, you hypocrite! Or do you want me to pull out of my files the very first letter you sent to me? An abject letter of gratitude for being permitted to work on the music for one of my playscripts, one of my very worst, which I didn't have time to tear up. And yet how happy you were to have even this bone thrown to you under the table. The very first bone of your miserable life!"

Ha! And now behold this wretched refugee from Switzerland who has for so many years enjoyed the hospitality of France, behold him now approving the barbarism of some of our priests who deny our French actors and actresses a Christian burial.

Is it possible that he has never bothered to read the history of his adopted country's literature? Or can his savage heart be so devoid of human pity that he did not find it necessary to weep when he read of France's greatest playwright, Molière, and how the priests mistreated him? How, when he lay dying, not a priest would come to speak a word of comfort to him? How could anyone possibly hold back his tears at the spectacle of Molière's wife having to run from church to church to beg for a burial permit? When again not a man of God had the courage to affront his superiors by giving her what Christ would surely not have denied her.

And of how she even ran to Versailles, to throw herself on her knees before Louis XIV, who shortly before had held her child over the baptismal font. Crying to him, "Sire! If my husband is a criminal, it was in your service. His crime of being an actor was not only authorized by Your Majesty, but even commanded of him!"

But what could this priest-ridden monarch do except dismiss her, giving orders that this matter be settled as quickly and as quietly as possible? With the result that Molière had to be buried at night. As if his death were a shame. With no hearse permitted. And no bells rung, no prayers allowed. And only by special last-minute dispensation granted an escort of six children carrying tapers to light the way. But accompanied by a great swarm of beggars in loathsome rags, who had somehow discovered that Molière's will authorized the distribution of a large sum of money to the poor, and who therefore thronged the cemetery in order to make certain of their share.

But then, what difference could all this make to a Rousseau? A Rousseau who hated laughter. Hated frivolity. And especially the laughter of Molière. For what does Molière consider funny, according to Rousseau? Is it not the scene where the inflexibly upright father is finally tricked by his pleasure-loving children? Is it not the scene where the husband, too concerned about the chastity of his wife, is finally triumphantly cuckolded? Is it not, in short, any scene in which virtue is held up to ridicule?

Virtue? As if this Jean Jacques, this venereally diseased guttersnipe of Turin, could really know the meaning of this word. As if this runaway apprentice, this lackey, could possibly know anything about the life and the morals of actresses.

All he could know was that Voltaire had loved so many of them. And that therefore anything evil he could think of saying about them would wound Voltaire. Voltaire, who had written one of his best poems to Adrienne Lecouvreur, the most beautiful and talented of them all. So distinguished, so elegant, that ladies of the court would go to the theater to listen to the modulations of her voice, which they tried in vain to copy. And would take along their maids and their couturières even, to study the dresses she wore and how smart she made herself look in them.

Virtuous?

Well, of course she was virtuous. Not, indeed, in the restricted sense that Jean Jacques would give to that word. To whom a woman could be stupid, could be vicious, could be as ugly as a potato, but would still remain virtuous for him provided only that she wore both her legs in one stocking, denying the urges of her body and the impulses of her heart.

No. In that narrow sense Adrienne had not been virtuous. She had loved too much and too many. But in every other sense there was never anyone more virtuous.

Priests came to her deathbed—she was so young! still in her thirties —and harangued her to repudiate her vile profession or, otherwise, be denied the last rites of the Church and be excluded from burial in a cemetery. Then it was that she exemplified everything that the word "virtue" can mean. Feverish and moribund as she was, and in great pain from an inflammation of the intestines, she nevertheless declared over and over again, "I will not give the lie to my career. I will not dishonor the profession that has honored me. I have left my parish church two thousand francs for the poor. Let my body be thrown into the gutter, if you cannot find a few feet of earth to cover me with."

Voltaire had suffered all the agony of watching her die. And then had found himself playing for her the same terrible role that Molière's wife had been forced to play. Found himself running from priest to priest, begging for a permit to bury her. But not even the unconsecrated area, that corner of the cemetery usually set aside for suicides and for those who have died cursing God, would they give to her remains.

Because she had been an actress. Because in ancient Rome, when Christianity was first forming its code of laws, actresses had been beneath contempt, and the Church had excommunicated them then and had continued to do so. With almost all Christian states following suit.

So that in France no priest would knowingly marry one of them. No court of law would hear their pleas. And if somehow, in some poverty-stricken parish where the priest needed the fee or where some powerful sponsor could force compliance, an actress managed to get herself married to the man she loved, she could still never be called Madame. She remained all her life nothing but Mademoiselle. And her children would still be considered bastards.

It was from a civil magistrate that Voltaire finally secured permission to bury Adrienne Lecouvreur's body in a vacant lot near the Seine. At midnight Voltaire hired a fiacre and saw her body put into it, as if it were no more than a package. And then he and a couple of other admirers more courageous than the rest walked bareheaded behind that vehicle through the dark streets, down to the river. Escorted by a couple of constables. As if they were all being marched to jail.

A hole had been dug in the earth. And by its side Voltaire, despite the orders against any ceremony, recited his poem "The Death of Mademoiselle Lecouvreur," a poem that would later be set to music by Frederick the Great.

> . . . *What will you say, people of the future,*
> *When you learn of the cruelty of our times?*

That she to whom the Greeks would have built altars
Was denied the right to burial . . .

He wept as her body was pushed into the hole and spaded over with
enough earth to keep dogs from digging it up. Thinking, Such may be
my own funeral someday. And most certainly will be if my theological enemies have their way.

The very next day he called together actors and actresses and addressed them thus: "Why do you consent to carry on a profession for
which you are destined to be punished? Are you not all employees
of the King of France? Why not announce that you will no longer
perform until the servants of kings are treated by the Church at least
as well as chimney sweeps and butchers?"

He spoke also to every playwright he could reach, asking them, "Is
any of us who write plays worth more than the interpretation that we
get? What would we do without these men and women who bring
our works to life? We should go down and strew Mademoiselle Lecouvreur's grave with roses."

When the authorities got wind of what was going on and began to
meet to determine upon action, Voltaire felt that it was time he made
himself scarce. And he fled Paris.

Of course, all that was long ago. Surely now, in Geneva, his life was
safe. And his burial when dead assured.

But was it? Voltaire was amazed to see Rousseau's *Letter* soaring
to a huge success. Jean Jacques's greatest acclaim so far. With book
dealers in Paris and Geneva unable to find enough copies to meet the
demand. And theologians everywhere rushing to their pulpits with
praises for his attack on the theater. And such a turmoil among
European intellectuals that over four hundred books and pamphlets
were printed pro and con. While Rousseau's mail grew so enormous
that it threatened to swamp him, and he had to declare that he could
not hope to answer even a fraction of it.

In Geneva so many clergymen found sermons in Rousseau's *Letter,*
and feelings rose to such a point that the authorities felt it advisable
to caution Voltaire against further theatricals in his home. The citizens
would not countenance this continued and flagrant violation of an
old Genevan law.

Enraged before this angry tide, Voltaire wrote to Thieriot, "Who
the hell is this fanatical Jean Jacques? Is he some modern hermit come
out of the desert, naked, sunburned and bearded, to preach damnation against us? Does he propose to be a new Father of the Church?"

Indeed, this feeling against Voltaire grew so strong, especially among the poorer classes of Geneva, who hated the rich and their luxurious way of life, that once when Voltaire was riding in his carriage through the streets of the town he suddenly heard himself vociferously jeered by a crowd of workingmen. Quickly he ducked back deep into his upholstery, out of the line of the windows, through which he expected at any moment a shower of rocks.

"What do they want of me?" he cried. "Will their preachers burn me, as they burned Servetus?"

Frightened, he gave orders to Councilor Tronchin to take steps to abrogate the lease on his house in Geneva, that house which only a couple of years before had seemed to him like an earthly Paradise, and which he had therefore called Les Délices.

"Where will you go?" the Councilor asked him.

"I don't know!" Voltaire moaned. "All I know is that I can't live here any longer. My life isn't safe. I must go!"

But when Councilor Tronchin reminded him that the clauses in his lease were such that if he dropped it before his death it would cost him twenty-five thousand francs, Voltaire wrung his hands in despair. "You mean that I must lose twenty-five thousand francs? All on account of this Jean-*foutre* of a Rousseau?"

He hesitated before such a huge financial catastrophe. But meanwhile the feeling against him continued to run high. Almost every morning ugly epithets could be found chalked up on the walls of his home. And threatening handbills could be found plastered on his gateposts.

"Cancel the lease!" he cried. "Take whatever you can get. I do not intend to be put to the torch either by the priests of Baal or by those of Basle!"

26: I LOVE YOU. I HATE YOU.

But then suddenly Voltaire changed his mind. Refused to sign the transfer papers for Les Délices. What? Was he mad? Was he really going to hand this Jean Jacques such a resounding victory, without so much as a fight?

Leave Geneva? So that this little squirt of a Rousseau might gloat that he had run the great Voltaire out of town? And that thus, inferentially, he had snatched from Voltaire the crown of being the most powerful writer of his day?

Never! Adrienne Lecouvreur had not flinched in the face of threats. Why should he?

Might it not be possible for him to buy some piece of property just beyond the jurisdiction of Geneva, so that his friends from town might still come to join him in his theatricals and the authorities be unable to offer any further opposition?

Just by chance there happened to be on the market two adjoining properties whose acreage extended almost up to the walls of Geneva. One of these estates, Ferney, in the French area known as Gex, was up for outright sale, and Voltaire quickly concluded a deal for its purchase. It was, however, a wretched piece of land, swampy and with barely a dozen tenant farmers on it, who grubbed there for an existence bordering on starvation. And its possession did not convey any special privileges guaranteeing him against interference by the French authorities.

The property that Voltaire really coveted was that of neighboring Tournay, an independent feudal remnant within the sovereignty of France, whose owners had the right to call themselves Counts of Tournay and still enjoyed certain medieval freedoms which had ceased to exist almost everywhere else. It was as if it were a separate little kingdom. A very tiny one, to be sure.

"That's the spot for me!" Voltaire cried. "From there a man can thumb his nose at the world. Geneva would be my neighbor still, but utterly powerless against me. And France, my protector, would nevertheless be barred from interfering in my private affairs."

Tournay, however, was not up for sale. But only for lease. And so Voltaire immediately addressed a letter to the owner, Charles de Brosses, president of the Parlement of Dijon, asking him how much he wanted for a lifelong occupancy.

Naturally the price for such a lease would depend on how long Voltaire might be expected to remain alive, de Brosses replied. But in a day when actuarial tables still did not exist, this was a matter for speculation, and therefore for haggling. So that almost at once each man was convinced that the other was trying to get the better of him, and each determined that this must never happen.

But when did Voltaire ever retreat from a battle of wits? Particularly when a bit of money was involved?

If, for example his carriage broke down while en route, he would bargain with farmers for a matter of a franc or two in the price of having his vehicle repaired or having it towed to town. In the city he would bargain with tradesmen until they would refuse to do business with him.

Once he wanted to buy a hunting knife to keep in his traveling coach. The merchant was asking a louis, twenty-four francs.

"Let's settle for eighteen," said Voltaire.

The merchant shook his head. Whereupon Voltaire began to figure out for him on paper just what the knife could be worth. He knew the price of tempered steel, the wages of knife grinders. He could estimate the worth of the handle. And as for the merchant's profit, that could be only so and so much. In short, eighteen francs would do splendidly.

But still the merchant shook his head. "One louis," he said.

Thereupon Voltaire began to work on the psychology of the man. The features of his face, which expressed honesty, love of mankind, faith in God—such a face could not possibly deny that eighteen francs was a reasonable price.

"So eighteen francs it is," said Voltaire, and began to count them out.

"One louis," said the merchant. "Otherwise I shall be cheating my family. Depriving my children of what is due them."

"Oh, you have children?" Voltaire asked.

"Five, monsieur. Three boys and two girls."

"Then everything is settled," said Voltaire. "Eighteen francs it is. And you shall see what positions I shall be able to find for your boys. And what husbands for your girls. I have friends in all the financial circles of Europe. I have influence in all government offices. All your family worries are over, my friend. And here's your money."

"I thank you, monsieur, for your interest in my family," said the merchant. "I shall never forget to mention you in my prayers. And my wife will do likewise."

"Then here are your eighteen francs," said Voltaire.

"But, monsieur," said the merchant, "the price of the knife is still twenty-four francs."

Voltaire cried out, "For six francs you sacrifice the future of your children?" That time, however, he knew himself beaten. But it wasn't often.

He still had the joy, every year, of collecting from the Marquis de Lézeau. Thirty years before, he had lent him eighteen thousand francs, to be repaid in annual sums until Voltaire died.

"I'll never pay a cent on it," the Marquis was reported to have said, rubbing his hands for having put one over on Voltaire. "I'll see him buried before six months are up."

It was the Marquis who had died, years later, and his heirs were still paying. And Voltaire who rubbed his hands year after year.

Such was Voltaire's stubbornness. Hadn't he been called *volontaire* as a child?

In this contest with de Brosses, Voltaire began by writing to him, "How long can I live? I'm sixty-seven years old. [He was really only sixty-five.] And I could almost give you my word of honor that I have not four or five years more to go. I am old and ailing. I would tire you out merely by listing the incurable diseases that afflict me."

But this de Brosses was no pushover. He was something of a *volontaire* himself. At any rate, he was no fool. He was a classical scholar of note. His work on the Roman historian Sallust was outstanding. He had had the good fortune to be present when Herculaneum was first exposed, after being buried beneath the cinders of Vesuvius since the year 79. His description of that event had made his name known over all Europe. In addition, his books on Australia and the South Seas would one day be acknowledged as laying the foundations for the geographical and ethnological study of that area of our globe. (He coined the word *fétichisme* for man's earliest religion.) And he was to become even more famous after his death, when his sprightly *Letters from Italy* would be printed and recognized as one of the master-pieces of travel literature.

De Brosses replied cannily, "What? You will live only four or five years? On that salubrious estate where my uncle lived to be ninety-one and my grandfather lived to be eighty-seven? For my part, I am convinced you will live out this century, which is already yours, and steal the palm of longevity from that centenarian *manqué*, Fontenelle."

All of which was very flattering. But rather frightening too. For a lease based on such a record length of life would come pretty high. And lest de Brosses be getting the wrong impression about Voltaire, Voltaire took to hobbling about on crutches and to wearing dark glasses. So that when de Brosses came to Geneva, he should have cause to worry lest he fail to get his prospective customer's signature on the lease before the Grim Reaper carried him off.

After some further cat-and-mouse play, it was settled that Voltaire was to pay 35,600 francs, based on a probable occupancy of ten years. And of course when Voltaire proceeded to live not ten but twenty years more, de Brosses would eventually have the right to feel that every additional year that Voltaire lived was just so much money filched from the de Brosses estate.

Voltaire, on the other hand, would always feel that he had been cheated in this deal, for de Brosses had failed to warn him of the inconveniences of being a feudal lord. For example:

Shortly after taking possession, one of Voltaire's peasants got into a brawl. Over nothing more important than a few pounds of nuts. And for that the peasant almost killed a man. The local magistrate decreed a fine of two hundred pistoles. And Voltaire, who hated physical violence, heartily approved the verdict. Until he discovered that, since the culprit was a serf, it would be the lord of the manor who would be expected to pay the fine. In short, himself.

Then, of course, Voltaire screamed. Two hundred pistoles! (Worth in money of today about ten thousand dollars.) Why, that was an outrageous fine for the beating up of a worthless scamp. And in any case it was the guilty man who should pay. He had caused the injuries. Not Voltaire.

But this man happened to be Voltaire's property. And the situation was exactly the same as if Voltaire's horse had leaped a fence and done damage to a neighbor's gardener.

Voltaire was incensed. A man no better than a horse? In this day and age? Why, such things were intolerable in modern France. He paid the fine, but he was to make it his business later to call attention to these last remnants of feudalism in his country, and to help eradicate them.

An additional grievance against de Brosses occurred when Voltaire complained that the house lacked enough firewood to carry it through the cold weather. De Brosses pointed out to him a certain large stack of wood that one of his peasants had chopped up. The strange thing about these fourteen cords of firewood was that Voltaire was expected to pay for them. The firewood, it seems, had been prepared before the lease was signed and was therefore not owned by either de Brosses or Voltaire, but by the peasant who had done the chopping.

Voltaire boiled. Hadn't he just paid out a huge sum of money and acquired some men who were not men but horses? How could these horses who could not pay their own fines own wood? Which he would have to pay for?

The sum involved was only 281 francs. But after the 35,600 francs he had just paid out, that seemed to Voltaire just the final straw to break the camel's back.

Whole volumes have been written about these miserable 281 francs.

But of course the quarrel ran much deeper. This paltry sum was just what seethed up to the surface. In particular there was a clause in the lease whose import Voltaire discovered only after he had signed it. That clause stipulated that everything at Tournay passed immediately into the hands of the de Brosses family the moment Voltaire died.

Did that mean that Voltaire's jewelry, Voltaire's books, Voltaire's manuscripts, all of that was immediately the property of de Brosses? And what about his files? Those enormous files of over fifty thousand letters that included communications from every personage of importance in Europe over the last half century, a file of material about which Casanova, when he visited Voltaire, had exclaimed, "Any publisher would give you a fortune for this!"

Inconceivable that this should become the property of de Brosses. And yet there was that clause. And when Voltaire realized that the law would uphold de Brosses, he began to withdraw from Tournay and set himself up permanently at Ferney, whose country house he rebuilt from top to bottom, incorporating a theater in it, and whose acres of swampland he drained, and whose population he increased until it became one of the richest estates of the neighborhood. Leaving Tournay more or less uncared for.

As if to say to de Brosses, "Let's see who outsmarted whom."

And to pound the point home, when de Brosses' name eventually came up for membership in the French Academy, Voltaire immediately issued the following slogan:

"If de Brosses gets in, Voltaire gets out!"

That was all he said. But it was enough. De Brosses' name was never again mentioned for the Academy. And the president of the Parlement of Dijon learned the hard way how difficult it was to win out against Voltaire.

Nothing to do now but wait for Voltaire to die. But here again he was unfortunate: Voltaire survived him by a year. And the feeling between the two sides was not to be resolved except in the law courts long after both parties were dead.

But despite all this byplay it was wonderful to be lord of Tournay, absolute ruler of a domain. Here he could have his theater undisturbed. No questions asked. And just let that nincompoop of a Jean Jacques set foot here, on his soil. Why, with his seignioral rights, Voltaire could have his peasants clap the man in irons.

Yes, sir! Chain him to the walls of his donjon keep. That would teach the fellow to meddle with a feudal lord! Why, he could hang him by the neck from the crenelations of his battlements! For the crows to peck at his rotting flesh.

It was in keeping with this new and exalted dignity that Voltaire made an ostentatious entry into his estate. Arriving in his sky-blue coach drawn by six horses. With Madame Denis sitting beside him, glittering with diamonds. And his peasants, fully armed, lined up like a hedge on each side of the road, as his vehicle swept through the gates and down the road to the manor house, where the drawbridge (of which Voltaire was particularly proud) came clanging down over the moat.

And then cannon roaring, grenades exploding and mortars (all rented for the occasion from the city of Geneva) discharging. And through the billows of smoke, a fife-and-drum corps erupting into shrill and noisy action.

And as Voltaire descended from his carriage, bevies of little girls in white confirmation dresses running up to curtsy to his lordship, to kiss his hand and to offer him beribboned baskets filled with oranges. While the more nubile girls, blushing and giggling, brought him great bouquets of flowers, and young boys awkwardly presented Madame Denis with cages in which were birds they had trapped. And older women waited to bring up their presents of cakes and of cheeses which they had specially whipped up for this holiday.

Then the parish priest made a welcome speech thick with compliments. Followed by a gala dinner in the open, with everything provided free by the lord of Tournay, including ample quantities of wine in which his farmers could toast their new master's health.

And then, after dark, private entertainment indoors for the vast numbers of distinguished guests who had arrived from Geneva and from the rich villas along the lake shore. And more food. And dancing. And then, to top it all off, a play!

Naturally, written by Voltaire. His most recent Parisian success, *Tancrède*. Dedicated to Madame de Pompadour, and dealing with medieval knights and ladies in a tale of tragic love and jousting, and therefore most appropriate for this castle and its new lord. Suggested by an episode in Ariosto's *Orlando Furioso* and subsequently to be adapted by Rossini for an opera of the same name. And now superbly mounted here on the stage of Voltaire's just-constructed bijou theater— "no bigger than my hand," as Voltaire himself would admit, but the principal roles were played by the sons and the daughters of some of the most prominent citizens of Geneva.

To d'Alembert Voltaire wrote, "So Jean Jacques is determined that there shall be no theater in Geneva, is he? Well, tell him that I've just opened one right under the walls of his city."

And that was just the first one. Another one would soon follow, built at Ferney. And in addition Voltaire would rent a building at Carouge, in Sardinian territory, and he would buy one at Châtelaine, on French soil, which he offered to groups of strolling players for their use. So that not only could the Geneva aristocrats see plays at his own various theaters, but the public could also see them.

Taking, so it would seem, a diabolical joy in ringing this puritanical town with theaters and with plays. Keeping the inns of Geneva crowded with visiting actors and actresses. Forcing the whole area either to succumb to frivolity or to be perpetually on guard against its temptations.

Naturally the Genevan consistory of clergymen fought him, using every avenue of influence at their command in order to persuade the authorities of Sardinia and of France to close these theaters the audiences of which were drawn from their congregations.

But despite endless hurdles put in his way Voltaire fought back. "I am determined," he cried, "to introduce gaiety among the Genevans!" And his plays succeeded each other on all his various stages: *Mérope, Alzire, Nanine, Zaïre, Mahomet,* and so on. At Carouge. At Ferney. At Tournay. And even right under the noses of the citizens of Geneva, at Les Délices, whose lease he still retained, but where Voltaire claimed no plays were being given, though he would not deny that there had been some trying on of costumes and of armor, some preparation of scenery and some studying of assigned roles.

Egged on by the ministers, the Magnificent Council of Geneva concluded that they could not see much difference between actors trying on costumes or armor, and reciting their roles before scenery, and what is usually called a play. Neither could the spectators who came and applauded and went home as satisfied as if they had witnessed an actual performance.

Still the authorities might not have taken any decisive action against Voltaire, had it not happened that right in the heart of Geneva a deceived husband took a shot at his wife's lover.

The crime of fornication inside the walls of Geneva? What was the world coming to? The whole citizenry was aroused and buzzed furiously over this incredible and scandalous occurrence.

The result was that the Magnificent Council ruled that Voltaire's theatrical rehearsals were just as bad as regular performances. And they forbade them utterly on every square foot of Genevan soil.

Angrily Voltaire wrote to his friend d'Argens: "This little rump church of Calvin, for whom virtue consists in austere living and the piling up of usury, has decided that if there are cuckolds in this world the reason is clear: Voltaire's plays. And these bumpkin preachers are now compelling the members of their flocks to swear that they will never have anything to do with my stages. It's that Jean-*foutre* of a Jean Jacques who is behind it all, of course. Every fortnight he writes a letter to these Calvinistic priests to steam them up against my theaters."

For some time Voltaire found himself performing to nearly empty benches. So that the strolling players of Carouge could not make ends meet and had to give up and move elsewhere. But the mood soon passed, and it wasn't long before Voltaire could report new successes, dashing off the following letter to d'Argental in Paris:

"Wait! Give me a chance to catch my breath. What a triumph! We had three hundred guests to my new comedy, *Le Droit du seigneur,* coming not only from Geneva but from Turin, from Dijon, from Lyons and so forth. And from Paris we have not only the Duke de Villars, the Duke and Duchess d'Enville and the Count d'Harcourt, but above all we have the Marshal de Richelieu! Yes, the conqueror of Port Mahon, the strongest fortress in Europe, next to Gibraltar, is in our midst. I have turned over my castle of Tournay to him and accommodated some of the others at my Geneva residence, Les Délices. We've had nothing but balls and banquets. And evenings when so many counts and dukes were present that I cried, 'This is not my home! It can't be. Crowded with all the peers of France.'

"And now more news: I have just written another play, *Olympia,* which we are planning to stage. . . ."

Is it any wonder that Jean Jacques, on June 17, 1760, felt impelled to write a letter to Voltaire, summing up his feelings in these wild words: *"I hate you!"*

And can there be any doubt that sobs must have racked his body when he gave in to this burning impulse to strip himself naked to his enemy, revealing all the secret torments of his heart?

I hate you, yes, but only because that is how you want it. For I hate you as one who would so much rather have loved you, if only you had been willing. . . .

Could any man prostrate himself more abjectly than in such a sentence? And was it possible that such a confession should fail to move even the iciest heart?

And yet it did fail. At any rate, with Voltaire.

The bitter outpouring continued:

How can I like you, when you have inflicted on me, your devoted disciple, on me, your most enthusiastic admirer, griefs which are almost beyond human endurance? When you are making every effort to ruin Geneva, despite the asylum that she has extended to you . . .

This is where Voltaire's heart was touched. But not with pity. With rage. "Despite the *asylum!*" he exclaimed.

Geneva extend an asylum to him? Does the Count of Ferney need asylum? Or the lord of Tournay? Does Voltaire, first gentleman of the King's chamber, need a refuge? He Voltaire, in daily correspondence with such exalted personages as Frederick the Great, Madame de Pompadour, the Margravine of Bayreuth, the Duke de Choiseul and God only knows how many other dignitaries, all of whom would be honored to have him as a guest?

Asylum! Did this Rousseau imagine for a moment that the great Voltaire was a mendicant like himself? Going around, hat in hand, begging for free housing?

Never had Voltaire read anything so impudent. Nor was that all. The letter went on in the same mad vein:

Instead of thanking me for the praises I have continued to heap on you . . .

As if Voltaire needed his praises. Praises had been showered on him for half a century now. Rousseau could keep his.

. . . you seem determined to alienate me from my countrymen. Already you have made it impossible for me to show my face in Geneva. Thus I find myself forced to live and die among strangers and will confront my last hour deprived of those consolations that the dying are entitled to. And my body, after that, is to be denied the comfort of the ground and thrown out on the town dump, while you will still go on enjoying every honor that my country can bestow.

Enough! Enough! All this was too ridiculous for words.

To d'Alembert Voltaire sent off a hasty note: "Never have I had such an impertinent letter as just now from Jean Jacques Rousseau. Tell me truthfully, has this man gone totally insane?"

And to Dr. Tronchin: "Haven't you got some specific against madness? I think Jean Jacques could stand some medical advice from you. He should be put on a regimen of warm baths and light foods. Or, since he admires everything savages do, on a diet of raw meat, and plunges in ice-cold water."

But a note to Rousseau? Voltaire never bothered with that. What, indeed, could he possibly say to a man who had just approved the denial of burial rights to French actresses and now, almost in the same breath, was pitying himself for the possibility that, as a Protestant living in Catholic France, he might be subjected to the same cruel treatment?

If there was anything Voltaire hated it was lack of logic. And it was therefore unlikely that he would have had the stomach to read this letter to the end. A letter that continued to dwell on Rousseau's mixture of hate and love for Voltaire:

I hate you then, monsieur, but only because you insist on it. And of all the rich emotions for you that my heart was once so full of, there now remains nothing but the love which I will forever bear for your works, and the admiration which no one will ever be able to deny to you because of your great gifts.

It is not my fault, then, if I cannot hereafter honor you for anything but your talents. You may rest assured, however, that I shall never be lacking in the respect that is due to them, nor in the conduct that such respect will entail on my part.

Goodbye, monsieur.

It was as if he did not know which emotion was uppermost in him, his love or his hate. And was certain of only one thing: his dream of being embraced by Voltaire could never be realized. Never.

27: SIGN YOUR NAME?
THAT'S FOR BISHOPS!

What a race was now run by these two! Pen in hand. As if in a breathless sprint to capture the applause of the world.

With Voltaire pouring out pamphlet after pamphlet in his *Écrasez l'infâme* campaign, under the militant slogan "Crush the monster!" Concerning which he would write to his disciples in Paris: "What?

Are we to acknowledge that Jesus, that illiterate Jew, with his almost equally illiterate companions, could sweep the world with a new religion, and we, the most intelligent men of our time, cannot spread our religion of good sense and tolerance?"

Letters which he would sign with a viciously scrawled *"écr. l'inf.,"* or some similar abbreviation reminding his correspondents of the necessity of freeing the world from fanatics. Fanatics of all kinds.

For it was no particular group, no particular government or church that he was after. But, in general, all those who presumed to force you to think as they did. Not by virtue of their more commanding logic, but because of their more commanding force. Because they could punish you if you dared to think differently. Forcing you thus to choose to abdicate either your brains or your life.

Anything and everything might give him the impulse for a new pamphlet in behalf of this great struggle for independence of mind. A bit of news. A passing fancy. A witticism, even.

As for example when he had been experimenting with snails and had observed how these little beasts joined themselves in sexual intercourse and remained thus for days.

"What an orgy!" Voltaire exclaimed. With admiration and with envy. "Quick, Wagnière! A pamphlet!"

And dictated at once to his secretary an essay to fling into the teeth of ministers and priests. "Is it possible," he asked, "that God should shower these slimy little beasts with such a blessing, giving them the power to love for days, whereas for us, supposedly the darlings of His creation, this, the greatest of all our pleasures, is over and done with in a matter of minutes? And yet theologians will continue to insist that God created the earth for us and not for snails?"

Or when he heard how, in France, Jesuit and Jansenist factions were stepping up their bitter religious dispute to the point where Jesuits, basing themselves on an old papal bull in their favor, would refuse the comfort of the last sacrament to expiring Jansenists, thus denying them the right to burial in this world and the right to heaven in the next—all because of a difference of opinion on matters which neither of them could know anything about.

"Quick, Wagnière! A pamphlet!"

And Voltaire, just out of bed, half undressed, still pulling on his breeches, as in the well-known sketch by Huber, would dictate a satire on the practice of greasing one's way into heaven. On extreme unction and other rituals supposed to guarantee one's safe arrival in Paradise no matter what may have been one's behavior during one's life on earth. Picturing an Asiatic, just deceased, bound for the abode of the blessed, but stopped at the pearly gates, to his great surprise, by a fakir armed with a sword.

"You cannot enter here!" cries the fakir.

"But why not?" the Asiatic protests. "Have I not been a good man?"

"Not enough!" the fakir declares.

"What? Not enough to have been a good husband? A good father? Lending my money to friends and neighbors without interest and giving it outright to the poor—all that is not enough?"

"Not enough!" the fakir insists. "What about spikes?"

"Spikes?" the good man exclaims. "What have spikes to do with my entry into heaven?"

"Did you practice sticking them into your behind?"

"I must confess that never occurred to me!" the good man is forced to admit.

"Then out you go! Forever! For God will not take into heaven those who did not prove their piety by sticking nails into their behinds!"

Anything, anything was enough to set him off. Is there a discussion among theologians as to how the followers of a Christ who was both baptized and circumcised, have come now to practice only one of these rites and not the other, straightway Voltaire has the answer.

"It is to the women that we owe this change," he writes. "They trembled at the thought of a slip of the knife."

Is there much talk about the goodness of God? Then Voltaire will write his article on the question. *La question*. That amazing device whereby in his day French justice elicited the truth from suspects in criminal cases.

A truly clever device. Nothing needed but a good cellar. Built out of solid stone. In the first place, to muffle the screams of the victims. And in the second place, to provide a sound wall for the attachment of a big iron ring.

It is to this ring that the prisoner, half naked, his face up, would have his wrists lashed, while his ankles, similarly lashed, were pulled, by means of a length of rope, toward another ring set in the stone floor about ten feet away.

Why so far? Because it is unbelievable how far the human body can be stretched once all its joints have been dislocated.

And this is only the ordinary *question*. There is still the extraordinary one, which requires fifteen pints of water to be poured through a funnel forced into the stretched victim's throat. Thus distending his body laterally as well as horizontally.

Who, Voltaire asked, first dreamed up this intricate system of giving pain? Such pain, that one sufferer would later report that he had been able to hear sweat bursting from his body and clattering to the floor with a sound like hail on a roof. A sound louder even than his screams.

Could this complicated notion have come from God? From that cruel God Who, in spite of the fact that He has already condemned us to death even before we are born, nevertheless still subjects us to the *question,* both ordinary and extraordinary? Using such ingenious devices as kidney and bladder stones, gout, inflammation of the bowels, dropsy, cancer—in short, distending us with more liquid and more gases than ever a torturer gave to an unfortunate suspect.

But that is a terrible thing to say: that God taught man cruelty.

You don't believe it? It is a blasphemous thing to accuse God of torturing human beings? Then explain, please, why, if God is good to us, we nevertheless stubbornly refuse to be good to each other.

For fifteen years, at the rate of almost one every fortnight, Voltaire launched these pamphlets against the oppressors of the human mind. With printers in Geneva, printers in Lyons, printers in Paris and London greedily copying them, translating them, publishing them, selling them. For their own profit, of course.

While more disinterested parties would broadcast them free. So that in any number of cities of Europe, householders would find them slipped surreptitiously under their doors. Or housewives discover them sneaked into some package containing their purchases. Or strollers see them lying on a park bench.

Authorities looking into the matter would report an apprentice paid a few pennies by some unknown gentleman to place one on every workbench, so that the journeymen returning from lunch would each find a copy. And errand boys would confess that they had been handed what looked like little catechisms and told to drop one on every desk of a certain school. While others told of having been given booklets that seemed to be psalms or hymnals, to judge by the binding, and paid to leave copies in all the churches.

What? You say the contents are damnable? But how is that possible? Look at these titles: *Serious Thoughts on God, Gospel for the Day, Letter Concerning the Holy Land, The Sermons of the Right Reverend Jacques Rossetes.*

What can be wrong with such booklets? And here, the names of the authors: The Archbishop of Canterbury. The Reverend Father l'Escarbotier. Pastor Gubstorf. An Ecclesiastic.

What? These are all by Voltaire? And all horribly anti-Christian. Then why don't you arrest him? He denies it? Then force him. Give him the question! Make him confess!

Ministers storm and priests rage. But what can one do against this man who owns four different estates located in two countries and two cantons, so that, like a fox with four burrows, as he himself phrases it, he can slip off in any direction, according to the quarter from which danger threatens?

And above all this man who never signs anything with his own name and furthermore will swear on the Bible that he is not guilty. No, not even of writing his famous *Catechism of an Honest Man!* Honest man, just note that! And right on the title page this "honest man" has no compunctions about signing himself as "J. J. R.," which everybody must take as the initials of his great rival, Jean Jacques Rousseau.

There's cheek for you!

But then, what difference? What difference to this Jean Jacques? Who didn't give a damn about anonymity. Why not add another irreligious work to his credit?

Whereas Voltaire wanted no authorship credit whatsoever. He was, in fact, so careful on this point that once, when one of his best friends —and, mind you, tête-à-tête, *in camera*—dared to speak to him as if he were the author of the *Philosophical Dictionary,* Voltaire screamed, "Liar! I the author of that vicious work? The most diabolical compilation that has appeared in centuries! Retract at once!"

Upset, but nevertheless laughing, the friend replied, "Come now, my dear Voltaire. We're alone here. You don't have to dissemble with me."

"You consider this a laughing matter?" Voltaire flew at him. "You think you can play tricks on me? And what if I should tell you that not I but you, yes, *You,* wrote that damnable volume?"

"Well, now, wait a second, my dear Voltaire. You can't be serious."

"I can't, eh? Well, you just wait until the authorities receive my denunciation of you. With proofs! Yes, just wait until *you* are arrested. Just wait until *you* are being submitted to the question. Wait until *your* property is being confiscated. Wait until— Haha! You are turning pale! You tremble. The shoe doesn't fit quite so well when it is on your foot!"

No, indeed, this was no laughing matter! All it took was one servant to overhear their conversation. One servant to turn informer. That's all that was needed.

As, for example, in his case with the rotting wooden crucifix that stood, or, rather, leaned crazily, in the cemetery of his church, on his Ferney estate. Ruining the view he had from his study window.

A fine sight for one's old eyes, every time he looked out his window: that Christ expiring on the Cross, done in wood that was going to pieces. Ravaged by weather and insects. As if to remind one all the more powerfully of death and decay. So that during the rebuilding of the church he ordered his workmen, "Get rid of that old gallows!" At any rate, that is what an old seamstress claimed she had heard, whether Voltaire really used those exact words or not.

And what a business then! With this old seamstress running to her priest in nearby Moens, and the latter at once raising the cry "Sacrilege! Sacrilege!" Because someone had referred to the cross as an old gallows. (Even though it might have been just that to the old Romans.) And this priest rushing off to Ferney to convince Voltaire's vicar that his church had been desecrated. So that the latter would at once set all his parish in an uproar.

Their Lord insulted! Insulted on His Cross! What calamities, what plagues, what murrains, this may bring down on the countryside!

And, gathering all the peasants of his flock to organize themselves into a procession, Voltaire's curé had them remove their precious church bells, their font, their confessionals and the Holy Sacrament and bear them all reverently to another building. Miles away.

Away from the blasphemous mouth of that antichrist, whom God would surely strike with lightning.

And now the summons from the regional ecclesiastical court. For Voltaire to appear and answer serious charges of blasphemy and desecration. Charges so ponderous that they might still, under the law, lead to burning at the stake. So ponderous that people locally were freely predicting that if Voltaire did not abscond he would hang. At the very least.

All because of one informer.

Compelling Voltaire to rush by express from Paris every book that could be found on ecclesiastical law, and to study them night and day. And forcing him to hurry to completion his church-building program. And to have the old crucifix refurbished, repairing it, strengthening it, giving it fresh colors and fresh gold leaf. And forcing him also to call upon whatever friends he could muster to persuade the powerful Duke de Choiseul to endorse a petition to the Pope, asking for the grant of a relic for Voltaire's church.

All this, while around him his peasants grew more and more surly, so that as he walked about his estate he could catch behind his back the muttered epithet "Christ hater!"

Which had to be endured until he had mastered his ecclesiastical law, until he could turn the tables on his priestly accusers. And file serious charges against them! For taking the law into their own hands, without waiting for their superiors to reach a decision. Indeed, without even consulting their superiors. Carrying their impudence so far as to remove the sacred Host from a church without any authorization. Irresponsible behavior specifically forbidden in 1623. And again in 1689. And so on.

Oh, he would make those priests sweat! Wait and see!

And especially when the Pope's relic arrived: a piece of the hair shirt of Saint Francis of Assisi. (Never mind that the Pope was obviously having his little sport with Voltaire by sending him a hair shirt. Anything connected with a saint was still a relic.) But a fine state of affairs: here's the relic, and no church to put it in. Voltaire's church completely rebuilt, yes, but minus everything that makes for a church: namely, Host, bells, confessional and baptismal font.

And priest.

Well, too bad. The relic would have to be returned and the Pope informed about the matter. . . .

No, it wasn't long before those two priests were waiting on Voltaire, begging him to reconsider his countercharges. And it wasn't long before they had summoned their flocks to form themselves into a new procession, this time to return to Ferney all the "stolen" sacred objects. And when Sunday came, there was Voltaire, sitting proudly in his pew again, clad in his best black velvet suit, with its old-fashioned Burgundian cut, its gold galloons and white piping, and on his head his special Sunday wig (equally old-fashioned with its triple row of curls). There he sat and received the proper number of odoriferous wafts of smoking incense swung in his direction, according to the tradition prescribed for the honoring of the feudal lord.

Ah, that was better! Much better.

And to think that all it took was one informer, one bigoted seamstress, and a couple of overanxious priests who would take her words seriously, and the world would have been capable of burning a man like himself. Whew! What a close call. With many a sleepless night, when it had seemed to Voltaire that he could almost hear the crackling of faggots!

True, it was years since anyone had been burned in France. But then, God only knows what might happen when fanatics got on the

343

loose. Fanatics and an informer. For there is the explosive mixture that destroys the world!

No wonder Voltaire wanted to be ringed with triple and even quadruple safety. And didn't care what lies, what frauds, what deceptions he had to practice to secure it. His titles. His four estates. His anonymity. Or, rather, his pseudonymity. To say nothing of his perpetually alert mind. Plus his fortune. Plus his powerful connections at home and abroad. And the loyalty of his tremendous readership.

But nothing, nothing was too much, where his precious life was concerned.

And thus he looked out from his machicolated and crenelated tower and observed with astonishment and with fury, far down below, among the common herd, a man to whom none of these precautions seemed important. A man who had neither property nor titles and yet took no thought of what he signed his name to. Turning out book after book, with his real name boldly printed on the title page: *Jean Jacques Rousseau. Citizen of Geneva.*

Exposing himself thus to inevitable pursuit. And apparently not caring.

What could be the purpose of such foolhardy behavior?

What else except to cast upon his rival Voltaire the stigma of cowardice?

Wasn't it as if this damnable Rousseau were shouting it to the whole world: *Coward!* Forcing everyone to face a comparison that must strike one between the eyes! Saying, in effect, *Look at me! Look at me: Rousseau!*

Do I hide behind a hundred different names? Do I pretend my books are catechisms? Do I slip them under doorways? Do I sneak them into churches? And then lie about it, denying that I ever had anything to do with them?

Yes, look at me. Jean Jacques Rousseau. Citizen of Geneva. Poor. Without even a roof overhead that I can call my own. But still a man of dignity. Standing back of everything I write. Honest and unafraid.

Not like your Voltaire. Who strikes in the dark and then runs. Rich, and yet a poltroon. Owner of estates, and yet afraid. Unwilling to take responsibility for his own works. A man without honor. Shifty and sly.

Well, no. Rousseau never actually saying this. Indeed, always behaving with respect. And, in front of witnesses, even correcting his servant girl Thérèse when she happened to use the name Voltaire, just short. Saying, "Mademoiselle, please. You must say *Monsieur de Voltaire*." But making his implications so obvious that no one could fail to see them. And leaving Voltaire no recourse but to retaliate that Rousseau signed his books not so much out of bravery as out of an inordinate thirst for fame. Dictated by a raging jealousy for the stature that Voltaire had succeeded in attaining.

Either that or he was just plain crazy.

For who in his right mind signed anything in these uncertain times? And if publishers nevertheless printed your name when you were unable to stop them, what author did not quickly deny the work?

Oh, minor works you might sign. Plays, for example, that had to be passed by the censor anyhow before they could be put on the boards. Essays and books carefully written to offend no one who was still alive. Pious sermons. That sort of thing. "Signing your name to a book? That's for bishops!" Voltaire used to say contemptuously.

But controversial matter? Did Baron d'Holbach, for example, with all his wealth and power, sign his name to his *Christianity Unveiled*? Did he even protest when the gazettes ascribed that work to Diderot? Or to Damilaville? Who both, of course, promptly repudiated this charge.

No. Not a word did the Baron utter. With the result that the authorities did not know whom to arrest. Whom to prosecute. And had to content themselves with the usual order for the book to be "lacerated and burned by the executioner at the foot of the grand staircase of the Palais de Justice." Which usually meant that some book or other was burned, but not necessarily the actual volume, since condemned books were generally too much in demand and one of the judges would no doubt have taken it home to read.

But burned nevertheless. Even if by proxy.

That's how it was. So that Hume and Diderot would not even publish some of their best works, but would leave them as manuscripts in their desks, where they were found after their death.

What else was one to do in this age when the Abbé de Prades, for example, would have to run for his life to Prussia, because he had been detected as the author of an article in the *Encyclopedia* judged full of heretical opinions? What else was one to do in this age when most of Voltaire's works still had to be sold under the counter? Few booksellers daring to expose them.

What could one do in this age when printers were still timid about giving out their correct addresses? And books printed in Lyons would generally be represented as "printed at The Hague," or marked "Geneva." Or any other city but the true one. When La Martellière, for getting out an edition of Voltaire's *La Pucelle,* could be condemned to nine years at the oars. And eight printers and binders in the shop that did the work got three years of banishment each. Just for setting type and sewing pages! And the only reason the Ministry did not suppress all printers was because it would have driven too many men out of work!

When at the Austrian border every piece of a traveler's luggage was carefully inspected for contraband books. By special order of Empress Maria Theresa. And in Rome, in Naples, in Milan and in general throughout Italy, Spain, Portugal, it was worth three years in the galleys to be caught with a forbidden book. And the authorities actually paid spies to worm their way into people's confidence and report on what books they found in various libraries.

And Boyer de Mirepoix, France's most powerful Jesuit, closest to the ear of the King, crying out, "Why burn books? That only publicizes them, so that they are surreptitiously printed again in even larger editions. Let's stop burning books. It's time to burn the writers instead!"

The scoundrel! Calling for the burning of human beings at this date! The donkey, as Voltaire always nicknamed him, because of a silly pun.

And how Voltaire rejoiced when Damiens, the man who had attempted to assassinate Louis XV but had scarcely done more than scratch him with a penknife, was found to possess only one book.

Too bad! For all the Jansenists had been hoping that a search of his quarters would yield a cache of Jesuit works, while the Jesuits had been hoping that, on the contrary, it would show a hoard of Jansenist publications—so that each could use such evidence in attacking their opponents as dangerous to the safety of the monarchy. And both of them together hoping that at any rate Damiens's room would reveal some works by Voltaire, so that together they could claim that it was the influence of that atheistic writer (atheistic in the sense of denying the divinity of Christ) who had raised Damiens's knife against the sacred personage of His Majesty.

And then the only book that was found in Damiens's room was the Bible. The Bible!

So that Voltaire could hop with glee, shouting, "Let's not burn this book. That will only publicize it, so that it will be printed again in an even larger edition. Let's burn the author instead. Or, if we can't find him, let's at least burn a couple of theologians!"

And for a while, during the period of Damiens's trial and torture, even after his barbarous execution, Voltaire would not refer to the Bible as anything but "that handbook for assassins."

And in this vicious melee of brawling parties there stood Rousseau. Seemingly calm. At any rate, scorning them all. As fighters in a battle that didn't really count. For what was there, after all, in this contentiousness that would help to produce better human beings? Better governments? Better schools? A deeper faith in God?

Nothing. It was all just a lot of fuss and fury that blinded people to their real problems.

How alone he felt in his mission! How derided. And ringed with enemies, who deliberately misunderstood him and his purpose.

"In the whole world," he would exclaim eventually, in his *Letter to Christophe de Beaumont,* "there is not a soul who understands me. Except myself."

How could any of these different groupings understand him, when they were so busy with their bickering that they could not see that all of them together, churches, governments, philosophers, however inimical, were nevertheless united in upholding the existing state of society? And thus, in spite of their apparent differences, all tightly joined in a common front against the one person in the world who really wanted to cure the ills of civilization.

That is to say himself. The one person in the world really determined to reform things from top to bottom.

And compelling him thus to fight the whole combined world. Singlehanded. With not a soul to help him.

Not that he hadn't been doing that all along. But never until now really launching himself out against his era. In one determined assault. Attacking everyone: Catholics and Protestants. Jansenists and Jesuits. Deists and pagans. Philosophers and censors. Governments and people. Rich and poor. Male and female.

Alone! Absolutely alone. Lining himself up with no coterie. And therefore no need to make any compromises with the truth as he saw it. *Faisant bande à part,* as the French would say of him. And utterly careless of what might happen to him.

Publishing, on the heels of his furious *Letter to d'Alembert* against the theater, his love story *La Nouvelle Héloïse.* Exposing all those barriers of money, of rank, of law and of custom which mankind has erected, as if purposely, in order to prevent men and women from experiencing in all its fullness life's most precious force: love. Our corrupt society determined to adulterate this pure and wonderful emotion with every sort of foreign consideration. Soiling it. Destroying it. Depriving humanity of its greatest treasure. Offering us instead the cheap surrogates of flirtation and fornication, plus loveless marriages arranged by lawyers. Instead of by God.

And then putting out his *Social Contract*.

Opening with that pistol-shot line: "Man is born free and is everywhere in chains." And going on to proclaim the sovereignty of the people, and how in a real representative democracy, with each person being both governed and governing, man might recover, if not his natural freedom, at any rate his dignity as a human being. And thus launching, for the generation of revolutionists that was growing up, the ideas behind those three words *liberty, equality, fraternity,* which were to bring politics for the first time down to the level of every human being on earth, no matter how poor or how ignorant.

And then his novel *Émile*.

Again opening with a pistol-shot line: "Everything issues perfect from the hands of the Creator. Everything degenerates in the hands of man." Thus denying right at the start a fundamental tenet of the great religions of his day, namely that man was born corrupt.

But this was just the beginning of a radical attack on all established methods of raising and educating our children. His purpose being to turn out no more geniuses. No more Voltaires. And certainly no more Rousseaus. Freaks, both of them. But to uncover gradually the true human being still concealed in the child. Letting him become just a healthy scamp at first. A rascal. A barbarian. Afraid of nothing. Neither of the cold nor of exhaustion. And not minding the dark, nor anything creeping or ugly, such as spiders or beetles.

In short, himself a little animal. Who would only gradually begin to discover that he was something more than an animal, namely a human being.

And then, but only slowly, letting that pupil's natural curiosity and natural need for information lead him into the world of knowledge. Never anything forced on him from without. Always the inner desire first awakened. And then satisfied. But never surfeited. Never stuffed. Never crammed.

And no books until the age of sixteen.

And only after that, introducing him to religion. (And what a furor that was to cause among all priests and religionists determined to foist their own religion upon the young while they were still pliable and before they had minds of their own to resist!)

And last of all: sex.

It seemed to Rousseau that in all this he was for the first time tearing the wrappings away from man. Man forever confined. Quickly bundled into swaddling clothes the moment he is freed from the enveloping womb. And then quickly seized upon by churches and schools and governments and customs, and beaten into shape, squeezed and boxed into conformity. And forced to remain thus as long as he lives.

Only to be nailed into a coffin when he dies.

As if to make certain that not even in death shall man be free. That never shall he spread his wings. Never unfold himself into the image of God.

And next, Rousseau's *Letter to Christophe de Beaumont,* pitting man's instinctual and honest religious feelings against the brutal efforts of theologian and Church to kill our hearts with ritual and dogma. And then his *Letters from the Mountain,* calling upon his fellow citizens of Geneva to throw out the treacherous aristocrats who had seized power in their once democratic city. Harping on the rights of man to make not only his own religion but his own government.

And finally his *Confessions* (though not to be published until after his death), casting aside all the accepted notions of modesty in the world, in order to expose himself naked and fearless to all. History's first complete portrait of a human being.

Could there be any doubt as to who was beginning to dominate the literary scene of France? Or even of Europe. Could Voltaire ignore him now, as these books cascaded from him in the space of a few years? Each one a mountainous success. With no mystery as to who the author was. No pen names. No tricks. No subterfuges.

Like a giant in a rage, little Jean Jacques ripped and tore at the whole fabric of existing society. Pitchforking and winnowing every accepted notion, every habit, every custom. Battling the kind of clothing that people wore, their amusements, the houses they dwelt in, their ways of earning a living, their forms of government, and even their manner of making love. And how they worshiped God.

Nothing pleased him. Not the roads that were being built, which destroyed the happy isolation of primitive communities, nor the money that was being minted, which continued to kill off the old and pleasant system of barter. Nor even the beds that people slept on, which he claimed softened the human constitution, opening the way for all manner of corruption and disease. Moreover, promoting excessive lascivious desires.

No, not even the music that was popular in Paris could secure his approval. "In France," he declared, "even the dogs bark out of tune."

Indeed, the very success of this fantastic cataract of volumes was to him only an additional proof of how lost the human race had become. And of how little hope there was for improvement. To think that man had wandered so far away from himself that he had to rediscover himself in a book!

While all around him every animal seemed to know instinctively how to live.

He himself, was he not as lost as everyone? And perhaps even more so? Further away than ever from that great man at whose feet he had so often dreamed of casting himself, crying, "Master! Master!" Further away than ever from that vision of being tenderly embraced by Voltaire, a vision that had sustained him through so many years of loneliness, of study, of failure.

What good did it do him now if people came flocking to him to tell him that he was greater than Voltaire? Or to inform him that Voltaire with his titles and his luxurious living, his versifications and his artificialities, was the past trying to outlive itself. And that the future belonged to Rousseau, with his simplicity, his naturalness, his democracy.

What good did it do him to find critics—Le Franc de Pompignan, for example—contrasting the two great writers and concluding that Voltaire was little more than froth compared to the solidity of Rousseau? That where Voltaire could only be superficial, Rousseau showed startling profundity.

What good did it do him to hear the gossips tell him that Voltaire had reached such a state of exasperation at the phenomenal rise of his rival that he would fly into fits of fury at the mere mention of Rousseau's name? That he was so consumed with jealousy that he could think of nothing but how to bring about the destruction of his enemy.

28: MY SON, COME TO MY ARMS!

Yes, of course Voltaire would have to be jealous of Jean Jacques. At the thought of how people everywhere were now saying, "Voltaire and Rousseau." Or, even more infuriatingly, "Rousseau and Voltaire." As if the mere fact that their works were now the most widely read, the most intensely discussed, was enough to justify this constant linking of their names.

Damnation! Voltaire didn't want to be associated with that man! Didn't want any part of him. He raged at the public for succumbing to those facile conclusions: that he, Voltaire, was nothing but a wit, while Rousseau was serious. That he, Voltaire, was the past, and Rousseau the future.

My God! Couldn't people see what the real difference between them was? That Rousseau was dead wrong, while Voltaire was consummately right?

That everything that came from the pen of Voltaire was designed to lead his readers toward a healthy skepticism? An open mind. While everything that dripped from that fool's pen tended, on the contrary, to lead his reader toward a violent fanaticism? A completely closed-in head!

That in places where Voltaire would proceed only with doubt, and therefore with lightness and with humor, Rousseau would rush in with convictions. And therefore with all the solemnity of an owl.

For who can be witty when he is so sure of himself?

Wasn't it plain, therefore, that what Voltaire was aiming at was the gradual improvement of mankind? The gradual amelioration of his lot and his customs. While Rousseau was calling for immediate perfection.

That the one was therefore coaxing humanity toward the possible.

While the other was lashing him toward the impossible.

Wasn't it clear, then, who was the true friend, the wise counselor of the reader? Who was showing him a goal that was not only attainable but desirable?

Voltaire, in short.

Whereas Rousseau was clearly misleading everyone. Directing us all onto a path that must lead us to perdition.

How was it that people could be so easily taken in by that charlatan with his bag full of deceit? That mountebank with his medicine bottles full of panaceas! Selling people the will-o'-the-wisp of perfect health, perfect parenthood, perfect pupils, perfect societies, perfect governments, perfect philosophies. And even a "perfect" religion, whatever that might mean, "whose dogmas" (yes, that is what this man had the effrontery to suggest, as if any religion with even the simplest of dogmas could possibly be anything but a form of fanaticism)—"whose dogmas," he said, "should be settled by a conference of wise men."

Was ever such nonsense uttered before? Luring men to the only thing that Rousseau really had to offer them: perfect disaster.

By creating new superstitions to mislead man, as fast as Voltaire could manage to destroy the old ones. New superstitions about perfections to be attained on earth. To replace the old ones about perfections to be attained in heaven.

And God only able to divine which of these two kinds of superstitions would in the end turn out to have been the most harmful, the most bloody: the one about perfect justice later, up there, or the one about perfect justice here and now.

But it was as if Voltaire could already see how the political dispute that Rousseau would generate in Geneva would grow and grow until it had engulfed all mankind. No one any longer disputing about religion. But everyone disputing about politics. No longer killing each other over articles of faith. Only over articles of law. In a Rousseauan world where no one would consent to be ruled. Everybody insisting on being a ruler. At no matter what cost in human lives.

And yet, good Lord! people so stupid as to gape at this misleader with admiration. Stricken with genuine awe. On their knees before the "wisdom" of this maniac who did not even have the common sense to destroy his enemies one by one, making friends with some while attacking the others. A strategy which the most ignorant guttersnipe could have taught him. But just pushing ahead, bull-witted, striking out blindly at everything and everybody. All at the same time. Like a man in a fit of grand mal, trying to tear off all his clothes at once. And managing only, all the more surely, to strangle himself in his epileptic convulsions.

Could anyone really explain what people could see in this calculating hypocrite endlessly babbling about his love for his fatherland—and meanwhile spending his whole adult life away from his home? What they could see in this petty ingrate writing his reams about true friendship, when it was so crystal-clear that the man couldn't hold on to a single friend?

Perpetually talking about the troubles of the poor, but himself taking good care never to live too far from the rich. Perpetually talking against the nobility, but living just the same in a château provided by a duchess. (Rent free, of course. No wonder this sponger could never see any use for money. And proposed to abolish it, if you please!)

And perpetually talking about morality, but all the same quitting the "hermitage" on the estate of Madame d'Épinay only to move into a friend's house and from there into a château put at his disposal by the Duchess de Luxembourg, even though that Duchess had had ten, or perhaps a hundred, lovers for every one of the three or four that Madame d'Épinay had had.

And never stopping his absurd talk about "nature." About man's being "naturally" good. Even though history was full of examples of man's being also "naturally" hellish. How ridiculous, this worship of nature! Couldn't Voltaire truthfully point out that "for seven decades nature has been trying to put me in my grave"? And eventually would succeed, too. Curse it! Yes, curse nature!

And launching that asinine slogan that everything came perfect from the hands of God, whereas it was so obvious that Rousseau and Voltaire both had come into this world as pretty sorry specimens of God's handiwork. Both near death.

Certainly Voltaire could say, as he often did, "If I have lived so long it is because I was born an invalid." Meaning that from his earliest days he had been compelled to study how best to circumvent that divine perfection that had created him. And only as a result of this study had he managed to hold off both God and nature for so many years.

But, in spite of all these paradoxes (to use the kindest word for his blunders and hypocrisies), Rousseau still convinced that no one had ever thought of anything sensible, no one had ever seen things correctly, until he came along. He, the one faultless thinker of all times!

And then, suddenly, the Parlement of Paris struck at him.

Why not? Wasn't his name there on the books he had written? Almost as a challenge to the authorities of France.

So that they not only ordered both his *Émile* and his *Contrat Social* (which Voltaire never called anything but "that *Unsocial Contract*") to be lacerated and burned by the public executioner, they went beyond and ordered the author's arrest too. In order to follow the Jesuit Mirepoix's advice to put him on trial and possibly burn him.

And guess what this brave man now did? This heroic author who had so boldly plastered his name to all his books.

Did he face the music? Like the martyrs of old? Who at least had the courage of their convictions.

He did not. He ran. Stuck his tail between his legs and ran. Brave, yes. But not so dumb as to continue to be brave when danger threatened. No, not quite that stupid.

Disappeared. Yes, became anonymous. And changed his name. Same as Voltaire.

Thus demonstrating again, the fraud that he was. The lionhearted soldier who dances on the parapet in front of the enemy, brandishing his gun, playing the devil-may-care. But only until a bullet whistles. Then, what a dive for cover!

Well, can one blame Voltaire now for rejoicing at this striking justification of his position?

And yet strange rumors would now begin to circulate. Rumors that when Rousseau was in flight for his life, with his whereabouts a mystery, Voltaire would be moved to tears and would cry out, "Why doesn't he come running to me? Why doesn't he take refuge with me? Here, where I've made myself so safe!"

Rumors so utterly ridiculous that Rousseauan scholars have rejected them with indignation. Characterizing them as inventions of the crudest manufacture. Designed to lighten the burden of guilt that Voltaire must bear before the bar of history for the manner in which he mistreated Rousseau.

Why, one has only to glance at any page of Voltairean invective against Rousseau. The names he called him. "Lackey" and "pederast" and "diseased monster," and "pup of the bitch of Diogenes." One Rousseauan authority able to make a list of nearly sixty such ugly epithets!

And yet Charles Pougens (who was later, after the tragic failure of his eyesight, to become known as "the blind philosopher") would report in his *Philosophical Letters* how M. de Végobre, the eminent Swiss lawyer, told him of a morning's breakfast at Voltaire's. This was just before the news had reached them of Rousseau's troubles in Paris.

There was quite a group of people sitting around, all drinking their coffee, when a lackey brought the mail in and handed it to Monsieur de Voltaire.

Voltaire had not intended to examine his mail at the moment, but a casual glance at the pile, with the gazettes on top, fixed his attention. He began to peruse the newspapers, becoming more and more interested and excited. And finally began opening one letter after another. While his face grew ever darker.

"Bad news?" he was asked.

"Read these out loud," said Voltaire to Madame Denis, handing her some letters and newspapers. And thus, from various sources, the company was able to form a picture of what had taken place. Of how the Parlement of Paris, in its anxiety to show how Jansenists (of whom the Parlement was almost exclusively composed) could be just as zealous as the Jesuits in stamping out books pernicious to the throne, had seized upon Jean Jacques Rousseau's works to make a public demonstration of their intense loyalty to Church and State.

"Why, oh, why did he have to sign his books!" Voltaire exclaimed.

In the dead of night some good friends of Rousseau's had pounded at his door, had roused him from his sleep and had placed a carriage at his disposal. He had dressed hastily, and lingered only to set a few papers in order, and then, all alone, he had taken off, no one knew exactly in what direction.

Since then there had been no news of him.

And suddenly, says Pougens, Voltaire burst into tears. While everyone stared at him in amazement.

"It's here he must come!" Voltaire cried. "To me. Where he can feel safe." He spread his arms. "He shall be master here, in my place. I will treat him as if he were my son!"

Rousseauan scholars laugh at this picture of Voltaire in tears over Jean Jacques. This urge to have Rousseau for his son. What will one be asked to believe next?

But Wagnière, Voltaire's secretary, in the memoirs he wrote after his master's death tells pretty much the same story. Adding even an additional detail. That Voltaire immediately called him to dictate a letter. A letter for Rousseau. Inviting him to come to Ferney. Offering him the refuge and the hospitality of his home. Or, if Rousseau preferred to be by himself, the use of a little cottage on the grounds of the estate.

"But where shall I address this letter?" Wagnière asked. "Rousseau's whereabouts are unknown."

"Make six or seven copies," Voltaire suggested. "We'll send them off to his closest friends, one of whom will surely know where to reach this unfortunate man."

Now, what is so unbelievable about that?

What is so unbelievable about that, considering the moves that Voltaire would make, or was already making, for a special refuge in Europe for all proscribed writers, thinkers, scientists and so forth? A refuge that Frederick the Great would promise them within his dominions, where they would have their own printing presses and other facilities for undisturbed activity. (A scheme that fell through because Parisians would not exchange Paris for Berlin even to avoid being burned at the stake.)

Why, then, should not Voltaire wish to give Rousseau a refuge? He was a proscribed thinker too, wasn't he? No matter how much at variance with the ideas of Voltaire.

And it must be recalled, too, that Voltaire had several times before invited Rousseau to be his guest. Not that he hadn't tinctured those invitations with some degree of malice (but he wouldn't have been Voltaire if he hadn't, would he?), saying, for example, "Come browse on our grass. Come drink the milk of our Swiss cows." That sort of thing.

But who will say that there was no sincerity whatsoever in these invitations? Seeing that Rousseau never put any of them to the test.

Certainly Voltaire's lavish hospitality was too well known for anyone to deny it. That was only typical of Old France. Where restaurant proprietors actually prided themselves on the number of bankruptcies they had sustained in the service of their clientele.

Voltaire's house was almost always bursting with guests. So much so that there were times when he would go into tantrums, screaming about the vast slaughter of his chickens and ducks, about the oceans of wine, the mountains of bread and pastry being devoured by this horde of gullets living at his expense.

And, rushing at his niece with fury, he would yell, "What is this? A scheme to bring me to ruin? What do these people imagine I am —the hotelkeeper of Europe? Now get them packing! Quick, before I drive them out. Before I turn into Christ scourging the money-lenders out of the Temple!"

Which would require Madame Denis to remind him of his fortune in bonds. Of his stack of annuities. Of the huge mortgage he had on the income of the Duchy of Württemberg. Of his four estates. Of his pensions from crowned heads. Of his income accumulating faster than he could find ways of investing it.

To all of which he would scream, "Wiped out in a moment! A change of Ministry—or one informer—and I could be declared a traitor. Banished. My fortune confiscated. And myself a poor man, forced to beg for a crust of bread."

A picture of himself that would evoke tears of pity from his own eyes.

But gradually he would become reassured again of his solid wealth. And the lavishness would be resumed, perhaps even on a grander scale.

Still, granted all this about his hospitality, how is it that, with so many people treasuring Voltaire letters, not a single one of these copies made by Wagnière has turned up in any collection? Especially considering that there would have been all the more reason to safe-guard just these particular missives, since they concerned not only Voltaire but also Rousseau, the two best-known names of the literary world. To say nothing of the startling nature of the contents!

Furthermore, when Rousseau had managed to escape from France and arrived at Yverdun, in Switzerland, and got out of his carriage to drop to his hands and knees and kiss the soil of freedom, and then sought refuge in the home of his wealthy admirer Daniel Roguin, and then almost immediately had to pack his things again and leave once more, because the authorities at Bern had heard that not only in Paris but in Geneva too, in Jean Jacques' home town, the author's books were going to be burned and the author himself arrested if he dared to show up there—did Voltaire then rise to protest?

Did he write a pamphlet about that?

Did he clamor for justice for this man who was, after all, only exercising that right that Voltaire so firmly believed in: the right of free speech. The right of speaking out.

Did he even commiserate with Rousseau's misfortunes? Or did he repeat that invitation of his now, when his letters had a better chance of reaching their destination?

He did not.

Apparently all he could think of was the folly of this supposedly intelligent man's kissing the soil of Switzerland as if it were the soil of freedom! Did this idiot really imagine that there were certain special soils that disposed man to freedom? Was he too one of those systematizers, whom Voltaire despised, a fault to which even the brilliant Montesquieu had succumbed when he had argued that climate made the character of individuals. As if people of every climate were not more or less the same: some evil and some good, and most of them a bit of both.

Kissing the soil of freedom, indeed! As if this hypocrite had not himself done his best to make Switzerland intolerant. As if he hadn't maneuvered to stop Voltaire and his friends from exercising their theatrical talents in the privacy of his home there. As if he had not been instrumental in forcing Voltaire to flee from Swiss soil to French soil. To find that same freedom that had made Rousseau flee the other way!

Because freedom consists in what men do, and not what the soil happens to be!

And now, nevertheless, playing the martyr because his books were no more safe from Genevan governmental persecution than had been Voltaire's plays.

What did he expect? To reap tolerance where he had sowed intolerance?

357

And to think, too, that it was Geneva. Yes, Geneva. Fancy that! Rousseau's precious fatherland. Model of cities. Ideal democracy of our globe. That city to whose honest magistrates, to whose industrious craftsmen and Spartan citizenry Rousseau had never been tired of pointing with pride, contrasting them with the effete, the corrupt, the lazy and foppish French—among whom he had nevertheless continued to live until forced to take to his heels.

And now this marvelous Geneva had nothing more pressing to do than imitate decadent Paris! Burn Rousseau's books and seek to nab the most famous of her citizens, as if he were no more than a common criminal.

Never could Voltaire in his wildest flights of imagination have dreamed of a more categorical vindication of everything he had stood for, against the arguments of his opponent.

Rousseau finally exposed! Hurrah!

No wonder that when Rousseau left Bern and there was speculation for a while that this brave man might actually go to Geneva, Voltaire cried out, "Don't! Fool! This is a hanging matter!" But then added slyly, "But perhaps you don't mind swinging. Anything, so long as it will elevate you above your fellow man!"

And then, not yet having exhausted all his malice, Voltaire went on: "No, an execution will not bother Jean Jacques. Not so long as his name will be on the sentence. An anonymous hanging—yes, that would no doubt jar him. From head to foot. But a public one? It would be his delight. Imagine—he the center of all that attention!"

The rumors, however, were false. It was to Motiers that Rousseau was going. And Motiers being just over the mountains from Geneva, in the Val-de-Travers, it had only seemed for a while that he was aiming to go to Geneva itself. But he had stopped short, to live in the house put at his disposal by Madame Boy de La Tour, daughter of the same Daniel Roguin who had sheltered him at Yverdun.

Motiers had the advantage of being in Neuchâtel, that is to say under the rule of Frederick of Prussia, and thus beyond the jurisdiction of either Geneva or Bern. Which was another good laugh for Voltaire: this democrat being forced to find refuge under an autocrat and thus learning that there were no blanket rules as to the behavior of peoples or governments, no matter how democratically or autocratically ruled.

But it was as if Rousseau could sense what an advantage Voltaire was hoping to derive from this curious situation, and was determined to disappoint him.

Sire [Rousseau wrote to Frederick—to this military-minded monarch who was only now managing to extract some sort of victory from the long and destructive Seven Years' War]:

I have written much against kings, and I shall no doubt write still more against them. I therefore deserve no mercy from you. Nor do I seek any. This letter is merely for the purpose of informing you that I have taken up residence in your states. I am therefore in your power. You will do with me what you please.

Frederick smiled at this scornful and studiously impolite note. And he sent word to his friend Marshal George Keith, the famous Scottish soldier of fortune, to whom he had allotted the governorship of Neuchâtel: "See to it that Rousseau is satisfactorily lodged. If necessary, let a hermitage be built for him in the forest. Have him amply supplied with flour, wine and firewood."

Which provoked an even prouder letter from Rousseau:

Sire:

You wish to give me bread. Are you so sure that none of your Prussian subjects lack it? For myself, I would be happy enough if only you would remove that sword of yours that continues to dazzle my eyes with its brightness. Has it not already exhibited its prowess sufficiently during your reign, while your scepter has lain neglected?

How wonderful it would be if, instead of waging war, you would wage peace and cover your states with a multitude of men to whom you would be as a father. Then I, Jean Jacques Rousseau, the enemy of kings, would rush to die at the foot of your throne.

Frederick was even more amused by this second letter. "Well, well," he wrote to Voltaire. "Now I too have been scolded by Jean Jacques."

But Voltaire was not amused. Not for long, at any rate. For when these letters were copied and circulated and found their way into print, into the gazettes of the time, people began to compare them to the correspondence between Voltaire and Frederick. Though surely there should have been no comparison possible between these briefest of short notes from Rousseau that Frederick had answered only indirectly and the voluminous exchange between Voltaire and the King.

Still, that didn't stop Rousseau's fanatical followers from saying that their hero had demonstrated to the world a new way of addressing monarchs. A proud and dignified way. With none of your old-fashioned bowing and scraping, such as Voltaire always exhibited. As for example when he called Frederick "the Solomon of the north," or "the new Marcus Aurelius," or "the Alexander of our day," and so forth. Fawning. Yes, fawning.

Not that Voltaire hadn't often written with the coarsest kind of humor to the Prussian monarch. Going so far, once, as to wish him relief from a proctological affliction. Saying (but, naturally, in poetry, where it seemed more permissible) that he wished the royal hemorrhoidal vein would no longer throb so painfully in His Majesty's rectum.

Which was comradely, no doubt. And brought royalty down to the common level of humanity. But where was the dignity of it? Where was that tone which in Rousseau had at last raised a common man to the level of royalty. And even above!

Ah, there was your difference, as people could not help but point out. Voltaire may have brought the King down. Yes, no doubt. But Rousseau had brought the common man up!

And people, looking for a new guide to life, could feel that difference. Could already feel it powerfully. As a great ground swell. As if the earth were preparing to heave itself. As Rousseau had, indeed, been predicting: "We are coming to the age of revolutions!"

So that, in spite of the authorities of Paris and those of Bern and Geneva (to say nothing of a number of other cities and communities equally busy burning the works of Rousseau), no sooner had he established himself with his Thérèse at Motiers, and the news of his whereabouts been diffused through Europe, than from everywhere people of means, people of education and of importance, began to flock to the Val-de-Travers to see the great Rousseau.

In numbers that at first rivaled and then threatened to surpass those that clamored to see Voltaire at Ferney. Who gave vent to his fury by making sneering remarks about Rousseau's recent decision to dress himself in Armenian costume.

As if, behind this decision, there must surely lurk some foul secret.

Though it was obviously nothing but the case of a sickly man wanting a more comfortable style of dress. Something less painful to a man troubled by periods of urinary retention. To a man with a double inguinal rupture. Whose lower regions must every now and then be taut with inflammation. At which times the least irritation from cloth might cause excruciating chafing.

Bodily infirmities that, in the prime of life, were turning an otherwise vigorous and active person into an old man.

Compelling him, for example, to deny himself the necessity and the pleasure of contact with his Thérèse.

Likely to prove more pain than pleasure, anyhow. Yes, and dangerous too. For who could say for sure that one might not have to pay for one's life just because of a yearning for a moment of delight?

But then again, without that relief, would not his old desire for exhibitionism come to torment him again? The urge to bare his behind. For what was his life, if not a trap? A trap from which the only escape was an exchange of one trap for another?

And then when, in desperation, he had to reach again for his old methods of cheating nature, had to let himself slide into the sin of Onan, all his former hatred of himself was powerfully revived.

So that several times already—in order to save himself—he had proposed to her that she leave him. Because he would not leave her. Never. Having given her his word that he would never abandon her. But now, now that he could no longer gratify her strong physical passions, might she not wish to leave him?

He had even promised her that he would give her half of all the money he had.

But that stupid she wasn't. Not to know that without her Monsieur Rousseau she was nothing but a servant. And even if the money he gave her was sufficient to keep her from having to work, then she would still be only a servant out of work. That's all.

For it was this man who gave her status. This wreck of a man. And she didn't intend to be separated from him so easily.

Besides, she loved him. In fact, they loved each other. For what else was that cement that bound them together? Were they not tied to each other by all these years of cohabitation? Tied to each other by five pregnancies? Five agonies of birth? Five children sinfully disposed of?

So that all that affection that might have been spread out through a large family had now to be concentrated on each other. So that they loved each other more than ever. Having no one else to love.

In fact, in a way, they were now each other's children. They were each other's family. He, certainly, was her only child. Her baby. Whom she had to mother. Whom she had, you might say, to diaper. Cooking for him and cleaning up after him. Performing for him the most intimate and menial and sometimes dirty services.

So that the mothering he had never enjoyed as a baby he now had. And the babies she had never been permitted to keep she now enjoyed. And, like a good mother, only she knew what to do when this baby of hers woke up at night. Feverish, feeling one of his uremic attacks coming on. Only she knew how to coddle this man when he had his strange pains, when his heart would flutter inexplicably and he was convinced that death was about to strike. Only she knew how to handle him during his difficult days of silence, his periods of dark brooding, his endless complaints and suspicions. Only she could guard him from interruption during those days when he was creating one of his books and wrote like a man in a rage.

Yes, he had become her baby. As if to make up to her for the five he had snatched from her.

And as for her sexual desires, these must not be permitted to interfere with what was, after all, a stable household. The world was full of other men, grown-up men, who could take care of her in that respect.

In the greatest secrecy, to be sure.

Brief muscular encounters in the inky black of a corridor, in some country inn. While he lay groaning in his room or furiously occupied in copying and recopying his laboriously polished sentences.

Or some night, in the quiet of a barn, in the softness of the hay. With some groom.

Or deep in a forest. With some unknown.

For it would never have occurred to her to parade her passions the way Rousseau had paraded his infatuation for Madame d'Houdetot. She was mortally afraid of gossip. Aware of her inferior position in that world of fame in which she had somehow found a place. And completely satisfied if, now and then, she had managed to make her need clear to some other prowler in the dark jungle of human lust. Resulting in a kind of quick mutual rape.

And leaving no trace. Or scarcely any.

Young Boswell being perhaps the only exception. The future biographer of Samuel Johnson, who, descending upon Switzerland with the firm intention of visiting the two greatest thinkers of the time (now living within a few miles of each other), appeared at Rousseau's home decked out like a fairy-tale prince. Absolutely dazzling Thérèse. With his greatcoat of green sateen, lined with fox fur that overflowed from cuffs and collar. And beneath that, buckskin breeches, waistcoat embroidered in gold thread, and jacket of scarlet.

No Armenian robes for him. That much was immediately clear to her.

And equally clear to him her trim little figure. Her dancing eyes. The skillfulness with which she arranged for his admittance into the great man's study. And the especially tasty dinner she prepared for the two men.

All clauses of an unwritten contract, which he quickly sealed with the secret gift of a pretty dress and a bracelet of garnets.

So that meeting her some time later, when they had the opportunity of traveling a stretch together, he was able to set down in his journal (which would not be discovered and printed until nearly two centuries later) how they had contrived to be guilty together "thirteen times."

And adding the further information that he had found her a very skillful sinner. A really talented "amorist." No doubt the result of considerable outside experience. Of which Rousseau knew nothing.

Not a thing. Except suspicions and torturing doubts. No, not a thing. Except the anguish and the shame of feeling himself cuckolded. But neither by whom nor exactly when. But any number of days when he could sense her inner glow of contentment. The glow of a completely satisfied woman. And along with that a scarcely expressed contempt for him as a male.

29: VOLTAIRE,
THAT SPANISH INQUISITOR

What, then, can one really hold against this much afflicted man Rousseau?

Whose troubles, whose problems, whose inner conflicts are almost beyond an ordinary man's understanding. Consider that just at this very time he was impelled not merely to change his costume, but also to take up a hobby (for relaxation, so he claimed)—namely, the art of making laces for women's bodices. And his sitting there, before a pillow, shuffling his threads, fashioning those laces, which he would then give away as presents to young married women of the neighborhood (and the unfastening of which would of course be preliminary to the exposure of the breast for suckling, reminding people thus, by this gift, of Rousseau's theory of the child's right to its mother's milk)—yes, Rousseau sitting there before his pillow, shuffling his threads, and dressed in a robe rather than in male breeches . . .

And something else too, something even stranger: beneath his robes a bougie pushed into his urethra (as was the case, for example, on at least one occasion when Boswell visited him), a sound to dilate the passage and relieve his distended bladder . . .

Well, yes, it must be admitted that there was something startlingly epicene, hermaphroditic, about the picture he must have presented on such occasions. (Though possibly no one in his day or since has so understood it.)

For with this bougie penetrating his body in that precise area, one might suppose that he was not just seeking to change his occupation or change his style of dress, but, rather, to change his whole anatomy. If such a thing were possible.

His bladder wanting to be a womb, but able to be big only with waste. And his urethra craving penetration, but getting only a piece of metal. His whole body doing its best to play a woman's role, but without the appropriate organs. And thus succeeding only in confusing everything.

So that really one cannot help wondering how he managed to endure life at all at certain times. Racked as he must have been. Needled by all his conflicting urges. Prodded by all his obscure passions. And goaded on, for all that, by his ambition, and his pity for mankind, and his conviction that he had the answer.

So powerful in him still, all those ancient confusions. Like uncharted torrents coursing secretly far underground, whose incomprehensible roaring may possibly have been the sound that perpetually filled his ears. Confusions as to what was front and what was back. As to what was male and what was female.

And all these distressing confusions playing a midnight hide-and-seek game with him. Nightmarishly intensified by his nearness now to the scenes of his youth, and by all the memories stirred up in him thereby. Memories of those days when his father would overwhelm him with kisses and with fondlings, as if he would turn his boy into the woman who had died giving him birth. So that little Jean Jacques, in the most formative years of his life, felt lost, not knowing whether he was boy or girl, son or mother.

But this time all these confusions no longer to be placated by so simple an exorcism as changing his religion. Nor by an escape to Paris with a wild project for changing the accepted notation for music. Nor by writing another book insisting that every human being change his style of living, or every school change its way of teaching, or every government its way of governing.

No, this time it was himself he had to change. Thus driving himself darkly to construct whatever plausible excuse he could out of his manifold illnesses, to lend some kind of spurious justification for a necessity that he could no longer deny: the necessity for changing his clothes from male to female.

Oh, yes, how racked he must have been! How driven! And himself unaware of exactly what was driving him. So that even in his *Confessions* he could only give hints of his problem, hints from which he would rapidly skirt away, as if afraid that this book, to be published only when he was dead, might still make him blush in his grave.

And Voltaire, lacking these *Confessions* could only guess at some vile sexual corruption in Rousseau. And make his ugly comments on that. Declaring that Rousseau, as a young boy, had run away from Geneva in order to play the pederast for priests in Turin.

And crying out with raucous laughter, "Look at that man who pretends to want to live in obscurity! Look at him now in his Armenian costume, the would-be hermit—who at last has succeeded in being what he has always wanted to be: the most easily spotted man in Europe!"

Causing Rousseau unending torment, and making him despair of ever being understood. Especially by Voltaire. Whose understanding he nevertheless still somehow craved, in spite of his hatred.

So that when a certain Meister visited Rousseau one day and asked him, "What is this I hear about Monsieur de Voltaire being really your very close friend? And offering you his home for an asylum?" Rousseau could hardly answer him for a moment, so choked up was he with bitterness and with passion.

Until he finally exploded. "Yes. Isn't that just what Monsieur de Voltaire would like people to believe—that he is my very close friend? But I tell you this: His kind of friendship—I reject it!"

Turning away abruptly. Already feeling himself feverish and dizzy.

And to the Duchess de Luxembourg, his most recent wealthy patroness, Rousseau would write without any hesitation: "All my troubles are the work of the Inquisitor, M. de Voltaire, who, seeing me harassed by the Parlement of Paris, has considered this the ideal moment to add further hardships to my misfortunes. And has managed things so cleverly in Geneva as to picture me, *me* whom the Catholics have expelled from France, as the enemy of Protestantism too. Thus closing my native city against me forever."

While Voltaire, for his part, would write gloatingly to d'Alembert (as if all these events were just a gift of Providence): "At last this baboon is getting what he has so richly deserved. Remember how he attacked both you and me because of our interest in the theater, just so that he could curry favor for himself among the clergy of Geneva? Well, now behold, that same Genevan clergy has influenced the Magnificent Council to burn his books and have the author arrested. That is, if ever they can lay their hands on him. Now, what do you think of that for poetic justice? *Écrasez l'infâme!"*

Well, of course Voltaire gloated. How could he help it, when this seemingly surprising turn of events was finally avenging him for everything he had once suffered from this hypocrite's writings? He could, in fact, only hope that Geneva's actions would be sufficiently drastic to reverse the tide that was carrying this man's works and ideas to a reputation so great that it was threatening his own.

But if only Voltaire hadn't gloated so much! So much that historians have been forced to wonder if perhaps he did not have a hand in guiding these events to their fortunate issue. But of this there is, in fact, not the least shred of evidence.

But then, evidence is hardly to be expected, is it? With a Voltaire? The man with four estates and a hundred and fifty pen names. Wasn't it enough that many of the aristocrats of Geneva were his friends? His commensals? Who came to applaud his theatricals? Rich men, to whom a word about the dangerous economic theories of this revolutionary democrat might be ample to sway them? In short, only hints, but just as effective as written letters, and leaving no record.

However something did get into the records. Not at the time of Rousseau's flight from France. But some time later, when Rousseau published his *Letters from the Mountain,* which were to make Voltaire especially furious. It was then that a charge was to be filed with the office of the prosecutor of Geneva, a formal charge against this work of Rousseau's. A charge which, while it would naturally not bear the signature of Voltaire (that would really be asking too much, wouldn't it?), would yet be so indisputably in the racy style of the master that the author might perhaps just as well have put his name to it.

And, furthermore, according to the students of this matter, without any doubt in the handwriting of Wagnière, Voltaire's secretary, who would hardly have written it for someone else. Nor acted on his own.

But what an incredible Voltaire confronts us in this formal requisition calling upon Genevan justice to strike swiftly in the case of Rousseau. A Voltaire armed with a hatchet! Crying for blood! Pointing an accusing finger at Rousseau—for being an anti-Christian, of all things! Charging Rousseau with insulting our Holy Scriptures! Charging him with casting doubt and ridicule on the miracles in the life of Jesus!

Yes. A Voltaire smelling out the religious heresies of Rousseau with all the craftiness and fury of a Spanish Inquisitor. And not forgetting his political and economic heresies either.

366

And documenting everything with quotations and with page references, lest there be any doubt of the extent of Rousseau's crimes.

And more than that!

Winding up these charges with an eloquent appeal to the dignitaries of Geneva to beware of taking these matters lightly. To beware of letting this malefactor escape with anything less than the full severity of the law. Scoffing at the silly punishment of burning a writer's books, which he calls nothing but an "amusement" that "never occasioned any writer the least bodily pain." In short, demanding the gallows! The stake!

No, this is unbelievable! This cry for burning Rousseau, penned by the very same man who supposedly stretched out his arms for him, who, with tears in his eyes, begged Rousseau to come and take refuge in his home. And live there as his son.

This anonymous charge filed by the same man who was still fighting his campaign for freedom of thought. And yet, at the same time, here conniving to suppress it! This plot hatched by the man who was signing his letters with his slogan *"Écrasez l'infâme!* Crush the monster!" And himself a monster to be crushed! This fanatic appeal for burning at the stake launched by the same voice that bellowed with rage against the Jesuit Mirepoix for calling upon the French authorities to do exactly the same!

This man who so often screamed against informers an informer now himself!

Impossible! Voltaire an informer? Nonsense. What was there to inform about? Hadn't Rousseau already done all the informing that was necessary? By never making any secret of his authorship. By signing everything he wrote.

How can one speak of informing, when all that Voltaire did was take care that the proper authorities should not fail to see exactly what their Citizen was writing in those famous books of his. Take care that they should not overlook a single important point.

That's all.

But no matter how an outsider might look at this question, it is obvious that Rousseau must have had a certain degree of information to go on for his suspicions of Voltaire. In particular when he began to refer to Voltaire, in letters to his friends, as "the Inquisitor." What could have suggested that nickname to him? And obviously he must have had some good reason when, in the presence of Meister, he cried out as if in pain, "His kind of friendship—I reject it!"

In short, that somehow he knew—or else felt—who it was that was pulling strings against him in Geneva. And also in Paris, in Bern, at The Hague and elsewhere. Attacking him at night. Stabbing him in the back.

Felt himself so surrounded by treachery that he would write to his friend de Luc, "Voltaire the Inquisitor is the most active man the world has ever produced. In one way or another he governs all of Europe." Declaring that Voltaire had his secret agents everywhere. The Jesuit Bertrand his agent in Bern. The Duke de Praslin his agent in Paris. And so forth. "And pulling the strings of his puppets everywhere."

While Voltaire, for his part, would challenge anyone to produce a single letter, a single sentence in any letter of his, which would show that he had ever tried to influence officials against Rousseau.

But Rousseau stuck to his convictions. As for letters, naturally there would be no letters.

And as for that scene at Voltaire's, that touching scene of deep emotion, deep concern for Rousseau's plight, acted out with the additional verisimilitude of tears, "genuine" tears, bursting from his eyes, that, to Rousseau, could be nothing but a well-thought-out screen behind which Voltaire might continue to do his worst. And remain unsuspected.

And at so little cost. For what could it demand from this consummate actor with fifty years of amateur stage experience behind him to produce a few "genuine" tears? Hadn't Rousseau himself pointed out what constitutes the so-called "talent" of an actor? The fundamental dishonesty of it? On a moment's notice to be able to assume any role, portray any character, no matter how different from one's true self. And play it to the hilt.

What, then, could it have cost Voltaire to present himself as having fatherly feelings for Rousseau?

Nothing. Absolutely nothing.

But any wonder that about this time Rousseau should begin to tremble at his own shadow? Feeling all these secret forces at work around him, weaving a net.

So that, at Motiers, when groups of people came to see him he would often have a kind of sixth sense about some particular individual.

Then, with a quiet nod of his head he would indicate the person to Thérèse and whisper, "Another one of Monsieur de Voltaire's spies. Take care that he is not admitted."

And though he had nothing to go on but this inner feeling, he would remain completely convinced and would refuse to see that individual. Despite pleas and protestations.

And when his mail came, he would distinguish between genuine letters from admirers and those that came from Voltaire and were intended to mislead him. Or upset him.

" 'Baron de Corval,' " he would mutter, reading the inscription on a letter. "An obviously invented name." And he would either return the letter to the clerk, refusing to pay the postage, or else tear it up.

But it was especially the large numbers of anonymous letters that troubled him. They were surely from the hand of Voltaire. True, they came from cities as far apart as Marseilles and the Hague. But no matter. Voltaire must have confederates in those towns, to whom he sent his letters for remailing. Which had the added advantage of increasing the charges that poor Rousseau would have to pay out of his meager pocket.

Was there anything that this man was not capable of, under the influence of his jealousy? For he was obviously jealous of Rousseau's success. That was at the bottom of his implacable pursuit.

Rousseau could remember Diderot, long ago, saying, "Voltaire can stand anything except a pedestal—on which someone else is standing." And there was the pedestal on which Jean Jacques was now standing. And that pedestal rising higher every day. And particularly as people began to talk more and more about the most striking chapter of Rousseau's *Émile*, the one entitled "Profession of Faith of a Savoyard Vicar," which many people did not hesitate to compare to everything that Voltaire had done on the same subject, reaching the conclusion that Voltaire had finally been surpassed.

This chapter, so it was being said, was the most daring essay on religion ever put on paper. And one of the most moving and convincing.

Yes. A chapter so impressive that it actually tore an exclamation of praise out of the man least likely to appreciate it: Voltaire himself. Who wrote to one of his friends, "There are fifty pages in that rascal's *Émile* that I have ripped bodily out of the rest of his miserable trash in order to have them bound in the finest Morocco leather."

What an admission to be wrung from his bitterest rival! That Rousseau had achieved the ultimate in the career of a writer: an authentic masterpiece.

What difference if it was just a chapter, rather than the whole book, to which Voltaire was willing to concede these laurels? What difference? A masterpiece remains a masterpiece no matter what its length, doesn't it?

And just how deeply impressed Voltaire was is seen in the statement of Condorcet, who was the great man's friend and first important biographer and who declared flatly, "Never before had Voltaire been goaded into jealousy by any man's talents, until Rousseau published his 'Savoyard Vicar.' "

Thus, in effect, putting into proper perspective all those other rivalries of Voltaire's: with Piron, with Jean Baptiste Rousseau, with Crébillon and so forth. Dismissing them as insignificant. Mere porcelain figurines in the circle of Parisian wits. Rivalries that didn't really count. Rivalries that would be lost to history. Ephemeral.

It was this diabolical Jean Jacques who had first taken his rivalry with Voltaire out of the courts of Versailles, Fontainebleau, Sceaux and Lunéville, and into the world's arena. For judgment by the public and not just by aristocrats or would-be aristocrats. Submitting his ideas not to the salons, nor even to the coteries of philosophers, but to everyone.

And winning! Thus threatening Voltaire's survival in the mind of posterity. Threatening his Newtonian funeral. Threatening everything he had been laboring for. For decades now.

But that wasn't all. Achieving this with Voltaire's ideas! With Voltaire's material! Stealing it! Taking it from the sort of thing that Voltaire had been writing since the days of his first antireligious poem, his *For and Against*. Taking it from his poem *Natural Law*. And his *Discourse on Man*. And from a thousand places in his historical works, his plays, his pamphlets.

Consider, for example, this passage from Rousseau's "Savoyard Vicar":

What makes you so sure that the Jews are not justified in their denial of Christ? How many Christians do you know, yourself included, who have taken the pains to examine with care what arguments the Jews may have? The little you happen to know in this matter comes to you exclusively from a few statements in books written by convinced Christians, does it not?

A fine way to learn your adversary's side of the case! But one for which there can be no remedy. For if anyone amongst us dared to publish books in which the cause of Judaism would be openly espoused, there would be severe punishment for all: author, publisher, printer, bookseller. And for the reader too. No one would escape.

Really, one can't see how any better system could possibly have been devised for always being in the right. And such a pleasure too, refuting people who don't dare open their mouths.

Voltairean, that's what that was!

But, even more exasperating, done better than ever Voltaire had done that particular argument.

370

Or such a passage as this, even bolder, from the same "Savoyard Vicar":

What? In that same Jerusalem where the Son of God lived and died, He had contemporaries who knew Him in the flesh and who still did not accept Him any more than do the people living to this day in that land which He made holy? Yet you insist that I, born two thousand miles too far to see Him, and two thousand years too late, should nevertheless be completely convinced of Him?

Is it reasonable to ask this of me merely because I am shown His story written up in a certain book which you assure me is Holy Scripture, whatever that may mean? A book set down originally in Greek or in Hebrew, neither of which languages I can read, so that I must be content with a translation. A book, moreover, which most of the population of the world has never heard of and could not read, anyhow, no matter in what language it might appear.

Is that how God chooses to reveal Himself to man—so distantly, so surreptitiously, so ineffectually?

Why, if Rousseau had not signed that passage, people might suppose that none other than Voltaire could have written it!

Ah, yes, but for saying it so well, Rousseau, my friend, you've handed Voltaire a weapon to use against you. And especially by underwriting it with your name.

And, furthermore, for being a Genevan. A Calvinist. From that tight little Calvinist oligarchy whose stringent laws you once used against Voltaire, didn't you? Laws which Voltaire now need have no scruples using against you.

That tight little Geneva, where still on Sunday mornings, when the citizens were all in church, the old custom prevailed of drawing a heavy iron chain around the building and padlocking it, so that no citizen might sneak out during the services. In such a city, as Voltaire well knew, the things that Rousseau was saying in his "Savoyard Vicar" weren't said. They couldn't be said.

All that was necessary was to call the attention of the various members of the Council of Geneva to certain of Rousseau's most flagrant passages. That was all. That wasn't informing. The passages were there, weren't they? And Rousseau's name was there too, wasn't it?

And just as there had been a time when you, Rousseau, had had your chance to throw Geneva at Voltaire, and you hadn't passed it up, so now there was an opportunity for Voltaire to throw Geneva at you. And he wasn't going to pass that up either.

371

No, not even though he knew, and though many of the Genevans also knew, that Rousseau's purpose in his "Savoyard Vicar" was not to *destroy* religion, but, on the contrary, to *restore* it. Not get rid of Christ, but, on the contrary, to evoke Christ all the more powerfully.

To re-establish the Christian religion on a firmer, purer basis. Relying neither on iron chains around a church nor on the existence of certain writings called sacred, nor on supposed miracles performed by Christ, nor on the kidnaping of children's minds before they could defend themselves. But securely and permanently erected on man's instinctual piety, going hand in hand with his reason. And thus acceptable without any inner conflict between one's intelligence and one's emotions.

And good for all the inhabitants of the world. Whose salvation must surely be equally precious to God. No matter how far they happened to live from the Holy Land.

"Can it be a crime in God's eyes," Rousseau asked, "for a man living at the antipodes not to know what happened at some obscure period in the Holy Land, on the other side of the globe?"

Oh, how Voltaire would have loved to have said that himself! Rather than be forced to denounce Rousseau for saying it.

Except, of course, for Rousseau's desire to retain Christ. On which point Voltaire could not agree. Between Voltaire and Christ lay all those centuries of religious warfare in which Christians had massacred Christians. To say nothing of massacring Jews, pagans, Mohammedans and so forth.

A river of blood, a mountain of skulls, lay between Voltaire and Christ.

But, just the same, Voltaire was so envious of Rousseau that he now began to issue a new kind of pamphlet. Written with more of Rousseau's seriousness. With more of Rousseau's respect for man's instinctual piety. *Le Sermon des Cinquante, The Sermon of the Fifty,* being the most famous.

Or, rather, the most infamous. At any rate in the eyes of the authorities, who everywhere condemned it to be lacerated and burned by the public executioner, describing it as one of the vilest things ever yet vomited forth by the Devil against the holy institution of religion.

Picturing a congregation of fifty gentlemen dissatisfied with the religious practices of Europe, who therefore assembled once a week to worship God (not Christ) in their own way. With the aid of no theologically trained priest. Without the use of any rigmarole of ritual or any vestment. But simply with a different member of the group standing up each Sunday and giving a sermon.

And on this particular occasion described in the pamphlet, the chairman reviewing the Bible and the various faiths it had sprouted, and concluding with this prayer to the Almighty:

May the great God who listens to us, the great God Who surely was never born of a Jewish virgin, nor put to death on a gallows, nor eaten in a wafer, Who surely was not the inspirer of those Biblical books that are so full of contradictions, so full of obvious lies and so full of bloody horrors —may this great God, Creator of all the universes, have mercy on all us Christians who belittle Him, and may He bring us back to the true faith in Him. And may He spread His blessings on our efforts to adore Him. Amen.

One can imagine the howl of rage that went up at the appearance of this pamphlet. From all the priests and preachers whose livelihood it undercut. From all those builders of churches, carvers of images, makers of vestments, and so forth, who made their living out of man's piety.

And yet there was genuine religious reverence here. Rousseauan reverence, you might say. And not just a touch of it, as in most of Voltaire's former pamphlets. But all through it. With that eternal Voltairean malice finally brought under a degree of control.

But—and here was the crucial *but* in this effort of Voltaire's to fight off the threat of Rousseau—there was still this important difference: that Voltaire still would not put his name to it. No, that he couldn't. That would have been too much of an imitation of Rousseau. That would have been an open confession that he was in the wrong when it came to the question of anonymity and the courage of the author to declare himself. That would have been the sign of a follower rather than a leader. The confession that Rousseau's courage had pointed out the way, and that Voltaire was now accepting it and treading meekly in the footsteps of the brave pioneer.

No. Instead Voltaire printed his pamphlet with a note attributing it to "a great and learned prince." And whom could he mean by that, except Frederick the Great? And why him? Was it not because Rousseau had only recently written to that monarch in a slighting manner, and Voltaire was now retorting that when it came to writing, the King was as good as, if not better than, Rousseau.

But this bit of tricky rapier fencing fooled hardly anyone. Rather, it showed up even more clearly than before Voltaire's incorrigible tendency to bow and scrape before kings. And gave rise to still another unfavorable comparison between himself and Rousseau.

Had Rousseau attributed to a great and learned prince his attack on the religious practices of his day? As if to rub off a little gold from the froggings of some potentate and place himself under the protection of one of the powerful of this earth? Oh the contrary. He had scorned such protection. Rousseau had ascribed his attack to a Savoyard vicar, a poor mountain priest and, what's more, in disgrace with his superiors for having got a poor girl pregnant.

In short, the lowliest of the lowly of this earth: a criminal and a sinner. While Voltaire had picked the highest of the high: the King of Prussia. Could one ask for a more striking illustration of the difference between the aristocratic Voltaire and the democratic Rousseau?

The frivolous Voltaire. The serious Rousseau.

With the result that Voltaire's fury only increased. As did the enthusiasm of Rousseau's followers. And Voltaire felt compelled to rush out his *Extraits des sentiments de Jean Meslier.*

Supposedly the work of a French country priest. In other words, as humble as your Rousseauan Savoyard. If not more so. And in fact a real priest, whose manuscript had come into the hands of Voltaire many years before. The testament of an obscure curé who did not wish to die without leaving behind him some evidence of his long-suppressed hatred for the tyranny of Church and monarchy that had compelled him all his life to believe in and to teach a pack of absurdities.

Voltaire's *Extracts from the Sentiments of Jean Meslier* caused a sensation.

But again, this was of little help in Voltaire's battle against Rousseau. People could only conclude that Rousseau had so far outdistanced Voltaire that the old master was racing after him just as fast as his ancient and creaky bones would permit.

As for Voltaire's anonymity, that still remained.

Wasn't it perhaps better, then, to drop the contest with Rousseau in that direction and concentrate one's attacks where Rousseau was more vulnerable? Since one could not imitate him successfully, might it not be wiser to go back to the old business of harping on Rousseau's contradictions?

Returning again and again to the ridiculous fact that Rousseau in his book on the reform of education takes a promising young lad, of a rich family, and in twenty years of educational effort succeeds in producing—well, what do you imagine?

A carpenter!

Yes, a carpenter. As if there were nothing so difficult to develop as a carpenter. As if that were what all the teachers of the world should

374

struggle to give us: another carpenter. And as if the making of a good poet, or a good architect, or a good scientist, weren't worth the effort.

And Voltaire returning again and again to ask: And who is it that writes all this drivel about making a boy a carpenter? Is it a man who has himself turned to carpentering? Laid down his pen and grabbed a saw and a plane? Which he ought all the more to have done, since in his book he has so little good to say of books that in fact he denies his pupil access to them until the age of sixteen.

But no. Any other man who hated books would throw away his pen and paper. But not a Rousseau. His advice is always for others. Never for himself.

Indeed, in his book, he doesn't even apologize for the fact that as a young man he ran away from the employer to whom he was apprenticed. Broke his contract and fled from his bench. Didn't want to be a workman.

Wanted to be a writer.

And the amazing fact that such a hypocrite should find intoxicated followers! That people should arise on all sides to cry out that books should be tossed aside. That man should leave his crowded cities. Cross rivers and climb mountains. And sing out with joy, "Down with writing! Down with books! Live your life! Don't read it!"

But how were these people expressing this new attitude toward life? In books, of course. How else?

And nevertheless unable to see anything wrong in their lack of logic. Stubbornly arguing that with books it was just the same as with money. Both of them substitutes for reality.

Asking whether anyone in his right mind could maintain that money improved anything. Whether an egg purchased at a store could ever be as good as an egg taken fresh from a hen. Or an apple from a greengrocer's stall could ever equal an apple plucked ripe from a tree.

But the fact that money is a deception is nevertheless not in itself sufficient for renouncing it. How can it be, in this world where everyone is brought up on deception? Where people will marry for money and even die for money. Where man's most generous impulses are quickly translated into money, lest they express themselves in genuine ways which we would be unable to control. Lest our lives turn out to be something more real than just a column of figures.

And the same with words as with money. Everybody chattering words all the days of their lives. Everybody giving words. Demanding words. Living and dying with words.

But of course one could hardly expect a Voltaire to understand Rousseau's strong position with respect to money and to words. Voltaire, to whom money and words were the solution for everything. Voltaire, to whom that most famous expression has been universally attributed: "I disapprove of everything you say, but I will defend to my death your right to say it."

Brave words, those!

Yes. But why? Whatever for? Die for words? Die for the right of people to talk? As if that were all that was lacking for the well-being of this world—that people should be even more loquacious than they already are. As if the salvation of mankind lay in people's talking just as much as they possibly could.

Which in fact they were already doing! Jabbering away for all they were worth. And with salvation nowhere in sight. On the contrary! Perdition daily coming closer.

Not that Rousseau had anything against freedom of speech. After all, since that was the kind of world we lived in, a furiously talking world, then everyone ought to have his share in it.

But with no illusions as to what could be achieved thereby.

Suppose, for example, that what we are all groping for is not to be found in words. What if, indeed, it is only killed, crushed, stamped to death in this incessant blizzard of words? What then?

Because light doesn't always illuminate, does it? For example, when you are trying to see the stars. When the more light you give yourself, the fewer stars you can see. While the darker the night is, the more brilliant the stars.

And with truth perhaps the same. The truth sooner grasped without words than with them. Yes, sooner glimpsed in silence than in speech. And in ignorance rather than in enlightenment. All you philosophers of the Era of Enlightenment to the contrary notwithstanding!

What? Truth in ignorance?

Yes, why not?

As in that story that Rousseau loved so much: of the bishop, who, in a remote mountain village of his diocese, came upon a woman who in her profound ignorance had no other form of prayer but to fall upon her knees and go: "Oh!"

And to whom this bishop, deeply moved, felt compelled to say, "Pray that way always, my good woman. Your prayers are perhaps worth more than mine."

Never would that make sense to a Voltaire. What? A silly woman's

"Oh!" is a religion? When it is so obviously nothing but an expression of stupidity.

Just as Voltaire would never accept carpentering to be as good as poetry. Even though the Saviour Himself had been a carpenter.

Because, for a Voltaire, if the truth, the great truth, should ever be revealed to man it would have to come in the form of words. And correctly spelled, too. Grammatical. Clear. Sparkling with wit!

In any case, nothing dull, or cryptic, or mystic.

Best of all, perhaps, in the form of mathematics. So that there could be no chance of any misunderstanding.

As in Voltaire's own favorite *exemplum*. The one about the long-lost shipwrecked mariners who, starved and despairing, finally land on a bleak and deserted shore. But in the sand their leader spies some geometrical tracings. With the result that he can point to them and say to the others, "Courage, friends, I see evidence of man."

And in the same way Voltaire, looking up at the skies at night and discovering there the operation of Newton's magnificent laws, could turn to his own long-lost and shipwrecked philosophers and say to them, "Courage, friends, I see evidence of God."

But of course not just anybody's God. And specifically not the God that Christians worship. But evidence of a Voltairean God.

For though Voltaire might poke fun at the pretensions of men to have a God in their own image, yet he himself was not above making his God in the image of Voltaire. What else? What better God could there be?

A God with whom Voltaire therefore did not so much plead as he argued. Did not so much adore as he was jealous of Him. And—supreme blasphemy of all—a God whose services Voltaire enlisted for the protection of his life and fortune. Naturally. Why not?

"To keep my servants from murdering me for my gold while I'm asleep in my bed," as he himself acknowledged. Without so much as a blush.

A God so necessary, not merely for the preservation of the universe, but also for the preservation of that society that Voltaire loved, with himself so near the top of it that he did not hesitate to write in his poem *Epistle to the Author of "The Three Impostors"*: "*Si Dieu n'existait pas, il faudrait l'inventer.*" If God did not exist, it would be necessary to invent him.

A task—inventing God—for which, of course, such an arrogant man as Voltaire no doubt felt himself splendidly equipped. Just as he had found himself capable of constructing a church for a faith he had no faith in. And stocking it with a relic for which he had nothing but contempt and ridicule.

In short, there was nothing to which this unscrupulous character would not lend himself. No hoax. No deceit. No disguise.

And yet this man could get into his coach, his beautifully upholstered coach, and have himself driven freely in and out of the gates of Geneva.

While Rousseau was excluded!

This man could go to his own church, on his own estate, and have incense wafted at him, any time he might be inclined to worship. Which assuredly wasn't often.

While Rousseau was practically excommunicated!

And yet which of the two of them had written more reverently about religion? And about Christ? Which of the two of them had defended Geneva? Proclaimed her in book after book?

Where was justice? Where was justice?

30: MONSIEUR LE FORNICATEUR!

Rousseau felt so angrily jealous of Voltaire, so angrily jealous of this man who was at the same time jealous of him, that one day, despite the rulings of the consistory, he wrote to the pastor of the church at Motiers that he wanted to attend services and to commune. And this pastor, who was in private his admirer and his friend, could not refuse.

But what a to-do when Rousseau actually went to church! And communed. For it was suddenly presumed that he was doing so in order to abdicate his theories and bow to the authorities in Geneva. Repudiate his books and beg God for forgiveness.

And when he quickly denied this, fury broke out in the city. It was rent in two by those who felt that Rousseau had the right to receive communion. And those who cried, "Sacrilege!" That this blasphemer should have dared break into one of the churches of the Calvinist faith and there receive the sacrament of the flesh and blood of Jesus!

"What?" Rousseau cried to the Genevans. "It is only those who mock religion, like Monsieur de Voltaire, who can have the freedom of your city?"

To which Councilor Tronchin, who was then writing his *Letters from the Plain* (against which Rousseau would later write his answering *Letters from the Mountain*), pointed out: "How dare you compare yourself to Voltaire? How dare you compare your works to his? In Voltaire one finds nothing against religion, except occasional indiscretions. Almost always in fun. While with you there is no beating around the bush; the attack is head on, and not just against the rites of religion, but against its dogmas and its morality, and against our whole society, which is founded on that religion!"

Which caused Rousseau's eyes to start from his head with fury. "So!" he cried. "Outrageous mockery is forgiven. It's just fun. But reason, argument, proof—they are forbidden! That's serious and can't be tolerated!"

And he wrote letters to his friends in the city demanding a hearing. "Can our city really permit one of its members to be condemned without having been heard? What must the world think of our so-called liberties?"

And he went into an analysis of the constitution of the city to prove to the Genevans that he was entitled to a hearing. And also to show that if the Council did not accord it to him, the citizens had a right to insist on it. For the citizens were superior to the Council, even though over a long period of time the Council had succeeded in contracting the governing power within a small circle of aristocrats.

"Citizens of Geneva!" Rousseau exclaimed. "Insist on your rights!"

As a result of which there broke out a kind of miniature civil war in Geneva. Between the so-called "representatives," who wanted Rousseau represented before the Council, and the "negatives," who were opposed to it. Between the aristocrats and the commoners. Between the rich and the poor. With the respresentatives under the leadership of Rousseau, who didn't live in the city, but outside it, at Motiers. And the negatives under the leadership of Voltaire, who also didn't live in the city, but outside it, at Ferney. In the opposite direction. So that the tug of war between these two men went back and forth right through the town, forming factions that even cut families in two.

But a controlled civil war. With little bloodshed. Only with much violent language and an occasional show of fists.

And a special weapon. Not too deadly. Originally a humble household necessity: the enema syringe. Cylinder type. Which furious Rousseauans and furious Voltaireans would fill with boiling water and squirt at each other.

To the chagrin of Rousseau, who deplored these scaldings. But to the vast amusement of Voltaire, who denied any part in all this nonsense except the interest of a man in all manifestations of human folly, and who later wrote a burlesque poem on it, called *Civil War in Geneva*.

And ordered a couple of dozen cottages built on the grounds of his Ferney estate.

Why? Why a couple of dozen cottages? On his estate?

Well, because he was still the unbeatable Voltaire, that's why. Because he had tricks in his armamentarium of which a Rousseau couldn't possibly have the vaguest notion. Because if he couldn't beat Rousseau on one front, he'd beat him on another. Or on a dozen others.

Because never in the world would Voltaire have made the mistake that Rousseau was making at this time when certain Protestant delegations came to wait upon him, to request his assistance in the matter of their coreligionists who were in trouble in France.

For it was still a crime to be a Protestant in France. Unless you were content not to practice your faith. But the moment you assembled in the service of the Lord (as a certain Pastor Rochette and his flock of glassmakers had done recently), and you were caught at it, then it was imprisonment for the women, the galleys for the men, for all the rest of their days. And death on the scaffold for the pastor.

Rousseau received such delegations with righteous anger.

"What?" he exclaimed. "You consider me good enough to be asked to help our religion? But not good enough to be a member? Good enough to fight for you, but not good enough to enter one of your churches?"

It was explained to him that despite what had happened to him lately in Switzerland he still remained the most important Protestant in Europe, one whose voice could not help but make itself powerfully heard everywhere.

"Yes, but, gentlemen," Rousseau cried, "can you promise me that when the world hears that powerful voice of mine it will not laugh? Will you promise me that there will not be smiles and even guffaws when I present to the world the spectacle of a Protestant unable to win his case before his own coreligionists and yet so arrogant as to suppose that he will win it handily against Catholics?

"No, my friends," Rousseau finished bitterly, "let those who persecute be themselves persecuted. That is only fair. That is, in fact, how one learns!"

Well, yes. What else could a Rousseau say? For isn't that how it must always be with the poor? On whom the weight of the world's injustice rests, giving them nothing to share but their misery? Whom years of poverty have compelled to be forever concerned about their own dire needs: their food, their clothing, their shelter. Always putting themselves first.

While with a Voltaire it was so different. A Voltaire with his millions. And his friends in all the seats of the mighty. A Voltaire with his four estates and his hundred and fifty disguises.

No. The wonder is not that the rich should find the time and the money to be generous, but that they shouldn't find even more. For what can be so difficult about giving from one's superfluity?

And indeed, when the Protestants, in their desperation, began to appeal to M. de Voltaire, despite his frequent ridicule of Protestants, and despite the Catholic church he had built—when they began to appeal to him as to that other great voice that might make itself heard all over the world, Voltaire did not hesitate for a minute.

He was ready to fight fanaticism wherever it might show itself.

Rousseau, in subsequent lonely and forgotten years, when he lived once again obscurely in a tiny apartment in Paris, must have pondered often on his race with Voltaire and how differently everything might have turned out if it could have been he, not Voltaire, who conducted all those great struggles for justice. Struggles that made Voltaire more famous than ever.

Because it had been for Rousseau that this fame had been meant, had it not? The delegations had come to him first with their entreaties, hadn't they? And naturally so. For which of them was the Protestant? Which of them was the persecuted man? Which of them had authored the *Discourse on Inequality?*

Which of them really understood the problems of the lowly?

Yes, how differently things might have turned out if only he had been able to accept. Then it would have been he, Rousseau, who would have formed all those committees for the defense of the victims. He, Rousseau, who would have organized the appeals for funds. Found refuge for the families of the accused, and for the unfortunate survivors of the executed. Coaxed the best lawyers of France to lend their skill. Persuaded people of the highest prominence, all over Europe, to lend their names and their money.

And written all those flaming pamphlets that shook awake the sleeping conscience of the world. Pamphlets on the Calas case. Pamphlets on the Sirven case. On the La Barre case. And so on, and so on.

Instead it was Voltaire. All Voltaire.

Voltaire who would draw every class of society into a popular demand for justice. Voltaire who would go down in history as the man who brought about the abolition of torture, the end of the cruel *question* and other brutalities. Voltaire who would spread everywhere his doctrine of religious tolerance. Voltaire who would become known throughout the world as the living symbol of justice for all.

So much so that one day a priest of France would write to him secretly, asking him if he was not really the Christ. Reborn at last. Come finally to the assistance of confused and struggling mankind. Bringing us again that wonderful teaching that all men are brothers. Spreading comfort and hope again in all our lonely and silent hearts.

A letter that would bring tears of irritation to Voltaire's eyes. Knowing himself too well ever to imagine that he might be the Son of God. And anyhow having no great love for Jesus, in Whose name so many people had been slaughtered. So many women put into convents and deprived of the joy of motherhood.

And besides, what was he doing now that he hadn't been doing all along? In his *La Henriade,* in his *Alzire,* in his *For and Against,* in his *Philosophical Letters,* in everything he had ever written. Had he ever preached anything but tolerance, tolerance, tolerance?

And forever hounded for his preaching—by whom? Mohammedans? Confucians?

No! Christians. In the name of Christ!

No, indeed. He wasn't the Christ reborn. Just Voltaire. But still with one undeniable difference between the Voltaire he had been and the Voltaire he was now, though never, of course, would he credit Rousseau with that change in himself. But scholars would. Distinguishing between the Voltaire who used to take his cases to the authorities, to the mighty, and the Voltaire who began to imitate Rousseau and take his cases to the people. To everyone.

Now he saw the people not merely as a stream of unfortunate human flesh perpetually pushing itself through God's pitiless meatgrinder of birth and death, but as a great force that might be enlisted in a glorious fight for justice.

"The people: the one force that can compel even a king," he would write.

Not that Voltaire had ever denied or disregarded the needs of the lower classes—he had just not thought of drawing them into his battles. But now he labored until in all France there was no man so ignorant as not to know the story of the Calas family of Protestants who had somehow managed to survive in Catholic Toulouse, though barred by law from the best professions and the best trades. One son having thus already been seduced—or, rather, compelled—into Catholicism, but the other, caught while attempting to conceal his religion in order to sneak through the bar examinations, sinking ever deeper into melancholia.

This was the young man who was found dead one evening. Hanged. Without a doubt a suicide. But according to a story that flew like wildfire through Toulouse, actually murdered by his sixty-four-year-old father, in order to prevent him from turning Catholic, following his brother's example.

So that the city was soon aroused by nightly processions of penitents in their awe-inspiring robes that covered them from head to foot, leaving mere slits for their eyes. And special church services for the martyred soul. And all the bells tolling during a huge funeral, and a flood of rumors circulating about strange apparitions and almost incredible miracles.

It was disaster for the Calas family. With all the sons and daughters immediately arrested. And the old mother too. And an ancient servant, even though she was a Catholic. And a friend who happened to be there that night, and who was also a Catholic. And all these people chained by their feet in separate dungeons and held there during all the weeks of the trial, until the sentence of the Parlement of Toulouse was carried out. Until the old man had been made to suffer the *question,* both ordinary and extraordinary, and then, with every joint dislocated and his body bloated with water, had been tied to a horizontal wheel, and, before the whole populace, all his major bones had been smashed with an iron staff. Eleven pitiless blows in all.

And thus left to suffer for two hours, before being strangled to death. And then his body burned and his ashes scattered.

While his daughters hastily elected to spend the rest of their lives in convents. And the sons fled in different directions, and the family property was sold for the benefit of the King of France. And the aged mother quickly disappeared.

And Voltaire, who was just then busier than ever, amidst his correspondence and his pamphlets, his fight with Rousseau and his *Écrasez l'infâme* campaign, and also an annotated edition of Corneille's works which he was doing for the benefit of a distant relative of the playwright, and the life of Peter the Great which he was composing at the special request of Empress Catherine, and the cottages he was building on his estate, and all his usual financial matters, plus his plays (for he could never cure himself of his habit of writing plays), this busy Voltaire with five desks already set up in his study now set up a sixth desk there and began the years of work that it would take him to reverse this horrible sentence.

Writing seven different anonymous pamphlets on the case, and above all his tremendously popular *Treatise on Tolerance,* which he claimed to be the work of a "M. Herman," saying to Damilaville, "Beware of imputing to me a little book on tolerance which you may happen to see," and explaining to the Marquis de Chauvelin that "it would hurt the cause of the Calas family if people took it into their silly heads that I might possibly have written it," and assuring someone else, "I myself can point out to you the preacher who penned it"—even though, as far away as America, Benjamin Franklin would recognize the style of Voltaire and would welcome this pamphlet as "a book so powerful that all alone it might destroy bigotry."

And in addition working to have all these pamphlets rendered into German and English and Dutch and other languages and distributed all over Europe. Even though copies would be burned by the Papacy, and by the Parlement of Paris, in which city, nevertheless, in spite of the efforts of the police, edition after edition would somehow get into the hands of people.

And pleading with the Queen of England to head the subscription for the relief of the Calas family. And with the Empress of Russia. And the King of Poland. And German princes and princesses without number. Writing, at one point in the fight, to the Duchess of Saxe-Gotha:

"A miracle in France! That private people should be able to reverse the decision of a high court. And even more unbelievable that this should be in a case that concerns justice for a Protestant, Madame Calas. And what a Protestant! Without reputation, without money, with her husband condemned as a criminal and broken on the wheel. Can you be under any misconception that this was achieved without money? No, no, no. On the contrary, we must get up a new collection at once. And we need your name at the head of our committee. And at the top of our list of donors too."

In fact, this anonymous Voltaire (with nobody fooled except the law) made Madame Calas so famous that even the King of France became curious about this long-suffering woman. So that she had her day at Versailles. In court. Before royalty. With the King graciously giving her a large sum of money to use against the justices of his own courts!

Voltaire clucking with satisfaction: "Go tell me now that there is no justice under monarchs. That the soil of Switzerland differs from that of France. No. There is justice everywhere! Wherever people want it. Wherever they demand it!"

Voltaire's fight for the Calas family was not finished before he was involved in the Sirven case. And then the d'Espinasse case. And the Lally case. And the terrible case of the Chevalier de La Barre. Not all the victims Protestants, by any means. But all the cases struggles for justice.

For example, the Chevalier de La Barre—a Catholic. Not yet out of his teens. Who, with several friends, was accused of behaving disrespectfully toward the crucifix. Though he protested that he had never mutilated a wooden cross, admitting only that he had failed to remove his hat once when the cross was being borne through the streets of Abbeville during a religious procession.

A search of his rooms, however, revealed a copy of that terrible *Philosophical Dictionary* whose first volume, of an eventual nine, had recently appeared. (And concerning which Voltaire had already written to Damilaville: "I beg all my brethren to shout to the world that it is a compilation by a Society of Men of Letters. This nobody will be able to refute, for a reading of it will convince anyone that only a consortium of twenty theologians, a couple of rabbis and a dozen assorted historians and scientists could have composed it—certainly not such a man as myself, over seventy, occupied with the affairs of my country estates, bent with afflictions and scarcely able to dictate my plays.")

While the friends of La Barre quickly fled in all directions, La Barre himself was seized and brought to torture. And then sentenced to have his tongue torn out, and his head cut off, and his body burned. And during this frightful execution, to have the *Philosophical Dictionary* of Voltaire between his feet.

For the purpose of linking up Voltaire with this crime. (Though it was obviously no crime at all. Nothing more than an indecency. Deserving of a slap in the face, for showing a lack of proper respect for the faith of others.)

And so as to execute Voltaire along with La Barre. Executing him in effigy. By proxy. As if to say, "Too bad we can't burn you too, Voltaire! But we'll show you, on the body of La Barre, what we would do with you if we could! At any rate, we'll show the readers of your pamphlets what may be in store for them if they don't watch out!"

Fanatics! Oh, yes, fanatics!

With the executioner actually kinder than the justices of Abbeville. For he only pretended to tear out La Barre's tongue. Only making it bleed a little, so as to give the authorities a show. And meanwhile whispering to the young man, "If you place yourself exactly as I say, I promise I will kill you quickly and with the least possible pain."

"Just tell me what I must do," La Barre whispered back from his bleeding mouth, "and you will see that I'm no baby." And he laid his head on the block exactly as directed.

He was nineteen years old.

Pamphlet after pamphlet escaped from the horrified Voltaire. And letter after letter. To vindicate this poor lad. Rehabilitate him. And also save himself from a like fate. To say nothing of others.

Years of work. . . .

And the case of Madame de Bombelles, discarded by her husband, along with her child, because she was Protestant and he was Catholic and the courts held that she had no rights whatsoever, that in fact she was not married at all, that she was nothing but a concubine and her child a bastard, the marriage ceremony having been performed by the Reformed Church and therefore without sacramental validity—null and void.

Case after case. Yes, until Voltaire was known from one end of the world to the other as the man of justice, of tolerance, of kindness. The man who pleaded for all peoples to remember that they are brothers and that "those who light candles at high noon to celebrate God's worship should tolerate those who are content with the light of His sun," and that "those who cover their garments with white linen when they adore their God should stop detesting those who adore him while clad in a mantle of black wool."

Case after case, until, in his old age, even peddlers and street cleaners would point him out as the man who had saved the Calas family.

How these giant legal engagements began to push little Jean Jacques back into the obscurity from which he had only so recently emerged! Not immediately, to be sure, but in the course of time.

And this fool of a Rousseau in the meanwhile continuing to imagine that Voltaire, the great Voltaire, was deeply concerned as to who would win out in that pipsqueak civil war of Geneva: the aristocrats of the Magnificent Council, who were supposedly on Voltaire's side, or the artisans supposedly on Rousseau's.

Why, Voltaire was so far from caring that, in addition to all his other battles, he deliberately undertook the case of Robert Covelle, which was equivalent to thumbing his nose at the Genevan Magnificent Council. And at their consistory too.

Covelle wasn't anybody in particular. And his case not especially pitiable. Just a young bourgeois of Geneva who had a healthy appetite for women and got one too many of them big with child. For which he was very properly condemned to pay the lady damages. But also, in accordance with an old Calvinist tradition, he was to go down on his knees before the authorities and grovel there while he begged God to pardon him for having been a fornicator.

At which Voltaire cried, "Don't you do it!"

The idea! People so proud of their chastity as to feel that they can force others down on their knees before them. People so confused as to imagine that the Creator did not have His own good reasons for making the flesh of man and woman tug toward each other. God evidently knowing only too well how many fools there might be around who would be so strict and so chaste as to put the creation of the Lord into jeopardy by their mad notion that they were thereby pleasing Him all the more.

(Strange spectacle for France: one of her two greatest writers proclaiming in his *Émile* the rights of the female breast, and the other in his pamphlets proclaiming the rights of other human organs!)

For this case of Covelle, Voltaire made a special study of genuflexion throughout history and then fought this humiliating punishment so vigorously that he had the satisfaction of seeing it eventually abrogated from the statutes of Geneva. Where, as a matter of fact, it was discovered that it had never figured, even though over three thousand people had been condemned to submit themselves to it!

So much for the feelings of those overenthusiastic followers of Rousseau who had been so quick to attack Voltaire for his bowing and his scraping. Unable to distinguish what Voltaire made amply clear in his study of the subject: the difference between a graceful form of French politeness, always reciprocated by both prince and beggar, and the demeaning, one-sided Genevan act of forcing a person to his knees.

And who, in their confusion, went so far as to ascribe some special merit to Rousseau's public rudeness to a monarch who, for his part, had shown nothing but kindness to Rousseau.

But there was an additional satisfaction to Voltaire from his efforts in behalf of Covelle. It was the laugh he got each time this young bourgeois came to consult him at Ferney, when Voltaire's lackey would throw wide the double doors and announce in a loud voice, *Monsieur le fornicateur!*"

And Sir Fornicator would enter smiling, while the lackey bowed him in, convinced that a fornicator must be some very high dignitary indeed, as was the case with all those many-syllabled words ending in

-eur, such as *ambassadeur* and *directeur* and so forth, and totally unaware of the fact that his own activities at night very likely entitled him to the same honorary distinction.

31: THE ROYAL STUDMASTER

For there was nothing Voltaire enjoyed so much as a little obscenity. And why not? Was it not of the very stuff of life? The most intimate part? The relish of which was the best specific against growing old? The nearest thing to a talisman against death?

Let Rousseau talk against sex. But as for himself, how greedily, how hungrily his beady eyes would devour the dainty virgins of Geneva, whose luminous skin contrasted so agonizingly with his own dry hands, corrupted by their maze of bluish veins and brown liver spots. And his spidery fingers, tipped with nails that were cracked, ridged and discolored.

Let Rousseau delay sex in the education of the youth. But as for himself, he enjoyed nothing so much as to whisper to those young girls, "Let me teach you about love," for the sheer delight of hearing their shrill squeals, as they clung to each other for protection. Protection against this dangerous Parisian aristocrat with his wild ideas, whose home and estate they nevertheless loved to visit. And for whom they would sew and embroider nightcaps and other pretty things.

(Much to the annoyance of jealous Madame Denis, who was afraid that her crazy old uncle, obviously rapidly getting senile, might some day take it into his head to marry one of these pretty little fortune hunters. For that is all they were, in her opinion. And thus cheat her out of an inheritance which was hers by right of keeping company with this old man so far from all the attractions of Paris.)

Let Rousseau chatter away about innocence. But as for himself, Voltaire adored these young women about him. And liked to spy upon them and catch them surreptitiously scratching their privates to relieve their pubescent itch. This guarded espionage communicating to him some indescribable renewal of energy. Making the air somehow tonic. Somehow full of zest. So that, breathing it, he felt himself more alive. And more able to spend eighteen hours a day at work without tiring himself. And nothing less than eighteen hours of work was required for all his manifold tasks.

"You must come and visit us," he wrote once to a niece of his in Paris, "and bring along some of your more immodest water colors and pastels." (This was the same niece, Madame de Fontaine, whom he would tease about her futile efforts to develop a bosom, and to whom he would gaily wish breasts jutting out like cannonballs.)

He also requested this niece to arrange to get the permission of the Duke d'Orléans to have some copies made of the Boucher and Natoire nudes which hung in the Palais-Royal. Voltaire admired these nudes above all others.

"They must have fed their models nothing but rose petals," he would say, pointing out the delicate sheen of their skin tones that made these nudes look as if they had just that instant disrobed, and as if their warm pink flesh, coming suddenly into contact with the cold air of the atelier, must in a moment be covered with goose pimples.

How alive they were! How deliciously alive. Really *croquantes*. Good enough to eat.

"I don't insist on originals," Voltaire wrote to his niece, in a letter which has often been quoted to show how little Voltaire appreciated true art (though that would depend on what one meant by "true," as well as what one meant by "art," would it not?). "Copies will do me just as well, so long as they show enough nudity to rouse my old nature, to put a little wantonness back into my sluggish blood, to restore my spirits."

To Voltaire that happened to be one of the functions of painting. To restore him. To rejuvenate him. To inspire him.

And it was for the same reason that Voltaire solicited from Count Le Voyer, who was at the head of the remount program of the French cavalry, the honor of keeping one of the royally approved stallions for the region of Gex.

What childish glee he had out of his new title, "Royal Studmaster"! And with what pride he would tell his friends and visitors about his new duties: "Not less than ninety ejaculations during the months of April, May and June.

"King's orders," he would add. "And as a loyal subject I can only bow my head and obey."

And he would sigh with pleasurable tiredness. As if his own emaciated frame had exhausted itself in service to His Majesty, delivering the required ninety ejaculations.

But admitting, "God has given us the command to fill the land with children, but alas, the best I can do is to fill it with good strong horses."

It amazed him to see how horses improved his fields. How thick and green grew the grass where pregnant cattle staled. And in his efforts to convert the scrubby acres of Ferney into fertile land, he adopted the practice of confining his cattle every night to a small area, so that their droppings and their urine, pounded into the soil by their hoofs, would eventually transform its character. And so that by gradually shifting his corral over an entire field, he could bring the whole of it into rich fruitfulness.

(And now let that stupid Rousseau say that by fencing this enriched field he was the source of all the world's miseries and wars! And let somebody dare to deprive him of what was so manifestly and justly his very own!)

This work with cattle fascinated him all the more since he had himself been afflicted with such a stubborn stoppage all his life and had swallowed oceans of drugs for relief. A matter that had taken such hold on his mind that once, half in humor, half seriously, he propounded a history of man as if studied from a chamber pot's point of view, showing how much evil and cruelty in man's history might perhaps have been caused by constipation.

Claiming that Cromwell had not been able to move his bowels for a week when he voted to send the King of England to the block. And Charles IX sometimes had his conduits so blocked that blood was ready to spurt from his pores. "Is it any wonder that a temperament so congested and inflamed would agree to give the signal for the Massacre of St. Bartholomew?" Voltaire asked.

How he envied those people whom he described as having "a little plumpness," whose intestines were "velvety smooth, their hepatic and cystic ducts flowing with juices, their peristaltic movements gentle and regular," and who could therefore "pay their respects to Madame Chamber Pot every morning as easily as one spits."

How he worshiped that which he didn't have! And how much he feared that those who still enjoyed the wonderful powers of youth might be unaware of their treasures and waste their precious, irreplaceable time. So that he would whisper to the dainty maidens of Geneva, "Come. Let me show you the most majestic sight in nature. Come no further than my barn, and I will show you a spectacle that is the most magnificent sight on earth!"

But they already knew what he meant, and they would flee from him like a flock of chickens before the shadow of a hawk.

"Just think," he would say later to his friends, "people will travel for weeks to see Stromboli in eruption. And what it is, when seen from a distance? Nothing but a bit of fireworks on the horizon. While right here on my farm anyone can watch an event far more marvelous. Will you tell me why people shun it?"

There exists a painting of Voltaire in his barn, entertaining one of those squealing young virgins of Geneva with this most magnificent sight in nature. The painter being that same Huber who for years hung around Voltaire, delighting to sketch him in every conceivable situation.

While Voltaire would scream at him, "Paint girls! Not me!" And when he managed to get his hands on Huber's sketchblock, he would tear to pieces the sheets that showed the crumpled face of an old man.

Imagine that idiot of a painter sketching a worn-out scarecrow when there were young girls around whom he should be undressing and painting, if he had any sense. Which obviously he hadn't.

No. Huber would go right on sketching Voltaire. However, when the great man was in one of his destructive moods Huber would hold his pad behind him and put down what he saw, with both hands out of sight.

So that Marmontel would marvel, "Have you got an extra pair of eyes at the ends of your fingers?"

To which Huber once answered, "Voltaire is the easiest man in the world to sketch. His face is so completely his own that one can hardly miss catching a likeness of him. Here! I'll bet you my dog can make a portrait of Voltaire."

This was an old trick of Huber's. He would take a large slice of bread and offer it to his pet, who would snap at it. But Huber would keep holding the bread and twisting it in such a way that the dog nibbled off just the right parts, and then Huber could triumphantly hold up the slice, and there, sure enough, was Voltaire's characteristic profile: the sharp projecting nose, the even more sharply projecting chin and the sunken eyes.

It was this Huber who painted the canvas of the Royal Studmaster in his stable, where grooms have just led the male into the presence of the quietly expectant mare, and an obviously experienced farm wench is already guiding the stallion's organ with her hand, lest the precious seed fail to find one of the ninety marks it was obligated to make each season. In the background of this painting, which Huber called "The Chaste Susanna," is the Royal Studmaster himself, struggling to restrain a blushing young maiden from flight. And no doubt talking to her in the same language that you can find today in his *Philosophical Dictionary* (written by a Society of Men of Letters, please!), where, under the heading "Love," it says:

Is there any better way to gain a conception of what love really is than by watching horses in the act of procreation? Contemplate a stallion rearing to mount a mare! There's real majesty for you! There's power! Can you think of anything more brilliant than his eyes at such a moment? As if lightning would flash from them. And his neighing! Listen to it. And look how he keeps his mouth open—because, for this supreme effort when he is about to generate a new creature, even those greatly distended nostrils of his cannot feed his lungs all the air they need. Who would dare interrupt him at this juncture, when his mane waves so fiercely and his body is as if on fire. . . ?

Jealous of Rousseau? He, Voltaire? Ha! Of a stallion, yes. Yes, indeed! But of Jean Jacques? That little man with the pox? Never!

But apparently this higher conception of love was too much for the chaste Susanna. For in the painting by Huber, at any rate, what with her youth and her strength, there would seem to be but little doubt that she must succeed in escaping from Voltaire's skinny hands.

A pity. According to the aged poet. Since she might thus fall into those notions of love propagated by the theologians, who tend to lump it with sin. Or the notions of that stupid Rousseau, so full of high-flown passion and flights of fancy about chastity and God, instead of the real thing.

Was it not a fact that, in his *Émile,* Rousseau had shown such a fear of the sexual drive as to advise parents to take their sons to a hospital for venereal disease, so as to frighten them away from concupiscence forever? Imagine! When it is precisely for youth that love was designed.

And this simpleton nevertheless continuing to have his admirers. Some of them so shameless as to come into Voltaire's home. As guests. And even to sit down at his table. And consume his food. And meanwhile babble nonsense about "the two great genuises of our day."

As if there could be two of them! As if anyone who read Voltaire could still have any respect left for Rousseau.

And yet there was, for example, a certain guest at table one evening who, with his mouth full of chicken (Voltaire's chicken, if you please, of which this guest was so fond that he kept asking for more, and smacking his lips over it, and saying, "What excellent chicken. My compliments to your cook, Madame Denis. What a fine nutty flavor!"), did not hesitate to laugh and bray, "Hoho! How surprised our good Jean Jacques would be if he could see his enemy Voltaire en-, joying the very life he always praises so highly—the innocent life of the country."

Which caused Voltaire to hunch forward and cup a hairy ear, in order to better study this impudent fool sitting across the table from him.

"Never," this guest went on, "never have I been so impelled to abandon all the advantages of city life as when I read Rousseau's rapturous descriptions of the delights of country living. For instance, that magnificent tribute of his to the grape harvest. In his *Nouvelle Héloïse,* you will recall. Ah, Monsieur de Voltaire, I know you too well, your generosity, your selflessness, to doubt for a moment that you would deny to your great rival the praise he merits for that passage. With what artistry this talented writer depicts that moment of the year, which he declares to be the last remaining evidence of man's golden age!"

"Bucolic," Voltaire suggested curtly, wondering how best to crush this chicken-eating idiot, along with his hero Rousseau. Both with one blow!

"Yes, bucolic," the guest agreed, smacking his lips over another bite of chicken, before going on. "That particular section of his novel is a poem, monsieur. Nothing less. Such genius in the rendering of the colors of the shriveling grape leaves as the cold night works its magic upon them. And such mastery in his description of the ripe grapes, as the clusters begin to glow through the diminishing foliage. Yes. It is as if he hadn't written with pen and ink at all, but with brush and pallette. And with crushed gems for pigments."

"Masterful," muttered Voltaire, itching with fury and aware that the whole table was now watching his mood, wondering how long he would permit this outrage to continue. And this guest, meanwhile, busy with both his chicken and his praise of Rousseau's harvest festival, running blissfully on:

"The whole countryside then awakening, and, amidst singing and drumming and general merriment, young and old going out to the sunny slopes where the vineyards are, and from early morning until late at night, all hands busy gathering nature's bounty. Truly Rousseau describes it so entrancingly that one feels one has wasted one's life by living in cities. By poring over books. By going to the theater. And especially when one reads the rewards of the evening: how, tired from honest toil, and with healthy appetites aroused, everyone gathers for the feast, and afterward for the music and the dancing and other innocent rustic joys."

"Idyllic," said Voltaire icily.

"Yes, yes," the guest agreed. "And when I see you, monsieur, here amidst this beauty, away from the crowded literary salons, away from the courtiers and the fops, the critics and the claques . . ."

"So peaceful here, and quiet," Voltaire supplied.

"Yes," said the guest.

"Yes, the innocent country," said Voltaire. And then suddenly he snapped, "By the way, just this morning I had the strangest experience. I was passing through our barnyard when it seemed to me that the gift that old Empedocles had enjoyed had also come to me. You remember the gift of Empedocles? All at once it was as if I could understand the language of animals."

He paused for just a moment before querying, "Are you not curious to know what I heard them saying to each other?" And he looked in particular at the Rousseau admirer.

Like all the others, this gentleman expressed his warm interest. Whereupon Voltaire first begged them all not to interrupt their meal and then continued: "Well, there was, for example, a young and sprightly capon, who was scratching and pecking in the dust of the barnyard for little bits to eat, when a dainty pullet approached him.

"Listen, now," said Voltaire, and he cocked his head to one side like a chicken, and in a voice that might very well have been that of the capon, he cackled, "Why, good morning, my dear chickie. Eh? What is this? You will not answer my greeting? Have I offended you? Or is there something else the matter with you? I must say, that is a rather tragic expression that I see on your face this morning. Tell me, have you got some dreadful sorrow?"

Then, returning to his natural voice, Voltaire asked, "Now shall I tell you what the pullet had to say in reply to the capon?"

And, cocking his head to the other side and pitching his voice to what might be the timbre of a young pullet's, a gentler, more treble sort of cackle, he went on: "My dear capon, it's not what I've got but what I haven't got that gives me this doleful expression."

Then switching back immediately to the capon's voice, and reversing the position of his head, Voltaire carried on: "Why, what do you mean? Explain yourself."

"I mean this," cackled the pullet. "That damned farm wench over there grabbed me up suddenly the other day, squeezed me upside down between her knees, stuck a long crochet needle into my behind, caught hold of my womb, rolled it up on her needle and tore it bleeding out of me."

The whole assembly was visibly shocked by this unexpected image of violence. And the reality of farm life was thus brought home to this table where but a moment before there had been nothing but the Rousseauan innocence of nature.

Voltaire, however, did not stop. Going on with the pullet's voice, to which he now added something of a sob, he cried, "And she threw my womb, my precious and only womb, to the cat. To eat! And now behold me, scorned by the barnyard rooster, the hero I worship, who wants nothing to do with me, since I can never hope to lay an egg."

"So you lost your womb," Voltaire replied, giving his capon voice a little semitragic snicker. "My dear, I do indeed pity you. But let me tell you this: That wench was only half as cruel to you as she was to me. For you lost only one organ. Whereas I lost two. And if this life now holds little consolation for you, then think of me, who might have been that very rooster whose favors you would have craved!"

"Oh, is there nothing that can ever sweeten our deplorable existence?" the pullet moaned.

"Nothing," said the capon bitterly. "Unless you are one of those who can still derive some joy out of the fact that others are more miserable than you. I confess that there is some of this ugly feeling in me, and that despite my better nature I was inclined to sip some satisfaction from recently overhearing two Italian abbots discussing a similar outrage to which they had been subjected."

"You amaze me," the pullet exclaimed. "What—man, the lord of the universe, treats his own kind no better than he treats us?"

"That is precisely what I mean, my dear pullet. Those two abbots had been destined for the Holy Father's own choir in Rome, and the removal of their organs was for the purpose of making them retain their innocent childish soprano voices, so that they might make sweeter music in their churches. Under the impression that God prefers voices obtained at such a price."

There was laughter around the table at Voltaire's barb against the papal custom of that time, of castrating children in order to have soprano voices for the Sistine Chapel choir, but Voltaire still did not stop. Going back again to the pullet's voice, he continued:

"Ah, then you give me at least one hope, my dear capon. That though we have lost our cherished organs of procreation, we shall have gained the voices of nightingales." Whereupon Voltaire, as the pullet, launched into a cracked bit of singing. Then stopped his ears as he changed over to the capon:

"Please, please, my dear pullet. Spare me. And undeceive yourself. No. Mutilate us as much as they please, never will our voices be anything but the clucks and screeches to which nature has confined us."

"Then why?" cried the pullet. "Why did they torture us?"

"In order to fatten us, my dear. That our skin may be softer and our flesh more delicate," the capon explained.

"But," said the pullet, preening herself, "I have no special desire to be fat. I like myself as I am and consider myself as delicate as anyone else."

"Oh, my dear chicken," said the capon impatiently, "don't you understand that they don't care what *you* happen to think about the delicacy of your flesh? It's the way *they* feel about it that counts. How delicate they will find *your* flesh. When they eat you."

"Eat me!" the pullet screamed. "Eat me? You lie! There cannot be such monsters in the world. The great God in heaven would never permit the continued existence of such criminals."

"You're wrong," said Voltaire with the capon's voice. "You're wrong, my dear pullet. You evidently have still much to learn of the ways of this world. They will not only eat you but will imagine themselves quite innocent while doing so. That's how they are. And it could be even worse. For if they should see that in spite of losing your womb you still remain scrawny, they will lock you up in a kind of prison and feed you a special mash. And if that doesn't do it, they may go even further and stab out your eyes."

"Oh, horrors!" cried the pullet. Voltaire's head sank as if the poor chicken was about to faint. He could see that not a single guest was touching any of the chicken now. Not even the chicken-munching guest, who, in fact, was beginning to look a little sick.

"Yes," the capon continued without pity, "that's what they will do for us. And then, when we are fat, they will cut our throats, tear out our feathers and roast us. And I give you ten to one, you have no idea of the funeral oration that they will hold over us. They will praise the taste of our flesh. They will say, 'What a fine nutty flavor!' And they will say, 'My compliments to your cook.' And this one will express preference for our thighs, and that one will praise our wings. And a third one will unashamedly dote on our bottoms, smacking his lips over this portion of us, which he would certainly never have done while we were alive, when we too might have appreciated it. And thus our little tale in this world will end. Done with, forever and ever."

For a moment Voltaire was tempted to stop. He had rubbed the noses of his guests into enough dirt for one day.

But something forced him to go on. The rogue in him. The wicked, malicious rogue in him.

Back he went again to the pullet's voice. He could see that Madame Denis was getting ready to scold him severely. But not now. She didn't dare interrupt him now. Not in front of company. So he went on:

"Oh, the scoundrels! How can they be so abominable? My dear capon, tell me, are not these ogres at least tormented with eternal remorse?"

"With remorse?" The capon laughed, with a laughter that was full of squawks and cackles. "My dear pullet, how innocent you are. Tormented with indigestion, yes. But never with remorse. For you must know that killing chickens is the least of man's crimes. Oh, the very least indeed."

"Why? What can be worse?" the pullet asked, opening wide her eyes with astonishment. "What can be worse than killing us and eating us. Unless you mean that while they eat us they relate amusing philosophical dialogues."

"Yes," said Voltaire in the capon's voice. "That too they do. But I wasn't even thinking of that. Let me tell you a few things about these human beings who eat us, and who give themselves such airs of superiority. Though, after all, they are nothing but bipeds like ourselves. But so naked and of such ugly skins that they envy us our feathers and do the best they can to cover themselves with fabrics which they put together themselves, but which can never replace or equal our feathers, neither in beauty nor in utility.

"And still another fact. They are disgusting creatures. Really. Without a single exudate from their bodies that they themselves do not reject with distaste and hasten to remove as fast as possible. Whereas among creatures which they regard as lesser, there are many that give eggs, or cheese and milk, or honey, or silk. But from them: nothing but ordure.

"But you are mistaken, my dear pullet, if you imagine that killing chickens is the height of their cruelty."

"You mean," said the pullet, "that they actually eat one another?"

"They did that too, at one time," said the capon. "And perhaps some

397

of them do still. But while now refusing to eat each other, they will still roast each other. Some at the stake, and others in great battles. Merely because they hold contrary opinions about subjects which we chickens would cheerfully admit we cannot understand, but which they claim they do, although apparently never able to explain them sufficiently clearly to convince each other."

"Oh, well," said the pullet. "Now you make it all very clear. And I am not the least disturbed to learn that such perverse creatures also torture each other. That is only right. But us? How can they torture us, who would gladly lay our eggs for them all our lives, in return for a little food? Why do they threaten *us* with castration, decapitation and roasting?"

"It is because they are Christians and claim this right from their God," the capon explained. "They claim that their Christian God gave them all the beasts of the world, to make them work, to use their skins or to eat them for food. Of course, not all people agree with that. I heard my two abbots declare that in other times and other parts of the world, for example in a great country called India, the sacred rule of their particular God was just the opposite: namely, that no beast was to be killed by man."

"But it is these Christians who are everywhere in power?" the pullet asked.

"Almost everywhere," said the capon. "Almost over the whole globe."

"Then goodness and kindliness can have no place?" the pullet moaned.

"Insofar as our lives are concerned," the capon answered her, "I'm afraid not. And this is in spite of the fact that the Christians worship a book which they call their Holy Bible. And there, in the ninth chapter of Genesis, verse four, it does say, so I heard my two abbots stating, that God ruled that 'flesh with the life thereof, which is the blood thereof, shall ye not eat.'"

"You tell me that this is in their sacred book?" the pullet exclaimed. "Then quick, let us remind them of it. Or are there no copies available?"

"There are millions of copies," the capon admitted. "But what you don't realize, my dear friend, is how these Christians have been able to twist and turn every verse of that book so that it is interpreted to mean just exactly what they wish. They have decided that this line means only that the blood and the flesh must not be eaten together, but can be eaten separately, and that anyhow when an animal is once killed the blood is no longer the life of it, so that one can do with the corpse what one pleases."

"Forgive me," said the pullet wanly, "but really I cannot follow you. You say on the one hand . . . and then on the other hand . . . It is all too much for me."

"My sweet pullet," said the capon quietly, "you must resign yourself. For this is far from being the only contradiction to be found amongst those monsters who pretend to be our friends and are really our eternal enemies. Human beings are forever making war and slaughtering each other, and you would be surprised to learn that these wars are always being fought for peace. And they are forever making laws for improving things, while at the same time they school lawyers who are forever finding new ways to outwit the very laws they make. Believe me, there are no subterfuges, no sophisms which they have not managed to discover in order to justify themselves for their endless injustices. One would think that God had given them speech only that they might the better conceal their thoughts.

"Just imagine that in this country where we live, and in several other countries where live people of the same belief, their own most sacred law orders that there be one day a week on which no flesh shall be eaten, on pain of eternal damnation. But in preparation for this one day vast hordes of men precipitate themselves on every ocean, every lake, every river, and kill millions of sea creatures, which, so it has been solemnly ruled, are not flesh—though what else could they be?—and therefore may be eaten without fear of going to hell. This they call fasting. Yes. And mortification of the flesh."

"Really, my mind whirls," murmured the pullet. "No, it can't be true. You have had a nightmare, my dear capon, and you have dreamed up these abominable creatures. Such sanguinary extravagances cannot actually exist."

"They exist," the capon said softly. "And indeed I am distressed to have to point out to you the proof of it. Look over there. What do you see?"

"Oh, no!" the pullet screamed. "Isn't that the scullion coming towards us with a long knife in his hand?"

"I'm afraid it must be so," the capon told her. "That extremely ignorant philosopher in whose barnyard we dwell no doubt has guests for dinner again. Guests who will tell him that the country is the scene of all innocence, and depravity exists only in the cities. It is another one of those ideas in a book which everyone is now reading, a book by a man who calls himself the Citizen of—"

"Don't talk!" the pullet cried. "Come, let us run!"

"What good?" the capon asked. "We are the weaker. And they are the stronger. Therefore our last hour has struck, and there is nothing we can do about it. Let us commend our souls to God."

"Must we really be eaten?" the pullet wept. "Then let the rascal who enjoys me be consumed with an indigestion that would burst the barrel of a cannon!"

"My dear," said the capon, "you talk now like all feeble souls. They think to avenge themselves against their oppressors with empty wishes, while those in power merely scoff and sneer."

"Very well, then," the pullet cried. "I pardon my enemies!"

"Little they care whether we pardon them or not!" said the capon, while Voltaire clutched at his own neck with one hand and with the other pretended to draw a knife across it.

"Farewell unto all eternity, my dear capon," the pullet breathed, as Voltaire let his head sink onto the table.

Then he straightened up, looked across the table, and said cheerfully, "I'm afraid that's the end of my little playlet." And he motioned to one of the lackeys to serve him some of the chicken.

Everybody stared with unbelieving eyes as Voltaire cut up into tiny pieces a little bit of chicken, preparing it for his almost toothless mouth.

Surely he was not going to eat chicken! Not right after his dialogue.

But he was. His fork caught up a few bits and put them into his mouth.

"Most succulent," he said. "Congratulations, my dear Madame Denis." And, looking around, pleased with himself, he said, "Fine nutty flavor."

They all stared at him as if frozen. While Voltaire smiled maliciously at them. "Eat, eat, my dear guests!" he encouraged them. And turned an especially broad grin toward the lover of Jean Jacques Rousseau, who, however, looked as if he would never again touch chicken in his life.

"I'm afraid," said this guest, "that I was more deeply affected by your performance than you yourself were."

"We took to heart," said a lady, "that verse from the Bible about which you spoke so movingly—God's law against the eating of flesh and blood. For myself, I don't believe I shall ever touch meat again in my life."

"The God of the Bible!" said Voltaire with scorn. "But what about the God who created the universe? What kind of world did He create for us? Is it the world that fool Jean Jacques Rousseau describes, where the countryside is the scene of peace? Have you ever seen a sheep grazing in a pasture? To Jean Jacques it may seem to be the very symbol of innocence. But can you imagine how many ants, worms, grubs, beetles, aphids that sheep is choking to death in his gullet, as he peacefully munches weeds and grass? Why, a tiger, with his jaws dripping with blood, is as innocent as a baby compared to that monstrous sheep!

"And as for my chickens, well, I shall certainly eat all of them I please. Do you imagine that they are so innocent? Why, the other day, when my trees were being devoured by caterpillars, what did I do? I ordered my peasants to shake the trees vigorously to make the caterpillars drop. And you should have seen the feast my chickens had under those trees, gobbling up those poor caterpillars. Can you conceive of the story those caterpillars might have told me of the cruelty of chickens, if I could have understood their language? For I am sure that caterpillars too object to being eaten. But then, I might ask them, why did they insist on eating up my trees?

"In this world, I am afraid, every living thing was created by God to devour some other living creature, and in turn be devoured by still another species. This is something we cannot hope to alter. And if only we human beings would stop murdering each other, I would be completely satisfied. I am not like your arrogant Jean Jacques, who expects to change everyone and everything."

It was at this point that one could hear the noise of a carriage on the cobblestones of the courtyard. And the chicken-eating guest, who was the only one so placed that by rising in his seat he could command a view from the window, exclaimed, "A guest so late! Yes. He is stepping out of his carriage. A foreigner. In some outlandish costume. Why, no! It can't be. Yes, it is! It's Rousseau, in his Armenian robes!"

"What?" Voltaire burst out. "Rousseau?"

"Yes," said the guest. "Now you will be able to tell him exactly what you think of his stupidity. Right to his face!"

"What? Scold that poor man?" Voltaire cried. "A man who has suffered so much? Madame Denis! The best room in the house for him. But bring him to me first, that I may embrace him."

Tears stood out suddenly in Voltaire's eyes.

But of course now the gentleman had to confess very humbly that it was all a hoax. Invented on the spur of the moment, when he had heard the noise of a carriage in the courtyard. But he had seen no one descend. It was just the grooms busy with their tasks. And he would have to beg Monsieur de Voltaire to forgive him for letting his momentary desire to get even drive him to this little deception.

And also his curiosity. To see how Monsieur de Voltaire would really conduct himself if he were brought suddenly face to face with his great philosophic opponent.

So there it was again. This time reported by the more authoritative Grimm, in his *Correspondance littéraire*. Another incident, which, if true, would show a feeling of kinship for Rousseau, a feeling of pity, in spite of all Voltaire's animosity.

Perhaps, if nothing else, that feeling of kinship which, in spite of himself, Voltaire—as the loyal opposition—had to feel toward Rousseau, the rebel. For are not these two, so to speak, father and son? Must not the one inevitably rise out of the other? The student always eventually oppose the master?

And precisely because of that kinship, must not love and hate here become both mixed and violent, such as could not happen except between close relatives?

32: NOT ANONYMITY, BUT FORGERY

Love? Hate? Yes, but which carried the day when Rousseau's *Letters from the Mountain* were published?

Those who were present would later relate how, when Voltaire ran across the paragraphs that referred to him, his body began to tremble, and he slammed the book to the floor and began to trample on it. While his eyes flashed fire and the veins on his forehead stood out like puff adders.

"Oh, the monster! The monster!" he cried.

Efforts were made to calm him. To remind him of his age. Recall to him the state of his nerves. The condition of his heart.

But nothing would cause him to moderate his fury as he picked up the torn book to read again that passage where Rousseau asks how it was that the members of the Magnificent Council of Geneva had not managed to imbibe any of Voltaire's well-known tolerance just from frequenting his company.

Surely [Rousseau wrote], Monsieur de Voltaire must, at some time or other, have spoken to you as follows:

"Gentlemen of the Council, inasmuch as I keep harping so much on the necessity of exercising tolerance, is it right that I should demand it of others and show so precious little of it myself? So let me now say a word in favor of tolerance for Jean Jacques Rousseau. It seems that in spite of all his criticism of the Gospels, the man is really steeped in religious reverence. Believes in Jesus Christ. Yes, deeply. Says that if the death of Socrates was that of a man, the death of Jesus was that of a god. That sort of thing.

"What of it? It's really no great crime to believe in Jesus. Of course, it does make him something of a bore, doesn't it? But then that's what often happens when a man insists on being not only logical but profound too.

"Just let's make sure never to have him at any of our supper parties. We'll continue to have our merry times, cracking our jokes, while he goes on trying to figure things out. And then, too, there are times—not too often, I assure you—when I myself try to be serious. As I did, for example, in my *Sermon of the Fifty* . . ."

Voltaire interrupted his reading of the passage in order to emphasize what he had just read: " 'As I did, for example, in my *Sermon of the Fifty.*' " And he screamed, "Do you see what he's done? He has me confessing that I wrote it!"

And he went back to his reading: " '. . . where, in spite of what Councilor Tronchin says in his *Letters from the Plain,* one does find a little more than occasional indiscretions against religion . . .' "

But that was more than Voltaire could take. He ripped the pages apart. "He dares stick me with that bit of blasphemous vomit! Yes, he publicly tags me with it—in a printed book, signed with his own name, so as to make certain that I shan't be able to deny it!"

And while those around him continued to try to restrain him, Voltaire bellowed, "Informer! Informer! So that's how far your jealousy of me drives you? To want to see me arrested! To want to see me burned at the stake! To see my head on the block and my fortune confiscated!"

He raved on and on: "Delator! Denunciator! Tool of the secret police! Spy! But let me warn you: If that's how far your jealousy goes, then I must take countermeasures! Yes, I must have you murdered. Do you hear? Murdered! In cold blood, by hired assassins! And I have the right to do so, you bloody scoundrel! For now it is your life against mine. And you will have to learn that I can be driven too far. That I too can strike!"

And he pushed away those who clung to him and who begged him to moderate himself. "Villain!" he screamed. "I shall have you strangled to death between the knees of that concubine housekeeper of yours. You sanctimonious hypocrite, you!"

How could he moderate himself? he asked those around him. How could he, when it was Jean Jacques who was betraying him? A writer to whom he had never shown anything but kindness. A writer who had once been a member, however obscure, of the philosophic coterie. Who had written articles for the *Encyclopedia!*

As far away as Paris, Voltaire's outcries against Rousseau were heard.

And d'Alembert wrote to Voltaire in great haste, pleading with him to avert a further split between the writers of France, who had need, more than ever, to be united.

"For God's sake," d'Alembert said, "if you feel that you absolutely must answer him—though I myself wish that you would choose the course of silence—at least let it be in a spirit of calmness, of dignity. What can you lose by taking this lofty stand? Doing, for example, nothing but publishing in juxtaposition all the fancy eulogies Rousseau once had for his fatherland, in the preface to his *Discourse on Inequality,* and all the ugly things he is now saying.

"Really, there's no end to his contradictions. But remember this: he suffers. I don't exactly know why. But that man is in pain, in terrible pain, and one must therefore forgive him certain things. Keep in mind how the Regent once replied to the governor of the Bastille, when the latter reported to him that one of the prisoners was really going too far in requesting an enema every single day. 'Shouldn't a stop be put to that?' the governor wanted to know. The Regent shook his head. 'Why deny it to him? Who knows? This may be the only pleasure he can still find in life.'

"My good Voltaire," d'Alembert concluded, "may I not urge upon you the kindness of the Regent?"

But Voltaire's fury was too great to consider Rousseau's informing as nothing more than the equivalent of a harmless propensity for enemas. In some way or other he had to give vent to the heat of his emotions. This man had irritated him long enough. And for the second time was bringing his life and his fortune into jeopardy.

The result was that anonymous brief of charges, in Wagnière's handwriting, filed with the prosecutor's office in Geneva. In which Voltaire turned informer on Jean Jacques, accusing him of the crimes of incredulity, of impiety, of blasphemy. Documenting it with references to Rousseau's *Letters from the Mountain*. And topping it off with a plea for the death penalty.

A shocking plea to come from Voltaire! Except that it was really quite harmless, and Voltaire knew it. For Rousseau was safe from any pursuit by the Genevan authorities, so long as he remained in Neuchâtel, in the realm of the King of Prussia.

So that this incident might have ended here, with no harm done, if a little volume had not just then come off the press, a little volume that had no justification for existence except one. A little volume grandiloquently entitled *The Complete Works of Voltaire* but actually only a random collection of a few old Voltairean pieces long available in many other editions.

With one exception, however: *The Sermon of the Fifty.* Yes, this pamphlet, condemned and burned by the public executioner in any number of cities, was here reprinted under Voltaire's name!

And who could be behind this new attempt to pin that work on Voltaire, if not Rousseau? For this volume came from the press of Rey of Holland, and Rey of Holland was Rousseau's favorite publisher, who had issued almost all of Rousseau's works. (In fact, just as much as Cramer of Geneva was known to be Voltaire's publisher, Rey of Holland was known to be Rousseau's.)

Who, then, but Rousseau could have put Rey up to this shabby trick?

Who else?

Well, that finishes it! No more pity now. No more harmless gestures. No more briefs that can be confidently left to gather dust in the files of some prosecutor who has no jurisdiction to act in the matter.

No! This calls for a genuine blow!

"Quick, Wagnière! A pamphlet!" We'll teach that dirty little informer a lesson that he will never forget. We'll stuff some of his own medicine down his throat! And see how he likes that!

But as Voltaire began to dictate in his usual nervous and lucid style, he paused.

Why? Wasn't informing on an informer justifiable? Could one afford to neglect a weapon which one's opponent did not scruple to use? Wasn't informing precisely what was called for here?

Yes. But didn't it drop one into the same slot as one's opponent? Depriving one of moral superiority? Opening one to the same charge?

Besides, would not the fanatic followers of Rousseau be inclined to discount at once everything that a Voltaire might have to say against their beloved Jean Jacques? The moment they recognized the pen of Voltaire—and that would be at the very first sentence—would they not toss the brochure aside?

And the mud Voltaire intended to cast on Rousseau—it would only splash on Voltaire's own face.

In order, then, to turn out a really effective piece of informing against Rousseau while seemingly remaining above such behavior, something more than Voltaire's usual anonymity would be required. Something more than his usual denials. This pamphlet would have to be written in such a way that its true authorship would never even be suspected. This time the anonymity would have to be perfect.

But how?

Could a Voltaire turn out something so utterly without Voltairean sparkle as to be unrecognizable? Devoid of all his usual facility and clarity of expression? With no trace of his rapid and captivating style —totally lacking in his infinite variety and ever bubbling humor?

Was that possible, for a man of whom it was said that he could not even write out a laundry list that would not somehow be engaging, instructive, amusing, poetic?

Yes, perhaps. If, for example, he assumed the character of a completely different person. Say that of an ardent and uncompromising Christian. Some narrow-minded, bigoted, orthodox Calvinist.

And perhaps better still: a man, who, in his righteous indignation against Jean Jacques, would drop his Parisian French, learned in school, and fall into all the errors of grammar and of spelling that Genevans tend to make.

Yes, that would do it. And, by God, there was the model right at hand. Lying on his desk. A recent work by the Reverend Jacob Vernes, long an enthusiastic friend of Rousseau's but now publicly taking a position opposed to him.

There was the man to imitate! For this would be a new kind of anonymity for Voltaire. One that did not point to him at all. But to someone else.

In short, not so much an anonymity as a forgery.

But forgery or not, Voltaire, after half a dozen pages of stodgy Calvinist orthodoxy refuting the Christianity of Jean Jacques Rousseau, went on to query, in wretched Genevan French:

Have not we Genevans had enough? When a man spits on our Lord Jesus Christ, when he goes so far as to say in print, "The Gospels are nothing but a pack of lies," and then has to escape from Catholic France, where his books are naturally being condemned, only to come into our neighborhood and there start splitting our good town into two camps, all on account of those wretched books of his, which of course we Calvinists have had to condemn, too, has not the time come for all of us to cry "Enough!"?

If he were just another impious author, of which our century is so cursed, one might consider chastising him lightly. But when he adds sedition to the rest of his follies, then is it not high time for patriots to raise the gallows?

For who is this fellow, anyhow, who thinks himself entitled to offend everyone—not only our citizens, but our Council and the very ministers of our churches, who are not only our friends but our consolers in our times of grief? Is he some scientist who upholds a learned thesis against other scientists? Is he a man of virtue, whose overzealousness has led him to make false charges against some of his fellow citizens?

No. He is no more than the author of an operetta—in addition to two plays that were hissed off the stage.

And more than that—blush though we must to put such things on paper —he is a man who will carry through life the disgusting marks of his early debauches. A man who dresses himself up like a clown, like a mountebank, and drags along with him from village to village that unfortunate creature whose mother he drove into her grave, and whose children he exposed on the steps of asylums for foundlings.

There! That last sentence ought to settle Jean Jacques for good and for all. Those last dozen words, "and whose children he exposed on the steps of asylums for foundlings"—they must crush him forever. Reduce him to silence and to dust!

Quick now, a message to Gabriel Cramer, Voltaire's loyal Geneva printer, to send a sure man or else come himself and pick up a very important, a very secret manuscript. One that must be set up in type immediately. This very night. With no one present but himself, or else his most reliable man. And then struck off without delay, and the sheets sewed with lightning speed.

And then distributed. With at least one copy—without the sender's name on the package—put into the mail at once. For "M. Jean Jacques Rousseau, at Motiers, in the Val-de-Travers."

33: NOT EXPOSED, BUT DEPOSED

Surely there could not have been anyone present when Jean Jacques tore off the wrapping of this pamphlet, so innocuously titled *The Sentiment of the Citizens*. For then there must surely have been left for us a record of how Jean Jacques, when he came to those last few words, crumpled to the floor, to lie there groaning and weeping and biting the flesh of his hands with all the fury and despair of a man gone mad. While Thérèse hovered over him, vainly trying to understand what ailed him.

All the record we have of his bitter grief is in his letters of the time. Letters where he conceals as much as he reveals. But from which we do know of his great pain. As when he writes to Duclos of Paris, "My dear Duclos, I cannot go on. My eyes are so swollen with tears that they are blind. Was there ever a man who had so many troubles strike him at one and the same time? Goodbye. I am in such pain I can hardly breathe."

From which it would seem that he must have had another attack of his bladder trouble at the same time, or at any rate have seized upon that as an excuse to justify his crawling into bed and there hiding himself from people. While wondering if there was any sense for him to go on living.

How could he ever face anyone again? Naked as he was. Shamed as he was. He, the man of virtue, revealed to the world as the man of sin. He, the reformer of everything, shown to stand in need of reformation himself.

Oh God, God! What would people say? He, the man who had been so severe on actors, shown to have been an actor himself. And what an actor! Playing his role for years. Convincingly. Deceptively. With more talent than any stage actor ever known.

He, the man who pretended to know better than anyone else how one must bring up children, now revealed as the man who refused to bring up his own at all.

He, who presumed to teach others the rights of the nursling to its mother's milk, shown to have been the most brutal of fathers, who had again and again torn his own babies from the breasts that he claimed they were entitled to!

The man of nature, think of it! The man of nature exposed as a most unnatural father!

The man who had so proudly taken for his motto "I dedicate my life to truth" exposed as a man who had, on the contrary, dedicated his life to a lie!

And Voltaire!

Good Lord, just the thought of Voltaire! For whom, after all, he had committed these crimes. Voltaire would surely read this vile thing. Someone would surely call his attention to it. Why, it was not impossible that he had already devoured it. That right now, this very

408

minute, he was gloating and chuckling and dancing, holding aloft this pamphlet and screaming, "Victory! Victory! Jean Jacques' hypocrisy, Jean Jacques' sophistry, long suspected, now fully confirmed!"

And utterly unthinkable now that one might kneel before him and unbosom oneself. Explaining to him how all this had happened. Out of such burning admiration for his works. Such love.

No. Everything finished. All the women to whom he had preached love of children and the necessity of suckling them at their own breasts, now turning from him in horror and contempt.

And Geneva? Geneva now a dead dream. Where his party of "representatives" must surely repudiate him. And in fact curse him. And join with his enemies to demand that he be put to death if ever he dared show his sanctimonious and hypocritical face in their city.

For would not the opposing party now have an irrefutable document to produce against him? Namely, that affidavit he had given years ago, when he had come to regain his citizenship. And where he had sworn that the condition of his organs was such that sexual intercourse with his nurse Thérèse was impossible.

And now there he was, exposed as a perjurer. Shown up as a man who didn't scruple to lie to the cloth. Before Jesus and the Bible.

And think of the consequences! Right here in Motiers, for example. Where one could already envisage what must take place. How the minister, Montmoulin, must turn from him in horror and preach sermons against him. Rousing the countryside to conspue him. Making it impossible for him or Thérèse to even show their faces out of doors.

Good God, what should he do? What hole could he crawl into? What land could he flee to where this pamphlet would not eventually reach out to point a finger at him? Was there anything left for him now except the grave?

Oh, who could have done this terrible thing to him: "those eight pages," as he would later speak of them, "that were not printed with ink, but with flames of hell."

Who could possibly have done it? Of the six or seven people who knew his secret, surely it could not be the men who had given him away. Not Grimm. Not Diderot. Not Duclos. No. Men do not betray each other. Not when they have been in this thing together. He could tell tales about them too, could he not? About Grimm and that actress. And about Klüpfel, Grimm's closest friend, and that young girl, barely twelve years old, whom they had all visited. Taking turns going into her room, where that poor child was held like a prisoner . . .

No. Men don't tell on each other.

And as for the women, neither Thérèse nor her mother would have told. Nor poor Madame de Francueil, dead these many years. Nor Madame de Luxembourg, who had wept along with him when, thinking he was about to die, he had sobbed out the story of his sins. No, she could not have told on him either.

Which left only Madame d'Épinay. But even she—would she have dared? Considering all that he knew about her? The scandal of her relations with various men, and the ugly disease she had caught and passed on to M. de Francueil. And even worse things, which he had threatened to reveal long ago if she ever forced him to it.

Still, if it was she, what a revenge he would take for this destruction of his life! He would tear down her life, too, yes, when it came time for him to tell everything. For now she had left him no choice: he would have to tell the story of his life. He would have to write his long-contemplated *Confessions*. Which his publisher Rey was urging him to write, anyhow. But which he would have to do quickly now, before he died of grief. Before he went mad!

Oh, how could anyone have been so cruel as to ruin his life? Wreck everything he had built up at such cost, such pain, such exertion, such unending labor! Who could have been so low and mean?

Had he not, so to speak, made a personal appeal to everyone who might know his secret? Had he not inserted in his *Émile* those few lines—which surely they must all have noticed, for if only one of them had, then that one must have called the attention of the others to it— where he had written, "He who cannot fulfill his duties as a father has no right to become one. For neither the excuse of poverty nor the press of duties can dispense one from the duty of feeding and raising one's children."

Ought that not to have sufficed to show that he had reformed? That he repented all his old sins?

And to make the matter thoroughly clear to them, had he not added, "Believe me, dear reader, when I tell you that whosoever has bowels of pity and has neglected these sacred duties, he is sure to weep often and bitterly over his sin and indeed never find consolation."

Could anything be clearer? Even too clear. Dangerously close to self-betrayal. And yet he had written that. So that those who knew his secret would take pity on him. For whom could he have meant by those words "dear reader" except those old friends of his who alone would have been able to understand the exact meaning of that sentence?

Was it not, in fact, as if he had got down on his knees before them? Crying out to them his remorse. Begging them, "Please, oh, please do not seek to punish me any further. I am punished enough by my own conscience. Can you not see how I suffer? How racked with pain my body is?"

But there had been one of them who had had no pity. And who had now betrayed him.

What was there to say now? How could he excuse himself to the world?

Poverty? But were there not millions in France who were poorer by far than he had ever been, and who had nevertheless brought up their children? Why, the very beggars of Paris, twenty thousand of them, behaved better than he. And one could see among them many a beggar woman in rags who nevertheless clutched to her bosom her precious baby, and who would have fought you like a wild beast if you had dared deprive her of it.

Besides, how would he explain the fact that even after the success of his operetta, *The Village Soothsayer,* when he certainly hadn't lacked for money, and a royal pension was even being held out to him, he didn't give his Thérèse the right to keep her offspring?

The custom of the times? Yes. But not so much so that millions didn't do otherwise. In fact, the large majority. Who raised their families as of old, despite what some small fraction might term the "custom" of the day.

Or the stubborn "I would do it again" with which he had justified himself in his code letter to Madame de Francueil? After his reform. After selling his watch, his wig, his gold frogging and his sword, when he could no longer plead the custom of his times. And instead took refuge with Plato. Plato, who, in his *Republic,* wanted all children brought up by the state. With equality. And simplicity. So that they would become strong, healthy farmers, laborers, artisans. Not fortune hunters. Or petty thieves, like the relatives of Thérèse.

No, that would not do, either. For it could be shown to him that, far from being brought up with equality and raised to be strong and healthy, the children of the foundling home simply went to their death. That putting them into the care of that institution was nothing but a convenient, "clean-hands" form of infanticide, so enormous was the death rate. Not one out of twenty children surviving the dubious care of that asylum.

Surely that was not what Plato had meant!

No. That excuse would not hold up, either. And certainly not the claim (which in any case he would not now dare to utter) that it was Voltaire's own fault, for having written books that had ignited in Jean Jacques such a yearning for glory.

And least of all that other unmentionable excuse: the dark stirrings of jealousy in him that would have made it absolutely intolerable to see the breasts of his Thérèse pre-empted by hungry mouths that had a better right to them than his own lips.

No. No excuses. No justifications. Snared by his own labyrinthine contradictions. Just as he had been trapped years ago in those black cellars of Turin, after he had been driven by mysterious forces to exhibit his naked bottom near the fountain where the girls gathered. Only a lie had been able to save him then: his convincing acting out of the role of a prince gone mad.

Or that other time, when, as a lackey, he had stolen a beautiful silver-and-rose ribbon and, being discovered in possession of it, had found no way out but to accuse a pretty little servant girl of having given it to him. Acting out that lie with such skill and effrontery that the girl was discharged as the thief!

Well, if he could save himself then by acting out a lie, why could he not do it again?

Surely there was some way out.

Where was that damned pamphlet, anyhow? Let us examine it. In the first place, who could have written it? A clergyman, obviously. So much was clear. And a Genevan. That too was easy, considering the miserable French of it. But which clergyman? Not Roustan. He was still sticking to Jean Jacques. Nor Montmoulin, even though he wasn't. Nor Moultou. He had too much honor. But perhaps Sarrasin. Or, even more likely, Vernes.

Yes, Vernes! That was exactly his style! Like the letters that Vernes used to send him. Or the book he had recently written. Why, that book was right here!

No doubt of it. That was his man! His former good friend Jacob Vernes!

And now that he knew who his opponent was, now that he was reading the pamphlet again, especially those terrible final lines of it, it seemed to him that it might not be so difficult to refute a Vernes. Taking advantage of the places where the man had gone too far.

In fact, there were at least five errors in this pamphlet. Which, being vigorously attacked, might make the thing look as if it were positively riddled with lies!

And so, as fast as he could, Rousseau affixed a few lines to the pamphlet and sent it off to a publisher in Paris. To Duchesne. Who immediately agreed to print it, since, with Jean Jacques's notes, it became a Rousseau item instead of a Vernes one and would sell off fast.

As for Rousseau's remarks, they were very brief. In fact, so brief as to constitute by their very size a kind of expression of contempt, for both the author and his work. The whole thing not really worthy of any extended comment.

Starting off with scorn for Jacob Vernes, for attempting to conceal his identity by leaving off his name. And then pointing out, "It is hardly from Geneva, a city where I have so many enemies, that the reader should expect to hear the truth about Jean Jacques Rousseau."

That is to say, cleverly slipping past the question of whether the pamphlet did or did not have any truth to it. In order to concentrate on the seemingly related question—though actually it had no bearing on the matter at all—of whether the reader might expect the truth about Rousseau to come from a Genevan.

And going on quickly to the next error: the matter of Rousseau's pox. Which, being utterly without foundation, was naturally the occasion for Rousseau to mount a truly formidable show of denial, attacking it with attitudes of noble indignation, as well as long lists of witnesses, plus challenges for a public hearing, and so on.

"Never," he wrote, "have any of the shameful diseases mentioned by the author soiled my body. As for my present afflictions, I was born with them, as people still living can testify. The nature of my suffering is known also to the following physicians, all of whom have examined me at various times: Doctors Malouin, Morand, Côme, Daran, Thiery, whom I here and now entreat to speak up and denounce me if ever they found on me any indications of a life of debauchery."

And then proudly on to error number three: "As for the respectable and well-behaved woman who nurses me in my infirmities and consoles me in my afflictions, thus being unfortunate only in sharing the fate of an unfortunate man, her mother was not only never driven into her grave by me, but is in fact alive at this moment. And even, considering her advanced age, in good health."

And so quickly on to the next point. For no use lingering here to explain that one of the misfortunes which this "respectable and well-behaved woman" had had to share with him concerned precisely the matter of those abandoned children! But that too Jean Jacques would manage to deny.

"Never—" so he wrote, and so it was printed—"never have I ex-

413

posed, or caused to be exposed, any children of mine at the door of any hospital or any other place!"

Which was really bold! And that last phrase "or any other place" especially brilliant. For though no other place had been even brought up by Vernes, by such a sweeping assertion Rousseau seemed to wipe the whole accusation off the face of the earth. Forever!

Taking advantage of nothing but the fact that Vernes had made the fatal error of accusing him of having *ex*posed his children. And to expose children means to do what the ancients used to do—namely, throw children out to die from cold, or from hunger, or from wild animals. Which is the dictionary meaning of *"ex*pose," isn't it?

So no need to mention the fact that Jean Jacques had *de*posed his children.

But now for a final fling at Vernes—the fatal fifth error: the lack of charity in this man of the cloth. To which Rousseau would administer this stinging little apostrophe: "I have nothing further to say here, except that I would rather have been guilty of the crimes charged against me in this pamphlet (short of murder) than have demonstrated so little charity as to write it!"

That was telling the man! And now he could relax. Now he could breathe freely again. Now he could recover his poise.

But not completely. No. For this had been a terrible jolt. And far from having nothing further to say, he would on the contrary have lots more to say. The whole of his several-volume *Confessions* would, in a sense, be his answer to this Voltairean pamphlet.

And far from wanting rather to be guilty of these crimes, he would, on the contrary, suffer endlessly from them. As, for example, once in his old age, while walking in Paris, when he would suddenly find his leg gripped and, looking down, would see a little toddler who had clamped chubby arms around his calf. Such agony would traverse his body at that moment that he would go home in tears and write of the love of a little boy that might have been his, if only . . . if only . . .

But now, for at least a moment or two, he felt better. Though the question of who had betrayed him, the question of where the enemy might strike next and the question of what effect his denial would have on Diderot and Grimm and Madame d'Épinay—all these questions would continue to harass him.

But now, for at least a moment or two, he had the right to feel better. He had lied, yes, but it was only in order to give himself time. And time he had to have in order to write his *Confessions* and in order to fight his battle against those who not only didn't understand him but didn't want to understand him. The ones who had hardened their hearts against him. The d'Épinays and the Grimms and the Diderots and so forth, who would no doubt be all the more confirmed in their opinion that he was a monster.

Well, let them think what they pleased. Fortunately the final judge of man's actions would be not the philosophic coterie of Paris, but God. And before God he would someday place his book, the book that would explain his whole life. And he had no doubt that this book would win him his rightful place in heaven.

"For the man of sin," he would write later, "at least knows repentance, which no one else can know. And there are repentances so profound, so precious, that they more than compensate for any sin."

And he would also write, "The greater one's fault, the more sublime one's admission of it!"

Matters that only a sinner can know! And in that respect the sinner has a right to feel a certain contempt for those who have never fallen. Those who are sinless largely for the reason that they have never really lived.

For if not as a saint, then as a sinner—one way or another—he would justify himself. Make his life count.

But these considerations were for later. For the moment he wanted to have copies of his reprinted pamphlet. Then let his visitors broach the subject—if they dared! And he would either treat them with righteous indignation or dismiss the whole subject with an airy reference to his published reply.

And, if necessary, stuff a copy of his pamphlet into the visitor's hand.

"There! Now you have my answer!" he could say. And add, "Do you know anyone else who has dared to reprint a pamphlet that attacks him? Give it even wider circulation than it might have had?"

He felt so proud of it that later, in England, when prodded by other articles and pamphlets, he would point to what he had done in the case of *The Sentiment of the Citizens,* to show how much he scorned such scurrilous literature. As if to say to it, "Do your worst. I am not afraid of calumny."

But suddenly a new blow pounded home—an angry communication from Jacob Vernes: "What do you mean by accusing me of having written a filthy pamphlet which, as a matter of fact, I never laid eyes on before I saw your reprint of it! What do you mean by writing that you would rather have committed certain crimes than show lack of charity? Is that what *you* call charity—blaming me without any evidence? I ask you, would not the charitable thing have been to communicate with me first before smearing my name all over Europe?"

Startled, Rousseau wrote back, "I have ordered the sale of the pamphlet discontinued."

To which Vernes replied bitterly: "Yes, now that one edition is already exhausted. And now that everyone concerned in this matter is already convinced that I am the author of an anonymous pamphlet. Now tell me, you with all your charity, what are you going to do to restore my good name? Yes, what are you going to do, you who are so concerned about your own good name?"

Rousseau was flabbergasted. If not Vernes, then who? No, everything he had done had depended on his absolute conviction that Vernes was the guilty one. That had been the keystone of it! So, to the delegates who came to see him on Vernes's behalf, Rousseau felt he had to take a firm stand.

"What does he expect me to do?" Rousseau asked angrily. "Isn't that his style of writing? Isn't that his wretched French? Isn't that completely in his character? But, of course, if he can prove his innocence, I will go and throw myself at his feet."

"So! You will throw yourself at my feet—if I prove my innocence!" Vernes retorted furiously. "Is it not rather up to you to prove my guilt? Must I teach the great Rousseau, the great moralist, the most fundamental principles of ethics? You pretend you can teach the world how to conduct itself, and you don't even know what every schoolboy knows: that a man must not be asked to prove his innocence. It is guilt that must be demonstrated."

As their quarrel grew hotter, someone threw in an even more disturbing thought: "Why don't you apologize to him, my dear Jean Jacques?"

"Apologize? Are you mad?" Rousseau flung back.

"But can't you see how all this bickering must delight Voltaire? In fact, is it not likely that it was he, not Vernes, who tossed this apple of discord among us, so that we should have this falling out?"

Rousseau was stunned. "Voltaire?" The thought had never occurred to him. Never.

"But can you think of anyone else who stands to profit so much from it?" he was asked.

In a flash Rousseau realized that if Voltaire had indeed written this pamphlet, then there would be really terrible conclusions that would have to be drawn. Far too terrible!

"Ridiculous!" he cried. "This miserable pamphlet from the most elegant pen of our century? Anyone who says that has obviously no taste for literature. No sense of discrimination. Can you really see Monsieur de Voltaire using up six pages out of an eight-page pamphlet for a stupid defense of orthodox Calvinism? Can you see Monsieur de Voltaire, the foremost playwright of our day, putting scientists ahead of authors of plays, as here? Can you see Monsieur de Voltaire using such crass Genevan spellings as *'quinze cent,'* without an *s* to *'cent'?"*

"Why not, if his purpose was precisely that—to deceive you?" was the answer.

Rousseau faltered. To deceive me? But he quickly became confident again. "Come now, gentlemen, don't make me laugh. What, this flatfooted piece of writing from Monsieur de Voltaire? Never will you get me to believe that!"

Of course not. Never would he permit anyone to make light of Voltaire's talents. You could say whatever you liked against Voltaire, but never that he wasn't still the best writer of his times. Why, even in his letter of hate Rousseau had assured Voltaire that he could never stop admiring his genius. After all, who had been Jean Jacques's model for years, if not Voltaire? For variety of style, for clarity of expression, for tightness and pace, for boldness of thought.

No, sir, Vernes was not going to slip out of this by casting aspersions on Voltaire!

Though of course, considered purely from the question of who stood to derive most satisfaction from this pamphlet, it had to be admitted that it could well be the work of Voltaire.

But that brought one up sharply against a most frightful possibility. For who could have told Voltaire about the dark secret of Rousseau's life? And when?

Madame d'Épinay. Obviously.

Madame d'Épinay, when, six years ago, she had begged her "bear" to accompany her to Geneva. And he had refused. And she, furious, had gone off without him. Hating him. And therefore betraying him. Betraying him during those months in Geneva under Dr. Tronchin's care, when she had been an almost constant guest at Voltaire's.

But think of what such a supposition meant! That for six years— for six long years!—Voltaire had been in possession of this dreadful secret. And had never said a word. Not a word!

Just think of it! Voltaire sparing him!

Voltaire sparing him again and again. Voltaire holding this gun in hand, pointed at Rousseau's heart and loaded with a bullet that could not miss, and still never pressing the trigger.

Was that believable? Of Voltaire? His enemy?

And in spite of every provocation offered to him by Rousseau? Sparing him in spite of the *Letter to d'Alembert* that had forced Voltaire to leave his home in Geneva, the home which he had called Les Délices and about which he had written poems, so much did he love it.

Sparing him in spite of the fortune it had cost Voltaire to leave that house and establish himself elsewhere. And in spite of the attacks that Rousseau had made on the acting profession, a profession which Voltaire adored and which was already under constant attack from the Church.

And in spite of Rousseau's constant sniping at Voltaire's philosophic coterie, whose arguments, he declared, he would "crush like lice." And doing this at a time when the *Encyclopedia* was already in danger of suppression.

And in spite of his involvement with Madame d'Houdetot, with its odious reflections thus cast on Voltaire's greatest love affair.

And in spite of his quarrel with Voltaire over the Lisbon earthquake. In spite of his "I hate you" letter. In spite of all the names he had called Voltaire in his communications to the pastors of Geneva: "clown, puppet master, juggler, Inquisitor," and so forth. And his repeated prophecy that "the refugee Voltaire, who obtained asylum in Geneva," would end up by "destroying that generous city." A remark that had infuriated Voltaire, who, with his millions and his powerful friends, considered it a defamation to call him a "refugee" or any city which he had freely chosen for his residence an "asylum."

Yes, sparing him, in spite of all that. Voltaire ridiculing him, yes. Criticizing him. Making sport of him. But never killing him. As he might have done all along.

But then, God help us, Voltaire might have been sincere—utterly sincere—when in those letters of his he had begged Rousseau to come to Switzerland. To come and live with him.

And sincere when he had written, "Please believe me, my dear Rousseau, that though I may often be guilty of jokes and sarcasm of questionable taste, of all those who read you none is more disposed to love you tenderly than your ever humble servant Voltaire."

And those rumors, those fantastic rumors, of a Voltaire who really loved him—they might be neither ridiculous nor fantastic, but true! And the tears he was said to have wept when he heard of Jean Jacques's misfortunes—they might have been genuine.

And he might have been telling the truth when he declared to people that he had had nothing to do with the burning of Rousseau's books in Paris, in Geneva, in The Hague, in Bern and elsewhere.

And more than that! It meant that year after year, at any time that Jean Jacques might have chosen to avail himself of it, that great man's house had stood open to him. And he needed no excuse, no justification, no period of trial during which he had to make himself worthy of that man's esteem to enter and cast himself at Voltaire's feet!

And Voltaire might—no, would, yes, would indeed—have lifted him up tenderly and embraced him as a son. As an equal.

But no! That far Rousseau wouldn't go. That much he refused to believe. For then the tragedy would be too vast, wouldn't it? All those years wasted, during which Voltaire's arms had been open to him! But now the opportunity gone.

Gone. Yes, of course gone! Now, after he had written and published those insulting words, "I have nothing further to say here, except that I would rather have been guilty of the crimes charged against me in this pamphlet . . . than have demonstrated so little charity as to write it!"

Charity! Charity! And meanwhile on whose side had the charity been? Who was the man who had been sparing him time and time again, while he, Rousseau, had, on the contrary, never missed an occasion to show that he had no charity whatsoever toward Voltaire?

And something still meaner, still nastier, was to be seen in that note to the pamphlet. The most disgraceful kind of hair-splitting. Rousseau descending to a cheap little pun on the words "expose" and "depose," in order to exculpate himself. Taking the most cowardly and deceitful sort of advantage of an error on Voltaire's part, an error so slight that it consisted of only two letters, in order to deny his guilt.

And handing this evidence of the smallness of his character to Voltaire. So that Voltaire now knew him through and through. Knew him as he might know a tiny insect stuck under a microscope. Knew him as he knew the snails and the slugs he experimented with. Knew him down to his last bit of pettiness and cowardice. Knew him as a man who claimed in public that he wanted no fame, desired only obscurity, whereas in fact he would lie, he would calumniate, he would even kill—yes, even kill his own children (and how those mendacious words "short of murder" now burned like drops of aqua regia, excoriating him). Whereas in fact there was nothing—nothing!—that he would not do for fame. Not short of murder. But murder included!

Oh, if only it were possible to recall that brief note, of which only

419

recently he had been so proud. Delete it from the records! Erase it. Expunge it. So that Voltaire should have no reason now to hold him in utter contempt. As something not even worth spitting on.

Great God! To have lived all those years so near to the peak of his desires, and to have missed it. In fact, to have become aware only now of what he had missed—now, when it was too late. Irretrievably too late.

And no longer any way out. No room for cleverness. Not now any more. No fatal error to be attacked with consummate slyness. Nothing left but madness.

No. Not even that. For now he was not trapped by a cul-de-sac in a cellar. Not trapped by the possession of a stolen ribbon. But trapped by himself. And within himself. And though he had written that "the finest subtleties of thought that the human brain is capable of come from our practice of bargaining with our own conscience"—and who but he could know the truth of that so well?—this time there was no subtlety so subtle that he could manage to deceive himself with it.

For the first time in his life he saw himself through and through—not just naked, but transparent—and what he saw he could not help but despise.

A gutter cur! Covered with his own vomit!

He hated himself at this moment so intensely that he could have murdered himself. Out of sheer stomach-upheaving self-disgust.

But precisely because of this furious hatred for himself, he could not help feeling a twinge of pity too. For himself. For this creature that was so utterly forlorn. So utterly cast out. So utterly without a single friend. Not even himself.

So that within this faint pity there even began to flicker a tiny bit of love. A new tenderness for himself. Glowing like a taper in a dark storm. Because he was spurned by everyone. Including himself.

And because he was a finished man. Who had nothing more to look forward to, except his death. For what could he hope to accomplish now in Geneva? With this thing hanging over him. With Voltaire holding that note in his hands, and able to use it as a weapon any time he chose. Revealing Rousseau as not just an ordinary liar, but one of the most devious and arrogant liars of all history.

34: THE WATCHMAKER OF GENEVA

Such were the reasons for Rousseau's sudden and amazing turnabout that left his followers openmouthed: advising them hereafter, in the battle for Geneva, no longer to look to him for guidance.

"But to whom, then?" they asked.

"Why not to Monsieur de Voltaire?" he suggested.

"To Voltaire?" they exclaimed. "To our worst enemy?"

They were stupefied. Had their leader gone out of his mind? Some laughed, and others were embarrassed. But Rousseau continued stubbornly to argue for M. de Voltaire.

And later, when he learned that no one had even made a move to consult Voltaire, he wrote to one of his closest friends in Geneva, to d'Ivernois:

I am distressed to learn that you have still not been to see M. de Voltaire. Was it because you thought I would be upset thereby? Ah, how little you understand my heart. I tell you, if God, working through that illustrious man, should bring an end to Geneva's troubles, then you would see me forgetting all the ways in which he has wronged me. You would see me dedicating my life, with unmixed feelings, to expressing my admiration for him.

Go, then, to M. de Voltaire. And give him all your confidence. He is, in fact, your only resource. Believe me, he will not betray you. Why should he, when, by saving you, he can only add to his glory? And if he does save you, then he may continue to harm me as much as he pleases, and I will not cease wishing for his happiness and his eternal fame until I draw my last breath.

Could anyone, even Voltaire, ask for a more abject surrender? True, instead of flinging himself at Voltaire's feet he was flinging his followers. But in any case, what was Voltaire's response?

A poem. One of the most vicious ever written. Which, in handwritten copies, began to circulate rapidly from person to person. An anonymous poem, of course, but one whose origin could not possibly be in doubt for a single minute, since it could only have come from a clever versifier who was at the same time maliciously and vindictively disposed toward Rousseau. And who could that be but the same master of rhymes who had tossed off the terrible *La Crépinade* against that other Rousseau, Jean Baptiste. Who else?

A poem picturing Rousseau and Thérèse as monsters out of some dreadful nightmare, two frightful skeletal abortions haunting the dark rocks and forests of the Val-de-Travers. Catching them just as they were moving into an act of sexual embrace. But what a sexual embrace! A performance of gargoyles, in which love had no part whatsoever. Hate taking its place.

> *L'aversion pour la terre et les cieux*
> *Tient lieu d'amour à ce couple odieux.*
> *Si quelquefois, dans leurs ardeurs secrètes,*
> *Leurs os pointus joignent leurs deux squelettes,*
> *Dans leurs transports ils se pâment soudain*
> *Du seul plaisir de nuire au genre humain.*

Showing how, in the ardor of their grotesque fornication, it was only the thought of the harm they were wreaking on the human race that enabled them to ignite their loathsome passion into a climax of raucous delight.

It was as if this horrible poem (later to be part of the third canto of Voltaire's *Civil War in Geneva*) gave all Val-de-Travers the signal for a free-for-all against Rousseau. With M. de Montmoulin, the pastor, hurling fiery sermons every Sunday from his pulpit. So that little boys were encouraged to run hooting after Thérèse with foul words in their fresh little mouths.

And Rousseau, when he went on his walks, imagined that he heard farmers, as he passed in the distance, crying to their wives, "Quick, my gun, so that I may take a shot at that blasphemer who dared soil our good church with his presence!"

And at night, despite the guard ordered thrown about the house by King Frederick, rocks would hurtle against the shutters of Rousseau's bedroom window.

Until it was finally too much for him. And, stricken to the core, he fled. Leaving Thérèse to pack as quickly as possible and join him. Fled to an uninhabited island in the nearby Lake of Bienne. Thinking that surely no one would mind his living in this unwanted, isolated spot.

But now he was once again on Bernese territory. And Their Excellencies were in no mood to tolerate this troublemaker who had caused the citizens of Geneva to rise in rebellion in order to win back their right to govern.

They ordered him to leave within two weeks.

So that scarcely had a bit of peace begun to creep back into his soul than Jean Jacques was forced to get his belongings together again and move on.

Plaintively he wrote to the bailiff at Nidau:

Isn't it too late in the year to send a homeless man out into the cold? And where am I to find a country that will accept me, now that my books have been burned in so many places? Would it not be a kindness, then, on the part of Your Excellencies, if a prison could be found for me—some castle in whose dungeon I could spend the rest of my life?

If it is a question of expense, let me assure you that I have enough money to pay for all my modest needs until my death. And I give you herewith my word of honor nevermore to be of any trouble to anyone. In fact, if it will set your minds more at ease, I will even consent to be deprived of paper and pencil and never write another line in my life. Let me keep only a few books. That is all I ask for—that and the opportunity of walking in a garden now and then.

Voltaire burst into laughter when he heard the details of this letter of despair received by the authorities of Bern. "This advocate of freedom for everyone," he cried, "this apostle of liberty, prefers a prison for himself!" And the idea was so amusing to him that he laughed himself into a fit of coughing.

As for Their Excellencies, they simply repeated their order that Rousseau leave immediately. And the author, once more abandoning to Thérèse the task of following him as best she could with books and manuscripts and other baggage, left for Strasbourg, not certain whether he would accept an invitation to go to England or another one bidding him come to Potsdam. As for Holland, to which country his publisher, Rey, had urged him to come, that was out now, ever since a recent decision to burn his books there too.

He reached the city of Basel, one night and sat alone at a table in an inn, and was overcome there with the thought of his misfortunes.

If only, years ago, he had not had that overpowering vision of a humanity enjoying life as God had meant us to enjoy it! If only he had never had that dazzling view of the true road destined for man. And from which we had so stupidly wandered. Spending our lives in the accumulation of money, of honors, of power, of possessions.

And thus missing out on the truly great experiences of life: The sense of freedom. The wonder of nature. The joy of love. The acquisition of useful knowledge.

He began to weep softly to himself, thinking of what this mighty moment of intuition had cost him: children, friends, position, wealth, everything—everything sacrificed in the hope of bringing man back to a better understanding of himself.

And Voltaire sacrificed, too.

Sadly, with the prong of a fork, he scratched on the table: "Jean Jacques Rousseau—outlawed, in flight, sick." A line that, years later, would still be pointed out proudly to guests and to visitors.

Soon, however, Rousseau began to feel himself somewhat restored. For he encountered evidence that his reputation had not really suffered so much after all. The recent news of his being hounded out of Motiers, the news of his desperate appeal for a prison cell in which to spend the rest of his miserable life—all that had served only to stimulate popular sympathy for him. And in city after city, as the report of the direction of his flight preceded him, increasing numbers of admirers gathered to greet him.

Were not these large crowds his most effective answer to Voltaire? Who could deny him this? How could one argue with this visible proof? And yet he was not completely at ease with these people. As if he suspected that, did they but know the truth, they might rend him limb from limb.

"No need to pity Rousseau any more," said Saint-Lambert in Paris. "He's taking a trip with his favorite mistress—fame."

But Rousseau was still troubled by the question of where to go, whether to Germany or to England. England seemed so far away. So strange and so cold. But on the other hand, Germany, with Frederick the Great—did that not bring him somehow all the more surely into the power of Voltaire?

It took repeated urgings from powerful friends to persuade Rousseau to accept the invitation of the philosopher and historian David Hume to go to England. And it was only when they took steps to secure for him a royal safe-conduct through France in order to meet Hume that Rousseau came to a decision. Very well, then. England it would be. Free England would henceforth be his home!

And when the two men met in Paris, what a scene! Those two great thinkers of their time, Hume and Rousseau, falling into each other's arms and weeping unrestrainedly. That is to say, Rousseau doing most of the weeping. Hume being far too phlegmatic to show more than a trace of moisture. Nevertheless, the whole city (with the exception of Diderot, d'Alembert, Madame du Deffand and so forth, that is to say those who might be considered followers of Voltaire) deeply affected.

Rousseau was once again so much the rage that, at the Temple, where the Prince de Conti gave him lodgings, he had to hold regular audiences, in a most imposing study, luxuriously furnished, with a valet to lead the visitors in one by one. Rousseau announcing that he would be visible from nine to twelve every morning, and again from six to nine in the evening. And to save time, the sculptor Lemoyne worked away at a bust of him while the audiences went on.

And the mob continuing so thick that Hume cried (in a letter to his friend Blair of Scotland), "Voltaire is eclipsed totally!"

And he reported so many people trying to push money into his hands to be given to poor Rousseau that if Jean Jacques had only relaxed his rule about gifts he might easily have counted on a fortune of fifty thousand pounds sterling. Enough to have made him a very wealthy man for the rest of his days.

And in England, when he was temporarily settled in Chiswick, just outside London, the mobs began again, coming from London every day in numbers that overwhelmed him. So that there was nothing to do but seek out a more remote place where he could devote himself to his memoirs.

And meanwhile he wrote to all his correspondents what a wonderful man Hume was. And how he had finally found in him a man of truth, like himself, with whom his friendship would be everlasting.

An everlasting friendship? With Rousseau? This was nothing less than a challenge to that philosophic coterie that for years had been pointing out Rousseau's inability to keep a single friend. Cynically they began to take bets as to how long this friendship with Hume would last.

While Voltaire, practical as usual, in order to make sure of the desired outcome, decided that the people of Britain ought to be better informed than they seemed to be about this great writer whom the English were taking to their bosom.

Did they have any idea how many ridiculous and contradictory remarks that man had made in his books? Did they have any notion how many insulting arguments he had raised against the English people, their government and their religion?

"Quick, Wagnière! A pamphlet!"

And, leafing rapidly through Rousseau's works, Voltaire began to cull out everything Jean Jacques had ever penned that might make him offensive to the British public. Such observations, for example, as Rousseau's statement that the people of England only imagined themselves to be free. While actually being slaves. And that the British nation was headed for certain collapse because of its greedy accumulation of wealth.

And as for the English women, Voltaire said, they would certainly want to have a look at this curious creature who openly declared that they had no business going to the theater, or being interested in the arts. That their duties were in the kitchen and in the nursery. Their only purpose in life being to make their husbands happy!

All of which Voltaire pasted together in a clever and stinging satire, which he called *Letter to Dr. Pansophe*. That is to say, to Dr. Know-it-all. And lest anyone be in any doubt as to who this Dr. Know-it-all might be, Voltaire gave him the initials J. J.

Translated into English, this letter was sold and distributed by the thousands and was widely excerpted by the press. And everywhere under the name of Mr. de Voltaire. Despite that gentleman's repeated protests that he had had nothing to do with it. Abbé Coyer being the author. As everyone ought to be able to see at a glance.

Which was by way of working in a little mischief for Abbé Coyer. Along with Rousseau. Nothing like killing two birds with one stone. Because this abbé, after a long visit to the home of Voltaire, had expressed his gratitude to his host in the following terms: "The three months I have spent with you have been the most rewarding of my life. I therefore propose to return here every year for a similar delightful visit."

To which the frightened Voltaire had retorted, "Really, you flatter me too much, my dear Abbé. But, by the way, do you happen to know the difference between yourself and Don Quixote?"

"No," the puzzled abbé had replied, "I don't."

"Then you must let me explain it to you without beating about the bush. Don Quixote, you will undoubtedly recall, was in the habit of mistaking inns for castles. And you are about to fall into the habit of mistaking my castle for an inn."

This rebuff the poor abbé had been forced to swallow. But that didn't mean that he had to stand by while Voltaire forced this corrosive pamphlet on him. And he protested so vociferously that Voltaire felt compelled to saddle a minor writer named Charles Borde with it. To whom he now wrote:

"So it's you, eh? You who got out that witty *Letter to Dr. Pansophe*. And you let me go on thinking it was Abbé Coyer. But of course I shouldn't have been so stupid as not to realize that you were in England just when that bitch-dog of a Diogenes landed there, and that you would not so soon forget the argument you had with Rousseau years ago over his *Discourse on the Arts and Sciences* . . ."

As for Rousseau, how could he possibly have any doubts as to who had written the *Letter?* Wasn't there a reference in it to Dr. Pansophe's "Jesuitical" skill in casuistry? That is to say, in the use of hair-splitting of the most specious kind in order to absolve one's conscience from a sense of guilt?

Was that not exactly as if Voltaire had said in so many words, "I haven't forgotten your little *expose-depose* trick, my friend, but I'll say no more about it—not at this moment, at any rate; just remember, it's hanging there over you, like the sword of Damocles, suspended by a thread?"

"What an atrocity!" Rousseau wailed. "Never was anything so calculated as this pamphlet to draw upon one man the hatred of an entire nation." But lest anyone suspect how frightened he really was, he added the following: "But it is bound to fail of its intended effect, because it is really too inept. Indeed, it can succeed only in adding to the disrepute in which M. de Voltaire is commonly held in this country, and in showing everyone how the thought of me gives him no peace."

But if the thought of Rousseau continued to torment Voltaire, how much more so must the thought of Voltaire have continued to torment Rousseau! Considering that it was Rousseau who had to worry when and where Voltaire's next blow might fall, Voltaire being so secure, while Rousseau was a man in flight.

And to think that despite Rousseau's insecurity, and despite this ugly attack of Voltaire's, Hume continued to maintain pleasant relations with the philosophic coterie of Paris! Could see no reason for interrupting his correspondence with all of Voltaire's intimate friends. His *Écrasez l'infâme* friends—Diderot, d'Holbach, d'Alembert and so forth.

What a strange linkage! Hume, Jean Jacques's savior, tied in so closely with Jean Jacques's worst enemies.

Forcing Rousseau to keep recalling a very peculiar occurrence that had taken place one night during their journey to the coast of France to take the boat for England. Had it really happened, that occurrence? Or was it only a dream? A vision? Whatever it was, it had made a terrible impression on Rousseau.

It had seemed to him that he was hearing Hume talking in his sleep. Saying in a portentous, strangulated voice, "I've got Jean Jacques Rousseau! I've got him!"

True or not, this frightful scene had continued to reverberate in

Rousseau's mind. Compelling him every now and then to wonder: In choosing England rather than Germany, had he not blundered into the very trap he had been hoping to avoid?

Perhaps Voltaire had planned things just this way?

Take, for example, this matter of the pension from George III. Why had Hume pressured him so about it? Why had he worked so persistently for it? Had not Jean Jacques explained to him often enough that he did not like royal pensions? That he had long ago made it a rule to refuse them? Had turned down one from Louis XV? And just recently refused the aid of Frederick the Great?

But Hume's insistence had been such that finally it was a question of either accepting it or affronting the King. And all that Rousseau could ask for was a promise that the matter be kept secret.

A promise that was not kept! The whole world knew about it. Making it necessary for Rousseau to turn the pension down and thus demonstrate that he was really what his enemies claimed he was: a boor. A bear.

(Concerning which Hume would later argue, "It seems to me that Rousseau deliberately courts offers of aid, only in order to give himself the glory of turning them down.")

Again, it had been Hume who had brought him together with the famous court painter Ramsay, who had done Rousseau's portrait in oil. But in such a way that Jean Jacques had been horrified to see himself as a hard-featured man with a contemptuous and brutal expression on his face. He, the most softhearted man in the world! And yet this dour portrait was to be engraved and distributed in the hundreds of copies.

No doubt to establish another proof that behind his moral books lurked a cruel and hypocritical author. Precisely what the philosophers of Paris were saying.

And still more: Was it not through Hume that Rousseau was led to accept the offer of a Mr. Davenport to move into his country home at Wootton, far in the lonely north of England?

(Hume would say that, on the contrary, he had tried to dissuade him, because he did not feel that a man of Rousseau's temperament should isolate himself. That it was Rousseau who had been stubborn.)

And there was the matter of Hume's stare. His bulbous glaucous eyes, which stared fixedly at one—indeed, transfixed one—and of which Rousseau would later say, "You cannot tell me that any man can be so unfortunate as to have received such eyes from nature." Implying that it was the evil in Hume that had caused his normal eyes to turn into these frightful organs.

"I could not stare him down," Rousseau would subsequently relate in a letter to Madame de Chenonceaux. "I tried, but I couldn't. Such a frightful look no man could possibly sustain. My whole soul was disturbed. My emotions went into a turmoil. But I cried to myself, 'Dare I misjudge this man? Dare I?' And my conscience pricked me so violently that, bursting into tears one evening, I flung myself into his arms, crying, 'No, no. David Hume cannot be a traitor. It is impossible. He must, on the contrary, be the best man in the world, for otherwise he would be the most wicked.'

"But what did David Hume do? Did he take pity on me? Did he invite me to unbosom myself, pour out my heart to him? No. He contented himself with some cold slaps on the back, repeating, 'There, there, now, my dear sir. There, there, now.' Truly, never did the effusions of a man's soul receive a more icy reception."

And then, still later, in that vast house in Wootton, where Rousseau went furiously to work on his *Confessions,* there was more of Hume's mischief to be endured, though Hume himself remained far away in London. But there were insolent servants about to carry on his work. Servants who opened his mail. Peered through his keyhole. Put cinders in his soup. And were obviously just waiting for a chance to do worse. Poison him, perhaps. By putting hemlock instead of parsley into his salad. Or frying his omelets with poisonous toadstools.

Well, of course. What else? Was he not writing in these *Confessions* the very proofs of the machinations of the philosophers against him? The plots of the Grimms, the d'Épinays, the Diderots, the d'Alemberts? And, above all, the conspiracy of Voltaire?

True, he was confessing his own crimes, too. His own often shameful deeds. But did not the very fact that he was not afraid to confess prove that he was better than those who refused to bare their sins? Did it not prove that they had hardened their hearts, while his heart had never ceased to be moved by his conscience? Did it not prove that though he had done wrong, he had repented? That in truth he had always meant to do good?

And would not these coldhearted conspirators be forced to unite now, in order to do everything in their power to prevent these *Confessions* from being published?

Perhaps even from being written? So that no man would ever know their guilt?

Murder, in short. Yes, murder! For would such men, who rejected Jesus Christ—would such frozen hearts have any scruples against murder? Provided they could carry it out with no witnesses around?

Who would believe, in faraway Paris, that Rousseau had not died of a normal disease? Who would proclaim his martyrdom to the world?

And thus, bit by bit, by going back in his mind, by piecing this fragment of evidence to that, Rousseau finally saw the whole nefarious plot. With crystal clarity! With Voltaire masterminding all the tentacles of the conspiracy. And d'Alembert playing the devious go-between, pretending sympathy for Rousseau while enlisting the necessary co-workers. And Hume consenting to play the role of "the good David," in order to lure Jean Jacques off to London. And then off to this lonely corner of Derbyshire.

And the trap perhaps now ready to be sprung!

With the result that all at once Rousseau knew that he must flee for his life!

Yes, at once! This very night! Grabbing up the manuscript of his half-finished *Confessions*—and, unable to burden himself with another book, a still incomplete novel, hastily stuffing the pile of sheets into the flames of the hearth, preferring to see the pages burn rather than leave them behind. Then, wrapping a dark-blue cloak about himself, lest his Armenian costume give him away to the peasants all about, who must surely have been alerted against him, he and Thérèse, with only the vaguest notion of where they were, taking off for Dover, to get a boat to France.

And somehow managing to make Dover, despite the crossing of hundreds of miles of hostile territory where, Rousseau was convinced, danger lurked behind every hedge, and every inn must be a trap.

And Dover itself an ambush, where all the sea captains were linked in conspiracy to deny him passage, declaring that the Channel was too stormy to be crossed. So that Rousseau mounted a stone at an intersection of streets and harangued the populace. "Good, kind English people," he cried with tears in his eyes, "you who inhabit a nation devoted to justice, are you prepared to stand by idly while a man is done to death in your midst? Help me!"

But he spoke in French, which no one understood. Some, however, were moved to toss pennies to him.

Long before leaving Wootton, Rousseau had already been filling the mail to the continent with his accusations against Hume. And all Paris and, indeed, all educated Europe were now agog over the violence of Jean Jacques's denunciation of the traitor Hume. While Hume, at first silent, was soon forced to defend himself with equal violence, calling Rousseau an unmitigated scoundrel. A monster!

With a storm of brochures following. And all the disputed incidents finally so confused with arguments and counterarguments that to this day there are scholars who will prove that a genuine conspiracy against Rousseau did exist. And certainly there was never any doubt of it in Rousseau's mind. Wasn't it, in fact, perfectly clear? For if he were really mad, would not everyone pity him? Would they not take him to their bosoms and comfort him? Would they not mingle their tears with his? Who would mock a madman?

But instead, what did one see? A chorus of rejoicing philosophers chanting, "I told you so. I told you so. This friendship could not last!" Was not this sufficient evidence that the friendship had never been meant to last? Had been planned for no other purpose but to fail?

And with whom did Hume immediately get in touch about this situation, when it began to come into the open? With d'Alembert. With d'Holbach. With Voltaire. Thus showing who his friends really were. And his communications with them were equivalent to a report from the military front: Our troops have won a resounding victory!

So that the Duchess de Luxembourg would no longer have anything to do with Rousseau. And Madame de Boufflers wrote to him, "Your conduct has been atrocious!" Even his good friend the elder Mirabeau declaring, "Sir, you are a fool."

It was nevertheless this elder Mirabeau who offered Rousseau and Thérèse a refuge on one of his many estates in France. But they soon left there and hid out on another estate, belonging to the Prince de Conti, at Trye. And for greater protection no longer called themselves Jean Jacques Rousseau and Mademoiselle Levasseur, but M. and Mademoiselle Renou. Their relationship? Brother and sister.

So as to baffle the French police. Who actually knew very well where Rousseau was, but no longer showed any interest in exercising the still standing writ of arrest. What for? Surely Rousseau could not be said to constitute a threat now.

Just an unfortunate man whom adversity had driven out of his mind. And whose books could therefore no longer be taken seriously by anyone.

"Bound to happen," was Voltaire's comment. "I saw it coming long ago."

But he was not disposed to take any chances, for all that. The wretch might still recover his wits. Voltaire therefore rushed into print an open letter to Hume. Reviewing his own years of contact with Rousseau and swearing that he had never had anything but the kindliest feelings toward him. Repeatedly inviting him to his home, and so forth. But how can one help a man whose body and brain are corroded with venereal disease? What can one do for a man who since childhood has been the pederast of priests?

"Now, however, with everyone finally clear about this man's tendency to bite the hand that wishes to feed him," Voltaire wrote in conclusion, "I would myself favor tossing him a crust of bread now and then, throwing it to him on that dungheap where he lies, and where he still grinds his teeth with fury and hatred for the human race."

Voltaire's best friends, d'Alembert and others, begged him not to publish anything more against a man who was obviously no longer in a condition to protect himself. But Voltaire refused to have any pity.

"Do you have any idea," he asked, "of the harm this man has done in his native city? Of the blood that may still be shed here on account of him, because of the fires of factionalism that he ignited here in Geneva before cravenly scuttling off into the dark—this demand for political equality which he has aroused in the population—whose embers still glow dangerously despite the water I keep throwing on them?"

These hot coals did in fact defy extinction. But Voltaire was not quite honest in describing himself as throwing water on them. Rather, as if to ridicule this Rousseauan insanity of everybody governing everybody, he did some fanning of the coals on his own. For there was a large segment of the population whom Rousseau had forgotten, the segment known as the "natives"—that is to say, the first and second generations of new settlers in the city, who were given no rights whatsoever. Who were not considered citizens at all.

Voltaire wrote out for them a flaming manifesto and pushed them into the fray. Why not? These were people too. And if politics is going to be everybody's business, then the more the merrier.

The result was the explosion of 1770, when enema syringes were tossed aside, and men took to their swords and their guns, and blood flowed in the streets of Geneva.

Which was something else that Voltaire had long been anticipating. For when people take to following madmen, they must all go mad.

And had he not built cottages on his estate for precisely this eventuality? Did he not know from his reading of history that once strife has been allowed to take root in a community, the end must be bloodshed?

And therefore refugees.

A century or more ago, hadn't Amsterdam and other cities built houses for the Huguenots? During France's long religious wars? And hadn't the Hugenots, France's best citizens, gone off to enrich England and Holland and other countries with their invaluable talents? Was not, therefore, the same thing likely to happen one day to Geneva, even though the quarrel was not about religion now, but about politics?

And indeed the outcome was the same. So that it wasn't too long before Voltaire had filled his cottages with Genevan jewelers, with Genevan silkworkers, spinners, weavers, velvetmakers and so forth. In fact, so many refugees came pouring down upon Ferney that Voltaire ran out of cottages. And he had to bed down one anguished family after another in his barns. And then in his home. While he rushed more cottages to completion.

And even those new cottages proved insufficient for the tide. So that finally there was no help for it: Voltaire had to turn over his theater to these workers! Partitioning his precious theater into sections for living quarters and for workrooms. And having the words "Royal Manufactory of Ferney" done in big gold letters over the entrance.

Royal? Why royal? What was royal about it? Was the King of France actually involved? Not in the least. That was just Voltaire's idea of how to drive home the difference between his workshops and those of *republican* Geneva.

It was meant to say to people—and especially to Rousseau—that the form of government of any country will always be less important than the character of the people. And that, in general, people have the governments they deserve.

Proudly Voltaire wrote to d'Argental of Paris, "My theater has become a factory! Yes. Come and see how gold is refined here instead of verses, and wheels polished instead of roles."

And though Voltaire had persuaded Frederick to take eighteen families of watchmakers off his hands and house them in Potsdam (where they proceeded to found the watchmaking industry of Germany), the poet soon had a town of over twelve hundred people on his estate.

And in six weeks he already had watches for sale.

Yes, those wonderful artisans of Rousseau's Geneva were working for Voltaire. Hundreds of them. He was their landlord. Their banker. Their wholesale supplier of raw materials—gold, silver and precious stones.

And also the dealer who found an outlet for their products.

Sending samples from his "royal manufactory" to all the crowned heads of Europe. And getting orders from Catherine of Russia and the peers of France. As well as from the dukes and barons of Germany. And circularizing all the French embassies throughout the world in order to advertise the matchless velvets of Ferney, the diamond-studded watch cases of Ferney, the long-lasting silk stockings of Ferney. Not only the best of their kind, but cheaper than any similar product of Geneva.

Why, there was even a time when—with Voltaire nearing eighty years of age—he dreamed of creating a new Geneva, another lake port, completely within the dominion of the King of France.

What fools men were to fight! When it was work, not contention, that held the answer to men's problems. Though Rousseau would ask how the poor were to achieve justice if they did not make some sort of trouble. Would the rich ever voluntarily give them their due? Would they really?

But look for a moment at what Rousseau's revolutionary ardor had managed to achieve! Those insane demands of his for political equality, for social and economic equality (when anyone could see that what made the world so fascinating was precisely the inequality of man, his endless diversity and variety). Yes, just see what Rousseau's revolutionary ardor had led to.

The enrichment of Voltaire! And more than that:

The Genevans unable to settle the discord that Rousseau had begun, and all parties finally tired of a strife which they no longer knew how to stop (Would it in fact ever stop? Has it stopped to this day? Has it done anything else but spread?), they had to agree to let others come in and do it for them. They invited France, Zurich, Bern, to send a delegate each, to form a commission that would study the city's political problems and bring about a solution, which all sides had pledged themselves to accept.

Scarcely had the delegates reached the city than Voltaire had them to dinner at his home. And for the French envoy, M. de Beauteville, Voltaire had a special message.

"Are you aware, my dear Monsieur de Beauteville, that once before, some thirty years ago, France was asked to intervene in Genevan affairs, on another matter? And have you any idea what our delegate's first demand was?"

M. de Beauteville did not know his history the way Voltaire did. And he had to ask the poet to please inform him.

"Our delegate," said Voltaire, "explained to the Council that he could not possibly spend dreary months in a city where he would be deprived of the one amusement that Frenchmen of all stations of

434

society have come to consider indispensable—that is to say, the theater. And can you imagine, Monsieur de Beauteville, what the reply of the Council was to this demand, in this city where the theater is forbidden? Why, their reply was to build with great dispatch a special theater where our chargé d'affaires, as well as other foreigners, could enjoy the works of our Racine and our Molière for as long as our man had to remain in the city. Now, don't you think that you have a right to the treatment accorded to our previous envoy, especially since your work here must take you far longer than his did?"

M. de Beauteville declared that he would not dream of settling for anything less than his predecessor. Nor did Geneva dare to raise any objections. Indeed, they rushed the opening of a theater so fast that the plaster was still not dry when the first plays were staged (with a troupe of actors quickly brought in from Savoy). The building was, in fact, still so damp that a brisk business was done in rented foot warmers to fight the cold.

And naturally the first play presented there was Voltaire's *Zaïre!*

With Voltaire sitting in a box and cackling with glee, "That crackbrain of a Jean Jacques! Imagine, with his talent he might be sitting here with us, if only he had worked with us instead of against us!"

For this was still another difference between Voltaire and Rousseau: that Rousseau had not the faintest idea how to take advantage of opportunities as they happened to offer themselves, while Voltaire never missed.

35: HIMSELF A SPARROW

They were after him! In full cry!

Yes, they! The philosophers.

With Voltaire in the lead. And the rest—the whole philosophic coterie—like a pack of hounds, in hot pursuit. Tongues lolling, mouths slobbering, throats baying. And, reinforcing them, all the lesser fry, all the apprentice philosophers: the false friends, the paid spies, the bribed servants. The wire pullers, the bootlickers, the hangers-on.

A vast clamorous throng. So that no matter how Rousseau dodged, no matter how he twisted and turned, no matter in what direction he rushed for cover, he could not shake them.

And, oh, how exhausted he was. How bone-tired. Of this fight that he knew must end in his death. While they, with all the advantage of their numbers, had no trouble passing on the chase to ever new conspirators just as soon as the old ones might grow weary. Or bored.

But for their victim, never any rest. Never. "Not so long as Voltaire remains alive," Rousseau would say.

While Voltaire could only laugh and shake his head when such remarks were brought to him. "I? Pursuing that fool? Now does anyone need further proof that the man is deranged and that he should have been locked up long ago while he was still over there in England —in that Bedlam of theirs, which is like our Charenton, only bigger? In a cell of his own, with his name over the bars, so that Londoners taking a stroll there, as they love to do, might have the pleasure of staring at our proponent of the goodness of nature. Which would please Jean Jacques too. All that recognition!"

Which would make Rousseau tremble with fury. The hopelessness of his situation! Because that plot of theirs was so diabolically conceived that just to recognize its existence was to draw upon oneself the accusation of insanity.

How natural, then, even for people of the greatest discernment, Buffon, for example, perhaps the outstanding scientist of his time, Buffon whose eagle eye saw every moving thing on the surface of our earth and even down into the depths of the sea—how natural for this all-seeing Buffon to write to Jean Jacques begging him to moderate himself. "Do be careful. Please. And don't keep provoking Voltaire unnecessarily."

"I! I shouldn't provoke Voltaire!" the flabbergasted Rousseau had to exclaim. Writing violently to his rich friend Du Peyrou:

Can you imagine being clubbed to death in broad daylight, on the open highway, by a brigand, and people standing around and, instead of helping, offering you the generous advice not to provoke the killer?

What must I do, then, appeal to this tiger for mercy—a tiger thirsting for my blood? Shall I perhaps get down on my hands and knees? Well, yes, gladly, if all that is involved is another moment of triumph for Monsieur de Voltaire. Why not? His genius perpetually deserves it. But the question is: Would that stop him, even for a single moment, from going right on and slashing my throat? Obviously not.

No, my dear Peyrou, life has already taught me to suffer. Now all I've got to learn is how to die. And when a man has learned that final lesson which life must teach us all, then he can never afterward be a coward.

As for the charge of being insane, well, he would have to learn to accept that too. Indeed, how could he escape it?

For who will ever believe that the magnificent Voltaire, the greatest writer of our times, is a killer? Who will ever believe that the good David Hume is actually an assassin? Who would imagine that the rich philosopher d'Holbach, the shy and sweet-natured d'Alembert, the bluff and hard-working Diderot, the clever and generous Madame d'Épinay, who would believe that all these fine people are working hand in glove at perpetrating the massacre of an innocent man?

This was clearly beyond belief.

The world would far sooner accept the idea that Rousseau was crazy. Far sooner.

In fact, so great was the authority of those philosophers that Rousseau would later write in his *Dialogues* (to be published after his death): "Why, if d'Alembert and Diderot were to assert today that Jean Jacques Rousseau has two heads, everybody—yes, everybody in the world—seeing Jean Jacques on the street tomorrow, would immediately notice that he had two heads. Plain as day. No doubt whatsoever. And the only surprise would be that no one had ever noticed it before!"

So what else could he be but mad? One had to choose, didn't one? Either he was mad, or the world. Either he or the philosophic coterie.

Good. So that matter was settled. Once and for all. Now let them leave him alone. No fear that he would ever write anything against them. At any rate, he wouldn't publish it. In fact, the only writing he'd probably ever do again would be to copy music. For a living.

He'd rather spend his time out in the fields and the forests, anyhow. There, in the out-of-doors, philosophers were less likely to trouble him. There was so little in nature for them. All they could see there was dog-eat-dog. All they could see there was red tooth and claw. Because they never saw anything anywhere that wasn't the reflection of their own vicious propensities. How, then, could they fail to read in innocent plants and animals the same evils they could not deny in themselves?

So pay no attention to poor Jean Jacques, gentlemen. Just a madman. But doing no one any real harm. Standing out there like a fool, in the damp of some neglected gully. And picking weeds. Picking them with all the tenderness that a gardener at Versailles might show to some gorgeous hothouse flower.

But that's because in a sense Jean Jacques was himself something of a weed. Wasn't he? Sprung up by chance amidst a lot of other weeds. Trampled upon. Uprooted. Jostled and crowded for space. And yet determined to live. Determined to succeed.

Raised by nature, you might say. Not pampered by a gardener, like Monsieur de Voltaire. Who had been so very carefully nurtured. His every need provided for. Schooled. Trained. Coddled. Never any question as to whether there would be room enough in the world for him. No. Never any question of that.

And now look what that idiot Jean Jacques is doing. Shedding tears over an insignificant flower growing in the moist soil at his feet. Bending down to kiss it, to fondle it, to talk to it. Nothing but a common blue periwinkle. But it was Mama's favorite flower. And Mama is dead now. . . .

But he can remember it all as if she were alive. Her beautiful snow-white bosom. And that wonderful, terrible moment when she first invited him to lie there, on her naked breasts. How he had bathed them with his tears! Afraid that he might not be able to prove himself a man with her.

And another memory: discovering the glory of spring for the first time in Mama's house. Spring in Savoy! Opening his window one morning, and there it was: the green of the foliage, the blue of the sky, the freshness of the wind and the delicious twitter of birds.

And all of it free! Free, and so beautiful! Beyond the brush and the chisel of the King's most expensive artists of Paris!

And to think that he had tossed all this aside. Renouncing all that beauty, which cost nothing, to go and live in cities in the vain pursuit of knowledge and literary fame, which was eventually to cost him everything. Including his life.

All because of Voltaire. All because of his worship of Voltaire.

How wonderful, then, to be insane now and recover all that joy. To come home evenings, pleasantly exhausted and yet somehow invigorated, his arms full of plants, and be able to spend long hours sorting out his specimens, drying them, looking up their names in his botanical guide, then carefully mounting them on sheets of fine paper, labeling all the various parts—the leaves, the pistils, the stamens, the petals and the fruit.

And decorating each page with a bit of blue or red ribbon. Because it was not knowledge alone that one found in a plant, but beauty. And he wanted to show his gratitude for that.

No one would bother him while he was botanizing. Not that they weren't still watching him. At all times he could feel them. At night especially. When it seemed to him, as he once confided to a friend, that for two hundred miles around he could see and hear everything that they were doing. Everything!

But it was his *Confessions* they were really after. The book that was to reveal the whole nefarious plot. It was worth his life even to touch it. And only in the darkest night would he venture to pull out the sheets from their secret repository and hastily scribble a few lines.

While he could feel ears stuck to every crack in the walls. And eyes at every knothole in the floor and the ceiling. Observing everything.

Was there anything that these conspirators were not capable of? Was there anyone whom they were not able to bribe? Why, even the gardener at the estate of the Prince de Conti was in the pay of the philosophers and would refuse to supply Rousseau and Thérèse with fresh vegetables and fruits during the absence of the Prince in Paris.

In fact, there was plot within plot. Wheels revolving amidst wheels.

Thus, the concierge of the château fell ill. Dropsy. Rousseau felt that it was only charitable to go visit this man, who was begging for some of Thérèse's cooking. But when he ate of it, he promptly died.

Poison! The Rousseaus had poisoned him! No doubt with those weeds he was always picking.

The rumors flew. All around the château. All through the village. Servant whispering it to servant. The floor waxer telling it to the coiffeur. The baker to the mason.

Now the plot of the philosophers really became clear to Jean Jacques!

So that was their game, was it? To have him charged with a frightful crime. To have him tried, convicted, executed! Before thousands of people. Leaving behind a name forever stained with innocent blood.

Well, yes! Of course. How could he have ever been so simpleminded as to imagine that these clever philosophers were after nothing more than his life? Risking the possibility that their victim, like Jesus Christ, would only flourish all the dearer in the minds of mankind because of his martyrdom.

No. Assassination is not how one destroys a Rousseau. Whose books must be made to perish, as well as his body. Whose character must be assassinated along with his life. So that in all succeeding centuries the world will shudder at the mere mention of the name of Rousseau: a cruel poisoner. Whose works must thereafter seem as pestilent as their author.

To the Prince, Rousseau had to send a special messenger. "Come quickly. My life—and far more—is in mortal danger!"

But the Prince knew all the details of the concierge's death from dropsy. And he saw no reason for rushing out to Trye. He contented himself therefore with a very friendly reply, calculated to calm the nerves of his guest.

Except that Rousseau was not so easily calmed. On the contrary, he was appalled by the Prince's reply. Who would have believed in this new and most sinister development of the plot? The Prince! His host. His very kind host was himself a cog in the conspiracy to annihilate Jean Jacques. Not consciously, perhaps. But what difference did that make? The facts were what counted. And they were incontrovertible.

Incredible, how far-reaching was the sly influence of those philosophers.

"I am placing myself under arrest!" was Rousseau's reply. "I am demanding an autopsy. I will not permit this man to be buried so that rumors and suspicions will forever hang over me. The world must know to what lengths my enemies are prepared to go in order to destroy me."

It made no difference to him that his complaints were forcing the Prince to leave Paris and make the long journey to Trye. Why not? Jean Jacques would even argue, "Why shouldn't the Prince serve me? Isn't his living already assured? Hasn't he all the time in the world? How can he better use his life than by relieving us who have nothing of some of the chains that the rich have loaded on the poor?"

So the Prince came to Trye. To beg Rousseau to moderate himself. Rid himself of his perturbations. Explain exactly what had happened. Point out the servants who were rumormongering. Point out those who seemed to be spies. And which ones were involved in a plot.

But so stupid Jean Jacques was not going to be. No, indeed. To reveal to the Prince the extent to which he had already uncovered the machinations of the conspirators. And the degree of their infiltration into the Prince's own household. So that the Prince could then, wittingly or unwittingly, pass on this invaluable information to the coterie.

No. Not a thing would he tell the Prince. Not a word.

The Prince was wounded by Rousseau's mutism, by this evidence of a total lack of confidence. But all he could say was, "My dear Jean Jacques, it is your privilege to remain silent if you choose. For it has always been my rule never to force my own terms on my friends. Permit me only to call my servants together and in your presence warn them to behave themselves toward you and Mademoiselle Renou no differently than they would toward me."

Unnecessary. Silly. The servants would do as they were bribed to do just as soon as the Prince's back was turned. But Rousseau didn't care. He had already made new plans. His one real friend, his one true friend, Du Peyrou of Neuchâtel, was to come to Trye, to the Prince's château, and save him. Take charge of all his manuscripts. For safekeeping. And arrange all his financial matters.

To frustrate his enemies. To prevent them from destroying his *Confessions*. And upset all their calculations.

But when Du Peyrou finally arrived at Trye, no sooner had Rousseau poured into his ear all the thousand and one ramifications of this intricate plot to have him arrested as a poisoner, and then tried and executed, than Du Peyrou himself fell ill!

And in his fever, in his delirium, Du Peyrou began to mutter incoherent phrases about poisoning. Once even, when Rousseau was offering him a cooling drink of water, Du Peyrou pushed it aside so vigorously that all at once Rousseau understood and was as if transfixed.

Good God! What now? His best and indeed his last friend on earth, Du Peyrou, not only was convinced that he had been poisoned, but suspected that Jean Jacques had done it!

The noose was ready!

Was there anything left now, except flight? At midnight. When the château would be asleep. So as to get a head start on his pursuers.

Except that Thérèse restrained him as he was about to leap out of bed. "You can't!" she said to him. "You mustn't. Think for just one moment. Isn't this exactly what your enemies want in order to have the laugh on you again—your breaking off relations with the Prince, and thus proving once again that you cannot last in any situation?"

She was right. But why did she talk so loudly? "For God's sake," he whispered to her, "lower your voice! Don't you realize that even in the dark they will know what we are doing? Don't you realize that they have ears at every crack in the walls? Do you wish to have yourself included in their fury?"

But he would follow her advice anyhow. He mustn't run away. Somehow he would have to manage to struggle through. He would have to stay and suffer.

Fortunately Du Peyrou recovered—though it might have been better if he had died and an autopsy could have established once and for all the innocence of Rousseau. For, as it was, Jean Jacques now had to keep to his room. Refuse to see Du Peyrou. With a double-locked door between them.

Naturally. In order to prove to everyone that there was absolutely no question of his wanting to poison his friend.

441

In vain Du Peyrou tried to explain that he had no such fears. That if he had muttered something about poisoning during his delirium—which he doubted—it was only due to the fact that Jean Jacques had talked of nothing else since he had entered this château.

A plausible excuse, yes. But suppose Du Peyrou had been won over to the other side? Suppose even that without being won over he was being used? No. Jean Jacques would not stir out of his room. With the result that Du Peyrou felt he had to constitute himself a prisoner, too. Since he, a guest, could not very well roam about the château as if he owned it. So he stayed in his room, too. And a lackey was kept busy conveying a constant interchange of notes between the two prisoners in their different rooms.

Until finally some sort of semifriendly arrangement was concluded between them, and Du Peyrou could take his departure. Carrying with him some of Rousseau's manuscripts and a sort of financial contract.

Not that Rousseau felt that he could really trust the man now. Yes and no. And just to make sure, he had other copies of the same manuscripts conveyed by Thérèse to the abbess of a nearby convent.

So that no matter under what conditions he perished, some part of his *Confessions* would survive.

In vain now Rousseau turned to Madame de Boufflers, the mistress of the Prince, spilling out in letters to her all his troubles and crying, "Save me! As you love God, do not abandon me in the abyss in which I am plunged! Find for me someplace to spend the last few days of my life in peace."

What could she do for him? Except assure him that at Trye the Prince had provided for him precisely what he craved: a haven of security. Where he was welcome to stay for as many years as God might please to keep him alive and well. But he must calm himself. That was all. Calm himself.

But such sweet reasonableness had no effect on Rousseau. On the contrary, his suspicions of some dreadful attempt upon him were only confirmed all the more. Even the Prince's coming out to Trye again, for still another visit, had no effect.

Rousseau threw himself upon his knees before the Prince. "You must give me permission to leave!" he begged.

"But you are not a prisoner here," the Prince assured him again and again, raising him from this humiliating posture. "You are permitted to go whenever you please. But you are doubly invited to stay. For as long as you like."

Was there ever a trap more carefully laid? And baited more enticingly? Just think of it! A Prince. A château. A lifelong invitation. What more could a man ask for?

But why? Why?

How his heart ached to pierce the mystery of good and evil in this world. How desperately he, the believer in the original goodness of man, was now in need of some shred of faith in his own philosophy.

But how could one believe in good, if evil was everywhere triumphant? How could one believe in the good, after that terrible pamphlet by Voltaire? So cleverly planned to trap him.

No. They had crumbled everything. They had undermined everything. For that was their plot: Not just to destroy Rousseau. Ah no. That would have been too easy. That they could have done long ago.

But to destroy the world. Destroy God's handiwork! For no other reason but that they might stand by and laugh to see Jean Jacques, the poor simpleton, wandering disconsolately over the ruins of God's creation. Cutting such a comical figure. Hahaha! Unable to understand what had happened.

What a great joke on Jean Jacques. Haha!

Yes. They were capable of that. Capable of anything!

Hadn't he tested it out? In very much the same way that years ago he had tested out the question of whether man had a soul or not. By throwing pebbles at a tree. Saying to himself, If I hit that tree, then I have a soul. And there is a Providence. And consequently there is immortality.

But this time experimenting with sparrows. Strewing his window sill every day with bread crumbs. Regularly. So that soon the sparrows had learned to gather there by the dozens, waiting for their daily largesse.

But never once would they permit him to stroke them. Not even just gently. Oh, very, very gently. But no. Never once. For just as soon as he stretched out his hand, off they whirred. In an explosion of wings and little feathered bodies. Not only the particular one he had aimed to pet. No. All of them. Retreating to a safe distance. From which they would watch him closely. Suspiciously. And not venturing back for his crumbs until his arm and hand were fully withdrawn

Taking absolutely no chances with that dangerous Jean Jacques Rousseau. So that he would turn to Mademoiselle Renou with tears in his eyes. "For months I have fed them. Never missing a day. And never harming a single one. And still they consider me capable of murder. Convinced that I have a dagger up my sleeve."

443

What did it mean? Could his enemies even bribe the birds against him? So that he, the most harmless of men, was suspected of entrapment and murder? Or was everything he had ever believed in, everything he had ever taught about the original goodness of nature, was it all false? All a pack of lies. Delusions!

The very caresses of his dog became obnoxious to him. "Overdone!" he would say to Thérèse. "Don't you think there's something fishy behind all that display? All that tail wagging and hand licking."

Thérèse just shrugged. "He loves you," she said.

Ah, yes. How wonderful. If only one could believe it. If only one could be sure of the love of just one living creature.

Confused, lacerated, terrorized, feeling himself as if sucked down into a whirling gloom of doubt, where every light was extinguished. Cataracted through a disintegrating universe, where his struggling fingers and toes ached for something solid to cling to. And his lungs cried out for air. . . .

Until suddenly he could stand it no longer. He fled. Fled in a veritable paroxysm of horror. Leaving Thérèse to follow him just as soon as he could convey to her that he had found a haven of safety.

Going first to Lyons. And then to Grenoble. And then to Chambéry. (To weep on the grave of Mama. Mama! Why did you ever give me reason to believe in the goodness of people? And then take your heart, the only good heart that ever was, into your grave?)

And then back to Lyons. And afterward to Bourgoin. And then on to Monquin. . . .

And everywhere he went people who managed to pierce his disguise. And everywhere his old admirers gathering quickly to honor him, to open up their hearts and their homes to this friend of mankind, whose books had communicated to them some of his own passion for equality, some of his own passion for democracy, his own passion for a perfect world.

If only there could have existed some touchstone by which to distinguish among these people, distinguish those who were true from those who were false, how perfect things might have been! What moments of peace one might have enjoyed again!

But wherever Jean Jacques went, his suspicions had to go with him. His terror of spies. And who would those spies be, against whom he had to be on his guard? Who else but those who were making the greatest show of being friendly? And thereby succeeded only in betraying themselves as being specially deputized by the conspirators? Instructed to put themselves out for naïve, trusting Jean Jacques. The more surely to snare him.

Or perhaps just the reverse now? Since he was on to the first kind.

For was it not fated that he should flee from one dangerous plot only to blunder into one still more horrible? As he had already done when from Switzerland and Voltaire he had fled to England and to Hume?

And now was in flight again. Himself a sparrow. Unable to have faith in the goodness of anyone.

For who could read from a person's face whether or not he was secretly in correspondence with the philosophic coterie? Who could read behind a friendly smile the faint trace of mockery? Who could read behind a compliment the faint sneer? Behind the warm hand, the cold glint of steel?

36: I AM NO CHRISTIAN

And everywhere, everywhere, in the very air Rousseau breathed, the vague feeling that horrible jests were being whispered around, jests about the public moralist who had been uncovered as a scoundrel.

Not that anyone ever told him so. Not that he could really hear any buzz of conversation. But somehow he could sense that letters were being circulated. That jokes were going the round. That laughter and derision were being stifled lest his enemies betray their presence.

And that people were repeating for the thousandth time stories about the man who had abandoned his country, abandoned his religion, abandoned his trade and his father, abandoned his children. The man who wrote about family life, but was himself neither son nor husband nor father.

And, in a way, that was really so. For Grimm, Voltaire and others were constantly having their little fun about Jean Jacques. Through the mails.

"Is it true," Voltaire asked, "that our little Rousseau has given up his Armenian costume and has once more joined the human race by dressing like everyone else? And that the reason is that he one day discovered that mistress of his locked in the embrace of a Capucin monk, making, as Rabelais puts it, the beast with two backs? Upon which our good Jean Jacques was forced to the conclusion that he was no different from the rest of mankind, being, like most of us, a cuckold;

and therefore that there was no longer any reason why he should set himself apart by dressing differently."

How it hurt to feel that one was the constant butt of crude merriment! That no matter what one did, one's actions were sure to be misinterpreted. And to give rise to half-stifled chuckles just as soon as one's back was turned.

Even so beautiful a moment in his life as his marriage to Thérèse. When, suddenly, at Bourgoin, he was overcome with remorse, thinking of the quarter of a century of services she had rendered to him, as mistress, as wife, as mother, as servant. And he was getting old and was likely to die at any moment, and was unable to leave her anything but the barest of pittances for an inheritance . . .

Even this beautiful gesture of his was made fun of. Though how else could he have shown his gratitude? And how else could he have arranged the marriage? There was no civil marriage in France. Only church marriages. And only one church: the Catholic. And just to show himself in a Catholic church would have been considered an abjuration of his Protestant faith.

So all he could do was arrange for a little dinner party. And for the presence there of the mayor of Bourgoin and some officers from the nearby cavalry post to lend the occasion some official color. And there he announced that he and Thérèse, master and servant, and just recently sister and brother, were now man and wife.

"Twenty-five years of mutual esteem," he said in a little speech, "precede this wedding, which is thus more auspiciously begun than most marriages."

Causing the letter-writing wits of Europe to exclaim, "Yes, but why expose twenty-five years of mutual esteem to all the hazards of married life?"

And others to comment: "What a stroke of luck for Rousseau's children! Granted in the first place that they are alive, which is doubtful, and in the second place that they are aware of being the children of this man, which is impossible. But even if they are dead and don't know whose children they are, still it's something to be illegitimate no longer, isn't it?"

And d'Alembert to write to Voltaire: "They say that our poor fool who just got married (and who wants us now to believe that every marriage should be like his—preceded by twenty-five years of concubinage) is now working on his confessions, and that it will be an enormous work, in many volumes. Which is inevitable, since everything in nature has some bearing on his life, so that the title of this

446

vast opus might well be 'Universal History, or the Life of Jean Jacques Rousseau.' "

But in spite of all this ridicule of himself that Rousseau could feel in the air around him, and in spite of the fact that he knew that it all had its magnetic pole in Voltaire, he could still not completely deny his youthful admiration for the master. And, in 1770, hearing of a reunion of Parisian men of letters at the home of Madame Necker (the wife of the famous financier) at which everyone present, in a burst of enthusiasm for their exiled leader, had decided that if ever a man deserved a statue while still in the flesh, it was Voltaire, Rousseau heartily concurred.

Even though Voltaire, while graciously agreeing to permit himself to become the recipient of such a signal honor, could not help remarking at the same time, as if he couldn't possibly have heard aright, "Isn't there some mistake? Isn't it to Rousseau that the men of letters of France wish to erect a statue? For I recall that Jean Jacques, in his *Letter to Christophe de Beaumont* some years ago, declared, 'I do not hesitate to say that if there were in Europe a single truly enlightened government, genuinely devoted to the welfare of all its people, it would proclaim a national holiday in my honor and raise statues to me.' Do you want to make a liar out of Jean Jacques? Do you wish to convict yourselves in the eyes of Rousseau of being unenlightened and corrupt, caring nothing for the welfare of the people? No, of course not. So it is obviously to him that you propose to build a monument, not to me."

But this bit of sarcasm did not stem the tide of enthusiasm, which was such that d'Alembert wrote, "A statue? Is that all? For Voltaire, whose soul is pure fire? Whose eloquence, whose fortune, whose every second of life, are consecrated to helping the unfortunate? No, not a statue, but a temple—that is what we must build for him!"

A chorus of approval in which Rousseau joined, writing, "All France—indeed, all humanity and this whole century of ours—is honored by this project."

And since it had been decided that only those who had become known to the literary world by means of some published work had the right to contribute—a maximum of two gold louis—toward the realization of this statue, Rousseau wrote to d'Alembert:

"In that case no man has paid more dearly than myself for this right to be numbered among those who subscribe to a monument for Voltaire. Here, then, is my contribution: only two gold louis, but no one can say how much they have cost me."

It was as if in a final burst of despair he tried to make known his real feelings toward Voltaire. That youthful impulsive worship of his. And d'Alembert evidently sensed it to some extent, for he replied to Rousseau, "I am sure that M. de Voltaire will be very deeply touched by this evidence of M. Rousseau's generous esteem. And I shall not fail to inform him of your contribution."

Deeply touched, was Voltaire? Yes, indeed. To the point of rage.

Writing to tell d'Alembert that he was through! Call off the campaign! Let them build a monument to Balaam's ass, if they must. But not to him. Not with Rousseau's money. Never!

And when d'Alembert wrote back to argue that it would be impossible to return Rousseau's contribution without the risk of a public scandal which might jeopardize everything, Voltaire pointed out that the affair was already a public scandal, and this precisely because of Rousseau's contribution.

Couldn't the committee see what was happening? That because of Rousseau's outrageous bit of irony, sly as everything else that snake did, all of Voltaire's enemies were beginning to take pride in sending in their contributions, too. That money was now pouring in from Fréron, from Palissot, from La Beaumelle, from Chaumeix, from all the notorious haters of Voltaire. And the next thing would be a contribution from that donkey, the bishop of Mirepoix! And from Le Franc de Pompignan! And God only knew from whom else.

And where would it end? With people all over Europe having their laugh out of the fact that Voltaire's friends had evidently not proved numerous enough, or generous enough, to raise the money for the project, and that the committee had thus been driven to appeal to Voltaire's enemies for contributions. With the result that instead of building a monument to his eternal glory, the committee had—through lack of funds—been forced to convert the project into one of erecting a monument to his eternal infamy.

Which was evidently proving far more popular.

Indeed, it seemed as if the only enemy of Voltaire's who was refusing to make a contribution was old Piron. Who was known, however, to be making the rounds of the Parisian cafés, launching this witticism: "Let others take care of the subscription. All I want is a free hand at the *in*scription!"

Of course, things hadn't gone that far at all. Nevertheless, because of Voltaire's irascible temperament, the committee had to meet in haste and draw up a rule that only admirers of Voltaire were to be permitted to make a contribution. The money of Fréron and others could therefore be returned.

But what about Rousseau's money? It was even more important that his contribution be sent back. Voltaire was adamant on that.

But the committee found itself unable to return Rousseau's money. Jean Jacques was so obviously an admirer of Voltaire's. Why, you had only to open up his works to find in every single one expressions of the highest admiration for Voltaire's genius. Indeed, enough for quite a respectable booklet. And this in spite of the fact that the contrary was certainly not true—you couldn't possibly extract from Voltaire's works any booklet of praise for Rousseau. Only the very opposite.

What? Had that miserable wretch somehow outfoxed the master? By hypocritically limiting his invectives against Voltaire to his private correspondence? So that in spite of all his vicious attacks on Voltaire, which had cost Voltaire a fortune, Rousseau could come into the court of public opinion looking like a snow-white lamb.

While Voltaire's hands would seem as if dripping with Rousseau's blood.

Really, the world was turned upside down. For it was Voltaire who had helped Rousseau reach his fame. And what had Rousseau ever done for him? What, I ask you?

So it was with no particular grace that Voltaire finally relented and allowed Rousseau's contribution to stand. Rousseau, however, complaining even years later, in his *Dialogues,* that the public was studiously kept in ignorance of his donation to the cause. Even though he, more than anyone else, had worshiped all his life at the shrine of Voltaire.

But that was again just another proof of their weasely effort to obliterate him and his works. Another proof of that vile conspiracy against him.

The scheme had in any case already lost much of its savor for Voltaire. A statue? Wasn't that as if people already wanted him dead? And wasn't that why so many people, Rousseau included, were so anxious to send in their contribution? Besides, the mere thought of his body, his wretched skinny body, being copied in marble, was upsetting enough. To Frederick the Great, Voltaire wrote, "You must be intending to study anatomy, since you are contributing to the statue of a skeleton."

And especially the arrival at Ferney of Pigalle, foremost sculptor of his day, could only remind Voltaire most forcefully of the terrible inroads that his great enemy, death, had already made in his body. Though without as yet capturing the final citadel.

"So you have signed a contract to model my countenance?" Voltaire said to Pigalle. "Did it never occur to you that you would first have to find it? With my eyes sunk three inches into my head, my teeth non-existent, and my cheeks nothing but crumpled tissue paper pasted to the bones of my head, I defy you to locate it."

An added annoyance was having to sit still. When, on the contrary, it was necessary that he should be more than ever active. To keep away the snub-nosed one. For the closer he felt its icy approach, the busier he had to make himself.

Crowding his life with ever more literary, ever more political and financial schemes. Planting miles of mulberry trees for his silkworms. Setting out hundreds of beehives. Growing almost frenzied in his latter years, so that in the final fourteen years of his life he would write more letters and more pamphlets than in all his previous seventy.

Unlike Rousseau. For in this aspect too they had to diverge sharply, did they not? Rousseau gradually restricting his life. Diminishing the number of his friends. Casting aside his literary activities. Even, for example, packing up most of his books when he went to live on the island in the Lake of Bienne, and never again finding any reason for unpacking them.

While one of Voltaire's last letters, from his deathbed in Paris, to his secretary Wagnière, back at Ferney, would contain a list of books he wanted, a long list, and tell exactly where on his shelves these books were to be found.

Rousseau as if practicing to meet death halfway. Knowing that it was part of nature's scheme. And accepting it as such. Refusing to quarrel.

While Voltaire only fought back all the harder. Even though there could be no doubt as to who would be the victor in the end. Determined not to waste a minute of life, not even the last.

And thus the old philosopher would sit before Pigalle and brood darkly. All of his old animosity against God aroused and multiplied. (Convinced, as Rousseau might have charged, that he, Voltaire, could easily have devised some better system for creation than this business of life and death.)

And at the same time the very contrast between the eventual polished marble in which his body was to be immortalized and the rough and ugly skin of his living self could only accentuate the funerary aspect of this project to build him a statue during his life. Bringing to mind too the skin he had seen nearly seventy years ago on Ninon de Lenclos when, as a young boy, he had been taken to see that famous hetaera, then already eighty-five years old. And he had been so frightened at the thought that if she smiled or spoke that tight desiccated skin of hers must surely crack open and bleed.

But lo! the years had gone by—as if in the twinkling of an eye—
and there he was with a skin as stiff and as thin and as wrinkled as
old Ninon's. In fact, so bad that shaving had become an impossibility.
Driving him to the use of a tiny pair of forceps, with which he would
seize one bristle at a time and viciously snatch it from out of the deep
slashes of his face.

And thus he would occupy himself while sitting before Pigalle.
Sometimes pouting, in order to give himself some semblance of lips.
And sometimes puffing out his cheeks, thus erasing some of the worst
wrinkles of his face.

Making poor Pigalle despair of ever recording in clay the expression
he wanted for his Voltaire (which only Houdon would really catch).
That famous mocking smile of pity. That famous philosophical derision, laced with tears of compassion, that was Voltaire's attitude toward the life of man. A life which he regarded as a great fraud perpetrated by God in a moment of cruel sport.

But a fraud of which we must somehow make the best. Accepting
the situation with humor and with wit, and, by sheer force of character, by sheer force of our energy and our will, raising ourselves to a
stature that must command even the respect of our Creator.

This secret battle between sculptor and philosopher might have gone
on endlessly, had not Pigalle quickly hit on the right approach.

"Have you ever considered, Monsieur de Voltaire," Pigalle began,
"that story in the Bible, in Exodus, that tells how Moses was delayed
on Mount Sinai, getting from God the laws and the Commandments
for the Jews? And how meanwhile Aaron made for this impatient
people a golden calf?"

"Yes," said Voltaire, his interest still not caught. "What about it?"

"Why, only that it must surely have occurred to you that Aaron
would have needed considerable time to make that golden calf. A
great deal more than the day or so which seems to be implied in the
Biblical account."

"Ah?" said Voltaire, his face beginning to light up with the thought
of possessing another argument to bring into play against that supposedly divinely inspired book.

"Speaking as an expert," said Pigalle, quickly attacking his clay in
order to capture Voltaire's aroused physiognomy, "speaking as an expert, which I certainly am, I would want at least six months for the
task."

"Six months!" Voltaire exclaimed.

"Not less," Pigalle asserted. "Only recall, please, how the affair
started. The Jews, you will recall, demand an idol. And Aaron asks

them for their golden earrings. And then it says that 'he fashioned it with a graving tool, after he had made it a molten calf.' In other words, he melted down the earrings, then cast the image, and then smoothed away all the roughnesses and brought out the finer details with various engraving tools."

"And that would consume six months?" Voltaire asked.

"Absolutely," said Pigalle. "That is, unless you wish to assume that God was working a miracle for Aaron on the plain while he was working miracles for Moses up in the mountains. Consider that Aaron had to have a mold in which to pour the molten gold, and that this required a very accurate estimate of how much gold he had and just what would be the largest and most impressive idol he could make with that given amount. Naturally, he would want to make his calf hollow, for only that way could he use his gold to any advantage. The gold had therefore to be stretched to its utmost, but without weakness in the resulting image. For if it collapsed, that would be a fine thing. At the same time, any overestimation in the amount of gold would find the mold half or a quarter empty, producing not a calf but a monstrosity.

"And don't forget that huge numbers of Jews had to be able to view this idol at one and the same time. Since the Jews had as yet no building in which to house it. No temple. And yet the number of Jews who worshiped it was enormous, since the Bible says that for this heresy Moses had many thousands of Jews executed.

"The method of casting must therefore have been the lost-wax technique. And with people wandering in the desert, without the required workshops and supplies, this must have constituted a project of immense difficulties. The inner clay mold would have had to have some sort of armature of iron or bronze in it, to prevent it from crumbling. Over this would come the wax coating, with all the detail modeled in, and corresponding in volume exactly to that of the available gold. And over the wax another heavy mold of clay, sufficiently strong to resist breakage or leakage under heat.

"Into this mold would have to be worked the necessary openings into which the gold would be poured, and the vent holes for the escape of wax and air, to make sure that the gold would fill the entire area formerly filled by the wax. For you can see that if anything went wrong, it would not be discovered until the mold was broken open, and then there would be nothing to do but recover the gold and start all over from the beginning."

Voltaire listened with fascination. Everything in this vast and varied world fascinated him. What a Creator! His admiration for God and for God's illimitable handiwork was without bounds.

Except in the matter of death.

It was some time after Pigalle's departure, but no doubt influenced by the discussion they had had, that Voltaire dreamed one night that he was standing in the midst of a vast cemetery. But a cemetery unlike any he had ever seen before. An immense area, stretching to the horizon, and planted only with long rows of mournful cypresses.

The most striking sight in this cemetery was the great number of towering piles of bones. Human bones! Shining white and chilly in the gloom. What countless human beings were represented by these bones! How many living eyes must once have peered through these skulls and gazed upon a brighter world.

For here was no cemetery for individuals, decently buried in separate graves. This was a cemetery reserved for mass victims. A cemetery for those who had suffered death in great massacres.

Not killed by God. No. But by man. As if in rivalry with God. To see who could be more pitiless: God or man.

How enormous were those mounds! What endless skeletons! And to think that most of these had died young, in man's endless wars and persecutions.

Here were the twenty-three thousand Jews slaughtered on command of Moses, because they had danced before the golden calf. And yonder, mound after mound of the innumerable victims of Christian religious zeal. Against paganism. Against Judaism. Against Mohammedanism. And bloodiest of all: against heresy. For then that pitiless Christian zeal confronted an equally pitiless Christian zeal. Fanaticism against fanaticism!

But the biggest mound of all, a veritable mountain: the twelve million American natives done to death because they were not baptized and therefore had no right to prevent Christians from taking over their continent. And their gold.

So ghastly was this spectacle of man's barbarity (and by far the largest share of it Christian barbarity) that Voltaire could not hold back his tears.

But at this moment he heard someone else weeping nearby, and looking up beheld a man of about thirty-five years of age, a man of gentle features, standing before these mounds and contemplating them with such compassion that it was as if his heart were breaking.

He seemed himself to be the victim of some sort of fanaticism, for his hands and his feet appeared as if cruelly tortured, all swollen

453

and bloody. So that Voltaire suddenly knew who he was: Jesus!

What? This Jew who was the cause of so much of this killing was now weeping over his handiwork? When, on the contrary, he should have been rejoicing? Voltaire could not restrain himself from shouting: "Hypocrite! Must you shed crocodile tears over the victims of your own fury?"

"My victims?" Jesus asked gently, looking at Voltaire with eyes of soft reproach.

"Yes!" Voltaire cried. "Can you deny that most of these dead are the result of your new religion?"

"What new religion?" Jesus asked. "I never preached anything else but 'love your God with all your heart, and your neighbor as yourself.' How can you call this, which has been known to all men since the beginning of time, a new religion? Besides how can you speak of me in connection with anything but the religion I was born in? Was I not circumcised like my fathers? Did I not pay my corban to the Temple treasury at Jerusalem? Did I not keep the Passover? Did I not recite my prayers in the synagogue? Did I not always insist that I had not come to abolish the Law, but to fulfill it?"

"Yes," said Voltaire, "but did you not also write that you had not come to bring peace, but a sword?"

"I never wrote anything in my life," said Jesus quietly. "And as for a sword, I never owned one."

"But these skeletons," Voltaire insisted, "was it not in your name that they suffered death? Do you not consider yourself responsible?"

"How so?" Jesus asked. "Did I ever kill anyone? Did I ever ask that anyone be killed in my name? Did I not come to die for others, rather than to ask others to die for me?"

"But your followers," Voltaire persisted, "you cannot deny that it was they who killed this mountain of Indians, in order to get their gold. You cannot deny that!"

"I never owned any gold," Jesus replied. "Nor coveted any. All my life I lived in poverty. And so did my companions."

"But then, these people who call themselves Christians, after you, do you reject them? Do you say that they are not of your religion?"

"If they loved God," Jesus said, "and if they returned good for evil, then they had the same religion I had."

"Then what about the battles of your churches?" Voltaire asked. "What about the great splits in Christianity? The millions of people who say you must be worshiped in Latin? And the other millions who say you cannot be worshiped properly except in Greek? And still other millions who say . . ."

"I myself knew neither Greek nor Latin," Jesus confessed. "I spoke only the language of my native land."

"And what about those who say that you cannot be adored unless one also abstains from meat on Fridays?"

"I always ate whatever was given to me," Jesus said. "For I was too poor to buy my own food."

"But to love God, as you say, with all one's heart, must not one retire to a monastery?" Voltaire queried. "Is not that what you say?"

"Why?" Jesus asked. "I never found it necessary to live apart from people."

"Or at least go on a pilgrimage to your church in Rome?" Voltaire pursued.

"I never built any church," Jesus said. "Nor did I ever go on any pilgrimage. Indeed, since God is everywhere, I cannot see why one place should be any more holy than another."

"But what about the Jansenists and the Jesuits?" Voltaire went on. "What about the Catholics and the Protestants? What about the Greek Orthodox and the . . ."

"For my part," said Jesus, "I never made any distinction between Jew and Samaritan. And I cannot see why those who profess to be my followers should behave any differently."

Whereupon Voltaire was about to cast himself at the feet of Jesus, crying: "Then let me be your follower! For like you, Jesus, I am no Christian."

But before he could carry out his impulse, his dream had vanished.

And he found himself in his bed, as before. But overcome with a strange inner glow: half sadness, because he realized that he was now very near to his own death, and half joy, because he felt that he had at last made some sort of peace with Christ.

Not that he was now any more resigned to death than before. No indeed. Writing in humorous self-pity, but not without passion and anger:

> *Affublé d'un bonnet qui couvre de ses bords*
> *Le peu que les destins m'ont donné de visage,*
> *Sur un grabat étroit ou gît mon maigre corps,*
> *Oublié des plaisirs, et mis au rang des morts,*
> *Que fais-je, à votre avis?*
> *J'enrage.*

Muffled in a nightcap that swamps
What little face I have,

My skinny body on a narrow cot,
Forgotten, left to die,
What do you think I do?
I rage.

Nor any more friendly to the Church. For he had only recently
gone through the sermons of the two greatest French preachers,
Bourdaloue and Massillon, and had found nothing but constant attacks against sexual impurity, and never a word against war.

"Miserable physicians of the human soul!" he had cried out. "You
declaim hour upon hour against the mere pricks of a pin and haven't
a word to say against that curse that tears the world to pieces!"

But he knew now that the time of his own death was fast approaching. How long could he still hold it off? Another few years, perhaps.

Meanwhile his functions were getting so bad that he would say, "I
live only from one enema to the next." Indeed, he hardly dared eat at
times, so frightful were his colics. Regularly, four times a week, he
purged himself with cassia. And when that didn't work he would fill
the house with his groans and his screams.

And pretty soon two husky Swiss girls, Babette and Barbara, would
go into action. Babette taking care of the hot water, and Barbara arm-
ing herself with the syringe. While Voltaire, naked between the sheets,
would shake his head at the sight of his own buttocks. "My cheeks
there," he would say, "are almost as wrinkled as my cheeks here."

But no sooner was the operation accomplished than he felt as if re-
newed. He would become gay, sprightly, active. Tease the two Swiss
girls about their stout bosoms and go off to superintend his watch
factory and his silk mill. And his barn with fifty cows.

Until the next attack.

And each attack reminding him again of that which he wanted to
forget. "One mustn't think of death," he wrote to Madame du Deffand,
old and blind and afraid to die. "After all, what is it but a sleep from
which one doesn't wake? And just as one is not aware of being asleep,
so one cannot be aware of being dead."

But he knew his advice to be fraudulent, for he couldn't keep his
own mind off death. He knew that the time had come for him to strike
his last blow against fanaticism. To drink his cup of hemlock before
all the world and show everyone that man could die without the aid
of superstitions.

But that meant going to Paris. To die in the full light of publicity.

But how was that to be done? How was he to come back again into the favor of Louis XV? In spite of his endless intrigues, in spite of the friendship of Madame de Pompadour and, later, of Madame du Barry, he could not find anyone in authority who could move the King from the position he had once taken, in a moment of irritation against one of Voltaire's pamphlets. "Is there no way of keeping that man's mouth shut?" the King had asked.

And that's how it stood. And even when Louis XV died, and Louis XVI mounted the throne and displayed the greatest respect for all men of learning, Voltaire remained an exception. The new King would not even go to the theater if he learned that a play by Voltaire was scheduled.

But Voltaire's friends urged him to come to Paris anyhow. Saying, "Who would dare stop you? What could they do to you? Surely the authorities would not dare arrest a man of your age. With your world-wide reputation."

Voltaire, however, had in mind his hoped-for Newtonian funeral. He had to play his cards carefully, so as to avoid some inglorious conclusion to his life ruining at the last moment a career so carefully and successfully cultivated. It would be necessary even to propitiate the Church, so as to avoid the danger of his body's being refused burial and being consigned to some cesspool.

"There are forty thousand fanatics in Paris," he would argue. "And with the least nod of approval from the authorities, they would bring a bundle of faggots to my stake, and I should have the honor of producing the biggest conflagration of any heretic in history."

"And what about your eighty thousand devotees in Paris?" his friends retorted. "Don't you think that each one of them would rush up with two pails of water to extinguish that conflagration? And soak the heads of your forty thousand fanatics, too?"

Yes, yes. In the end he would have to resolve himself to some such move. But it would bring on such risks that it would be folly to misjudge his timing.

And meanwhile he had to endure the infuriating spectacle of Rousseau living in Paris. To his old friend the Duke de Richelieu, Voltaire wrote, "A fine state of affairs! That apprentice clockmaker, with an order of arrest hanging over his head, can go and live in Paris, and I can't!"

It was true. On his simple say-so to the authorities that he did not intend to disturb the peace and would write, or at least publish, nothing, Rousseau had been permitted to return. The Prince de Conti and some others being willing to guarantee that he would keep his word.

How could Voltaire take this, except as a personal affront? What else could it be? It was the same as Jean Jacques's passion for Madame d'Houdetot. Motivated by nothing but spite for Voltaire.

When a man with such a mania for living in the country goes to live in a city, and at that in the most populous city on the continent of Europe, when a man who professes to hate Paris, and castigates it in the most virulent manner in his *La Nouvelle Héloïse,* with page after page of scorn . . . When such a man nevertheless goes to live in Paris, what can it be but an attempt to show that in this particular aspect of their battle he could still defeat Voltaire? And was determined not to miss the opportunity.

Paying back Voltaire for the time when he, Rousseau, a born Genevan, could not enter Geneva, while Voltaire was free to come and go there. And now Voltaire, the born Parisian, couldn't enter Paris, while Rousseau went in and out freely.

No, there could be no other explanation, except this personal one, for this man of nature going to live in the midst of the most artificial society in the world! But of course this imbecile would have another explanation to give to those who dared to say anything to him about another paradox in his life.

"Where else can I be so alone?" he would answer sharply. "Where else than here in Paris? Where I am as lost as if I were living in the mountains of the Caucasus."

37: THE VERY COBBLESTONES
DESPISE ME

And in a way it was true, what Rousseau claimed. He was alone in Paris. With Thérèse. They lived in a tiny fifth-floor apartment on the Rue Platrières, today the Rue Montmartre. There had been, of course, a certain period, in the beginning, when he was still something of a sensation. When women of wealth would once again, as years ago, climb the steep flights of stairs to his rooms, to request the copying of some music.

Just to glimpse the famous Rousseau.

When he would again be his old self, barking with impatience, "Yes, yes. Come back in three months."

"Three months?" they would exclaim. "That long? To copy twenty pages of music?"

Whereupon he would hand them back the music. "Take it elsewhere," he would say. "There are faster copyists. And better. Who need the work more than I do."

But of course they would leave it anyhow, and try to prolong the talk so as to get a good idea of where and how the famous writer lived. A couple of tiny rooms. Dormer windows. Twin beds spread with clean Indian cotton. Striped white and blue. A bit of a kitchen. Everything spotless under Thérèse's care. A small combination dining room and study. The table near the window, where the great author copied music and prepared his collections of plants. And against the wall a little spinet, on which, when the weather was wretched and he could not stir from the house, he would sometimes play old-fashioned tunes. From the days of his youth. Singing softly to himself in a melancholy untrained voice.

"Enough to break one's heart," one visitor reported.

But he was not a sensation for very long. He made it too difficult for those who would have wished to keep him in the public eye. Soon hardly anyone paid any attention to him, even when he went to one of the better-known cafés and ordered himself a chocolate and invited one of the customers to play him a game of chess. Which of course he would win without any great trouble, for he still possessed the mastery he had drilled into himself years ago.

He even gave a reading or two from the manuscript of his *Confessions*. Yielding to the importunities of aristocratic admirers. With members of the highest nobility present. And all the listeners so fascinated that the sessions would go on and on. For eighteen hours or more. With only brief pauses for refreshments. And not a single person who did not shed tears.

But the police soon warned him about that. And Jean Jacques stopped his readings. He had no idea that it was Madame d'Épinay who had gone to the police and complained, fearing that her former protégé would now besmirch her character with his biased memoirs. But he was not in the least surprised that the police should have interfered.

He had, in fact, expected it. They were still after him! Voltaire and the whole philosophic coterie. They never rested. Never.

They were bound to pursue him. In Paris too. He realized only that he had been foolishly mistaken in imagining that they intended to assassinate him.

How could he have been so silly? When they obviously had a much more vicious revenge in mind.

They wanted to bury him alive! They wanted him to go on living, year after year, and feel each spadeful of dirt being shoveled on his coffin. Gradually see himself deserted. Covered with hatred. Ignored. Forgotten.

Why, already they had spread around him such contempt among people that wherever Jean Jacques passed, on the street, he could hear behind him the clearing of throats and a vigorous spitting with disgust. Every glob of mucus intended for him!

Such massive contempt that the moment he entered some public place, the crowd would part before him. Everyone staring at him and drawing away, as if he had the plague, as if he would infect anyone he happened to brush against.

Never, no, never once, when he came to the river and wanted to use the ferry, at the Four Nations place, never was the ferry there. Always he would have to wait. And this even when from a distance he could plainly see that the ferry was there. Loading. But run as fast as he could, the ferryman would have already anticipated him and, suddenly declaring the boat full, would quickly cast off and pull away from the shore, just as he arrived there all out of breath.

And it was the same when someone was passing out handbills on the street. He no longer even tried to get a copy. For he knew that the moment he pushed through the crowd, just at that moment the man would have handed out his last copy. And would go off. Leaving him there, looking foolish.

Oh, how assiduously they worked against him! How minutely! Enlisting every inhabitant. So that if he went into a store to get something, whatever it might be, he could be sure that the article would not be in stock. In fact, there would not be a shop in Paris that carried it.

Imagine! Such vast labor, just to spite one man. One poor man.

Ink, for example. Chinese ink. Of which, naturally, he had to use a great deal. For his copying. Anybody and everybody could manage to buy ink. Just walk into any stationery shop and ask for a stick of tusche. Yes, anybody could get it. Except Jean Jacques. For *him* they were always out. Sorry. Just sold the last one.

And if by chance he did find a stick in some out-of-the-way shop, which, for the moment, it seemed that the conspirators might have overlooked, then it was sure to be of such bad quality that one might rub it in water for hours and still be able to drink the water, so clear and thin would it be.

Anything, anything to humiliate him!

It was only by good fortune that he still possessed a large stick of Chinese tusche, bought years before the plot against him. And a little of this would go a long way toward darkening whatever poor ink he could manage to get, making it somehow usable.

How lucky that his enemies had not yet found out about that stick of good ink. Which you can be sure he kept well hidden.

Of course, there were articles in such constant demand that no storekeeper could claim that he did not have any in stock. For such articles there were different forms of humiliation to be employed against him.

It turned out, for example, that this or that article had just been reduced in price. Yes. Sharply reduced.

But why? And why speak of it so loudly in front of all these other customers?

For no reason except to shame him. Shame him with a disguised form of charity. As if to say, "Poor Jean Jacques. Poor Jean Jacques. Such a failure. So little money. We must manage somehow to slip him a few pennies. Without his knowing it."

But he didn't want their charity! He didn't want their pity! He would show them that he was no beggar. Why, he was Jean Jacques Rousseau. Who had turned down pensions from kings! Pensions which, had he accepted them, would have enabled him to buy out the whole stock of all their stores. A hundred times over!

Huh! Giving him charity! What for? So as to be able to gossip behind his back? To be able to boast that but for this generosity Jean Jacques would starve? No, indeed! No special reductions for him! Here's your money. Every cent of it!

And he would toss the money down on the counter and walk out. Fast. While the storekeeper called after him excitedly.

Naturally he would take care never to visit that particular shop again.

How was it possible for those conspirators to be everywhere? How was it possible for them to enlist so many people in this hounding of an innocent man? What was the crime with which they charged him, so that people recoiled at the very mention of it?

Could there really be such a crime? So monstrous that just to be accused of it was enough to convict? But was it not even more monstrous to leave a person in ignorance of this charge?

Wasn't that the most abominable kind of injustice?

How could anyone do that to a person?

Arousing him to the point where he would stop a passer-by on the street—just anyone—and challenge him on the right to condemn without a hearing.

"Speak up!" he would cry. "Bring it out into the open!"

But the challenged man would evade the issue. Indeed, he would behave as if he were utterly at sea. He would even pretend to be frightened. As if he had to do with a madman.

Oh, how well the coterie had trained people to disguise themselves. Everybody trained from childhood. To close doors. To blow out candles. To lead double lives. One open. The other concealed.

Liars! Actors! Deceivers!

People would stop on the street to watch Jean Jacques haranguing a passer-by. And they too would pretend not to understand. And would end up by shaking their heads with pity for this poor man who had obviously lost his wits. And then they would move on. Leaving Jean Jacques to cry out his complaint to an empty street, "What have I done? What? Tell me, for God's sake!"

Not that Jean Jacques was utterly friendless. How could he be? With his works growing ever more famous. Ever more read and studied and discussed.

He himself might live obscurely, copying music for a living. Almost twelve thousand pages during less than seven years. And—considering his age and his slowness—that was labor. Taking up all his mornings and most of his evenings.

But his readers still admired him and sought him out. Wrote to him, or else came personally to see him. And even wept as they kissed his hand. Young men such as Saint-Just, Robespierre, Mirabeau. Politically-minded, and moved to wild dreams of perfect government by Jean Jacques's *Discourse on Inequality* and his *Social Contract*. Men who seemed as if they could already see ahead those Revolutionary days when in the Assembly no new law could be proposed, no speech made, that did not have liberal quotations from Rousseau to bolster it.

And women still adored him. For his *Émile*. And his *La Nouvelle Héloïse*. And they would write long letters to him. Which sometimes he would answer with replies full of charm and tenderness. And sometimes with brutally curt notes, when his sharp eye had detected another secret spy.

462

Musicians came, too. Now and then. Gluck, for example, who respected Rousseau's works as a composer, and had high regard for his *Dictionary of Music*. And such men of importance as the Prince de Ligne, of almost royal family, a field marshal of the Austrian Army, who came to visit Jean Jacques several times and would later write, "What a man! What eyes—like stars! And a genius that electrifies."

And another frequent visitor was the half-engineer Bernardin de Saint-Pierre, not yet famous as a novelist, but already a personage because of his infectious enthusiasms, his wild passions that would propel him and his disciples to adventurous lives.

Rousseau enjoyed Bernardin's company. They were as one in their hatred of the philosophers. And as one in their love of fields and forests. Bernardin would tell Rousseau about his travels in the tropics, and he would evoke such pictures of distant islands where he had lived that Rousseau would feel that he had had for a moment a glimpse of the terrestrial Paradise and would wish that he might have spent his whole life in such a place. In blissful innocence.

Not that the course of any of these friendships was smooth. How could it be? With Rousseau having to be on perpetual lookout for emissaries from the coterie. Why, for example, should Bernardin de Saint-Pierre send him a sack of coffee, a full hundred pounds of it, when all that Jean Jacques had begged for was a pound of the fine variety that Bernardin had brought back with him from his travels?

What was the man trying to do? Show up Jean Jacques as too poor to provide his own coffee?

And Rulhière, the poet, Bernardin's friend, who was later to become famous for his histories of Poland and Russia.

"What are you after?" Rousseau once greeted Rulhière when he came knocking at Jean Jacques's door.

Rulhière stood there amazed. Hadn't they been seeing each other rather regularly of late?

"Yes, yes. But what are you after right now?" That was what Rousseau wanted to know. "Why do you come just at this time, when it's too early for dinner and too late for business?"

The flabbergasted Rulhière was left speechless.

"Well," said Rousseau, "now that you're here, let's not say you've come in vain. Enter. Look around. Take your fill. Come, Thérèse, my dear, let's not hide anything from our gentleman friend. What might be in that pot that you have on the stove? Lift the lid. Let him see what you're cooking. Taste it, kind sir. What do you say? Enough salt? Enough carrots? Do you approve of our little stew? Not very much of a stew, I agree. But the best we can afford. And nutritious. Besides honestly earned. Every bit of it. By my own labor. And now is your curiosity satisfied? Or shall I open this drawer? Would you like a peek in this chest?"

Rulhière fled in dismay.

Too bad. But then, one couldn't be too careful.

"The league against me," Jean Jacques would write, "includes everyone. It is universal. And so secret that I shall never plumb its depths. I shall go on to my grave without ever having solved its mystery.

"For who," he would ask, "can be expected to solve a conspiracy so all-encompassing that it includes insects trained to sting Jean Jacques, and sly girls instructed to use their innocent smirks to overcome his mistrust, and even whores carefully coached on how to behave like virgins in his presence."

Nothing, nothing was sacred to these frenzied plotters. Not even so solemn an event as the death of Madame Geoffrin, kind hostess to these very men, her home being actually known as "the hatchery of philosophers." When d'Alembert came to write her eulogy, he did not scruple to besmirch her memory with no other object than to get in a good blow at Jean Jacques.

Affirming that Madame Geoffrin had once said, "I would like to ask every condemned criminal, before his execution, the following question: 'Were you ever fond of children?' I am positive that the answer would always have to be no!"

A lie! Never had Madame Geoffrin said anything of the kind. Invented out of whole cloth in order to stir up the people to even greater hatred of Rousseau.

His name not mentioned, to be sure, but only too wickedly transparent. For to whom else could d'Alembert possibly be referring when he used those words "condemned criminal"? Except to Rousseau. Rousseau, around whose gibbet those philosophers of Madame Geoffrin's salon were all hoping to dance someday. Rousseau, the only man in the world about whom there was any such discussion as whether he loved children or not.

How d'Alembert must have gloated at this image he had conjured up of Jean Jacques facing execution. And forced finally to come out with the truth. Unable to lie at this moment when he was about to meet his Maker, and therefore admitting at last that he had never loved children.

Which showed to what lengths these unconscionable people would go in order to travesty him before the world. Because it wasn't true! No, it wasn't! He was fond of children. He was so! Very fond of

464

them. Yes, and at the foot of the scaffold where his body must soon swing, he would still be able to maintain that he had always loved children. Had kept his pockets filled with sweets for them. Had stopped during his walks to admire them. Pet them. Yes, and even weep with them, unable to restrain his tears whenever he saw a child mistreated. Had written endless pages to urge parents to cherish them more—mothers to nurse them at their breasts, fathers to bring them up with more love and more intelligence.

Just another example of their unending persecution of him, in order to drive him from "every public gathering," as he would charge, "from every theater, from every café and every public walk and eventually from the very streets of Paris, by a campaign of open and whispered insults, by a campaign of sneers and snickers, by looks either savage or mocking, and even by blows and mob violence."

But they had miscalculated. Yes. They had failed to reckon with his strength. With his endurance. With the power that comes to a man who knows that he is innocent. So let them be warned! Beware! For he would bring his case to the public. And the public would have the courage to take his side.

And so he composed an *Appeal to the Public.* An appeal to "all Frenchmen who still love justice and pity." And, making dozens of copies, he passed them out on the streets.

But people took his appeal and scarcely glanced at it, or else read it through without a flicker of interest, or else stuffed it in a pocket, or, worse still, threw it away, even crumpling it first. And his heart would break at the thought of what the world might be coming to when one human being had so little sympathy for the miseries of another.

But if this generation had no pity for him, might not another generation—after his death—render him the justice that was his due? Might there not be better generations of men to come?

That's why it was so extremely important that his great work of self-defense, his *Dialogues,* on which he had labored so diligently since putting aside his *Confessions,* should survive him, and see the light of day, in spite of the efforts of enemies who were no doubt determined to destroy it.

But who would guard it for him? Whom could he possibly trust with this precious manuscript?

The name of the Abbé de Condillac came to his mind. Years before, as a poverty-stricken young man, Rousseau had been for a short while a tutor for the children of one of the branches of the Condillac

465

family, and thus he felt some sort of vague right to approach this particular Condillac, who, moreover, because he had already made himself independently famous for his investigations into the five senses of man, would have little reason to persecute Jean Jacques in order to curry favor with the philosophers.

In any case, Rousseau did not intend to take any risks with his only copy of the *Dialogues*. No. First he sat down and patiently copied out the many hundreds of pages of his book. Copied them out in his neatest hand, with never a word illegible or misspelled. Laboring on it every day for an hour or two, and sometimes more, after he had done his usual stint of music copying.

Then, when it was finished (and how well one can understand why those who saw him during this period of his life never failed to comment on his exaggerated carriage, one shoulder being so much higher than the other) he took it to the Abbé de Condillac and left it for him to read.

And the abbé turned out to be quite willing to take care of Rousseau's book. Promising to guard it carefully and see to its publication when Rousseau died. Or, if he himself should die first, to instruct the executor of his estate to carry out Jean Jacques's orders.

But might he be forgiven if—well, if he urged upon the author the advisability of some further work on the novel? In view, that is, of the greatness of Rousseau's other novels, his *Émile* and his *La Nouvelle Héloïse*. This novel being, in comparison, quite deficient. Lacking in a consistent plot, for one thing. And then, no female character. And . . .

What? You say this is not a novel? All this is factual? Well, of course one can indeed recognize some roots in reality. For example, this defense of Jean Jacques's musical ability against those who would deny it. But why two characters, one named Jean Jacques and the other Rousseau? Wasn't that confusing? And strange? And then this about insects taught to sting him. And this about Madame Geoffrin . . .

No, no, there was no intention to offend. And if that was how Monsieur Rousseau wished to leave it, then he might rest assured that his wishes would be carried out. Here, right in this drawer, see? under lock and key, the manuscript would be absolutely safe. And Monsieur Rousseau might set his mind at ease.

But how could Jean Jacques set his mind at ease? Of what value was the promise of this abbé who thought of Rousseau's self-defense as nothing but a badly written novel. He was obviously only waiting for

Jean Jacques to die, that was all, in order to throw it out as a worthless bit of rubbish. Or else give it to some of his philosopher friends for a good laugh at Rousseau's expense.

But if there was no one in France who would help him, if all sense of honor and decency had vanished from this country, then what about a foreigner? There was, as a matter of fact, just then living in Paris a certain Boothby, an English gentleman who had been a neighbor of Rousseau's at Wootton and who, upon coming to the Continent for a stay, had graciously paid his respects to Jean Jacques.

Quick, before this man should return to England, Rousseau must make a new copy and bring it to Mr. Boothby.

"My message to the world from the grave," Rousseau said. "And worth one's life, just to have in one's possession. Therefore keep it hidden. And when you learn of my death, have it published."

Boothby expressed the hope that this eventuality might not be for many years to come. But in any case he promised solemnly to take care of the matter.

But of course Rousseau could not trust this cold Britisher either. No more than he could trust the abbé. (Though actually both men were to prove themselves as honorable as their word.) And since he had found no succor, neither from a Frenchman nor from an Englishman, Rousseau sat himself down to make still another copy.

This one would be for God.

More carefully written than the others. Much more. Beautiful. Faultless. And, when completed, carefully packaged and addressed.

"Committed to the care of Providence," he wrote. And then, as if even the heart of God had to be awakened to a sense of pity, he added, "My last hope."

Using his best hand, and remembering how years before it was just such copperplate script he had used when composing a letter to Voltaire. And wondering, too, if this letter to God would get him any more than he had got from that great poet. Who had been his god in those days.

"Protector of the oppressed," he wrote on the package, "receive this appeal from one who has been hounded, outraged, defamed by a whole generation. Who for fifteen years has been subjected to harassment without equal, to indignities worse than death. And this without any explanation, with nothing but insults, lies, treacheries. Eternal Providence, receive my manuscript, and see to it that it shall come eventually, and without forgeries, into the hands of a new and better generation."

Then for several days he studied the Cathedral of Notre Dame. Cautiously marking the time of the masses, the coming and going of beadles, priests and acolytes, so that he might figure out the best moment to enter the edifice unperceived and penetrate to the very chancel, and run up to the high altar to lay his manuscript there.

What a sensation the discovery of this manuscript would make! This desecration of France's most important sanctuary. Everyone, from the new King on down, would be forced to grant Jean Jacques a hearing. And what a story of nefarious persecution he would be able to lay before the world!

Let the philosophers tremble!

With his every move calculated ahead, he tucked his manuscript under his arm one morning and made his way to the cathedral. And, timing his entry perfectly, he rushed to the chancel.

But the way to the altar was blocked. There was a high iron grille between the choir and the steps to the altar. Never had he noticed this grille before. Who could have built it overnight?

He thought at first that it must yield to his touch. But no. It was solid. Locked. Impenetrable. Anchored to the stone underfoot. He tugged at it, but it would not give.

His head swam, and he had to clutch the ironwork to keep himself from falling. While from his mouth there escaped such a loud groan that it reverberated from the ribbed vaulting overhead, frightening him.

With legs that could scarcely support him, convinced that God Himself had magically erected this iron barrier between Jean Jacques and His sacred altar, Rousseau staggered and crawled out of this church.

Out into a strange, dark city.

Paris itself had suddenly altered. Turned into a labyrinth. Where Jean Jacques felt utterly lost, despite his thirty years of residence.

"In vain—" so he would write of this day—"in vain I groped for a single helping hand. I was trapped in a city without signposts. Without advice. Without consolation. Where the very cobblestones seemed to despise me and lie in ambush for me, to trip me up. And the dogs in the gutter would abandon the nameless offal on which they were chewing in order to come over and snarl at me."

But in the depths of despair and horror in which he now found himself, he had one satisfaction: that of having touched bottom. God, for His own inscrutable reasons, had taken the side of Voltaire. Jean Jacques had struggled. Yes. But he had failed.

And now he could rest. For this was the end.

What was he, after all, in the light of divine creation? What was he but a nothing? A transient bubble. Appearing for a moment, by God's mysterious will, in the froth of a wave. One bubble among countless other bubbles. Lucky if he endured for a fraction of a second. And even luckier if, in that tiny moment of his existence, he had managed to sparkle for an instant in the light of the sun.

Before bursting. And returning his tiny bit of borrowed wetness to the ocean of water whence it had come.

Years ago it had seemed to him as if he could hear the scream of an eagle, flying high above the clouds. Voltaire! Voltaire! Rousing little Jean Jacques to seek the sun of glory, too.

His little bubble of life wanting to sparkle likewise. Because everything else was sparkling. And Voltaire sparkled above all.

And indeed, for a moment, he too had sparkled.

But that was over now. He had surrendered everything into the hands of God, Who makes and unmakes. He had surrendered everything into the hands of that eternal nature, in which even the sun is only a brief bubble of flame, sparkling only for an instant before it too must burst.

There was nothing that Jean Jacques wanted now. Neither from his own generation nor from any other.

He would still go on long botanical walks with Bernardin de Saint-Pierre. Sometimes he would even go for strenuous climbs. But in general he was satisfied with less ambitious, less arduous excursions. Spent more time over his plant specimens. Or sat at his spinet, singing old songs. And gradually beginning to restrict the number of orders he would take for the copying of music.

Not that he was ill. On the contrary, he had rarely felt so well. Even his bladder no longer seemed to bother him so much. He rested. Relaxed. His passions as if extinct.

38: CONFESS, SINNER, CONFESS!

Suddenly, one bitterly cold day in January 1778, when the temperature had dropped so low that the Seine was rolling large floes of ice, Bernardin de Saint-Pierre appeared at Jean Jacques's door.

Muffled to the nose against the intense frost. But full of excitement. "Have you heard the news?"

"What news?" Rousseau asked.

"About Voltaire!" Bernardin exclaimed. "He's in Paris. Arrived this morning."

Jean Jacques's heart almost stopped beating. Voltaire in Paris? He and Voltaire in the same city again? After over a quarter of a century?

What would happen now? What?

Something. Yes, surely something must happen.

A meeting. By chance. Or else arranged by friends. Or by enemies. But in any case how could they help but meet? And then Rousseau's heart must finally unload all that it had felt for this great man through so many checkered years, pouring it all out, his worship and his admiration, his love and his disappointment, his envy and his hatred. And finally his fury and his fright. Every passion that it was conceivable for one man to have for another.

And Voltaire—who knew?—perhaps the same.

The very thought of such a scene of mutual confession, both men pleading for each other's forgiveness and ending at last in a stormy embrace, was enough to bring tears to the eyes of Rousseau. How many wasted years might have been spent in affection, in conversation, in helping each other with their work . . .

Abruptly he stopped his dreams. Froze the glands of his eyes before the tears had a chance to well over.

For it was as if he could already hear in his mind that voice which he had never really heard, but which he couldn't help imagining as strident and commanding.

Saying, "Rousseau? *Le petit* Rousseau? You mean the hyena?" And explaining that he called him the hyena now because he had learned recently that in all nature there was only one animal that would devour its own young in preference to any other food, and that was the hyena.

Or some other cruel witticism that would stab Rousseau to the heart. The one, for example, about Jean Jacques's having started out to make the world envy him, and then, having failed at that, deciding to make the world pity him, and in the end succeeding only in making the world forget him.

Yes, what was to be expected from Voltaire but such vitriolic remarks? Of which he had already made hundreds at Jean Jacques's expense.

Then why? why was one nevertheless drawn to all this hubbub about Voltaire? To all the stories in the gazettes? Why did one even bother to listen to Bernardin de Saint-Pierre and his gossipy reportage?

"The man's nothing but a clown!" Rousseau exclaimed.

"I'm sorry," Bernardin said quickly. "I didn't mean to irritate you. Yes, the man is something of a clown."

"Not that I've ever denied him his genius," Rousseau went on. "I never have and never will."

And he encouraged Bernardin to continue. Asking himself at the same time, What was there to learn from all this silly show?

That Grimm, for example, had immediately exclaimed, "If a prophet from the Old Testament, or one of the Twelve Apostles, or the ghost of Julius Caesar, had appeared in broad daylight in our city, Paris could not have been more astounded than at the sight of Voltaire in our midst."

Well, what else would Grimm say? Naturally it would be something in wild praise of Voltaire, and couched in such a form that everyone would want to repeat it. Everybody taking a free ride on everybody else's success.

That's what a clique was for, wasn't it? For mutual admiration?

In the same way d'Alembert too would have his enthusiastic remark to contribute: "Voltaire come to Paris at the age of eighty-four to see to the staging of his latest play, *Irene,* exactly sixty years after the opening of his first play, *Oedipus.* Not since the days of Athens, two thousand years ago, when Sophocles put on his last play at the age of ninety, has man witnessed such a record in the theater!"

How familiar! Was there ever a time when Europe was not excited about Voltaire? And Voltaire in the midst of all that excitement, forever making the appropriate witty remarks? Voltaire, playing Voltaire. His oldest and best role. And always bringing down the house to violent applause.

Take, for example, that perfect line that Voltaire had delivered when he had reached the gates of Paris. Can one imagine anything better for a proper Voltairean entry into the city? And as if tossed off. Extemporaneous. Impromptu. (As if there hadn't been a six-day trip from Ferney to Paris, during which the line and its perfect delivery might have been rehearsed a hundred times!)

Voltaire arriving in the frosty morning, in his imposing sky-blue, star-spangled coach equipped with a little built-in stove for warmth, and accompanied by his servant, his cook and his secretary. And

471

halted at the gates of Paris by the officer of the guard, for the usual customs examination.

"Any contraband to declare?" the officer would naturally ask. The usual question.

And Voltaire's voice immediately crackling from the interior of the coach: "Nothing contraband here, Officer. Except myself."

And the officer quickly leaning into the dark interior from which had come that strange answer, and recognizing there that emaciated frame, that unmistakable living skeleton, even though huddled in the folds of a most extravagant red pelisse lined with sable (such a magnificent fur piece as only Empress Catherine the Great could give to the writer whom she admired above all other writers, and who had only recently written for her a *Century of Czar Peter the Great*). And recognizing too that squeezed-up face drowned in the curls of a huge wig. And shining from out of that face those two unforgettable jet-black eyes, glowing like carbuncles, that were the master's hallmark.

"My God, it's Voltaire!" the officer had cried. So overcome at the sight of this world-renowned figure that he could not even remember what Voltaire had just reminded him of—namely, that the poet's presence was not permitted in Paris. Just waving him on into the city.

Into the city, and to the Quai des Théatins (today, naturally, the Quai Voltaire) where the master was to live in the luxurious palace of the wealthy Marquis de Villette, rumored to be his son as a result of a very secret affair many years ago.

That too staged. Like every other aspect of this show.

Everything. Starting with the traditional heart-rending farewell scene when he had left Ferney, his beloved estate. Ferney with its orchards planted by Voltaire, its barns with fifty cows, its five hundred beehives, its scores of devoted peasants all enriched by following Voltaire's wise counsel and example, to say nothing of all the grateful watchmakers and silk weavers. And his immense library. With its six desks, on each one of which stood a partially completed manuscript. And the tomb he had built for himself, half in and half out of his church. Leaving all that. With tears in his eyes, but leaving it just the same. Why? Because the script called for him to leave it.

Because as an experienced playwright he knew that this tomb was not for him. Too small, and too far away from Paris. Because he knew that the last act of the great Voltaire drama needed a bigger stage setting than this little village. That a life like his had to have a more imposing backdrop for its final act—nothing less than the biggest city of its time: Paris.

What difference then how one might like to live out one's life? For a showman, the play was the thing!

And all Paris responding. As a properly trained audience should. To the savior of the Calas and Sirven families. To the man who had only recently called for the abolition of all forms of torture in the administration of justice. And for the liberation of all the remaining serfs of France, principally those still existing on certain church lands, such as that of the Abbey of St.-Claude.

And so successful was this farewell appearance of Voltaire on the stage of Paris that almost immediately crowds began to collect around his coach. And people took to leaping on the step of the carriage, or on the box, or even on the turning hub, in order to try and catch a glimpse of the great man, or even kiss his hand. Or reach in and try to pull out a tuft of fur from his cloak to treasure as a souvenir.

A man selling card tricks figuring to increase his sales by crying, "Look at these tricks that Monsieur de Voltaire taught me at Ferney!"

And a woman running from her bookstall to plead, "Monsieur de Voltaire! Make my fortune. Please!"

"How am I to do that?" he asked.

"Write a book for me to publish and sell. Just a little book. On any subject. Please, please!"

So that it seemed as if only the King and the Church were annoyed at Voltaire for selecting Paris as the stage for his final act. (Which was quite understandable, since for centuries this had been their theater, and they had no intention of letting this king of reason, this pontiff of popular appeal, rob them of their big scenes.) Paris and Versailles had been created as a stage for the Bourbons, not for the Voltaires.

And Louis XVI could not help but ask angrily, "Why was this man permitted to enter Paris, when there is an order of exile against him?"

Which required someone to confess to His Majesty that such an order must certainly have been drawn up against Voltaire at one time —or at least so everyone had reason to believe—but a thorough search had failed to uncover a single copy in the files. (What file clerk, lover of Voltaire, had secretely destroyed it?)

"Let him remain, then," the King decided sullenly. For to exile Voltaire now, a man so old and so famous—that would only make France look ridiculous. (And France too was involved in this theatrical competition.) But let no member of the court have anything to do with this blasphemer.

As for the Church, it began to put itself forward at once. From pulpits everywhere violent sermons were thundered against this antichrist. This man who had dared to make fun of Jesus. This man who called Jesus a failure, saying He had come to save the world but obviously hadn't succeeded.

And especially the Abbé de Beauregard delivering himself of a powerful castigation of Voltaire at the Cathedral of Notre Dame, and being invited to repeat it in the royal chapel at Versailles. A sermon that attacked the whole philosophical school, describing thêm as madmen armed with hatchets and with axes, come to despoil the temples of God. Smash throne and altar. Profane our holy of holies. Wreck our society and our civilization. And, above all other philosophers, this most gifted one, with his subtle poison, this sly heretic, this shameless pagan, against whom, however, the Church would surely know how to defend herself: "For our charity has its limits and can turn to fury. And our zeal knows revenge as well as forgiveness." And declaring that never would the body of this insulter of God be permitted to contaminate the earth where lie the worshipers of God.

"How can he refuse to bury me," Voltaire asked, "when I would be only too happy to bury him?"

A jest that became such a sensation in Paris that it swelled the already enormous crush of visitors who came to the home of the Marquis de Villette to pay their respects to the poet. So that Voltaire's legs ached and his ankles puffed up from nothing but rising from an easy chair and sitting down again, in the process of greeting three hundred or more guests a day—selected from the many more who came to the palace, but failed to pass the scrutiny of Madame Denis and the Marquis de Villette, who acted as a kind of admissions committee and also ushered out those who had been allowed in, so that the room would never become too overcrowded.

And Voltaire taking pains to see to it that each guest received some memorable word from him to carry out into the world, to be passed from mouth to mouth and printed eventually in gazettes all over Europe.

The noblest names of France—Richelieu, Montmorency, Polignac, Lauzun, Armagnac, the Duchess de Cesse, the Countess de Boufflers, even blind Madame du Deffand—all humbled themselves by waiting in line for their opportunity to see the great Voltaire.

Gluck, the composer, even delaying his departure to Vienna, where he was due for a performance, in order to have a chance to see Voltaire. And immediately after him his great rival, the Italian composer

Piccini, whose style of music was at war with Gluck's, splitting Paris into two camps.

"What is this?" Voltaire asked. "Piccini trails Gluck?"

A happy phrase that reached the ear of Queen Marie Antoinette, a rabid Gluckist, who was now all the more determined to see Voltaire, despite the King's orders.

And delegations from the Academy, including Saint-Lambert, the Prince de Beauvau, Marmontel and so forth. And another from the Comédie-Française.

And Benjamin Franklin, from America, just successful in his efforts to associate France with the cause of the American Revolutionary forces. And bringing with him his grandson.

"I've studied your great Declaration of Independence," Voltaire said to him. "And I tell you, if I were only half my eighty-four years, I would go to live in your country. Your land of freedom."

He spoke of his admiration for General Washington too and wrote a couple of impromptu verses, and then begged leave to have them struck on a medal of gold, which he hoped Franklin would present to the General. (Which Franklin did.)

In turn Franklin begged Voltaire to bless his grandson. An act that Voltaire performed, saying, as he put his hand on the lad's head, "My child, I give you two words to live by: God and liberty." And no one in the room could keep tears from his eyes when Voltaire added, "You are young. You will live to see great days."

Even the British ambassador, Lord Stormont, due to leave Paris now that France was at war with England, had put off his departure until he could have his moment with Voltaire.

And Voltaire found it completely possible to be equally gracious to him, the enemy of the moment. "It is your great people," he said, "who first taught me the most precious virtue that any human institution can possess: tolerance."

Priests came too. Each one excited over the prospect of converting Voltaire back to the Church. And in spite of the vigilance of the Marquis de Villette, in spite of Madame Denis and Wagnière, who did their best to keep these proselytizers out of Voltaire's room, several of them managed to slip through during the height of the crush.

One wild prophet, for example, his face stamped with religious fury, who burst in shouting: "Confess, sinner, confess! For I've come to save your soul for God."

"Who has sent you?" Voltaire asked.

"God Himself!" the priest declared.

"Let me see your credentials," Voltaire retorted. And the prophet was escorted out amidst laughter.

And still another priest, who insisted that God would willingly forgive Voltaire if only he would repudiate all his works.

"All my works?" Voltaire asked.

"Every one of them!" said the priest. "Without exception!"

"Do you mean to tell me that you've read them all?" Voltaire asked. "And you know for a fact that I must repudiate everything I've written?"

"I have read none of them!" the priest cried. "For I never touch an impious book except to throw it into the flames."

"You are asking me, then, to repudiate the Bible!" Voltaire flung at him. "Yes, the Bible! For don't you know that among my works is the Song of Solomon, which I translated into French verse in honor of Madame de Pompadour? Don't you know that my writings are full of arguments proving the existence of God and confounding the atheists? And don't you know that I dedicated my play *Mahomet* to His Holiness, with the Holy Father's own gracious permission? Shall I then repudiate Pope, Bible and God? Is that what you say? All because you burn my books instead of reading them? And are you here to tell me now that this is what I must do in order to gain admission into heaven?"

But among these priests there was one, a certain Abbé Gaultier, attached to the Hospital for Incurables, who, unlike the others, did not burst into Voltaire's room to rant of eternal damnation and hellfire, but sent him a kindly, a respectful, a sympathetic note offering his services, if ever they should be needed.

And him Voltaire kept in mind for that *fichu moment,* that villainous, dreadful time, when he would have to make what Henry IV called "the perilous leap" into the unknown.

Ah, if only somehow, somehow, one might go on living forever, working forever, studying forever, mounting forever from triumph to triumph!

And the curtain never coming down on a play whose scenes would unroll forever.

But since that was impossible, then at least "let me be buried decently," as he said one day to d'Alembert. "I don't want my poor body, ugly as it may be, to be thrown into the sewers. Or shoveled into the ground, at night, like that of poor Adrienne Lecouvreur. As if I were no more than a dead dog."

"You have only to do what Montesquieu had to do," said d'Alembert. "And Fontenelle too. And how many others. All of whom had to submit in the end to the priests. Confessing themselves as sinners, and repudiating all their writings. Accepting Communion and extreme unction. We will understand, we men of letters. And we'll forgive you. Since for us the same hour will strike someday."

But Voltaire shook his head vigorously. No! Die in the Catholic faith? Yes, that he would do. Or at least he would try. Because he had been born in that faith, and he might as well go out by the same door he had come in. What was he, a Rousseau? To change his religion again and again? As if a Calvin or a Luther could possibly know more than the Pope in matters where all men are equally ignorant, death being a dark tapestry that no man has ever lifted.

But repudiate all his writings? That was one thing he would never do.

"They will go on being read, you may be sure," said d'Alembert.

"I trust so," said Voltaire, "for there will never be a time when man will not have to fight fanaticism and tyranny."

But just the same he would not consent to a deathbed repudiation of his works. Notwithstanding the fact that he himself had repudiated his works often enough, by publishing them anonymously, and even by denying his authorship. Yes, repeatedly.

But that had been only a matter of lying to men. Compelled by circumstances. So that he might go on writing.

But this would be lying to God.

"All that the fanatics are asking me to do is stick a few nails into my behind. So that millions more will continue to stick nails into theirs. And why not? Where's the harm of it? If one is dying beside the Ganges, I suppose it is only right to die with a cow's tail in one's hand. Such is the custom. But for *me* there has to be a place where *I* draw the line. Because of the fight that I have made all my life against superstition."

"And where will you draw that line?" d'Alembert asked.

"I will acknowledge nothing but the existence of a Creator," Voltaire replied. "For every second of my life has been to me a convincing and a most precious proof that He exists. Beyond that I do not know anything. Nor does anyone else."

And he could only hope that this line would somehow be found sufficient to secure him his burial permit. So that his survivors might give him a fine funeral—if they deemed him worthy of it.

But all these thoughts about death could not prevent Voltaire from still using every remaining minute of his life to the fullest. The fact that a man must die is no reason why he should bury himself while still alive. As it seemed Rousseau had done. No more than a man on a sinking ship need start to swim before he is actually in the water.

Not for a moment did Voltaire interrupt his furious activity with respect to his visitors and his friends. Nor with respect to his play: to the selection of a cast, to the coaching of actors and actresses, the planning of costumes, and the last-minute changing of lines in order to intensify his drama.

Nevertheless, the thought of death could not be kept from intruding. Most sharply, perhaps, when he went to visit the Marquise de Gouvernet, who, sixty years before, as the delightful but not too talented actress Suzanne Livry, had been his mistress. And also, when Voltaire was ill, the mistress of his closest friend. And when Voltaire was well again, the mistress of both of them.

But after that she had been wooed and won by the Marquis de La Tour du Pin de Gouvernet, who married her and set her up in a palace so sumptuous that it was known as "the Thousand and One Nights," and Suzanne reigned there as the Sultana of Flowers.

When that happened she became very proper and shut out her past, and when Voltaire came to visit her she had her porter close the door in his face. That was when he had gone home to write his beautiful poem *Épître des "Vous" et des "Tu."* About the change in Suzanne Livry when she rose from the familiar *tu* to the formal *vous*.

But now, fifty-seven years later, now that she was a widow and old, her door was open again to a Voltaire equally old.

She received him while seated in an easy chair, backed against a wall. And above her, on that wall, hung a painting by Largillière, the portrait of Voltaire as a youth.

This tableau was obviously meant to say, "That's how I want to remember you—young and handsome. Try, then, to think of me in the same way: young and beautiful."

But who can do that? The result was so unsuccessful that it resulted only in locking their tongues. Neither one could say a word. They only sat facing each other, their eyes overflowing.

With Voltaire no doubt remembering the lines of the poem he had written the day she had turned him away from her door.

> *Non, madame, tous ces tapis*
> *Qu'a tissus la Savonnerie,*
> *Ceux que les Persans ont ourdis*
> *Et toute votre orfèverie*

Et ces plats si chers que Germain
A gravé de sa main divine
Et ces cabinets où Martin
A surpassé l'art de la Chine,
Vos vases japonais et blancs,
Toutes ces fragiles merveilles,
Ces deux lustres de diamants
Qui pendent à vos oreilles,
Ces riches carcans, ces colliers,
Et cette pompe enchanteresse
Ne valent pas un des baisers
Que tu donnais dans ta jeunesse.

No, all that fantastic luxury of *your* palace was not worth a single one of *thy* youthful kisses.

So they separated without a word. Voltaire returning to his home to say, "This afternoon I crossed the Styx. And had to cross it again, coming back." And thinking of the inroads that death had made. Thieriot gone. And Vauvenargues. And how many others!

And the very next morning, early, sitting up in bed, propped up with pillows, and dictating to Wagnière some new lines, declaiming them with all his usual theatrical fire, he was suddenly attacked by a fit of coughing.

He was disturbed by a tiny trailing spiral of red in the clear of his spittle. He cleared his throat again. And now the red was more prominent. He tried again and got more blood. And all at once his throat and nostrils were hot with blood gushing out so violently that it inundated clothes and bedding.

Wagnière leaped up, crying out, and rushed to pull the bell rope. Madame Denis came in, shrieked and flew out the door to send a lackey on the run for Dr. Tronchin, who was now established in Paris. Soon the whole household was gathered in Voltaire's room, with everybody offering advice and some few busy with wet towels, but Voltaire's blood continuing to pour.

Dr. Tronchin arrived, had the room cleared immediately and, by bleeding three pints of blood from the patient, brought the hemorrhage under control. Down to no more than a delicate trickle. He was also able to establish the fact that the flow was from some ruptured blood vessel in the throat and not from the lungs, which would have been even more serious.

A nurse was put in charge. To keep out all visitors. And a surgeon-barber remained on duty, available at all hours to bleed the patient again if the hemorrhage should ever threaten to become more than this trickle.

And Voltaire was cautioned not to speak, but hardly needed that injunction, for he was so weak that he could scarcely have made a sound if he had wanted to. Which he didn't. All his faculties being involved in his struggle to hold on to whatever bit of life he could still feel within himself. Asking himself if he was to be deprived of that moment of triumph which he had been looking forward to for so many years. As Moses had been denied his entry into the Promised Land for which he had struggled all his life.

Ah, if only one could pray! But to whom? To God?

How insane that would be. God! The Creator! Before Whom he had knelt one night, many years ago. One night when he and the Marquise du Châtelet had been on the road, and their coach had broken down. And they had sat outside, looking at the spread of stars in the sky. And the Milky Way as if flung across the heavens from a lady's powder puff.

But each tiny dot of powder—and there were millions of them—was really a sun, and only God could know how many planetary bodies wheeled about each one of those suns. And each such planetary body a possible earth inhabited by countless species of life represented in numberless individuals.

One gasped for breath at the extent of creation. And the Milky Way was only one universe out of many universes. No one knowing how many millions or billions of other universes there might be.

No wonder he knelt that night before the Creator!

But pray? How could he? How could man pray to such a God? As if one were on familiar terms with Him and could describe Him as being, for example, blue in color, or square in shape.

As if at Ferney, in his castle, a fly caught in a spider's web in some dark corner of his cellar might pray that the master of the castle would save him. Prolong his life. Kill that spider. And then that wretched fly daring to presume that there was no lord to the castle, daring to deny the existence of Voltaire, simply because no one came in answer to his prayer. No one came to rescue him from death.

No. One could only adore God. And Voltaire did adore God. He lay there on his bed and adored God, but never a plea for mercy escaped him.

Meanwhile the news of his illness spread through the city, and his house was now more besieged than ever, with inquiries as to the poet's condition, and requests to be allowed to help. The Academy went so far as to post a daily bulletin for the information of their members. As if the King of France were ill. And the Théâtre-Français held a special meeting to decide whether to go ahead with the rehearsals of *Irene* or not, the vote being to go on with the production no matter what might happen.

Bernardin de Saint-Pierre brought the bad news to Rousseau. "Voltaire is dying," he said.

After a moment Rousseau replied, "He will live."

That was not Bernardin's opinion. "At his age? After the kind of hemorrhage he has had?"

"He will live. He will live," Rousseau repeated. "You will see."

Voltaire couldn't die. He had to live. Had there ever been a time without a Voltaire? Rousseau could not remember such a time. Could not even conceive of it. Why, when he, Jean Jacques, had been a vagabond, in his teens, a nobody, there had already been a Voltaire, whom people applauded wildly and who was spoken of with respect and excitement. And now, half a century later, with Jean Jacques once again a nobody, people were still applauding Voltaire and still speaking of him with respect and excitement.

How, then, could Voltaire fail to go on living? It was impossible.

And the fact was that he did not die. He lingered on, day after day, until one morning he felt himself strong enough to ask for writing materials and to scribble a note for Abbé Gaultier at the Hospital for Incurables.

The moment had come for Voltaire to face the Church on the question of a burial permit. To decide whether his body would go into the carrion pit or into a Christian grave.

When the abbé arrived, Voltaire closeted himself with him and gave him his confession, which the abbé must have considered satisfactory, for he went on to ask the poet to agree now to a repudiation of all his works.

But the old moribund, his face and body the color of gray parchment from lack of blood, would not give in. His toothless mouth gummed his arguments: "Would I not be committing new sins, now after confession, if I repudiated *in toto* works that surely must contain some shred of good? Therefore, in order not to burden my conscience, I have written out the following statement, which I am willing to sign."

He gave the abbé a paper on which was to be read: "The undersigned states that, being eighty-four years of age, and suffering from hemorrhages, he has been unable to drag himself to church, but hereby declares his wish to die in the Catholic faith in which he was born. He also declares that if ever he offended either God or the Church in any of his works, he hereby begs forgiveness from both."

The abbé was not too pleased with this formula, but since Voltaire, weak and sick as he was, would not budge from his position, the abbé let it pass and prepared to give him the sacrament of the Eucharist. But once again the old man demurred. He even called in his nurse and his barber-surgeon, and others, to be witnesses to the impossibility of it.

"Please observe," he murmured, "that I cannot take any food. That my stomach will not suffer the slightest particle of it. That I am constantly spitting up blood. What a desecration if I should vomit up the flesh of our Saviour mingled with my blood."

The abbé argued for a moment, but, finding that Voltaire was adamant, he shrugged, put away the wafer and said, "You understand, of course, Monsieur de Voltaire, that I shall have to submit my report to your parish priest, Monsieur de Tersac, of the Church of St.-Sulpice. It will be up to him to decide whether you have died in the Christian faith, and whether your body shall be entitled to Christian inhumation."

It soon became evident that M. Faydit de Tersac did not think so. Most emphatically not.

A heretic in consecrated soil? A man whose every work had been condemned as fast as it fell from his pen? No! Not while the parish of St.-Sulpice was in M. de Tersac's hands.

And especially not this heretic, worse by far than even Luther. This propagator of that infamous doctrine that every human being, intelligent or stupid, well-meaning or evil, should be free to live and worship according to his own ideas. Free, if you please, to spout any and all the insane blasphemies that he might wish. Voltaire cavalierly regarding such blasphemies as nothing more than differences of opinion. That's all. And to him one opinion about God or Jesus being just as good as any other, and thus any fool granted the right to go up and down the land, insulting the Deity according to his whim.

Ah, no indeed!

Religion was too serious a matter for that. Eternity, the soul, divine grace, the punishment of sin—these were far too important to be left to the ignorant, the unthinking and the corrupt. Putting into jeopardy the salvation of millions of innocent people! As if it had not been to guard against this very thing that Christ instituted His Church. And appointed the shepherds of His flock.

No. Never should this destroyer of civilization have a Christian burial. Not without the most abject apology. The most ringing renunciation of everything he had hitherto stood for. A firm and complete and final rejection of all his false philosophies, all his lies, all his sarcasms. And a humble plea to the Church and to the world for forgiveness.

And let him not imagine that he could escape by returning to Ferney and getting himself laid to rest in the tomb he had built on his own estate. For that church was in the diocese of the bishop of Annecy, and M. de Tersac had already put himself in touch with that gentleman, and it had been agreed that in Ferney too Voltaire would find himself shut out.

Not that the Church was not merciful. Indeed, no institution was ever so lenient or so easily placated. Just this piece of paper to sign. Just these few words. Already written in and ready for your signature. Thus bringing you back into the fold of the Church with the least possible exertion.

Except that Voltaire too had pondered these last bitter moments of his life. Often. Often. On how many nights of suffering! When, hour after hour, he died and died again. Then he would hear the cry of the monks and priests, shouting, "Sign! Sign!"

And he would visualize himself pleading with them, "Have pity on me. Don't you see that I am dying?"

And they would argue back, "It is precisely for that reason—because we consider ourselves the guardians of your most precious possession, your soul. And because we pity you and want to open the gates of heaven for you."

But how could Voltaire sign this document that rested on five propositions which he considered that no man was competent to rule upon? "So I must take sides with Lanfranc against Bérenger, must I? And I must take sides with Saint Thomas against Saint Bonaventura? And with the Nicene Council against the Council of Frankfurt? Is that what you are asking me to do?"

"Yes, yes. And hurry! No more arguments."

"But what about perjury? Is it all right for me to lie—now, when I am about to appear before God's throne?"

In this and other imaginary conversations he had asked priests why a man who had owned a cabaret where dozens, or even hundreds, had wasted their lives getting drunk could die without renouncing his works—why there was no problem about burial for him. And why diplomats and military leaders who had involved their countries in futile wars, in which thousands had died in the flower of their youth, were not called upon to disown their philosophy of national greed.

No, it was always Voltaire who was the sinner. Voltaire whose mind they had to bend to their will. Voltaire who had to be subdued.

And Voltaire had even foreseen (in his *Treatise on Tolerance*) the most frightening possibility: that after all his years of fighting superstition, he might be tricked into signing away whatever victory he had managed to secure during his lifetime of work.

"Ah! I am dying." So he pictured himself in a scene with a priest. "This is my last breath," he murmured, "but with it I will pray to God that He may touch your heart and convert you to charity for all. Believers and unbelievers alike. Farewell . . ."

Then he imagined the priest so annoyed at seeing his prize slip away that he would say, "The Devil take this fool! To die like that, without signing. But no one is watching. And I can easily forge the palsied signature of a dying man."

And then there were also the atheists. Fanatics too. In their own way. Who were determined that Voltaire should expire denying the existence of God. And it was to guard himself against both these groups, right and left, that Voltaire had written his statement that he was dying in the Catholic faith, and begging both God and Church to forgive him if he had slandered them.

And to make himself entirely clear, he had written for the world his one-line bible, his testament for modern man: "I die adoring God, loving my friends, not hating my enemies, and detesting superstition."

There was his entire religion.

He had signed and dated it. And given it to Wagnière for safekeeping. And it may be seen to this day in the Bibliothèque Nationale of Paris.

No. He would not give in. To either side. Not that he was afraid of God. Indeed, it could only be a matter of supreme indifference to the Creator that some inconsequential and almost toothless old wretch named Voltaire, member of that short-lived species of bipeds called *Homo sapiens,* happened to be perishing on a distant planet of the solar system and refusing to scribble his name on a tiny piece of paper. Simply because he did not agree to what was written on it. Even though that writing was invisible two yards away.

No, surely the great Creator of the universe couldn't care less. Microscopic disputes!

But Voltaire cared.

And to his last breath he would refuse to add his signature to the confusion of beliefs that had caused Europe so often to run with blood. Yes, to his last breath.

39: KILL ME WITH GLORY

And somehow Voltaire didn't take that last breath. Not just yet. Once more, as so often in his life, he managed to postpone his agony. Perhaps because all this religious bickering, for all that it was carried on in a typically eighteenth-century fashion—that is to say, with unfailing courtesy—was nevertheless a duel of wills. A sharp clash, unyielding on either side.

Thus exerting a curiously revitalizing effect on Voltaire. As if an old war horse, expiring on the field of battle, heard once more the trumpets calling the charge and could somehow find within his wounded body the strength to rise again on shaky legs.

Voltaire began not only to sit up in bed, but even to get out of bed and relax in his easy chair. He did not, of course, dare to go so far as to attend the opening of *Irene,* but his friends had arranged for a brigade of messengers to run back and forth between the theater and the poet's bedside and keep the old master supplied with so many reports that it would be almost as if he were actually present.

"House packed!" was the first of these communiqués.

And then: "Your friends so numerous that your enemies daren't open an attack."

Next: "All Versailles has turned out. The King's brothers are just entering their box. And Queen Marie Antoinette is already in hers, in spite of the King's express orders against showing you any attention."

Then the curtain going up. And: "First act a terrific success. The Queen is seen with paper and pencil, taking down your most striking verses."

And: "Your lines against the clergy are being especially appreciated because of your recent *affaire* with them."

And so forth and so on.

Later, to be sure, the critics would all agree that *Irene* was one of the poorest of all Voltaire's plays. But not that night. Not in the atmosphere in which it was being shown, which made it one of Voltaire's most exciting and most significant.

And Voltaire was so stimulated by this success that he was soon up and about as if there never had been such an incident in his life as a massive hemorrhage. Even though Dr. Tronchin warned him, "As a *rentier,* haven't you got enough sense to spend only your health's income instead of drawing on your capital at your age?"

Once again Voltaire's coach was seen traversing Paris. With greater crowds than ever shouting "Voltaire! Voltaire!" wherever they caught sight of him. And the *Journal de Paris* deciding that the old poet had made such a sensational and total recovery that "not a trace of his recent illness can be detected." Whereupon the Comédie-Française scheduled rehearsals for a gala performance of *Irene* on March 30, at which the author himself promised to appear.

That, and his attendance at the meetings of the Academy of Belles Lettres, were the highest moments of Voltaire's Parisian visit. The short distance from his home to the Louvre, where the Academy then held its sessions, was lined with admirers. More than two thousand forming themselves into a living hedge in his honor.

And inside (with the chair of every clerical member conspicuously vacant) the Academy was amazed to find itself gathered to hear a violent tirade against itself. No one had expected anything but the usual mutual compliments, but Voltaire suddenly launched into an unmerciful castigation of the membership. For laziness. For their failure to carry out their main obligation, which was the cherishing and preservation of the French language.

"Why is it that a dictionary has still not been compiled?" Voltaire demanded. "Was not that one of the purposes of the founding of this body? And are the honorable members not aware that in the meantime the French language has been losing some of its most picturesque and energetic expressions? Such, for example, as those to be found in the works of Amyot, of Charron and of Montaigne?

"Shall our French language become poverty-stricken, cold and flat, while the tongues of other peoples grow in expressiveness and beauty? Let us not forget that a language too can become sick and die. Are we to stand by idly while the many wonderful examples of word usage created by our poets are allowed to perish and even the derivation of our words is lost for lack of an adequate etymological record? All that must be the function of a dictionary. And the French language must have it or else die.

"And what, pray, is so difficult about the making of a dictionary? Are there not more than twenty-four of us here? If each one of us will but take a single orphan into his home, a single letter of our

486

poor homeless alphabet, and clothe and love that one letter, all of us together shall have built a mansion for the whole French language!

"I myself will begin. Give me the letter *A*. I adopt it. And, gentlemen, I promise you I shall take good care of it."

To see the old Voltairean zeal in operation again, and—the irony of it—to see this eighty-four-year-old man, just up from his deathbed, taking upon himself the letter *A*, perhaps the hardest of all, was enough to put the Academy to shame, while at the same time it aroused every member, so that amidst bursts of applause Voltaire's proposal was passed by acclamation and all the letters were quickly distributed.

Then Voltaire rose to beg for the floor again. And when the hall was hushed, he was heard to say simply, "Gentlemen, I thank you in the name of our alphabet."

Whereupon Academician de Chastellux, the same who was shortly to go with Rochambeau to fight in the American Revolution, replied: "And we thank you, Monsieur de Voltaire, in the name of French letters."

It was in the theater, however, that the wildest scenes took place. When Voltaire calmly entered a box reserved for the gentlemen of the King's chamber, as if a quarter of a century had not elapsed since he had used any of the rights connected with that office.

He had placed Madame Denis and the Marquise de Villette up front and had sat himself down behind them, almost invisible. But the whole house erupted with cries of "Up front! Up front!" and the ladies were forced to squeeze their magnificent toilettes aside so that Voltaire might sit forward between them.

Then the popular actor of the day (Lekain having just died), the former painter Brizard, who was to play the lead in *Irene,* stepped up with a crown of laurel leaves to put on Voltaire's head. Voltaire naturally resisting, and attempting to put the crown on the Marquise instead.

But again the audience shouted its displeasure, and the Prince de Beauvau himself reached into the box to snatch up the crown and force it upon the patriarch's brow.

Whereupon the whole house was on its feet. Roaring.

The number of people present was at least twice what it should have been. Aisles and lobbies were packed. Crowds had been lined up since dawn to make sure of getting a chance to buy a ticket. And anyone so lucky as to secure one could sell it for five or even ten times what it had cost. The whole area around the theater had been blocked since early afternoon by stalled carriages. And it was a wonder how actors and employees managed to make their way through this jam of vehicles and humanity into the house to assume their duties.

Inside, the fracas would not end. People had their clothes ripped to shreds in their efforts to find a better position from which to glimpse Voltaire. (And later exhibited these torn clothes with pride, as evidence of their attendance on that magic night.) And the commotion raised such dust that at times no one could see much of anything. In spite of which, the clapping and the shouting would not die down. Not even when the curtain had risen and the play was beginning.

Lines and even occasional whole scenes had to be repeated, not once, but twice, because of the tumult. And then, at the end of the play, while the audience was still applauding frantically, the curtain rose once more. To show a stage occupied with nothing but a pedestal on which was a bust of Voltaire.

Actors and actresses now appeared from the wings to form themselves into a semicircle about the bust. For Voltaire was now to be honored, not just for *Irene* but for all his plays. And there were recitations of poetic eulogies, and still another crowning, and no end to the demonstrations of popular enthusiasm.

While Voltaire, in his box, kept moaning, "It is a conspiracy to kill me with glory." And his eyes would not cease overflowing with tears, which he would wipe away furtively, as though he were half ashamed of them.

Even when Voltaire had finally managed to leave the theater, the uproar would not stop. The driver could scarcely get his horses into motion, so great was the press of the crowd. From somewhere torches were produced, and a hundred men quickly formed themselves into a guard of honor to force a path for Voltaire's carriage and to light his way back to his residence. While others even went so far as to strew rose petals in advance of his horses and kiss and fondle the beasts, as if they should be honored, too, for pulling Voltaire's vehicle.

"Can they really mean it?" Voltaire asked the Marquis de Villette.

"Of course they mean it," he replied.

Voltaire shook his head unbelievingly. "But are not these the same Parisians," he asked, "who eight years ago flocked to the antechamber of the Prince de Conti, waiting to catch a glimpse of Jean Jacques? And yet today they hardly know if that poor fool is alive or dead. And probably care less."

The Marquis would not agree. "You're wrong," he said. "The Parisians care a great deal. For both of you."

"But that makes no sense!" Voltaire cried. "We are as different as night and day. Anyone who agrees with him cannot very well agree with me. Impossible!"

"Just the same," the Marquis insisted, "they do love you both. And they do care!"

"Bah!" was Voltaire's skeptical response. Nevertheless, his eyes continued to shed tears.

In the opinion of both Dusaulx and Bernardin de Saint-Pierre, this gala performance had gone far beyond the bounds of good taste. Overplayed, was Bernardin's opinion, which he brought to Rousseau's little apartment. And Dusaulx—who had also come to bring Rousseau a report—agreed, describing it as puffed up and exaggerated, full of air and water, like a big heat blister.

Would not one laudatory poem have expressed everyone's feelings? Why, then, a dozen? And did not one coronation make Voltaire the king of French literature? Why then did there have to be two? And people so aroused that they gladly risked not only their clothes, but life and limb, in a melee from which they hoped to gain a better view of the poet.

And then the torches! One would have been ample to light the way. And ten would have made it a memorable occasion. But no. There had to be a hundred. And then the culmination of the whole silly spectacle: rose petals under the hoofs of his horses. Could anything be more ridiculous?

Rousseau said nothing for a moment. Then, in an icy voice, he asked, "I presume, then, that you gentlemen know of someone else more worthy of these honors?"

Neither Bernardin nor Dusaulx was prepared for such a question, and neither of them had any answer. They could only wonder if perhaps Rousseau was so envious as to want such honors for himself.

And since they remained speechless, Rousseau went on angrily: "Then how dare you make fun of our theater for paying these honors to Monsieur de Voltaire? Who else has been the god of that temple for the last fifty years? Two generations of actors and actresses have made their living out of his pen. And it would be impossible to count the audiences all over Europe who in this half century have derived entertainment and excitement, beauty and moral precepts, from his plays. How, then, could the theater overdo itself in demonstrating its gratitude? And whom else should they crown, if not Monsieur de Voltaire?"

Neither Bernardin nor Dusaulx chose to argue the matter. Though they must have asked themselves whether that was really how Rousseau felt about his literary opponent. The man who had ridiculed and exposed him. The man of whom Rousseau himself had several times said, "There can be no peace for me so long as that man is alive."

But if that was how he really felt, then why had he not himself gone to the celebration and participated in these honors for Voltaire? What had kept him away? It wasn't as if he hadn't known about the gala performance. Everybody in Paris had heard about it. And it wasn't as if his attendance might have cost him anything, since, as an established writer, he was still entitled to his free ticket there in that house supported by royal funds.

Then what could have kept him away?

The conversation, however, never reached that point. Perhaps because there were tears to be seen in Jean Jacques's eyes. And neither visitor had the courage to break into this heavy moment with words that might have proved completely inappropriate.

Lacking the still unpublished *Confessions* and the correspondence of Jean Jacques with his Mama, they could not have guessed what scenes of his life must be unrolling behind those tears. And in particular that time in Grenoble when he had witnessed his first performance of a Voltairean play, *Alzire*. And felt that he would die right there in his seat because of the mixture of admiration and envy that was being stirred up in him. Passions so powerful that he had to rush from the theater and take to his bed. Lying there for days, in a fever, overcome with the terrible injustice of it: that one man should be born with so much talent and another with so little.

Bernardin de Saint-Pierre, however, must have come close to guessing the cause of Rousseau's tears: Jean Jacques matching himself against Voltaire. And it must have been then that he conceived that fine essay of his, which he wrote years later, comparing and contrasting the two men.

The one so rich. The other so poor. The one so talkative. The other so taciturn. The one writing poetry so fluent that it reads like prose. The other writing prose so eloquent that it reads like poetry. The one letting his reason get in the way of his genius. The other letting his genius get in the way of his reason.

As if Bernardin might have been seeking some deeper explanation of this strange phenomenon, this like and unlike and dislike, this bond that both chained and divided. Groping for an understanding of the relationship between the man who became a watchmaker and the man who was a watchmaker's son. And catching perhaps more than a glimpse of a symbolic father and a symbolic son, admiring and envying each other. Loving and hating. Gradually moving toward a predestined relationship.

And this must have been the moment, too, when Rousseau suddenly felt that he must get out of Paris. Fast. Just exactly as he had found himself forced to rush out of that theater many years ago. For nothing had changed. All these violent passions of his that he had thought were dead were still there, alive, and ready to cut him to pieces again.

So that he had to leave at once. Out of this city that had become the stage for a starring Voltaire.

Saying nothing to either Dusaulx or Bernardin. But quickly making his arrangements, and leaving for later his explanations that he just couldn't stand Paris any longer. Where trees died from noise and dust.

As if all along some royal decree had been forcing him to stay in Paris against his will. As if for seven years he hadn't been turning down one offer after another of a house in the country. Just recently, for example, Count d'O's offer. And a little later Count Duprat's. And then that of the Chevalier Flamanville. And that of the commander of Menon, a friend of Duprat's.

But now, suddenly, he let Corancez, the son of one of the founders of the *Journal de Paris,* know that he would accept his proffered house at Sceaux, just outside Paris. A house which he had previously several times refused. However, no sooner had Corancez made arrangements to come to Jean Jacques's apartment in the morning, with a carriage large enough to move them out, than Rousseau took up another invitation that also lay to hand: that of the Marquis de Girardin, who was willing not only to give him a little pavilion on his estate, but to take him out of Paris that very afternoon. Out to Ermenonville, where the Girardins had one of the most beautiful properties in all of France, on which millions had been lavished.

Thus Rousseau left. In a departure that can be regarded only as a flight from Voltaire. And from his own past.

Without so much as a word to Corancez. So that when the latter found himself at Rousseau's door the following morning, ready to help move them, there was no Jean Jacques. Just Thérèse. Packing up and grumbling. And shrugging at the questions that Corancez put to her. Not really knowing where her husband had gone. Or else not caring to tell. Just that he had gone off. And that he would send for her eventually.

And Bernardin de Saint-Pierre also appeared. He too had had an appointment with Rousseau. To walk with him to Sèvres. And he too had heard nothing of Rousseau's moving away.

And all this mystification because of that unspoken and unanswerable question that neither Bernardin nor Dusaulx had dared to ask. And that Rousseau would never have answered.

The question: "Why weren't you in the theater, if that is how you felt about honoring Voltaire? Why weren't you there, in that stamping crowd? Why weren't you there, clapping your hands, shouting your praises, getting the clothes torn from your back? Letting yourself go so far, in your drunken affection, as to strew roses before his coach, and kiss his horses?"

Yes, why? Why, when there was really never anything else you wanted more to do in all your life?

But now, safe at Ermenonville, Jean Jacques could enjoy his peace and quiet again. With Thérèse soon joining him, and life again routined, so as to give him no reason for thinking about Voltaire. Once again taking his early-morning walks and coming home loaded with various plants. Having his breakfast, and then working on still another herbarium. He had compiled quite a number already, giving them to friends as presents.

Never imagining that they were of any great value. In fact, the first to admit that he had no real head for botany. So little, indeed, that after all the years he had devoted himself to this subject he still could not get along without constant consultation of his guidebooks. But pursuing it nevertheless. Finding pleasure in pasting up his plants, identifying and labeling them. If for no other reason than that it took up his time.

Time, for which he no longer had any use. Though he had now constituted himself as the musical instructor of the Girardin children. And in the evenings would sometimes dine with the family and afterward engage in some not too serious discussion with M. de Girardin. Or else play some melodies for Madame.

But no more than two weeks of this when, one day, the Marquis came to him with important news. "About Voltaire," he said excitedly. "Have you heard? All Paris is buzzing about it."

No. Rousseau had heard nothing. And he seemed as if uninterested until he heard M. de Girardin say, "There's a rumor that Voltaire is dead." Then he stood stock-still, hardly breathing.

"Some are saying that Voltaire died several days ago," the Marquis went on quickly. "In fact, on Saturday night. But what is strange is that no one really knows for sure. And at the home of the Marquis de

Villette there is no information to be got. Not a soul is being admitted.

"That's what's so odd. The secrecy. As if orders had gone out not to let the public know. The newspapers, until recently so full of him, now suddenly seem to have forgotten his very name. Not a word anywhere. And certainly no obituary. Not in the *Journal de Paris,* not in any of the papers. And for the first time in perhaps half a century, there is not a single performance of any Voltaire play scheduled by the theater.

"Those who maintain that Voltaire is still alive argue that if he were dead the Franciscans would be holding a special mass for him, attended by all the members of the Academy, that being the custom since the founding of the institution. What is certain is that no such mass has been held and that none is contemplated. Nor is anyone campaigning for Voltaire's vacant seat, about which there would be such a stir if Voltaire were really dead.

"But meanwhile all sorts of epigrams are being passed from hand to hand that seem to take Voltaire's death for granted. Some violently for the man, such as one addressed to the Archbishop de Beaumont: 'You can deny him a tomb, but we will build him an altar.' And others violently against Voltaire—for example, one that goes: 'Here lies the spoiled child of the world that he spoiled.' Then there's another one—"

M. de Girardin stopped, struck by Rousseau's appearance. Jean Jacques's face had gone quite ashen.

"Are you unwell?" the Marquis asked. "Would you like some water?"

"I'm all right," said Rousseau quietly. But as the Marquis continued to look at him wonderingly, Rousseau added, "Only now I must die, too."

"What do you mean, you too must die?" the Marquis exclaimed.

"Don't you know that our lives are linked?" Rousseau said. As if it were the most obvious thing in the world. "Monsieur de Voltaire is dead. I shall not be long in following him."

A scene that M. de Girardin would never forget. And that he would report in a letter to Musset-Pathay, Rousseau's first important biographer.

Voltaire! Voltaire!

How can you possibly be dead? Leaving one with nothing to live for? Nothing to do from now on but wait for one's own death?

No. You can't be dead. Sick, maybe. But you will recover. And rise to still greater heights. . . .

But it was true: Voltaire was dead. His death kept as secret as possible by his family, in order to trick the Church. And news of it ordered suppressed by the King, who hated the poet and feared his tumultuous admirers.

But dead he was. Although supremely alive almost to the last. Writing a poem to the notorious *bon vivant* the Abbé de L'Attaignant a few days before expiring.

And busy almost to the brink. Busy writing a new play, *Agathocles.* Busy shopping for a new house, and buying eventually the palatial residence that the Duke de Richelieu was in the process of constructing. And which Voltaire would now plan to complete in order to have a permanent home in Paris. And busy sending Wagnière back to Ferney to look after rents, after the sale of crops, after his watch and silk factories and a host of other accumulated business details.

And busy with the letter *A* too.

Determined to wake up those lazy Academicians by his example. Writing to Wagnière at Ferney: "Fix up a crate of books for me immediately, and ship it to me in all haste. My Port-Royal grammar, to begin with. And then Restaut's little grammar too. And Girard's *Synonyms.* Also Dumarsais's *Figures of Speech.* And Pélisson's *Letters.* Vaugelas's *Remarks.* My little *Dictionary of Proverbs.* And anything else on the French language.

"Also the quarto on surgery, by Thévenin. And a two-volume study on French orthography which ought to be on the desk in my library. I'll be wanting my Italian *Vocabolario* too, as well as Buon Mattei's grammar. And the big Italian dictionary, that two- or three-volume affair which ought to be on the first shelf of my Italian books in the new addition to my library. Then that nicely bound two-volume English work *Origin of Languages . . .*"

Books and more books, from his library of over six thousand volumes. Of which fewer than three dozen were novels. And which would nevertheless be described later as "a miserable collection of light reading, the sort of thing that a farmer would gather for his winter pastime." An opinion first issued by that Voltaire hater Joseph Marie de Maistre, the same who maintained that the foundation of man's civilization was the executioner. And who claimed to have examined the collection in St. Petersburg.

And this ugly lie about Voltaire's books would be repeated thereafter by all the haters of Voltaire. Kreiter of Germany would repeat it as if it were gospel. And so would Madame de Genlis. And the Abbé Maynard in his book. And Nicolardot in his. And most recently Sister O'Flaherty in hers.

Just as it would be repeated indefinitely that Voltaire had died in the most frightful torments. Bemoaning with great cries that he had wasted his life in blasphemy and that his soul must now burn in hell. Going out of his mind at the sight of the Devil lurking beside his bed, and, in his frenzy of despair, seizing his chamber pot and pouring its awful contents down his gullet.

Again and again this incredible story has been repeated. As if, in a household of wealth such as that of the Marquis de Villette, overflowing with servants, a dirty chamber pot would be left lying around. As if Voltaire did not have his personal valet, Morand, at his bedside. And a personal nurse too. And a bell rope always at hand, to summon a lackey any time he wanted one.

And as if Voltaire himself had not written to Tronchin, his doctor, who wished to examine some specimen of the exudate from his bowels, that he regretted that he had nothing to show him.

Because for days he had not been able to eat. And, to keep himself active and working, despite the increasing pains of his body, he had swallowed nothing but black coffee. And also some opium pills that the Duke de Richelieu had given him.

"Absolutely harmless," the Duke had told him. "I use them myself all the time, and I'm at least as old as you."

What better recommendation could Voltaire want? So he began to take them, too. And, in fact, more and more of them—as they seemed to have less and less effect on his pains.

Until suddenly his body stopped functioning altogether. Bladder and bowel simply locking up. And still Voltaire full of life, and unwilling to lie down and die, even though the machinery for living had stopped and uremic poisoning and gangrene were setting in. Unwilling to surrender a life that had been so exciting, so beautiful, so rewarding.

And with so much still to be done! So many books, plays, poems, pamphlets still unwritten. So many innocent people to be defended from cruel and unjust sentences. So much money still to be made. So many letters still to be written. . . .

But finally nailed to his bed in spite of himself. Fever and a great lassitude making it impossible for him either to rage or to laugh. Though surely he would have raged and laughed magnificently against death if he had been able to. Instead he found himself forced to concentrate whatever power he still had in order to forgive God for His cruel joke on man.

Giving him life. And taking it away. God's will—or, rather, God's willfulness—be done.

And this was a joke, too: that some might consider Rousseau more fortunate in going to his death by easy stages, losing first his mind and then his fame, and being led through deepening obscurity toward final extinction; while he, Voltaire, was being tumbled abruptly from the height of fame into eternal who-knows-what.

He lay thus for several days, with only now and then a show of his old spirit. As, for example, when the news was brought to him that the King's Council had set aside the verdict against General de Lally. That too one of God's jokes. For the General was now long dead. Executed twelve years ago. First paraded through Paris with a gag in his mouth, so that he could not cry out his innocence to the people. And then beheaded. For having betrayed the French forces in India, thus losing that colony to England.

For years Voltaire had been almost alone in daring to fight for a man proclaimed throughout France as a traitor. An accusation so terrible that merely by pinning it on a person one had already succeeded in disgracing him, even before any trial. And any effort to appear on that man's behalf exposed people to the charge of being fellow conspirators.

But that didn't stop Voltaire from screaming, "Judicial murder!" Or from writing a book on the French-English war in India in order to demonstrate General de Lally's innocence.

And now, at last, the King's Council agreed with him. Ordering a retrial.

To the son of the "murdered" man, Voltaire wrote: "A dying man has been revived by the great news. He embraces you most affectionately. And now can return to his dying, happy in the thought that there is justice under our King."

He went further. In order to spare himself the necessity of arguing the matter (talk having become a painful ordeal to him), he begged that a sign be painted and affixed to the tapestry, to show all visitors that justice was possible under kings. Foreseeing the day soon to come when people would have a new superstition: that merely by the elimination of kings, justice, perfect justice, would come automatically.

And day after day, under that sign honoring Louis XVI, Voltaire somehow clung to a shred of life. Half ashamed of himself for lingering on. Sending Dr. Tronchin, when he needed his services, a most humble note. "Please excuse a dying man," he wrote, "for taking up a doctor's time in such a hopeless matter."

And showing irritation only with the priests who still wished to convert him. Saying to one of them, "If God were really so determined that man should have a religion, would He not have given us another protuberance somewhere about our body—a religious protuberance. In the same way that he gave us two eyes so that we might see, and a nose so that we might smell?"

Evidently still trying to die laughing, but soon so far gone that he could not react to religious stimulation either. And when M. de Tersac visited him with another retraction ready for signing, Voltaire was so close to death that he could not even reply to a question as to whether he believed in the divinity of Jesus Christ.

Whereupon M. de Tersac, under the impression that Voltaire had not heard him, leaned down to cry into Voltaire's ear, "Confess your faith in Jesus Christ! Confess Jesus Christ!"

"Jesus Christ? Jesus Christ?" Voltaire murmured. "Please let me die in peace."

With that M. de Tersac folded up the retraction, saying, "The man is obviously out of his mind." Though it was obvious that, on the contrary, Voltaire was still in his old Voltairean mind. Although that was going fast.

Late that same Saturday evening, he groped for his valet's hand, mumbling, "Goodbye, my dear Morand, I'm dying."

Laughter would have been too much of an exertion for him. But surely there must have been the faintest smile on his face when he died. For he had still a final trick up his sleeve. At any rate, his nephew, Abbé Mignot, seemed to act as if he knew exactly what to do. As if he had received previous instruction from the master trickster himself. The man who had successfully tricked Frederick the Great and had tricked Piron, and the husband of the Marquise du Châtelet. The man who had tricked censors, priests, aristocracy and kings. And death itself, for eighty-four years.

And who now intended to trick himself into a decent grave.

The deceit had been started while Voltaire was still alive. By concealing, insofar as it was possible, how close he was to death. And by having his body embalmed almost immediately after his decease. So that within a few hours, early Sunday morning, Abbé Mignot could already appear before the curate of St.-Sulpice for permission to remove Voltaire's body from his parish.

M. de Tersac could only suppose that Voltaire was to be taken back to Ferney, and, having already arranged matters with the bishop of Annecy, he was perfectly willing to give Abbé Mignot the necessary certificate.

Armed with this certificate, signed by M. de Tersac, and also with

Voltaire's statement of faith, signed by Abbé Gaultier, Abbé Mignot hired a post chaise and drove off as fast as he could to the village of Romilly-sur-Seine, a little over a hundred miles from Paris. This was Abbé Mignot's official residence, and he also had many friends at the nearby Abbey of Scellières, and thus he had little trouble inducing the prior to agree to bury Voltaire in the crypt of the abbey church.

Why not? With two documents signed by priests, everything seemed in perfect order, and the prior, who knew nothing of what had been going on in Paris, had no reason to deny this small service to a good friend.

Meanwhile, in Paris that evening, Voltaire was dressed up, as if still alive, in a dressing gown and a nightcap, such as a rich old gentleman might wear during a night voyage. And this impression of Voltaire returning while still alive to his estate at Ferney was further carried out by sitting him up as if half dozing, leaning against the cushions of his carriage. With his valet, Morand, sitting close enough to keep the body from toppling.

For who could know what certain religious fanatics might wish to do to Voltaire if they thought he was already a corpse?

Six horses were harnessed to the carriage to lend an air of wealth and authenticity to this picture of the rich, ailing Voltaire being rushed to his country seat. With several of Voltaire's nearest male relatives, a grandnephew and two cousins, following in another carriage.

The two equipages drove out of Paris as if going in the direction of Switzerland, but they turned northeast just as soon as they were out in the country and headed for the province of Champagne.

Not until they arrived in Romilly the following day was a carpenter called upon to make a coffin, out of pine wood. Vespers were then sung, and the body was laid out in state. At five o'clock in the morning a mass was said, and later a high mass, and then the body was lowered into the vault beneath the church floor.

When the priests of Paris bethought themselves that Voltaire might not have been taken to Ferney, but to Romilly, his nephew's place, they hastily dispatched a messenger to warn the prior there not to bury Voltaire. He was even threatened with "the most serious consequences" if he disobeyed.

The prior immediately rushed to Paris to defend himself and his position. Arguing that he had buried Voltaire because of the two documents that had been shown to him, both signed by reputable priests. How could he possibly know that this was a body that was to be denied religious services and inhumation?

Government and Church, which had combined to forbid any discussion of Voltaire's death and burial, did not dare go so far as to throw Voltaire's body out. That might have been too scandalous, and there was a question as to how the courts might rule on such a matter if the relatives of Voltaire should sue.

But an elaborate stone, already being chiseled for placing over the vault where Voltaire lay, was forbidden. Only a simple inscription was permitted: "Here lies Voltaire."

Less than a month after this burial, Jean Jacques Rousseau was dead, too.

He had wakened one warm day, July 2, feeling too tired to take his usual morning walk. And had lingered about the house until about ten o'clock, when Thérèse, upstairs, heard her name being repeatedly called in a harsh, choked voice. Terrified, she rushed downstairs and found her husband lying on the floor. Half paralyzed, groaning.

He was in pain, and suffering from strange chills. But once helped into an easy chair, he decided that all he needed was a physic, because he had eaten too richly the previous evening at the Girardins'. Thérèse therefore locked the door for privacy and went to get the medicine, but when she returned and Rousseau leaned forward to take it, he fell from the chair and struck his head so hard against the stone tiles of the floor that blood spurted from his forehead. And Thérèse, struggling to put him back on the chair, was soon drenched in blood.

She screamed for help. But help couldn't reach her until M. de Girardin came with a key to unlock the door.

By that time Jean Jacques was dead.

In the village—on account of that locked door—the rumor arose that Rousseau had first tried to poison himself and, when that had failed, had shot himself. And thus, that it was a bullet, not a fall, that had occasioned the head wound from which his blood had poured.

But Houdon, the sculptor, who hastened out from Paris to take a death mask of the writer, found no evidence of suicide. And neither did the physicians who performed an autopsy.

The body was buried on July 4, 1778. On the Island of Poplars, a lovely little island on the lake of the vast Ermenonville gardens. A night burial, with a couple of peasants holding torches to give light. And no church ceremony, because of his Protestantism.

Of his Parisian friends, only Corancez was present.

So now they were both gone, buried in graves more than a hundred miles apart. And leaving behind them their female companions, who seemed as if anxious to put them both out of their minds.

Madame Denis promptly selling off Ferney to the Marquis de Villette. And Voltaire's library to the Empress of Russia. And giving herself (and all the bonds and the diamonds she had inherited from Voltaire) in marriage to a man of less than fifty, when she herself was already close to seventy. Much to the disgust of all the admirers of Voltaire, who considered her conduct unbecoming the niece of so great a man.

And Thérèse taking up with a groom employed on the Ermenonville estate. A behavior that so shocked the Girardins, who continued to worship the memory of Jean Jacques, that they could not bear to have her living with them any more.

She settled in a nearby village and took to drink, becoming more and more disreputable, and making herself obnoxious by insisting that all the valuable manuscripts left by Rousseau, which should have become her property, had been dispersed without adequate compensation to her, taking advantage of her ignorance. Yet, when a de luxe edition of her husband's songs was issued, from which she might have realized the vast sum of thirty-four thousand francs in royalties, she signed away the entire amount to the foundling home of Paris.

The Revolutionary government of France later granted her an annual pension, sufficient to live on. She died at eighty-one. In Napoleon's time.

40: EPILOGUE

Climb Rue Soufflot some summer's day when you are in Paris, and enter that vast dome, the Panthéon. (Where, years ago, Foucault set up his famous pendulum demonstration, so that man, for the first time, could actually see the planet earth revolving under his feet.) And wait there in its marbled emptiness until the guard goes around summoning those who wish to visit the crypts.

There will be a gradually increasing patter of echoing footsteps as the little sprinkling of sightseers slowly converges upon the guard, who leads the way to a corner, where he unlocks heavy doors.

As he guides you downstairs, deeper and deeper into the foundation of the structure of the old Church of Ste. Geneviève (the weight of whose dome caused architect Soufflot such anxieties that he died of a heart attack when the rumor suddenly flew through Paris that his church was collapsing), the guard will point out to you the microscopic exactness with which the chiseled stones are fitted to each other. A layer of mortar might allow some damp to penetrate; these stones therefore rest massively against each other with nothing but a thin sheet of lead crushed between them. Thus excluding the corruption of moisture forever from this last resting place, once intended for rich Catholics, but later assigned by the French Revolution to those whom the Republic most wished to honor.

It is chilly here. And hushed. And one's eyes must accustom themselves to a gloom that is only faintly relieved by dark purplish lamps.

The crypts succeed each other off the corridors like chapels in a cathedral, each glimpsed through a small aperture worked into a ponderous door. Inside one spies a clutter of urns, some stone caskets and a number of busts and memorial tablets. All inscribed with the names of celebrated men, who in the course of time unfortunately tend to become so numerous as to become confused and forgotten.

Two crypts, however, stand out. Each reserved for a single body. Each wide open, without a door, and each containing only one giant sarcophagus. A signal honor granted only to the bones of Voltaire and Rousseau.

The tomb of Voltaire is further distinguished by his statue, placed in front of it. As if his restless spirit, which made such a big splash in the eighteenth century, would still not permit him to lie quietly in a box.

Across the aisle is the cenotaph of Rousseau. With a truly startling carving on it: a pair of almost-closed doors, through which a heavily veined hand grasping a flaming torch is forcefully thrusting itself just as the leaves of the door are about to slam shut forever. As if to illustrate how even the finality of death could not stop this man from passing on to future generations the fiery purpose of his life.

But most gripping, for one who knows anything of these two men and who stands here between these two confronting tombs, is the silence. The complete and utter silence. Only the guard's voice droning on for yet a little while, until he has exhausted his singsong recital of names and dates. With never a word about any controversy between the two men.

And when the guard leaves, the little knot of people leaves with him. And then the silence becomes truly unbearable.

The irony of it! That these two men, who never met in life, should now face each other. In silence. Through eternity.

But what would they say? What would they say, if they could speak? Voltaire was the first to inhabit this subterranean masonry. Shortly after the beginnings of the French Revolution. When, in the theater, of all his plays the one being most wildly applauded was *Brutus*. (Not about the familiar Marcus Junius Brutus, but about another, earlier Brutus, the Roman patriot Lucius Junius Brutus, who did not shrink from condemning his own son to death when he discovered him involved in a plot against the republic.)

Though written sixty years before, it was a play made for these times. And it was in the midst of an inspiring performance of this *Brutus* that the Marquis de Villette leaped to his feet and harangued the audience. Calling it a shame, a national disgrace, that the author of this play should still lie in an almost unknown grave, to which the despotism of priests of a former day had condemned him.

"Who sowed the seeds of our glorious Revolution?" he cried. "Who called for the abolition of torture? Who demanded equality of taxation, an end to privileges of Church and aristocracy? Who called for every Frenchman to have some property, and thus a stake in the welfare of his country?"

People wept and applauded. And the result was such a wave of popular enthusiasm for bringing Voltaire's body to Paris, and giving him the funeral he should have had, that the National Assembly passed a decree to that effect and Louis XVI, already the prisoner of his people, was forced to sign it.

Whereupon an ornately decorated funeral wagon was built to pick up the body at the Abbey of Scellières. And spontaneously, all along the route to Paris, in village after village, festivities were held. Triumphal arches were erected. Girls sang and danced. Citizens paraded. And at night there were torches and lanterns to light the way, and voluntary groups organizing themselves as escorts. While thousands lined the road, cheering. And mothers lifted up their children for a better view.

In Paris an altar had been raised on the site of the recently destroyed Bastille. An altar built out of the stones of that fortification. And Voltaire's body was placed in state there. With an inscription beneath, reading: "Voltaire! Here, where despotism chained you twice, receive the homage of a free people!"

Then, for the final part of the journey, there was a bronze funeral car. Designed by the great David. A truly imposing affair, tall as a four-story building and rich with a hundred allegorical figures. And men clad in antique robes led the twelve milk-white steeds that pulled this gigantic catafalque.

With more music, and more dancing. And no end of flowers and garlands. And a hundred thousand people joining the procession.

And special halts made. For special ceremonies and speeches. For the Calas family to come forward and honor their defender. And another at the Pont-Royal, so that Louis XVI might watch from the Tuileries, where he was under house arrest, and see what honors were being paid to the man whom he had hated.

And then, at nighttime, when a dismal rain started, there were thousands of torches to dispel the gloom as the cortege finally drew up before the Church of Ste. Geneviève, now rebaptized the Panthéon (to all the gods), with a new inscription just carved under its pediment: *"Aux grands hommes, la patrie reconnaissante."* That is to say, "Dedicated by a grateful fatherland to its great men." So that the Newtons of France might have their proper funerary honors, too. Despite the Church.

And Voltaire's remains, encased in a fresh sarcophagus, were placed in one of the crypts.

With Rousseau soon following.

Although the Marquis de Girardin, proud of having on his property the body of the now universally acclaimed Jean Jacques Rousseau, bitterly opposed any effort to have him moved.

"Take Jean Jacques to Paris?" he argued. "Yes, if you build for him another Island of Poplars, perhaps in the middle of the Seine, with weeping willows planted all around. But not if you intend to stick him in a cellar, in the middle of your city. Nothing could be more offensive to the memory of this lover of nature and the out-of-doors."

But forgotten was that aspect of Rousseau. Forgotten, too, the bitter dispute the two men had waged against each other. All drowned in the clamor of the Revolution. Orators leaping to their feet in the Assembly to shout that if Voltaire, who despite his struggle for humanity still supported the royal power, could lie in the Panthéon, then all the more so Rousseau, for he too had fought for humanity and, in addition, had condemned all kings and had even announced that the age of revolutions was at hand.

Indeed, Voltaire and Rousseau were so closely associated in the popular mind with the great turmoil that was going on through the whole of French society that it was impossible to keep them from being joined in the Panthéon. And amidst celebrations very similar to those given to Voltaire—with flowers and music and dancing girls, with speeches and with men carrying copies of his great works, especially his *Social Contract,* bible of the Revolution—Rousseau was laid to rest at Voltaire's feet.

To lie there forever.

But actually not for very long. For by 1815 the Bourbons were back on the throne of France, and by 1821 began the great reaction that resulted in the Panthéon's being restored to the Catholic authorities, who once more named it the Church of Ste. Geneviève and ordered the remains of Voltaire and Rousseau removed from their crypts and deposited in a remote part of the cellars, beyond the grounds of the sacred edifice itself, in a profane area dug out under the columned portico.

But still together.

For nine years. Because with the Revolution of 1830 the Church was once more out of power, and Ste. Geneviève became the Panthéon again, and Rousseau and Voltaire were brought back to their respective crypts.

Until the days of Napoleon III, when once again the Panthéon was returned to the Catholics, but this time with the understanding that the bodies of Voltaire and Rousseau would not be moved or made to suffer any indignities.

To which the priest assigned to the edifice objected strenuously. Saying to the Emperor, "How will I feel, preaching a sermon, with those two damned souls lying under my feet?"

"And how do you suppose they will feel, with you preaching your sermons above them?" the Emperor is said to have replied.

But it would seem that in spite of that the priest somehow obtained permission to move the bodies. According to other reports, however, the question of whether they were moved or not no longer had any meaning. It was only big boxes that were being pushed around. For it was claimed that both sarcophagi had long been empty. Some daring young Catholic royalists having broken into the crypts, many years before, and stuffed Voltaire's and Rousseau's bones into a sack. Thrown the whole business out on some dump.

Thus no one being able to say where Voltaire and Rousseau might lie buried. Though presumably still together, wherever that might be.

And it wasn't until December 18, 1897, when the Church of Ste. Geneviève had once more become the Panthéon, that a commission was appointed to look into that matter. A commission of important men, such as the historian Ernest Hamel, the famous chemist Berthelot, the novelist Jules Claretie, the financier and art collecter Berger and many others.

With reporters from all over the civilized world attending. On a dismally wet and wintry day, when everyone was in his heaviest overcoat, so that the little space around the crypts was absolutely packed, leaving the workmen with scarcely enough room to operate. And the dignitaries massed so solidly about the workers that they were like a wall, squeezing the reporters to the rear and preventing them from seeing anything that was going on.

It led to bad feeling almost immediately. Moreover, the workmen were exceedingly slow about it, complaining that they had been misinformed about their task and that the job really required something of a derrick, the lids—which weighed hundreds of pounds—being so massive and unwieldy. Rousseau's coffin, furthermore, was encased in a leaden casket, which had to be sawed apart.

So that the reporters became not only impatient, but eventually impertinent. Many deliberately keeping their hats on, as a gesture of disrespect. Some clambering on the shoulders of others, to try and get some inkling of what was going on. The others, bored, beginning to talk of different matters. Of the recent Italian defeat at Aduwa. Of the meeting of nations at St. Petersburg in an attempt to get England to stop the use of the cruel dumdum bullets against the natives of India and Africa. Which England refused to do, asserting that with her small Army and her large Empire she needed a more effective weapon. A more frightful deterrent.

The reporters discussed Klondike gold and the Panama scandal. They discussed girls. They told improper stories, and there were bursts of unseemly laughter.

And suddenly there was Hamel's voice crying, "Voltaire is here!"

The reporters shrieked, "Where?" "Show us!" "Let us see!" And they pushed and scrambled for a glimpse.

"Disgraceful!" said Hamel, an elderly gentleman, who, incidentally, was to catch a cold from this investigation and die of it in a matter of days. He suggested to the committee that a workman be sent out to fetch the police and that the reporters be ejected.

The historian Georges Lenotre said to him, "I thought you were an admirer of Voltaire and Rousseau."

"So I am," said Hamel. "And precisely for that reason I will not tolerate this disrespect."

"But if you admire Voltaire and Rousseau," Lenotre argued, "then you should admire their product, modern man. Manufactured by these two skeletons whom we are uncovering—Monsieur Voltaire, who killed man's reverence for religious authority, and Monsieur Rousseau, who killed our reverence for political authority. And there you have the result: today's people, with reverence for nothing."

"I beg your pardon," said the financier Berger. "They have reverence for the authority of money."

"That too will go someday," declared Francisque Sarcey, the novelist and critic. "You'll see."

The reporters were still clamoring for their rights, but with absolutely no room available to give them a view. Until the chemist Berthelot thought of reaching down into Voltaire's casket and coming up with his skull. Holding it up high for all to see.

"Here he is! Voltaire! He can be recognized by his lack of teeth and his sawed-off brainpan, the result of an autopsy."

"What about Rousseau?" several reporters asked.

"He's here, too," Berthelot declared. And he bent down and came up holding aloft both hands, a skull in each.

That was quite a sight, the skulls of Voltaire and Rousseau held up like that. And for a moment there was a kind of awed silence.

Then one reporter cried out, "Let's see them kiss!"

"Yes. Have them kiss!" came from various newspapermen.

But the correspondent for the *London Illustrated* said, "I wonder what they might be saying to each other."

His somber mood somehow caught on. And upon leaving shortly afterward, the reporters were considerably more subdued. Each wondering about those eternal mysteries in which we all find ourselves trapped.

Yes, one wonders what they might be saying to each other. These two. Together at last.

The one who let his mind take precedence over his heart. And the other who let his heart take precedence over his mind.

The thinking man, for whom, as Horace Walpole said, the world is a comedy. And the feeling man, for whom the world must be a tragedy.

What do they say to each other, in the ghostly silence of their crypts? The mind-man, to whom the world is so understandable and who catches on to its ways so quickly. And the heart-man, to whom the world will always be a puzzle and who will never catch on.

The mind that accepts the existence of human inequality. And the heart that rebels against it. The mind that can laugh at sex, chastity and virginity. And the heart that consumes itself with jealousy.

Yes, what can they possibly say to each other? The mind that can be courteous to all. And the heart that can only either love or hate. The mind that admires the city and the noise and bustle of human competition. And the heart that yearns for the country, for untouched nature, where the silence is broken only by wind and the cries of animals.

What can they say to each other? The mind that demands reforms. And the heart that cries, "Revolt!" The one planning progress, and the other demanding utopia. The one counting profits and the increase in human comforts, and the other accepting only the values that cannot be bought. The mind calling man to his duties. The heart clamoring for man to demand his rights.

What can they possibly say to each other, these two archetypes of man? So far apart. Unbridgeable in their differences. And yet only inches apart in each one of us. No farther away than the head is from the chest. And the two of them endlessly whispering their dissonances and their confusions into our blood stream, which secretly nourishes them both. The mind that can always find words to express itself. And the heart that can never quite say what it feels.

What can they say to each other, these two who are forever complicating our lives?

The mind that promises us the stars—and will ultimately take us there, too! So that we'll cry, "Hurrah! Hurrah!"

While our hearts ache with homesickness for the earth.

ABOUT THE AUTHOR

Novelist, scholar, biographer, linguist, pamphleteer, Guy Endore practically invented a new form of literature with his widely read King of Paris *(1956), a Book-of-the-Month Club selection. This was a dual biographical novel about Alexandre Dumas* pere et fils *in which every detail was historically true except the principal theme of the story— and even this was "true" in the psychological—or poetic—sense. One felt it* must *have happened this way, even if there are no documents to prove it did.*

Voltaire! Voltaire! *is the same sort of dual biographical novel, and Mr. Endore's background was ideal for creating the form. Part of his childhood was spent in France, and for the purpose of writing the book he did several months of research in France and Switzerland, including days and nights in the Voltaire library in Ferney.*

Mr. Endore's previous works had also prepared him to master his new form (see the list of these works in the front of the book). For many years now he has made his home on the West Coast, writing for the motion picture industry between books. He is married and has two daughters.